ATOMIC COLLISION THEORY

Second Edition

LECTURE NOTES AND SUPPLEMENTS IN PHYSICS
John David Jackson and David Pines, *Editors* (Nos. 1-13)

Volumes of the Series published from 1962–1974 are not officially numbered. The parenthetical numbers shown are designed to aid librarians and bibliographers to check the completeness of their holdings.

(1)	John David Jackson	Mathematics for Quantum Mechanics: An Introductory Survey of Operators, Eigenvalues, and Linear Vector Spaces, 1962
(2)	Willem Brouwer	Matrix Methods in Optical Instrument Design, 1964
(3)	R. Hagedorn	Relativistic Kinematics: A Guide to the Kinematic Problems of High-Energy Physics, 1964 (5th printing, 1980)
(4)	Robert S. Knox and Albert Gold	Symmetry in the Solid State, 1964
(5)	David Pines	Elementary Excitations in Solids: Lectures on Phonons, Electrons, and Plasmons, 1963 (3rd printing, 1978)
(6)	Gabriel Barton	Introduction to Dispersion Techniques in Field Theory, 1965
(7)	David Bohm	The Special Theory of Relativity, 1965 (2nd printing, 1979)
(8)	David Park	Introduction to Strong Interactions: A Lecture-Note Volume, 1966
(9)	Hans A. Bethe and Roman W. Jackiw	Intermediate Quantum Mechanics, 1968 (5th printing, 1982)
(10)	Gordon Baym	Lectures on Quantum Mechanics, 1969 (9th printing, with corrections, 1981)
(11)	K. Nishijima	Fields and Particles: Field Theory and Dispersion Relations, 1969 (4th printing, 1980)
(12)	B. H. Bransden	Atomic Collision Theory, 1970
(13)	R. D. Sard	Relativisitc Mechanics: Special Relativity and Classical Particle Dynamics, 1970

LECTURE NOTES AND SUPPLEMENTS IN PHYSICS
David Pines, *Editor*

Volumes published from 1975 onward are being numbered as an integral part of the bibliography:

Number		
14	Hans Frauenfelder and Ernest M. Henley	Nuclear and Particle Physics, A: Background and Symmetries, 1975
15	H. W. Wyld	Mathematical Methods for Physics, 1976 (3rd printing, 1981)
16	Werner O. Amrein, Josef M. Jauch, and Kalyan B. Sinha	Scattering Theory in Quantum Mechanics: Physical Principles and Mathematical Methods, 1977
17	B. H. Bransden	Atomic Collision Theory, Second Edition, 1983

Other volumes in preparation

ATOMIC COLLISION THEORY

Second Edition

B. H. BRANSDEN

University of Durham

Durham, England

1983

THE BENJAMIN/CUMMINGS PUBLISHING COMPANY, INC.

Advanced Book Program

Reading, Massachusetts

London · Amsterdam · Don Mills, Ontario · Sydney · Tokyo

CODEN: LNSPB

Library of Congress Cataloging in Publication Data

Bransden, B. H., 1926-
Atomic collision theory.

(Lecture notes and supplements in physics ; 17)
Bibliography: p.
Includes index.
1. Collisions (Nuclear physics) 2. Scattering
(Physics) I. Title. II. Series.
QC794.6.C6B7 1983 539.7'54 82-16272
ISBN 0-8053-1181-5

Reproduced by The Benjamin/Cummings Publishing Company, Advanced Book Program, Reading, Massachusetts, from camera-ready copy prepared by the office of the author.

Printed in the United States of America
ABCDEFGHIJK-MA-898765432

CONTENTS

PREFACE TO THE FIRST EDITION

Although the theory of atomic collisions is fundamental to many branches of physics and astrophysics, hardly any text books are available at an introductory level, although at a more advanced level, the established research worker is well served by N.F. Mott and H.S.W. Massey's treatise on 'The Theory of Atomic Collisions' (Oxford, 3rd edit., 1965) which originally appeared in 1933 and which will remain the indispensable classic in the field. This book, which is based on my lectures delivered in the Spring of 1968 at the University of Washington, is intended to fill this gap in the literature. It is primarily addressed to graduate students, but in addition, it contains a survey of the most recent developments in the field that will be of interest to more senior physicists. The book is not addressed solely to intending theorists, but it is hoped it will be of equal value to experimentalists in assessing the theoretical interpretation of their investigations. It should be understood easily by all those who have attended a good undergraduate course in non-relativistic quantum mechanics.

The first four chapters provide a self-contained account of non-relativistic quantum scattering theory. In Chapter 1, the theory of scattering of particles by a central potential is developed and is followed in Chapter 2 by a discussion of a number of important practical methods for the approximate calculation of cross sections, including those based on variational principles and semi-classical approximations. The long range potentials between atoms decrease as some inverse power of the inter-atomic distance. Such potentials require special treatment and this topic forms the subject of Chapter 3. In Chapter 4, the theory is generalized to treat the collision of complex systems and the idea of the scattering or S-matrix is introduced.

In the second half of the book, the theory developed earlier is applied to a variety of problems in atomic physics. In each case the present state of the theory is outlined and the theoretical predictions are compared with the latest experiments. Chapters 5 and 6 are concerned with the interactions of electrons with atoms, while Chapter 7 contains a detailed account of the auto-ionizing states that are responsible for the recently discovered resonances in the scattering of electrons at energies below the excitation thresholds of the target atoms. Chapters 8 and 9 review the theory of heavy particle collisions between atoms and ions and particular attention is paid to the theory of charge exchange. The application of scattering theory to the collisions of electrons with molecules is a complex problem, but recently some successes have been achieved and these are described in the last chapter.

Although no attempt has been made to provide a comprehensive bibliography, extensive references to the original papers are collected together at the end of each chapter and it is hoped that these will help to overcome the often considerable difficulties facing the new research worker in finding his way through the literature.

It is pleasant to thank Professor R.Geballe and his colleagues at the University of Washington for their hospitality during the period that the major part of this book was written, and for providing the ideal conditions for study and research, and my particular thanks are due to Jim Martin and Harold Zimmerman who gave me invaluable help in collating the manuscript of my lectures and in the preparation of many of the figures and diagrams, and to Dr. M.I. Barker for his careful reading of the proofs. I am indebted to the Editor of the 'Proceedings of the Royal Society' for permission to reproduce Figures 5-3 and 6-4. Finally, I should like to express my appreciation to Mrs. Dorothy Birtles for her expert typing of the final manuscript.

Durham, England
September 1969

Brian H. Bransden

PREFACE TO THE SECOND EDITION

Since the first edition of the book was issued in 1970, something of a renaissance in the subject of atomic collisions has occurred, fired by an increasing demand for collision data from those working in research on controlled nuclear fusion, on astrophysics and in quantum chemistry. Despite the large number of experimentalists and theorists working in fields related to atomic collisions, there are still very few texts available at an introductory level for those taking up the subject for the first time, and this has led to requests for a new edition of this book to be prepared.

Most of the material in the first edition has stood the test of time, but methods which are now of less interest have been deleted, making room for accounts of some important new developments, and in addition the bibliographic material has been completely updated. As an aid to study, problems have been added at the end of each Chapter, which should be attempted to gain a complete understanding of the textual material.

The revision has the aim of preserving the essential character of the book, which is intended to be introductory in nature and addressed primarily to beginners in the field, although with sufficient advanced material to be of interest as a reference for established scientists. Clearly in a book of this size not every interesting topic in atomic collision physics can be covered and only a selection of the applications of the theory to specific systems can be described, however many references are given to the review literature where further specialist information can be located easily.

The preparation of this second edition was made possible by the generosity of the University of Durham, which granted me leave of absence and of the Joint Institute of Laboratory Astrophysics at the University of Colorado which provided a Fellowship and hospitality affording me the time to concentrate on this project. My thanks to both institutions is gladly acknowledged.

I am deeply grateful to my wife who in addition to her patient support during the revision of the text, undertook the typing and preparation of the camera-ready copy.

Boulder, Colorado
July 1982

Brian H. Bransden

Chapter 1

POTENTIAL SCATTERING

The interactions between atoms, or between electrons and atoms, are studied through scattering experiments in which a well defined beam of particles is allowed to interact with the atoms of a target and the products of the collision are detected and measured. It is necessary to describe such an experiment in quantum mechanical terms[1] and to achieve this several simplifying assumptions will be introduced, that are satisfied in most of the experiments in which we are interested. The target will be supposed to be so thin that the probability that any particle in the beam is scattered by more than one atom in the target can be neglected, and it will be assumed that the density of particles in the beam is so low that the beam particles do not interact with each other. We shall further suppose that each particle in the beam has the same well-defined value of the energy, E, and the same well-defined value of the momentum $\vec{p}$. In view of this, the wave function of an incident particle is an eigenfunction of energy and momentum and, by the uncertainty principle, it is not localized in space or time. In the position representation, this wave function is the plane wave.

$$\Psi_i(\vec{r},t) = \phi(\vec{k},\vec{r})\exp(iEt/\hbar), \tag{1-1a}$$

where

$$\phi(\vec{k},\vec{r}) = \exp(i\vec{k}\cdot\vec{r}), \tag{1-1b}$$

and the direction of propagation is parallel to the wave

vector $\vec{k}$.

As we shall deal exclusively with particles moving at non-relativistic velocities $v \ll c$ the relationship between the energy E and the momentum $\vec{p} = \hbar \vec{k}$ is:

$$E = \frac{p^2}{2m} = \frac{\hbar^2 k^2}{2m}, \tag{1-2}$$

where m is the mass of the incident particle and $\hbar = h/(2\pi)$, where h is Planck's constant.

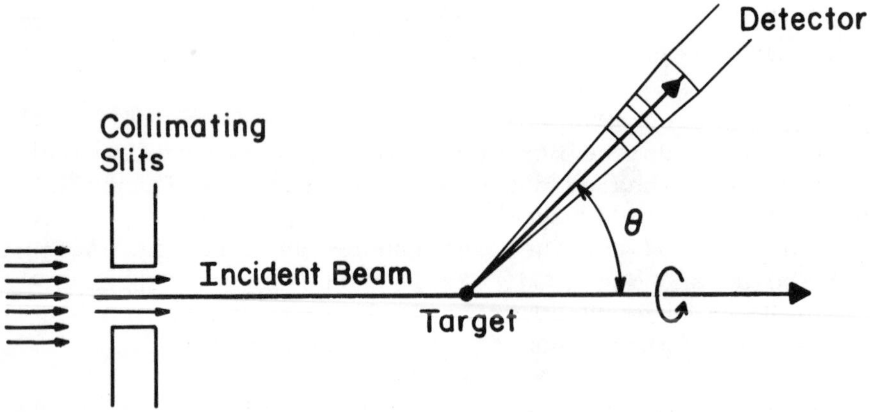

Figure 1-1. Schematic diagram of a scattering experiment

In a real experiment, the incident beam is defined by collimator slits, shown schematically in figure 1-1, and is therefore localized in space, but because the radial dimensions of the beam are at least of the order 10^{-1} cm, while the dimensions of an atom in the target are $\sim 10^{-8}$ cm, the uncertainty introduced in the momentum can be neglected and the wave function can be taken to be the plane wave (1-1a). In the same way, the beam is switched on for times that are long on the atomic time scale. This allows us to treat the wave train as being of infinite duration in time and the uncertainty in energy of the beam particles can be neglected. The results that we shall obtain, based on these approximations, can be justified rigorously by explicitly constructing a localized wave packet to represent the incident particle and following its motion (Brenig and Haag, 1959).

If the atoms of the target are very heavy compared with the incident particles (which may be electrons for example), they can be treated as fixed centers of force. The Schrödinger equation for the system is then, in the position representation,

$$\left(-\frac{\hbar^2}{2m}\nabla^2 + V(\vec{r})\right)\Psi(\vec{r},t) = i\hbar\,\frac{\partial\Psi(\vec{r},t)}{\partial t}, \qquad (1\text{-}3)$$

where $V(\vec{r})$ is the effective potential field exerted by the target on the incident particles, and the position vector $\vec{r}$ of a particle is measured from an origin situated at the fixed center of force.

In this chapter we shall consider potentials that are spherically symmetrical, $V(\vec{r}) = V(r)$, and of short range so that $V(r) \to 0$ as $r \to \infty$ faster than any inverse power of r. Examples of such potentials are the exponential well, $V(r) = A\exp(-r/a)$, the Yukawa well, $V(r) = r^{-1} A \exp(-r/a)$ and the spherical well, $V(r) = A, r < a$, $V(r) = 0$, $r > a$. The parameter A is known as the well depth and a is the range. For the moment it is assumed that V is real, $V = V^*$.

Under the steady state conditions that we have postulated, the system is in an eigenstate of energy and we express the wave function $\Psi(\vec{r},t)$ as

$$\Psi(\vec{r},t) = \psi(\vec{r})\exp(-iEt/\hbar) \qquad (1\text{-}4)$$

where the time independent wave function $\psi(\vec{r})$ satisfies

$$(\nabla^2 + k^2 - U(r))\psi(\vec{r}) = 0, \qquad (1\text{-}5)$$

and $U(r) = (2m/\hbar^2)V(r)$.

At large distances, the scattered particles emerge radially from the center of force and are represented by a spherical wave with an amplitude depending on the direction of scattering. If $\psi_a(\vec{r})$ is the asymptotic form of the wave function $\psi(\vec{r})$ at large distances from the scattering center, we have

$$\psi(\vec{r}) \underset{r\to\infty}{\sim} \psi_a(\vec{r}) \qquad (1\text{-}6a)$$

and

$$\psi_a(\vec{r}) = \phi(\vec{k},\vec{r}) + f(\vec{k},\theta)\, r^{-1} \exp(ikr) \qquad (1\text{-}6b)$$

where (θ,ϕ) are the polar angles of $\vec{r}$, taking the incident direction $\vec{k}$ as axis. The first term represents the incident plane wave and the second the radial outgoing wave. Both terms satisfy the free particle Schrödinger equation, obtained by setting $U = 0$ in (1-5). In the exceptional case of scattering by a Coulomb potential, for which $U(r) \propto {}^1/r$, it is not possible to neglect the potential in the asymptotic (large r) region and the asymptotic form (1-6) does not apply. As the system is symmetrical about the direction of incidence, the scattering amplitude $f(\vec{k},\theta)$ depends only on k and the angle of scattering θ. This is of course true only for spherically symmetrical potentials and in general the scattering amplitude is a function of both θ and ϕ.

1-1 THE CROSS SECTION

The wave function $\Psi(\vec{r},t)$ is not normalizable, but it can be interpreted by identifying $\rho \equiv |\Psi(\vec{r},t)|^2$ with the particle density in a beam of identical non-interacting particles. The rate of change of the total number of particles within a certain closed volume v is given by

$$N = \frac{\partial}{\partial t}\int_v \rho dv = \int_v \left(\Psi^*(\vec{r},t)\,\frac{\partial}{\partial t}\,\Psi(\vec{r},t) + \Psi(\vec{r},t)\,\frac{\partial}{\partial t}\,\Psi^*(\vec{r},t)\right) d^3r \tag{1-7}$$

Using the Schrödinger equation (1-3) for Ψ and the corresponding equation for Ψ^* we have, provided the potential V is real,

$$N = \frac{i\hbar}{2m}\int_v (\Psi^*\nabla^2\Psi - \Psi\nabla^2\Psi^*)\,dv. \tag{1-8}$$

This can be converted by Green's theorem to an integral over the surface s that bounds the volume v, giving

$$N = -\int_s \vec{j}\cdot\vec{n}\,ds, \tag{1-9}$$

where

$$\vec{j} = \frac{\hbar}{2mi}(\Psi^*\vec{\nabla}\Psi - \Psi\vec{\nabla}\Psi^*), \tag{1-10}$$

and $\vec{n}$ is a unit vector in the direction of the outward drawn normal to the surface. The term $\vec{j}\cdot\vec{n}$ is equal to the number of particles crossing unit area of the boundary surface per unit time in the direction of $\vec{n}$, $\vec{j}$ is called the current density vector and satisfies (from 1-7 and 1-8) the conservation law,

$$\frac{\partial\rho}{\partial t} + \vec{\nabla}\cdot\vec{j} = 0. \qquad (1\text{-}11)$$

The incident flux F is defined as the number of particles per second in the incident beam crossing unit cross sectional area normal to the beam, and F can be calculated by inserting the plane wave $\phi(\vec{k},\vec{r})$ given by (1-1b) into (1-10),

$$F = |\vec{j}| = \frac{\hbar k}{m}. \qquad (1\text{-}12)$$

The radial current of scattered particles j_r, where $j_r = (\vec{j}\cdot\vec{r})/r$, can be found from the second term in (1-6). For large r, and neglecting terms of order $1/r^3$, we have

$$j_r = \frac{\hbar}{2mi}\left(\Psi^*\frac{\partial\Psi}{\partial r} - \Psi\frac{\partial\Psi^*}{\partial r}\right) \underset{r\to\infty}{\sim} \frac{\hbar k}{mr^2}\,|f(\vec{k},\theta)|^2. \qquad (1\text{-}13)$$

From the radial current, we can calculate the number of particles, W, entering a detector per unit time. If the detector subtends a solid angle $d\Omega$ at the scattering center in a direction (θ,ϕ), then

$$W = j_r r^2 d\Omega(\theta,\phi) = \frac{\hbar k}{m}\,|f(\vec{k},\theta)|^2\, d\Omega(\theta,\phi). \qquad (1\text{-}14)$$

The results of an experiment are usually expressed in terms of a differential cross section $(d\sigma/d\Omega)$, which is defined as the number of particles scattered in direction (θ,ϕ) per unit solid angle per unit incident flux:

$$\frac{d\sigma(\theta)}{d\Omega} = |f(\vec{k},\theta)|^2. \qquad (1\text{-}15)$$

To obtain a measure of the intensity of scattering without regard to angle, a total cross section σ is defined by integrating $d\sigma/d\Omega$ over all solid angles,

$$\sigma = \int_{4\pi}\left(\frac{d\sigma}{d\Omega}\right) d\Omega \qquad (1\text{-}16)$$

In defining the cross section, the flux of the incident wave is calculated separately from that of the scattered wave. This procedure is justified provided that the detector is situated so that it lies well outside the incident beam as in figure 1-1 and collects only the scattered particles.

In potential scattering the energy of the scattered

particles is the same as that of the incident particles and the scattering is said to be elastic. However other kinds of process are possible. For example, if electrons are scattered by an atom, an electron may give up part of its energy to the atom, leaving the atom in an excited state. Such collisions are said to be inelastic. If only elastic collisions are possible, as many particles with the incident energy E, must leave any sphere drawn about the scattering center as enter it, in a particular interval of time. It follows that the net radial flux calculated from both terms in the asymptotic wave function (1-6) must vanish. In inelastic scattering, some particles give up their energy to the target, so that the number of particles of energy E leaving such a sphere per unit time must be less than the number entering it. As far as elastic scattering is concerned, the presence of such inelastic processes can be simulated by allowing the potential to become complex,

$$V = V_R - iV_I, \qquad V_I > 0.$$

The Schrödinger equations for Ψ and Ψ^* are now

$$\left(-\frac{\hbar^2}{2m}\nabla^2 + V - i\hbar\frac{\partial}{\partial t}\right)\Psi(\vec{r},t) = 0$$

$$\left(-\frac{\hbar^2}{2m}\nabla^2 + V^* + i\hbar\frac{\partial}{\partial t}\right)\Psi^*(\vec{r},t) = 0 \qquad (1\text{-}17)$$

The rate $\bar{N}$ at which the number of particles within a volume v decreases is given by

$$\bar{N} = -\frac{\partial}{\partial t}\int_v |\Psi|^2 d^3r = -N$$

From (1-8) and (1-17) we have

$$\bar{N} = -\frac{i\hbar}{2m}\int_v (\Psi^*\nabla^2\Psi - \Psi\nabla^2\Psi^*)\,d^3r + \frac{2}{\hbar}\int_v V_I|\Psi|^2 d^3r \qquad (1\text{-}18)$$

The first term in (1-18) is, as before, equal to $\int_s \vec{j}\cdot\vec{n}\,ds$, the net number of particles leaving the volume across its boundary, so the second term must be identified with the number of particles absorbed per unit time within the volume v.

1-2 PARTIAL WAVE AMPLITUDES

If the potential is spherically symmetric and the incident wave has no azimuthal variation, the wave function $\psi(\vec{r})$ is axially symmetric about the direction of incidence $\vec{k}$. Taking spherical polar coordinates (r,θ,ϕ), with $\vec{k}$ as axis and with the center of force as origin, it follows that $\psi(\vec{r})$ is a function of r and θ only and that $\psi(\vec{r})$ can be expanded in a series of Legendre polynomials, which form a complete set in the interval $-1 \leq \cos\theta \leq +1$,

$$\psi(r,\theta) = \sum_{\ell=0}^{\infty} r^{-1} f_\ell(r) P_\ell(\cos\theta). \tag{1-19}$$

Each term in this series is an eigenfunction of L^2 and of L_z, where $\vec{L}$ is the orbital angular momentum operator, since

$$L^2 P_\ell(\cos\theta) = [\ell(\ell+1)\hbar^2] P_\ell(\cos\theta)$$

and $L_z P_\ell(\cos\theta) = 0$,

where

$$L^2 = -\hbar^2 \left\{\frac{1}{\sin\theta}\frac{\partial}{\partial\theta}\sin\theta\frac{\partial}{\partial\theta} + \frac{1}{\sin^2\theta}\frac{\partial^2}{\partial\phi^2}\right\}$$

and $L_z = -i\hbar\dfrac{\partial}{\partial\phi}$.

To find the wave equation satisfied by the radial wave function $f_\ell(r)$, the Schrödinger equation is written in the form (1-5) as

$$[\nabla^2 - U(r) + k^2]\psi(r,\theta) = 0,$$

where $k^2 = 2mE/\hbar^2$ and $U(r) = 2mV(r)/\hbar^2$. Using the result

$$\nabla^2 = \frac{1}{r^2}\frac{\partial}{\partial r}\left(r^2\frac{\partial}{\partial r}\right) - \frac{1}{\hbar^2 r^2} L^2,$$

and expansion (1-19), it follows that

$$\sum_{\ell=0}^{\infty} r^{-1} P_\ell(\cos\theta)\left[\frac{d^2}{dr^2} - \frac{\ell(\ell+1)}{r^2} - U(r) + k^2\right] f_\ell(r) = 0.$$

The radial equation is now obtained by multiplying by $P_{\ell'}$ $(\cos\theta)$ and integrating over $\cos\theta$, to give

$$\left[\frac{d^2}{dr^2} - \frac{\ell(\ell+1)}{r^2} - U(r) + k^2\right] f_\ell(r) = 0, \tag{1-20}$$

where the orthogonality property of the Legendre polynomials has been used

$$\int_{-1}^{+1} P_\ell(\cos\theta) P_{\ell'}(\cos\theta)\, d\cos\theta = \left(\frac{2}{2\ell+1}\right)\delta_{\ell\ell'}$$

For potentials that are not too singular at the origin[2], so that

$$\lim_{r\to 0} r^{2-\varepsilon}|U(r)| < C, \qquad \varepsilon > 0 \tag{1-21}$$

the radial function $f_\ell(r)$ can be expanded in a power series

$$f_\ell(r) = \sum_n a_n r^n.$$

An examination of the indicial equation then shows that there are two solutions, one regular at the origin behaving like

$$f_\ell(r) \propto r^{\ell+1}, \tag{1-22}$$

and one irregular with

$$f_\ell(r) \propto r^{-\ell}. \tag{1-23}$$

To describe a physical scattering situation, the wave function $\psi(\vec{r})$ must be finite everywhere so that we must choose the regular solution. If the potential decreases sufficiently rapidly[3], for large r we may neglect V(r) in comparison with k^2. In this case $f_\ell(r)$ is determined for large r by the equation

$$\left[\frac{d^2}{dr^2} - \frac{\ell(\ell+1)}{r^2} + k^2\right] f_\ell(r) = 0. \tag{1-24}$$

Two independent real solutions of this equation are $s_\ell(kr)$ and $c_\ell(kr)$ which are related to the spherical Bessel and Neumann functions[4] $j_\ell(x)$ and $n_\ell(x)$ by $s_\ell(x) = xj_\ell(x)$; $c_\ell(x) = -xn_\ell(x)$. These functions have the properties,

$$s_\ell(x) \underset{x\to 0}{\sim} \frac{x^{\ell+1}}{(2\ell + 1)!!}, \quad s_\ell(x) \underset{x\to\infty}{\sim} \sin\left(x - \frac{\ell\pi}{2}\right)$$

$$c_\ell(x) \underset{x\to 0}{\sim} \frac{(2\ell - 1)!!}{x^\ell}, \quad c_\ell(x) \underset{x\to\infty}{\sim} \cos\left(x - \frac{\ell\pi}{2}\right). \tag{1-25}$$

The functions $s_\ell(x)$ and $c_\ell(x)$ can be expressed in terms of polynomials in $(1/x)$ multiplying cos x and sin x. For $\ell \leq 2$, s_i and c_i are

$$s_0(x) = \sin x, \quad c_0(x) = \cos x,$$

$$s_1(x) = \frac{\sin x}{x} - \cos x, \quad c_1(x) = \frac{\cos x}{x} + \sin x,$$

$$s_2(x) = \left(\frac{3}{x^2} - \frac{1}{x}\right)\sin x - \frac{3}{x}\cos x, \tag{1-26}$$

$$c_2(x) = \left(\frac{3}{x^2} - \frac{1}{x}\right)\cos x + \frac{3}{x}\sin x.$$

Sometimes we shall find it convenient to use in place of $s_\ell(x)$ and $c_\ell(x)$, the functions $e_\ell^\pm(x)$ defined so that

$$e_\ell^\pm(x) = c_\ell(x) \pm is_\ell(x). \tag{1-27}$$

For large x, the functions $e_\ell^\pm(x)$ have the asymptotic form

$$e_\ell^\pm(x) \sim \exp\left[\pm i(x - \ell\pi/2)\right] \tag{1-28}$$

For large r, $f_\ell(r)$ must have the general form

$$f_\ell(r) \sim f_\ell^a(r),$$

where

$$f_\ell^a(r) = A_\ell[s_\ell(kr) + K_\ell c_\ell(kr)]; \tag{1-29a}$$

$$f_\ell^a(r) \underset{r\to\infty}{\sim} A_\ell \left(\sin\left(kr - \frac{\ell\pi}{2}\right) + K_\ell \cos\left(kr - \frac{\ell\pi}{2}\right)\right) \quad (1\text{-}29b)$$

and where A_ℓ and K_ℓ are constants . The A_ℓ are multiplicative normalization constants and the scattering amplitude is determined by the parameters K_ℓ. To find the connection between the scattering amplitude and K_ℓ the asymptotic part of $\psi(\vec{r})$, which is $\psi_a(\vec{r})$ given by (1-6), can be expanded in Legendre polynomials.

The first term in (1-6), the plane wave $\phi(\vec{k},\vec{r})$ has the expansion (Bransden and Joachain, 1982, Chapter 2).

$$\phi(\vec{k},\vec{r}) = \sum_{\ell=0}^{\infty} (2\ell + 1)i^\ell (kr)^{-1} s_\ell(kr) P_\ell(\cos\theta)$$

and for large r,

$$\phi(\vec{k},\vec{r}) \sim \sum_{\ell=0}^{\infty} (2\ell + 1)i^\ell (kr)^{-1} \sin\left(kr - \frac{\ell\pi}{2}\right) P_\ell(\cos\theta). \quad (1\text{-}30)$$

The second term in (1-6), representing the outgoing scattered waves, can also be expanded in a series of Legendre polynomials,

$$f_k(\theta)\exp(ikr)/r = \left(\sum_{\ell=0}^{\infty} (2\ell + 1)k^{-1} T_\ell P_\ell(\cos\theta)\right)\exp(ikr)/r. \quad (1\text{-}31)$$

The coefficients of the expansion, T_ℓ, are called the partial wave scattering amplitudes. From (1-19), (1-30) and (1-31), we see that

$$f_\ell^a(r) \underset{r\to\infty}{\sim} (2\ell + 1)\left(k^{-1} i^\ell \sin\left(kr - \frac{\ell\pi}{2}\right) + k^{-1} T_\ell \exp(ikr)\right) \quad (1\text{-}32)$$

Writing

$$\exp(ikr) = \exp\left(i\frac{\ell\pi}{2}\right)\left(\cos\left(kr - \frac{\ell\pi}{2}\right) + i\sin\left(kr - \frac{\ell\pi}{2}\right)\right) \quad (1\text{-}33)$$

and comparing with (1-29b), we find that K_ℓ is given in terms of T_ℓ by

$$K_\ell = \frac{T_\ell}{1 + iT_\ell} . \tag{1-34}$$

In terms of ingoing and outgoing radial waves, $f_\ell^{\,a}(r)$ has the asymptotic form, using (1-32)

$$f_\ell^{\,a}(r) \sim \frac{-(i)^\ell\ (2\ell + 1)}{2ik} \left(\exp -i\left(kr - \frac{\ell\pi}{2}\right) - S_\ell(k) \exp i\left(kr - \frac{\ell\pi}{2}\right)\right) \tag{1-35a}$$

where

$$S_\ell(k) = (2iT_\ell + 1). \tag{1-35b}$$

The conservation laws discussed in Section 1-1 require that the total outgoing radial flux never exceeds the total ingoing radial flux. It follows that $S_\ell(k)$ must always satisfy

$$|S_\ell(k)| \leq 1. \tag{1-36}$$

For real potentials, only elastic scattering is possible and the outgoing and ingoing radial fluxes are equal, so that $|S_\ell(k)| = 1$. It follows that $S_\ell(k)$ can be represented as

$$S_\ell(k) = \exp(2i\delta_\ell) \tag{1-37}$$

where δ_ℓ is a real constant called the phase shift of order ℓ. In terms of phase shifts, the partial wave scattering amplitude T_ℓ is (from 1-35b)

$$T_\ell = \frac{1}{2i}\left(\exp(2i\delta_\ell) - 1\right) = \exp(i\delta_\ell)\ \sin\ \delta_\ell, \tag{1-38}$$

and $K_\ell = \tan\ \delta_\ell$.

S_ℓ is known as an S-matrix or scattering matrix element, and K_ℓ as a reaction matrix element. The complete scattering amplitude $f(k,\theta)$ can be written in terms of the phase shifts (from 1-31), as

$$f(k,\theta) = \sum_{\ell=0}^{\infty} \frac{1}{2ik} \left(\exp(2i\delta_\ell) - 1\right)(2\ell + 1)P_\ell(\cos\theta). \tag{1-39}$$

The total cross section σ can be written as

$$\sigma = \sum_{\ell=0}^{\infty} \sigma_\ell,$$

where

$$\sigma_\ell = \frac{4\pi}{k^2}(2\ell + 1)\sin^2\delta_\ell. \tag{1-40}$$

The quantities σ_ℓ are known as partial cross sections and, since $\sin\delta_\ell$ cannot exceed unity, the partial cross sections satisfy the inequalities

$$\sigma_\ell \leq \frac{4\pi(2\ell + 1)}{k^2} \tag{1-41}$$

The partial wave expansion reduces the partial differential equation (1-5) in three variables, to a system of second order ordinary differential equations, but this is only useful if the expansion converges and we shall now discuss this point in a nonrigorous way. If a potential vanishes beyond a certain distance a, then according to classical mechanics particles with impact parameters $b > a$ (see figure 1-2) are not scattered. The impact parameter is related to the momentum p and angular momentum L, by

$$b = L/p$$

so that particles with angular momentum,

$$L > pa,$$

are not scattered. Writing $L \cong \hbar\ell$ and $p = \hbar k$, it is seen that scattering is expected to be small in angular momentum states for which

$$\ell > ka \tag{1-42}$$

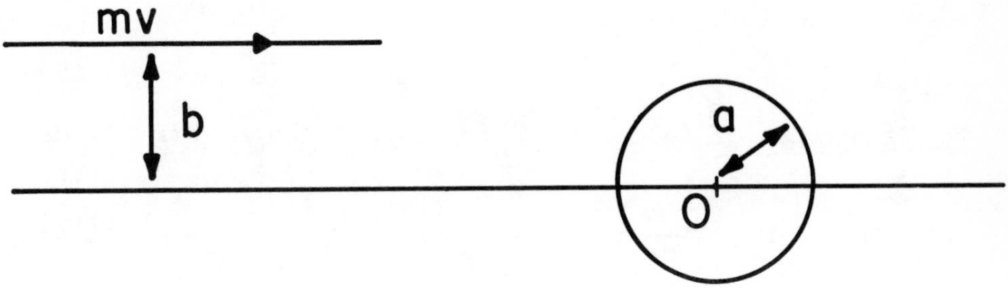

Figure 1-2 Particles with impact parameters b > a are undeflected classically.

When the scattering in a given partial wave is small the corresponding phase shift is small. It follows that only a finite number of terms in the partial wave expansion of the scattering amplitude are important, the number increasing with energy. To estimate how rapidly the phase shifts decrease with increasing ℓ, we shall find an integral equation for the reaction matrix elements $K_\ell = \tan \delta_\ell$.

1-3 INTEGRAL EQUATIONS FOR THE PHASE SHIFT

Wronskian relations

Integral equations for the radial wave function and for the phase shift are most easily obtained by considering the Wronskian of two solutions of the radial equations (1-20). Let f_ℓ and F_ℓ be two solutions of the radial equations for different potentials, U_1 and U_2, but for the same values of k and ℓ. Then f_ℓ and F_ℓ satisfy the equations,

$$\left(\frac{d^2}{dr^2} - \frac{\ell(\ell + 1)}{r^2} - U_1(r) + k^2\right) f_\ell(r) = 0, \qquad \text{(1-42a)}$$

$$\left(\frac{d^2}{dr^2} - \frac{\ell(\ell + 1)}{r^2} - U_2(r) + k^2\right) F_\ell(r) = 0. \qquad \text{(1-42b)}$$

Multiplying equation (1-42a) by $F_\ell(r)$ and equation (1-42b) by $f_\ell(r)$ and subtracting, we find

$$F_\ell(r)\,\frac{d^2}{dr^2}\,f_\ell(r) - f_\ell(r)\,\frac{d^2}{dr^2}F_\ell(r) = [U_1\ (r) - U_2\ (r)]f_\ell(r)F_\ell(r). \tag{1-43}$$

The Wronskian of $f_\ell(r)$ and $F_\ell(r)$ is defined as $W(r)$, where

$$W(r) = F_\ell(r)\,\frac{d}{dr}\,f_\ell(r) - f_\ell(r)\,\frac{d}{dr}\,F_\ell, \tag{1-44}$$

From (1-43), we find on integrating,

$$W(r) - W(0) = \int_0^r [U_1\ (r) - U_2\ (r)]f_\ell(r)F_\ell(r). \tag{1-45}$$

If $f_\ell(r)$ and $F_\ell(r)$ are independent solutions of the same equation, that is if $U_1 = U_2$, the right hand side of (1-45) vanishes showing that the Wronskian is independent of r. As an example, we can calculate the Wronskian of $s_\ell(x)$ and $c_\ell(x)$ from the asymptotic forms of these functions at large r and the result will be correct for all r. We find

$$c_\ell(kr)\,\frac{d}{dr}\,(s_\ell(kr)) - s_\ell(kr)\,\frac{d}{dr}\,(c_\ell(kr)) = k, \tag{1-46}$$

and in a similar way

$$e^{\pm}(kr)\,\frac{d}{dr}\,(s_\ell\ (kr)) - s_\ell(kr)\,\frac{d}{dr}\,(e^{\pm}(kr)) = k. \tag{1-47}$$

Integral equations for the radial wave functions

Using the result (1-46), it is easy to verify by substitution that $f_\ell(r)$ given by

$$f_\ell(r) = s_\ell(kr) + \int_0^\infty g_\ell{}^P(r,r')U(r')f_\ell(r')dr'. \tag{1-48}$$

is a solution of the radial equation (1-20), where

$$g_\ell{}^P(r,r') = -\frac{1}{k}s_\ell(kr_<)c_\ell(kr_>), \tag{1-49}$$

and $r_<$, $r_>$ are the lesser and the greater of r, r' respectively. This solution clearly vanishes at the origin and for large r satisfies the boundary condition

$$f_\ell(r) \sim s_\ell(kr) + K_\ell c_\ell(kr), \tag{1-50}$$

with

$$K_\ell = \tan \delta_\ell = -1/k \int_0^\infty s_\ell(kr) U(r) f_\ell(r) dr. \tag{1-51}$$

This integral equation can also be obtained from (1-45) directly. We first set $U_2 = 0$ so that $F_\ell = s_\ell(kr)$ and take $U_1 = U$. On the left hand side of (1-45), we see that $W(0) = 0$ and if $f_\ell(r)$ satisfies the boundary condition (1-50), we find that

$$W(r) \underset{\text{large } r}{\sim} -kK_\ell$$

and we again obtain equation (1-51).

The function $g_\ell^P(r,r')$ is known as a Green's function. By comparing (1-48) with (1-20), it is seen to satisfy the equation

$$\left(\frac{d^2}{dr^2} - \frac{\ell(\ell+1)}{r^2} + k^2\right) g_\ell^P(r,r') = \delta(r - r'). \tag{1-52}$$

Different forms of Green's function can be found that allow integral equations incorporating different boundary conditions to be constructed. For example by choosing

$$g_\ell^+(r,r') = -\frac{1}{k} s_\ell(kr_<) e_\ell^+(kr_>) \tag{1-53}$$

in place of g_ℓ^P in eq. (1-48), we find solutions satisfying

$$f_\ell^+(0) = 0, \quad f_\ell^+(r) \sim s_\ell(kr) + T_\ell e_\ell^+(kr) \tag{1-54}$$

where the partial wave amplitude T_ℓ has the integral representation

$$T_\ell = \exp(i\delta_\ell) \sin \delta_\ell = -1/k \int_0^\infty s_\ell(kr) U(r) f_\ell^+(r) dr. \tag{1-55}$$

Born's approximation

At sufficiently high energy, the functions $c_\ell(kr)$ and $s_\ell(kr)$ oscillate so rapidly over the interaction region $0 < r < a$, that the integral term in (1-48) is negligible compared with the first term. We then have (large k)

$$f_\ell(r) \cong s_\ell(kr). \tag{1-56}$$

Born's approximation for the phase shift is found by using this approximation for $f_\ell(r)$ in the integral equation (1-51):-

$$\tan \delta_\ell \cong - 1/k \int_0^\infty |s_\ell(kr)|^2 U(r)dr. \tag{1-57}$$

It will be shown that this expression can be used to estimat the phase shifts for large ℓ (any k), which allows the convergence of the partial wave series to be studied. The incident wave $s_\ell(kr)$ behaves like $(kr)^{\ell+1}$ for small (kr) and then increases exponentially up to a point of inflexion at $(kr) = \sqrt{\ell(\ell+1)}$, $(\ell \neq 0)$. Beyond this point the function oscillates with roughly unit amplitude. It follows that for sufficiently large ℓ the overlap of the incident wave and the potential in the range $0 < r < a$ can be made as small as we please. Under these conditions the wave function for the ℓth partial wave will be equal to the incident wave to a good approximation and the integral term in (1-48) will be very small. This will occur for values of ℓ roughly given by the condition $(\ell >> ka)$. The Born approximation (1-57) can now be used to estimate δ_ℓ. Setting $s_\ell(kr) \cong (kr)^{\ell+1}(2\ell + 1)!!$ (which is valid for $(kr) << \ell$) in (1-57), the approximate phase shift δ_ℓ is

$$\delta_\ell \approx \tan \delta_\ell \cong - \frac{k^{2\ell+1}}{[(2\ell +1)!!]^2} \int_0^\infty r^{2\ell+2} U(r)dr. \tag{1-58}$$

This expression is valid only for potentials vanishing for $r>a$, or which decrease exponentially for $r>a$. For potentials with tails that extend significantly into the region $r>a$, the Bessel function cannot be approximated in this way. As an example, for the square well potential

$$U(r) = A, \; r<a$$
$$= 0, \; r>a, \tag{1-59}$$

we find

$$\delta_\ell = -\frac{(ka)^{2\ell+1}(a^2A)}{[(2\ell+1)!!]^2(2\ell+3)} \tag{1-60}$$

which decreases rapidly with increasing ℓ.

The condition that the overlap of the potential and wave function is small, $\ell \gg ka$, can be satisfied by taking small k, rather than large ℓ, so that (1-58) displays the behaviour of the phase shifts at low energies, that is

$$\delta_\ell \underset{k\to 0}{\propto} k^{2\ell+1} \tag{1-61}$$

This behaviour is correct for all potentials decreasing faster than a power of r, at large r.

<u>The sign of the phase shift</u>

The Born approximation estimate of the phase shift, given by (1-57), shows that for potentials that do not change sign, the phase shift is positive for an attraction (U negative) and negative for a repulsion (U positive). This is not only true in the Born approximation. From the Wronskian relation, we easily find,

$$\tan\delta_\ell(2) - \tan\delta_\ell(1) = 1/k\int_0^\infty f_\ell(r)F_\ell(r)[U_1(r)-U_2(r)]dr, \tag{1-62}$$

where $\delta_\ell(1)$ is the phase shift of the partial wave $f_\ell(r)$ for scattering by the potential U_1, and $\delta_\ell(2)$ is the phase shift of the partial wave F_ℓ, for scattering by U_2.

If the difference $(U_1 - U_2)$ is small, so that $f_\ell(r)F_\ell(r) \cong [f_\ell(r)]^2$ we see the sign of the difference $(\delta_\ell(2) - \delta_\ell(1))$ is the same as that of $(U_1 - U_2)$. By constructing a series of comparison potentials between U_1 and U_2, it follows that this result remains true for all $(U_1 - U_2)$. Finally by taking $U_2 = 0$, we establish the result that the phase shift is positive (negative) for attractive (repulsive) potentials.

As an example of the decrease of the phase shifts with increasing ℓ and of the connection between the sign of the potential and the sign of the phase, some results are shown in Table 1-1 for scattering from the potentials

$$U_\pm(r) = \pm 2(1 + 1/r)e^{-2r}. \tag{1-63}$$

Table 1-1

Phase shifts $\delta_\ell^{\pm}$ for scattering from the potentials $U_\pm$ (see 1-63).

(Phase shifts in radians)

k(a.u.)	δ_0^+	δ_1^+	δ_2^+	δ_0^-	δ_1^-	δ_2^-
0.1	-0.058	-	-	0.721	0.0003	-
0.2	-0.1145	-0.0017	-	0.9731	0.0021	-
0.3	-0.1680	-0.0055	-	1.0458	0.0066	-
0.4	-0.2181	-0.0121	-0.0005	1.0575	0.0147	0.0005
0.5	-0.2640	-0.0200	-0.0013	1.0448	0.0260	0.0014
0.6	-0.3043	-0.0322	-0.0028	1.0210	0.0406	0.0030
0.8	-0.3713	-0.0584	-0.0082	0.9633	0.0752	0.0087

U_- is the effective potential expressed in atomic units between an electron and the ground state of a hydrogen atom calculated in lowest order, while U_+ is the corresponding potential for positron-hydrogen scattering.

1-4 THE SQUARE WELL AND HARD SPHERE POTENTIALS

The general features of the phase shifts calculated from the square well potential (1-59) are given by the formulae (1-60) for large ℓ (fixed k) and for small k (fixed ℓ). We shall now obtain the exact phase shifts in this case.

If the potential is attractive (negative), the well depth A can be written as

$$A = -\lambda^2, \tag{1-64}$$

in which case the radial wave equation can be written for $r<a$, as

$$\left(\frac{d^2}{dr^2} - \frac{\ell(\ell+1)}{r^2} + p^2\right) f_\ell(r) = 0, \tag{1-65a}$$

where

$$p^2 = k^2 + \lambda^2. \tag{1-65b}$$

The solution vanishing at the origin is

$$f_\ell(r) = N_\ell s_\ell(pr), \; r<a \tag{1-66}$$

where N_ℓ is a constant. In the region, $r>a$, the wave function satisfies the equation,

$$\left(\frac{d^2}{dr^2} - \frac{\ell(\ell+1)}{r^2} + k^2\right) f_\ell(r) = 0, \tag{1-67}$$

for which the general solution is

$$f_\ell{}^a(r) = s_\ell(kr) + K_\ell c_\ell(kr), \; r>a, \tag{1-68}$$

where K_ℓ is (from equations 1-29a,b) related to the phase shift by

$$K_\ell = \tan \delta_\ell .$$

To determine K_ℓ, we must join $f_\ell(r)$ to $f_\ell{}^a(r)$ smoothly at $r=a$. To do this, we equate both $f_\ell(r)$ with $f_\ell{}^a(r)$, and $(df_\ell(r)/dr)$ with $(df_\ell{}^a(r)/dr)$ at $r=a$, from which we find,

$$N_\ell s_\ell(pa) = s_\ell(ka) + K_\ell c_\ell(ka)$$

$$C_\ell p s'_\ell\,(pa) = k\,[s'_\ell\,(ka) + K_\ell c'_\ell\,(ka)]$$

In this equation, we have denoted derivatives by primes,

$$s'_\ell(x) \equiv \frac{ds_\ell(x)}{dx}, \quad c'_\ell(x) \equiv \frac{dc_\ell(x)}{dx}$$

We then find immediately that K_ℓ is given by the equation,

$$K_\ell = \tan \delta_\ell = \frac{ks'_\ell(ka)s_\ell(pa) - ps_\ell(ka)s'_\ell(pa)}{pc_\ell(ka)\; s'_\ell(pa) - kc'_\ell(ka)s_\ell(pa)} \tag{1-69}$$

<u>$\ell = 0$</u>

In the case for which $\ell = 0$, making use of the relations $s_o(x) = \sin(x)$, $c_o(x) = \cos(x)$, we find

$$K_o = \frac{k \tan(pa) - p \tan(ka)}{p + k \tan(ka) \tan(pa)}, \tag{1-70}$$

from which

$$\delta_o = -ka + \tan^{-1}\left[\frac{k}{p}\tan(pa)\right].$$

The behavior of the cross section at zero energy is particularly interesting. In general, the ratio tan $\delta_o(k)/k$ as $k \to 0$ tends to a finite limit a_s, known as the scattering length[6]

$$a_s = \lim_{k\to 0} [\tan \delta_o(k)]/k. \tag{1-71}$$

In the present case, we have that

$$a_s = \left[\frac{1}{\lambda}\tan(\lambda a) - a\right].$$

In terms of the scattering length, the zero energy partial cross section for $\ell = 0$ is,

$$\sigma_o(0) = \lim_{k\to 0} \frac{4\pi \sin^2 \delta_o}{k^2} = 4\pi a_s^2 \tag{1-72}$$

while the zero energy partial cross sections for higher partial waves, vanish in general. Although a_s is usually finite, exceptional cases occur if $a\lambda = \tan(\lambda a)$, when a_s vanishes, or if $(a\lambda)$ is an odd multiple of $(\pi/2)$, when a_s is infinite. These results are connected with the existence of bound states in the potential well. If there is a bound state at an energy $-E_B$, then the wave function for $r>a$ is of the form

$$f_o(r) = e^{-\xi r}, \tag{1-73}$$

where $\xi^2 = 2mE_B/\hbar^2$. This must be joined to the internal wave function (1-65), where p^2 is now $p^2 = \lambda^2 - \xi^2$. The equations joining the solutions in and outside the well are $(\ell = 0)$

$$N_o \sin(pa) = e^{-\xi a},$$

$$N_o p \cos(pa) = -\xi e^{-\xi a}.$$

On dividing, we see that ξ is determined by the roots of the equation

$$\frac{1}{p}\tan(pa) = -\frac{1}{\xi}. \tag{1-74}$$

When the depth of the well is small and

$$(\lambda a) < \frac{\pi}{2},$$

equation (1-74) cannot be satisfied (remembering that $\xi > 0$) and the system has no bound state. Under these circumstances a_s is finite, and if we normalize the phase shift so that $\delta_o(k) \to 0$ as $\lambda \to 0$, we see that $\delta_o(k) \to 0$ as $k \to 0$.

Increasing λ until (λa) lies in the interval

$$\frac{\pi}{2} < (\lambda a) < \frac{3\pi}{2} ,$$

equation (1-74) can be satisfied by just one value of ξ and the well supports one bound state. The scattering length a_s remains finite, but in the intermediate case when $(\lambda a) = \pi/2$, we have already seen that a_s is infinite and this implies that $\delta_o(k) \to \pi/2$ as $k \to 0$. Since $\delta_o(k)$ for finite k, increases monotonically with λ, it follows that in the interval $\pi/2 < (\lambda a) < 3\pi/2$ $\delta_o(k)$ does not vanish as $k \to 0$, but that

$$\delta_o(k) \to \pi.$$

Repeating the argument, it is seen that if λ is increased so that the system supports n bound states, then the phase shift satisfies

$$\lim_{k \to 0} \delta_o(k) = n\pi \tag{1-75a}$$

In the intermediate case in which λ is increased until the $(n + 1)^{th}$ bound state is about to appear and $a\lambda = (2n + 1)\pi/2$,we have

$$\lim_{k \to 0} \delta_o(k) = (n + \frac{1}{2})\pi \tag{1-75b}$$

These results turn out to be true generally and are an example of Levinson's theorem, which will be discussed at a later point.

Considered as a function of increasing k, the phase shift δ_o rises from its threshold value of $(n\pi)$ to maximum, which examination of (1-70) shows is usually less than $(n + 1/2)\pi$, although for certain values of λ and a, the maximum of δ_o can be slightly greater than $(n + 1/2)\pi$. As k increases further, δ_o will decrease and ultimately as

$k \to \infty$, $\delta_o \to 0$. As δ_o decreases, with increasing k, it will pass through the values $n\pi$, $(n-1)$, $(n-2)\pi$..... and at the corresponding energies the $\ell=0$ partial cross section is zero. At the intermediate energies for which δ_o takes on the values $(n-1/2)\pi$, $(n-3/2)\pi$.... the $\ell=0$ partial cross section attains its maximum value of $4\pi/k^2$.

Using arguments based on causality, Wigner (1955) has shown that the rate of change of the phase shift with momentum satisfies the inequality

$$\frac{\partial \delta_o(k)}{\partial k} > -a$$

for all interactions with a finite range a. It follows that the rate of decrease of the phase shift through an odd multiple of $(\pi/2)$ cannot be arbitrarily rapid, and that the peak in the cross section must be broad (compared to the energy interval between successive peaks). Such a situation can be termed a broad resonance in contrast to the narrow resonances that can occur when a phase shift <u>increases</u> rapidly through an odd multiple of $(\pi/2)$.

<u>$\ell > 0$</u>

The phase shift for $\ell=0$, given by equation (1-70), is the sum of a smoothly varying term, $-ka$, and a term containing tan (pa) which can show rapid variations, as k or λ changes. The phase shifts for $\ell>0$, are also the sum of two terms, which behave in a similar manner. This is seen most easily if we consider the special case for which $(ka)>>\ell$. This allows us to replace the Bessel function $s_\ell(x)$ and $c_\ell(x)$ by their asymptotic forms for large x, (1-25), and we find at once that

$$\delta_\ell(k) \simeq -(ka - \ell\pi/2) + \tan^{-1}\left[\frac{k}{p}\tan(pa - \ell\pi/2)\right] \qquad (1\text{-}76)$$

The phase shift again tends to $(n\pi)$ as $k\to 0$ and to zero as $k\to\infty$, but for small values of k, it is possible for δ_ℓ to <u>increase</u> rapidly through $(n + 1/2)\pi$ before decreasing.

To discuss the low energy variation of $\delta_\ell(k)$, we can use equations (1-25) to approximate $s_\ell(kr)$ and $c_\ell(kr)$ for small k, and the corresponding derivatives $s'_\ell(kr)$, $c'_\ell(kr)$. Using these approximations in (1-69), we find

$$\tan \delta_\ell \approx \frac{(ak)^{2\ell+1}}{(2\ell+1)!!(2\ell-1)!!} \left(\frac{(\ell+1)s_\ell(pa) - (pa)s'_\ell(pa)}{(pa)s'_\ell(pa) + \ell s_\ell(pa)} \right) \tag{1-77a}$$

If in addition λ is large, $(\lambda >> k)$, so that $s_\ell(pa)$, $s'_\ell(pa)$ can be replaced by their asymptotic forms, a good approximation to $\tan \delta_\ell$ is

$$\tan \delta_\ell \approx \frac{-(ak)^{2\ell+1}}{(2\ell+1)!!(2\ell-1)!!} \left(\frac{(pa)\cot(pa-\ell\pi/2) - (\ell+1)}{(pa)\cot(pa-\ell\pi/2) + \ell} \right) \tag{1-77b}$$

In contrast to the $\ell=0$ case, it is possible for δ_ℓ $(\ell \neq 0)$ to increase rapidly through an odd multiple of $\pi/2$ and this occurs at a value of k for which the denominator in (1-77b) vanishes. If this value of k is k_R, and remembering that $\lambda >> k$, we can expand $\tan \delta_\ell$ about $k = k_R$, to obtain

$$\tan \delta_\ell \approx \frac{(ak)^{2\ell+1}}{[(2\ell-1)!!]^2} \quad \frac{1}{b(k^2 - k_R^2)},$$

where, provided $p^2a^2 >> \ell(\ell+1)$,

$$b = \frac{\partial}{\partial k^2} \left(pa \cot(pa - \ell\pi/2) \right)_{k=k_R} \approx - \left(\frac{a^2}{2} \right).$$

In terms of the energy, $E = \hbar^2 k^2/2m$, we find that when E is close to E_R the phase shift is given by:

$$\tan \delta_\ell = - \frac{\Gamma(E)}{2(E - E_R)}, \tag{1-78a}$$

where

$$\Gamma(E) = \frac{(ak)^{2\ell+1}}{[(2\ell-1)!!]^2} \left(\frac{2\hbar^2}{ma^2} \right). \tag{1-78b}$$

Under the conditions $\lambda >> k$, $pa >> \ell$, $\Gamma(E_R)$ is small compared with E_R, so that $\tan \delta_\ell$ is small except in a region of width $\Gamma(E_R)$ centered about $E=E_R$, at which energy the phase shift increases rapidly with increasing energy passing through an odd multiple of $\pi/2$. This behavior gives rise to a sharp peak in the cross section which we may describe as a narrow resonance. The scattering amplitude T_ℓ has the form, for E close to E_R,

$$T_\ell = e^{i\delta_\ell} \sin \delta_\ell = \frac{-\Gamma/2}{(E - E_R) + i\Gamma/2}\,, \tag{1-79a}$$

and the total cross section for the ℓth partial wave is

$$\sigma_\ell = \frac{\pi}{k^2} (2\ell + 1) \left(\frac{\Gamma^2}{(E - E_R)^2 + \Gamma^2/4} \right) \tag{1-79b}$$

This is known as a Breit-Wigner resonance formula, in which the energy E_R is known as the position, and $\Gamma(E_R)$ as the width, of the resonance.

The physical significance of a narrow resonance can be seen if the amplitude N_ℓ of the wave function, $N_\ell s_\ell(pr)$, inside the well is computed. To produce a standard of comparison, we shall normalize the wave outside the well so that it is of unit amplitude,

$$f_\ell(r) \sim \sin (kr - \ell\pi/2 + \delta_\ell), \; r >> a$$

and we then find

$$N_\ell \approx \left(\frac{\hbar^2}{ma^2}\right) \frac{(ak)^{\ell+1} P_R}{(2\ell - 1)!!\,[(E - E_R)^2 + \Gamma^2/4]^{\frac{1}{2}}}\,. \tag{1-80}$$

The amplitude of the wave function inside the well is very small, except near $E = E_R$ when the probability of finding the scattered particle in the well becomes large. At the energy of a narrow resonance, the particle is nearly bound in the well, forming a metastable state. Such states are of great importance in determining the characteristics of atomic and nuclear scattering phenomena and we shall study their properties in some detail in later sections of the book.

The theory of the repulsive square well (A<0) is left as an exercise for the reader. It may be developed most easily by replacing λ by $i\lambda$ in the formulae that we have obtained.

Hard sphere scattering

Another interesting example is that in which $A \to +\infty$, that is there is an infinite repulsion for $r<a$. The wave function cannot penetrate into the region $r<a$, so the boundary condition that determinates the phase shifts is

$$f_\ell(a) = 0.$$

For $r>a$ we have

$$f_\ell(r) = s_\ell(kr) + \tan\delta_\ell c_\ell(kr),$$

so that

$$\tan\delta_\ell = -\frac{s_\ell(ka)}{c_\ell(ka)} . \tag{1-81}$$

When $\ell=0$, this shows that $\delta_0 = -(ka)$, and the scattering cross section at zero energy becomes

$$\sigma(0) = 4\pi a^2 \tag{1-82}$$

which is four times the classical value.

For large k, ($ka >> \ell$) we can use the asymptotic forms of the Bessel functions to obtain

$$\delta_\ell \cong -ka + \ell\pi/2. \tag{1-83}$$

The total cross section is then

$$\sigma(\text{tot}) = \frac{4\pi}{k^2}\sum_{\ell=0}^{\ell_{max}} (2\ell + 1)\sin^2(-ka + \ell\pi/2). \tag{1-84}$$

If we take the maximum value of ℓ in the sum to be (see page 12) $\ell_{max} = ka$, successive terms in the series can be paired, giving

$$\sigma(\text{tot}) = \frac{4\pi}{k^2}\Big\{[\sin^2(ka) + \sin^2(ka - \pi/2)] +$$
$$+ 2[\sin^2(ka - \pi/2) + \sin^2(ka - 2\pi/2)] + \ldots\Big\}$$
$$= \frac{4\pi}{k^2}\sum_{\ell=0}^{\ell_{max}} (\ell) \approx 2\pi a^2 \tag{1-85}$$

This is double the classical value, which at first sight would seem contrary to experience. The explanation is that at high energies, half the cross section is concentrated into a narrow diffraction peak in the forward direction, which is unobservable under macroscopic conditions.

The differential cross section, in the high energy limit can be shown to be

$$\frac{d\sigma}{d\Omega} = \frac{1}{4} a^2 \left[1 + \cot^2 (\theta/2) J_1^2(ka \sin \theta)\right] \tag{1-86}$$

where J_1 is the first order Bessel function. For small x $J_1(x) \cong x/2$ while for large x it oscillates according to

$$J_1(x) \sim \left(\frac{2}{\pi x}\right)^{\frac{1}{2}} \cos (x - \frac{3}{4}\pi) \tag{1-87}$$

The first term in (1-86) is isotropic and is the same as the classical differential cross section, while the second describes the diffraction scattering, which is concentrated in a peak of angular width $\sim(\pi/ka)$.

1-5 INELASTIC SCATTERING AND THE OPTICAL THEOREM

In section (1-1), we saw that absorption or inelastic scattering can be described by a complex potential. The radial wave function in this case will still be the regular solution of equation (1-20), but the asymptotic form of $f_\ell(r)$ must be modified. When absorption takes place, the outgoing radial flux in each partial wave must be less than the ingoing flux, so that in place of (1-37) we may write

$$S_\ell(k) = \eta_\ell e^{2i\delta_\ell} , \tag{1-88}$$

where η_ℓ which is called the inelasticity is a real number in the range $0 < \eta < 1$. When no absorption takes place η_ℓ is equal to one. The partial wave scattering amplitude T_ℓ which is connected to $S_\ell(k)$ by (1-35b) is now expressed as

$$T_\ell(k) = \frac{1}{2i} (\eta_\ell e^{2i\delta_\ell} - 1) \tag{1-89}$$

Correspondingly the complete scattering amplitude $f(\theta)$

becomes

$$f_\ell(\theta) = \sum_{\ell=0}^{\infty} \frac{1}{2ik}(\eta_\ell e^{2i\delta_\ell} - 1)(2\ell + 1)P_\ell(\cos\theta). \quad (1\text{-}90)$$

We can define an absorption cross section for the ℓth partial wave as being equal to the net ingoing flux divided by the incident flux. The contribution to the outgoing radial current from one partial wave can be found by using one term in the expansion (1-19) in the expression for j_r, (1-13). For large r, neglecting terms in r^{-3}, we find

$$j_r \sim \frac{\hbar}{2mir^2}\left(f_\ell^* \frac{\partial f_\ell}{\partial r} - f_\ell \frac{\partial f_\ell^*}{\partial r}\right)[P_\ell(\cos\theta)]^2. \quad (1\text{-}91)$$

This can be calculated from $f_\ell^a(r)$ given by (1-35a), giving

$$j_r = \frac{-\hbar}{4mr^2}\,\frac{(2\ell + 1)^2}{k}(1 - |S_\ell|)^2\,[P_\ell(\cos\theta)]^2 \quad (1\text{-}92)$$

$$= \frac{-\hbar}{4mr^2}\,\frac{1}{k}(1 - \eta_\ell^2)(2\ell + 1)^2\,[P_\ell(\cos\theta)]^2 \quad (1\text{-}93)$$

The flux absorbed in a sphere of radius r surrounding the scattering center is

$$-\int_{(4\pi)} j_r r^2 d\Omega = \frac{\hbar}{mk}\,\pi(2\ell + 1)\,(1 - \eta_\ell^2). \quad (1\text{-}94)$$

Dividing by the incident flux $F = (\hbar k/m)$ (see 1.12), the absorption cross section σ_ℓ (abs) is

$$\sigma_\ell\,(\text{abs}) = \frac{\pi(2\ell + 1)}{k^2}(1 - \eta_\ell^2). \quad (1\text{-}95)$$

The elastic scattering cross section for the ℓth partial wave becomes

$$\sigma_\ell\,(\textbf{el}) = \frac{4\pi(2\ell + 1)}{k^2}|T_\ell|^2 = \frac{\pi(2\ell + 1)}{k^2}(1 + \eta_\ell^2 - 2\eta_\ell\cos 2\delta_\ell), \quad (1\text{-}96)$$

and the total cross section for the ℓth partial wave is

$$\sigma_\ell(\text{tot}) = \sigma_\ell(\text{el}) + \sigma_\ell(\text{abs}) = \frac{2\pi(2\ell + 1)}{k^2}(1 - \eta_\ell \cos 2\delta_\ell). \quad (1\text{-}97)$$

Several important inequalities are apparent from these expressions:

$$\sigma_\ell(\text{el}) \leq \frac{4\pi(2\ell + 1)}{k^2}, \quad \delta_\ell(\text{abs}) \leq \frac{\pi(2\ell + 1)}{k^2}, \quad \sigma_\ell(\text{tot}) \leq 4\pi\frac{(2\ell + 1)}{k^2}. \quad (1\text{-}98a)$$

When the absorption cross section attains its greatest value, the inelasticity parameter η_ℓ must vanish and under these circumstances from (1-96) and (1-97) we see that

$$\sigma_\ell(\text{el}) = \sigma_\ell(\text{abs}) = \frac{1}{2}\sigma_\ell(\text{tot}). \quad (1\text{-}98b)$$

It should be noted that the ratio $\sigma_\ell(\text{abs})/\sigma_\ell(\text{el})$ can only become large when both $\sigma_\ell(\text{abs})$ and $\sigma_\ell(\text{el})$ are well below their maximum values.

Examining (1-97) and (1-89) we see that

$$\sigma_\ell(\text{tot}) = \frac{4\pi(2\ell + 1)}{k^2}\text{Im}T_\ell \quad (1\text{-}99)$$

and the complete total cross section is

$$\sigma(\text{tot}) = \sum_{\ell=0}^{\infty} \sigma_\ell(\text{tot}) = \sum_{\ell=0}^{\infty} \frac{4\pi(2\ell + 1)}{k^2}\text{Im}T_\ell \quad (1\text{-}100)$$

On the other hand, the forward elastic scattering amplitude is, (setting $P_\ell(1) - 1$ in 1-90),

$$f(\vec{K},\theta=0) = \sum_{\ell=0}^{\infty} (2\ell + 1)T_\ell/k, \quad (1\text{-}101)$$

On comparing (1-100) and (1-101) we obtain the result

$$\sigma(\text{tot}) = \frac{4\pi}{k}\text{Im}f_k(0) \quad (1\text{-}102)$$

This is the optical theorem. It is a statement of conservation of probability and is valid under all circumstances. In particular, it does not depend on the assumption of a local potential.

1-6 INTEGRAL EQUATIONS FOR THE WAVE FUNCTION

We shall now turn our attention to the problem of finding integral equations for the wave function $\psi(\vec{r})$ and for the scattering amplitude $f(\vec{k},\theta)$. Let us start by writing the Schrödinger equation in operator form, using the Dirac notation

$$(H - E)|\psi(E)) = 0. \tag{1-103}$$

The Hamiltonian can be split into the kinetic energy operator H_o and the potential energy operator V, so that

$$(H_o - E)|\psi(E)) = - V|\psi(E)). \tag{1-104}$$

The incident wave $|\phi(\vec{k}))$ satisfies the homogeneous equation

$$(H_o - E)|\phi(\vec{k})) = 0, \tag{1-105}$$

so that a formal solution of (1-104) can be written

$$|\psi(E)) = a|\phi(\vec{k})) + G_o(E)V|\psi(E)), \tag{1-106}$$

where a is a constant and $G_o(E)$ is the Green's operator associated with the free particle Hamiltonian H_o.

$$G_o(E) = \frac{1}{(E - H_o)} . \tag{1-107}$$

The state vector $|\psi(E))$ will be normalized by setting a=1 in what follows. The problem is to construct $G_o(E)$ in the particular representation that we wish to use. Unfortunately, $G_o(E)$ as we have written it is not completely defined. To see this we can express $G_o(E)$ in terms of the eigenvectors $|\phi(\vec{k}))$of H_o.

We shall adopt a normalization for the basis vectors $|\phi(\vec{k}))$ which is consistent with that of the plane wave function $\phi(\vec{k},\vec{r})$ (eq.1-1),

$$(\phi(\vec{k}')|\phi\ (\vec{k})) = (2\pi)^3\delta(\vec{k} - \vec{k}'), \tag{1-108}$$

with the closure relation

$$\left(\frac{1}{2\pi}\right)^3 \int d^3k\ |\phi(\vec{k}))\,(\phi(\vec{k})| = 1. \tag{1-109}$$

The required representation of G(E) is

$$G_o(E) = \left(\frac{1}{2\pi}\right)^3 \int d^3k' \; \frac{|\phi(\vec{k}'))(\phi(\vec{k}'))|}{E - E'} \qquad (1\text{-}110)$$

with $E' = (\hbar^2 k'^2/2m)$.

We are interested in positive real E, and in this interval it is seen that the integration over E′ is singular. In general, the resolvent $(H - Z)^{-1}$ of a self-adjoint operator H exists for all complex Z except on the eigenvalue spectrum of H. The eigenvalue spectrum of H_o consists of all real positive values of E and the singularity in $G_o(E)$ is a branch cut in the interval $0 \leq E \leq \infty$.

The singularity in the integrand of (1-110) can be avoided, and the integral defined, by adding a small positive or negative imaginary part ε to E, and defining $G_o^+(E)$ or $G_o^-(E)$ as the limit $\varepsilon \to 0^+$, (a more extended account of the properties of Green's functions can be found in Morse and Feshbach (1953)).

$$G_o^{\pm}(E) = \lim_{\varepsilon \to 0^+} G_o(E \pm i\varepsilon); \quad G_o(E \pm i\varepsilon) = \frac{1}{E \pm i\varepsilon - H_o} \qquad (1\text{-}111)$$

We have now to find which of the operators G_o^+ or G_o^- to use, and this is determined by imposing the boundary conditions of our problem. There are several ways in which this may be done, and we shall start by giving an argument based on the evolution in time of the state vector. First we define state vectors $|\psi^{\pm}(E))$ by using $G_o(E \pm i\varepsilon)$ in eq. (1-106). These state vectors are eigenfunctions of energy, with a time dependence of the form $\exp(-iEt/h)$. In a real scattering situation, the wave train is not of infinite duration and we must superimpose solutions to form a wave packet of finite duration. The corresponding state vector $|\Psi^{\pm}(t))$ can be constructed as follows:

$$|\Psi^{\pm}(t)) = \int_0^{\infty} \rho(E'' - E)\,|\psi^{\pm}(E''))\,e^{-iE''t/\hbar}\,dE'', \qquad (1\text{-}112)$$

where $\rho(x)$ is a function that is zero except for a narrow range of values of x about x = 0. From (1-106), and using the representation of $G_o(E \pm i\varepsilon)$ given by (1-110), the integral equation satisfied by $|\Psi^{\pm}(t))$ is found to be

$$|\Psi^{\pm}(t)) = |\phi(t)) + \int_0^{\infty} dE'' \int_0^{\infty} dE' \rho(E''-E) e^{-iE''t/\hbar} \times$$

$$\times \frac{|\phi(E'))(\phi(E')|V|\psi(E''))}{(E'' \pm i\varepsilon - E')} \tag{1-113}$$

where the first term describes the incident wave packet, unperturbed by the interaction,

$$|\phi(t)) = \int_0^{\infty} \rho(E'' - E)|\phi(E''))e^{-iE''t/h}\, dE''. \tag{1-114}$$

Provided the interaction is of limited range, the state vector at the start of the experiment is identical with the incident packet $|\phi(t))$. As time goes on, the incident packet will begin to interact with the scattering center and the state vector will no longer be identical with $|\phi(t))$. Evidently the boundary condition to be imposed on $|\Psi^+(t))$ is:

$$|\Psi(t)) \xrightarrow[t\to -\infty]{} |\phi(t)). \tag{1-115}$$

For this condition to be satisfied the second term in (1-113) has to vanish at $t \to -\infty$. The contributions to the integral over E'' arise from the singular point at $E'' = E'$. Since $|\psi(E''))$ is assumed to be a well behaved non-singular function of E'', we can set $E'' = E'$ in the matrix element $(\phi(E')|V|\psi(E''))$ and take it outside the integral over E''. The integration then involves the expression

$$I^{\pm}(t) = \lim_{\varepsilon\to 0} \int \frac{e^{-iyt/h}}{y \pm i\varepsilon}\, \rho(y + E' - E)\, dy, \tag{1-116}$$

where a change of variable from E'' to $y = (E'' - E')$ has been made. As $t \to \pm\infty$, the infinite oscillations in the exponential factor ensure that the integral will vanish except at the singular point $y = 0$ which corresponds to $E' = E''$. To evaluate the contribution from this point, we may extend the integration over y to the whole of the real axis, and for $t > 0$ close the contour by an infinite semicircle in the lower half y plane, as in figure 1-3. No contribution to the integral arises from the semicircular contours in the limit $|t| \to \infty$, because the integral becomes exponentially small along the semi circles in this limit.

The pole in the integral of $I^+(t)$ is at $y = - i\varepsilon$. For $t<0$, this pole is outside the closed contour, and for $t>0$ it is included within the contour. Thus by Cauchy's theorem

$$\lim_{t\to-\infty} I^+(t) = 0 \;;\; \lim_{t\to+\infty} I^+(t) = -2\pi i\rho(E' - E) \tag{1-117a}$$

Correspondingly, the pole in the integrand of $I^-(t)$ is at $y = + i\varepsilon$, which is within the closed contour for $t<0$ and outside the contour for $t>0$, so that

$$\lim_{t\to-\infty} I^-(t) = 2\pi i\rho(E' - E) \;;\; \lim_{t\to+\infty} I^-(t) = 0 \tag{1-117b}$$

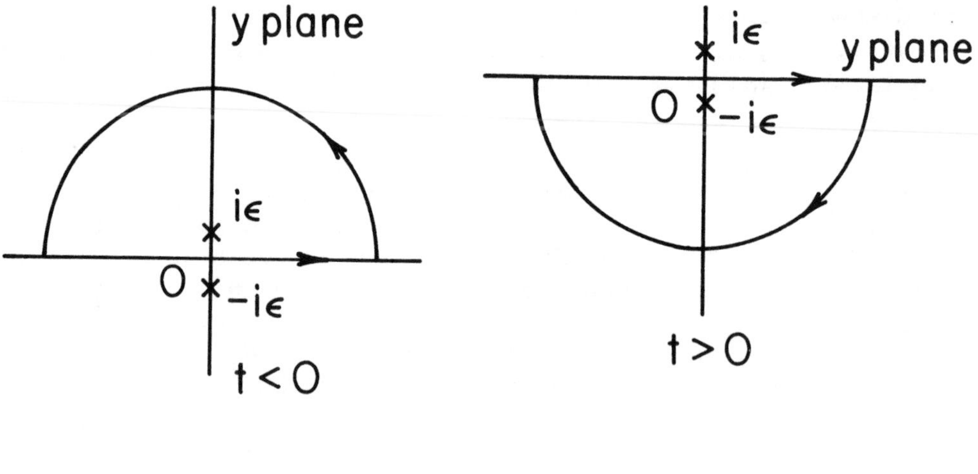

Figure 1-3 Contours for the evaluation of singular integrals

Thus it is the solution $|\Psi^+(t))$ that satisfies the boundary condition, since it coincides with the incident packet as $t\to-\infty$. We have that

$$\lim_{t\to-\infty} |\Psi^+(t)) = |\phi(t)), \tag{1-118a}$$

and

$$\lim_{t\to+\infty} |\Psi^+(t)) = |\phi(t)) - 2\pi i \int_0^\infty \rho(E'-E)e^{-iE't/h}|\phi(E')) \times$$

$$\times (\phi(E')|V|\psi^+(E'))dE'.$$

(1-118b)

Later we shall be interested in the solution $|\Psi^-(t))$. This is a solution which coincides with the unperturbed packet in the infinite future:

$$\lim_{t\to+\infty} |\Psi^-(t)) = |\phi(t)). \quad (1\text{-}119)$$

Green's functions in configuration space

The method of specifying which of the Green's operations G_o^+ or G_o^- satisfy the physical scattering boundary conditions that we have given is rather general and will be useful to us later. We shall now return to the position representation. The wave equation is (1-5).

$$\frac{-2m}{\hbar^2}(H_o - E)\psi(\vec{r}) = (\nabla^2 + k^2)\psi(\vec{r}) = U(r)\psi(\vec{r}). \quad (1\text{-}120)$$

The integral equation for $\psi\pm(\vec{r})$ is of the form

$$\psi\pm(\vec{r}) = \phi(\vec{k},\vec{r}) + \int G_o^{\pm}(\vec{r},\vec{r}')U(r')\psi^{\pm}(\vec{r}')d^3r'), \quad (1\text{-}121)$$

where $\phi(\vec{k},\vec{r})$ is the incident plane wave (1-1). In order that $\psi^{\pm}(r)$ should satisfy the Schrödinger equation, it can be seen by substitution that the Green's function $G_o^{\pm}(\vec{r},\vec{r}')$ must be a solution of the equation

$$(\nabla^2 + k^2)G_o^{\pm}(\vec{r},\vec{r}') = \delta(\vec{r} - \vec{r}'). \quad (1\text{-}122)$$

Apart from a factor $(2m/\hbar^2)$, $G_o^{\pm}(\vec{r},\vec{r}')$ is just the matrix element of $G_o^{\pm}(E)$, and from (1-111),

$$G_o^{\pm}(\vec{r},\vec{r}') = \frac{\hbar^2}{2m}(\vec{r}\,|G_o^{\pm}(E)|\vec{r}'). \quad (1\text{-}123)$$

Using (1-110),

$$G_o^{\pm}(\vec{r},\vec{r}') = (2\pi)^{-3} \, d^3k' \, \frac{(\vec{r}'|\phi(\vec{k}'))(\phi(\vec{k}')|\vec{r}')}{(k^2 \pm i\varepsilon - k'^2)} \tag{1-124}$$

The wave functions $(r|\phi(\vec{k}))$ are the plane waves $\phi(\vec{k},\vec{r}))$

$$(\vec{r}|\phi(\vec{k})) \equiv \phi(\vec{k},\vec{r}) = \exp(i\vec{k}\cdot\vec{r})$$

from which

$$G_o^{\pm}(\vec{r},\vec{r}') = (2\pi)^{-3} \int d^3k' \, \frac{\exp\,(i\vec{k}' \cdot (\vec{r} - \vec{r}'))}{k^2 \pm i\varepsilon - k'^2} \tag{1-125}$$

The same expression can be found more directly by expanding $G_o(\vec{r},\vec{r}')$ as $G_o^{\pm}(\vec{r},\vec{r}') = \int d^3k \; a\,(\vec{k}) \; \exp(i\vec{k}\vec{r})$, and determining $a(\vec{k})$ by inserting this expression in (1-122).

We shall first treat the case of G_o^+. The integral is easily evaluated using contour integration. In spherical polar coordinates (k,θ,ϕ):

$$\int d^3k' = \int_0^{2\pi} d\phi \int_{-1}^{1} d(\cos\,\theta) \int_0^{\infty} k'^2 dk'.$$

from which, on integrating over ϕ and θ,

$$G_o^{+}(\vec{r},\vec{r}') = \frac{1}{4\pi^2} \int_0^{\infty} k' \, \frac{\exp(ik'R)-\exp(-ik'R)}{iR(k^2 + i\varepsilon - k'^2)} dk' \tag{1-126}$$

where $R = |\vec{r} - \vec{r}'|$. The integral is easily transformed into the form

$$G_o^{+}(r,r') = \frac{1}{8\pi^2} \, \frac{1}{iR} \int_{\infty}^{\infty} \exp(ik'R) \left(\frac{1}{k + i\varepsilon' - k'} - \frac{1}{k + i\varepsilon' + k'} \right) dk'.$$

where ε' is a small quantity of the first order $(\varepsilon'>0)$. In fact neglecting the second order quantity ε'^2, we have $2k\varepsilon'=\varepsilon$.

The integrand vanishes exponentially as $\text{Im}k' \to \infty$ so that the integral can be closed by an infinite semi-circle in the upper half k' plane. Using Cauchy's theorem, the first term in curved brackets makes the contribution,

$$\int_{-\infty}^{\infty} \frac{\exp(ik'R)}{k + i\varepsilon - k'} dk' = -2\pi i \exp(ikR).$$

The pole in the second term in curved brackets at $k' = -k - i\varepsilon$ is excluded from the contour and makes no contribution. The final result is then:

$$G_o^+(\vec{r},\vec{r}') = \frac{-1}{4\pi} R^{-1} \exp(ikR). \tag{1-127a}$$

In just the same way we can find G_o^- which is

$$G_o^-(\vec{r},\vec{r}') = \frac{-1}{4\pi} R^{-1} \exp(-ikR). \tag{1-127b}$$

From the analysis of the time dependence of the wave function, we expect the second term in the equation for ψ^+ (1-121) to represent scattered outgoing spherical waves, which is the correct boundary condition for physical scattering. For large $|\vec{r}|$ we have that

$$R^{-1}\exp(ikR) = r^{-1}\exp \; ik(r - r' \cos \alpha)$$

where α is the angle between $\vec{r}$ and $\vec{r}'$. The asymptotic form of $\psi^+(\vec{r})$ is then

$$\psi^+(\vec{r}) \sim \exp(i\vec{k}\cdot\vec{r}) + f^+(\vec{k},\theta) r^{-1} \exp(ikr) \tag{1-128}$$

where the scattering amplitude $f^+(\vec{k},\theta)$ is[7]

$$f^+(\vec{k},\theta) = -\frac{1}{4\pi} \int \exp(-i\vec{k}'\cdot\vec{r}') U(r') \psi^+(\vec{r}') d^3r' \tag{1-129}$$

$$= -\frac{1}{4\pi} (\phi(\vec{k}'), U\psi^+)$$

$$= -\frac{1}{4\pi} \left(\frac{2m}{\hbar^2}\right) \langle \phi(\vec{k}') | V | \psi^+ \rangle$$

where $\vec{k}'$ is a vector in the direction of $\vec{r}$, and of magnitude $|\vec{k}'| = |\vec{k}|$ so that $kr' \cos \alpha = \vec{k}'\cdot \vec{r}'$.

The solution $\psi^-(\vec{r})$ has the asymptotic form

$$\psi^-(\vec{r}) \sim \exp(i\vec{k}\cdot\vec{r}) + f^-(\vec{k},\theta) r^{-1} \exp(-ikr) \tag{1-130}$$

with

$$f^-(\vec{k},\theta) = -\frac{1}{4\pi}\int \exp(i\vec{k}'\cdot\vec{r}')U(r')\psi^-(\vec{r}')d^3r'$$
$$= -\frac{1}{4\pi}(\phi(-\vec{k}'),U\psi^-) \qquad (1\text{-}131)$$

It corresponds to an incident plane wave travelling in a direction parallel to $\vec{k}$, but with incoming rather than outgoing spherical waves. From the boundary conditions (1-128), (1-130) we see that

$$\psi^-(\vec{k},\vec{r}) = \left(\psi^+(-\vec{k},\vec{r})\right)^*$$

where the wave functions are labeled by the incident wave vectors $\vec{k}$, or $-\vec{k}$.

Time reversal invariance

To interpret the solution $\psi^-(\vec{r})$ further, we notice that if the Hamiltonian does not depend on time and is real, the Schrödinger equation is invariant under the combined operations of $t\to -t$ and complex conjugation. This combined operation is known as time reversal. Under these circumstances if $\Psi(t)$ satisfies

$$H\Psi(t) = ih\frac{\partial\Psi(t)}{\partial t} \qquad (1\text{-}132)$$

then so does the wave function $\Psi_T(t) \equiv \Psi^*(-t)$. The wave function Ψ_T is known as the time reversed wave function. It is clear that under the time reversal operation, the momentum and position vectors behave like

$$\vec{p}\to -\vec{p} \text{ and } \vec{r}\to\vec{r}$$

so that the wave vector $\vec{k}$ transforms as $\vec{k}\to -\vec{k}$ (1-133) and the angular momentum vector $\vec{J}$, like $\vec{J}\to -\vec{J}$.

It follows that the time reversed wave function corresponding to $\psi^+(\vec{k},\vec{r})$ is $[\psi^+(-\vec{k},\vec{r})]^*$ which is equal to $\psi^-(\vec{k},\vec{r})$. The scattering amplitudes $f^+(\vec{k},\theta)$, $f^-(\vec{k},\theta)$ are then connected, using an obvious notation, by

$$[f^+(\vec{k}\to\vec{k}')]^* = f^-(-\vec{k}'\to -\vec{k}). \qquad (1\text{-}134)$$

The amplitude $[f^+(\vec{k})]^*$ describes scattering from $\vec{k}$ to $\vec{k}'$

and $f^-(\vec{k})$ describes scattering from $-\vec{k}'$ to $-\vec{k}$, which is the time reversed situation.

The partial wave Green's functions

The Green's functions g^+ introduced earlier (1-53) are just the coefficients of the expansion of G_0^+ in Legendre polynomials. To see this we use the expansion (Morse and Feshbach, 1953, p.1466)

$$|\vec{r}-\vec{r}'|^{-1}\exp(ik|\vec{r}-\vec{r}'|) = \sum_{\ell=0}^{\infty}(2\ell+1)ikj_\ell(kr_<)h_\ell(kr_>)P_\ell(\cos\theta), \tag{1-135a}$$

where $h_\ell(x) = j_\ell(x) + in_\ell(x)$, θ is the angle between $\vec{r}$ and $\vec{r}'$, and $r_<$, $r_>$ are the lesser and greater of $\vec{r}$ and $\vec{r}'$ respectively.

In terms of the functions s_ℓ, c_ℓ and $e_\ell^\pm$ introduced earlier we see that

$$|\vec{r}-\vec{r}'|\exp ik|\vec{r}-\vec{r}'| = \sum_{\ell=0}^{\infty}(krr')^{-1}(2\ell+1)\ s_\ell(kr_<)\ e_\ell^+(kr_>)\ P_\ell(\cos\theta) \tag{1-135b}$$

and from (1-127a) and (1-53), we obtain:

$$G_0^+(\vec{r},\vec{r}') = \sum_{\ell=0}^{\infty}\left(\frac{2\ell+1}{4\pi rr'}\right) g_\ell^+(r,r')P_\ell(\cos\theta). \tag{1-136}$$

The Green's function $G_0^P(\vec{r},\vec{r}') = 1/2[G_0^+(\vec{r},\vec{r}') + G_0^-(\vec{r},\vec{r}')]$ is real and the coefficients in the Lengendre polynomial expansion of this function are the Green's functions $g_\ell^P(r,r')$ (1-49), which generate the standing wave solutions of the radial equations,

$$G_0^P(\vec{r},\vec{r}') = \sum_{\ell=0}^{\infty}\left(\frac{2\ell+1}{4\pi rr'}\right)g_\ell^P(r,r')P_\ell(\cos\theta). \tag{1-137}$$

The Born approximation

The Born approximation for the scattering amplitude is found by substituting the incident wave for the exact wave function on the right hand side (1-129),

$$-4\pi f^B(k,\theta) = \int \exp(-i\vec{k}'\cdot\vec{r})\ U(r)\exp(i\vec{k}\cdot\vec{r})\ d^3r \qquad (1\text{-}138)$$

This will be justified if the difference $|\exp(i\vec{k}\cdot\vec{r})-\psi^+(\vec{r})|$ is small over the range where U is large. From our discussion in section 1-3, this difference is seen to be small provided that the phase shifts δ_ℓ are small for all ℓ. The critical case is ℓ=0 and from (1-57) a sufficient condition is seen to be

$$\left(\frac{a\bar{U}}{k}\right) << 1, \qquad (1\text{-}139)$$

where $\bar{U}$ is the average depth of the potential well[8]. The condition is sufficient, but is too restrictive, for example it will not work for small k, and under some circumstances the Born approximations can be accurate at all energies. To obtain another condition valid for all k, we may estimate $|\psi^+(\vec{r}) - \exp(i\vec{k}\cdot\vec{r})| \equiv I(\vec{r})$ by substituting the incident plane wave into the right hand side of (1-120),

$$I(\vec{r}) = -\ (4\pi)^{-1}\int R^{-1}\exp(ikR)U(r')\exp(i\vec{k}\cdot\vec{r}')d^3r'$$

where $\vec{R} = \vec{r}' - \vec{r}$. Changing the variable of integration to $\vec{R}$ we have immediately

$$I(\vec{r}) = (4\pi)^{-1}\int R^{-1}\exp\ i(kR + \vec{k}\cdot\vec{R})U(|\vec{r}+\vec{R}|)d^3R$$

so that

$$|I(\vec{r})| \leq (4\pi)^{-1}\ R^{-1}|U(|\vec{r}+\vec{R}|)|d^3R$$

The value of the integral is approximately $a^2\bar{U}$, so a sufficient condition for the Born approximation to be accurate at all energies is

$$|a^2\bar{U}| << 1. \qquad (1\text{-}140)$$

By examining eq. (1-74) we see that in the case of the square well, this is the condition for the potential to be too weak to support a bound state, and in fact it can be shown generally that if bound states are absent, the Born approximation will converge.

In terms of the momentum transfer $\hbar\vec{K}$, where $\vec{K} = \vec{k} - \vec{k}'$, the scattering amplitude in the Born approximation is

$$f^B(\theta) = -(4\pi)^{-1}\int \exp(i\vec{K}\cdot\vec{r})U(r)d^3r \qquad (1\text{-}141)$$

and it is seen that the scattering amplitude in Born's approximation is proportional to the Fourier transform of the potential. The Fourier transform of a potential well of range a is only large for values of K such that

$$K \lesssim \frac{1}{a}$$

and it follows, on expressing K in terms of the scattering angle θ, $K = 2k \sin \theta/2$, that at high energies, where Born's approximation is valid, scattering is confined to an angular region about the forward direction of extent

$$\theta \lesssim (ka)^{-1} \qquad (1\text{-}142)$$

As an example, we may again take the zero order or static interaction between an electron and a hydrogen atom (1-63). On performing the integration (1-141) we find (in atomic units)

$$|f^B(\theta)|^2 = \frac{4(8 + K^2)^2}{(4 + K^2)^4} = \frac{(2 + k^2 \sin^2 (\theta/2))^2}{4(1 + k^2 \sin^2 (\theta/2))^4}\ . \qquad (1\text{-}143)$$

This is expected to be accurate at energies over a hundred electron volts, and is strongly peaked in the forward direction. For large k^2, it is easy to show that the total cross section

$$\sigma = 2\pi \int |f^B(\theta)|^2 d(\cos \theta) \qquad (1\text{-}144)$$

is proportional to 1/E, where E is the incident energy.

The Born expansion

If the integral equation (1-121) is written in operator form as in (1-106)

$$|\psi^+) = |\phi(\vec{k})) + G_0^+(E)V|\psi^+), \qquad (1\text{-}145)$$

a further equation can be obtained by substituting

$|\phi) + G_o^+V|\psi^+)$ for $|\psi^+)$ on the right hand side:-

$$|\psi^+) = |\phi(\vec{k})) + G_o^+V|\phi(\vec{k})) + G_o^+VG_o^+V|\psi^+). \tag{1-146}$$

Repeating this iterative process, an infinite series for $|\psi^+)$ can be obtained

$$|\psi^+) = (1 + G_o^+V + G_o^+VG_o^+V + \ldots.)|\phi(\vec{k})). \tag{1-147}$$

The scattering amplitude can also be expanded by substituting this series for $|\psi^+)$ on the right hand side of (1-129),

$$f(\vec{k},\theta) = -\frac{1}{4\pi}\left(\frac{2m}{\hbar^2}\right)(\phi(\vec{k}')|V|\psi^+) \tag{1-148a}$$

$$= -\frac{1}{4\pi}\left(\frac{2m}{h^2}\right)(\phi(\vec{k}')|V + VG_o^+V + VG_o^+VG_o^+V + ..|\phi(\vec{k})), \tag{1-148b}$$

where we have labeled the incident unperturbed state as $|\phi(\vec{k}))$ and the final unperturbed state as $|\phi(\vec{k}'))$. The amplitude $f(\vec{k},\theta)$ can be written as

$$-\left(\frac{2\pi\hbar^2}{m}\right) f(\vec{k},\theta) = T(\vec{k}',\vec{k}) = (\phi(\vec{k}')|V + VG^+V|\phi(\vec{k})), \tag{1-149}$$

where

$$G^+ = G_o^+ + G_o^+VG_o^+ + \ldots. \tag{1-150}$$

Comparing (1-148a) and (1-149), we see that G^+ is also a Green's function, with the property

$$|\psi^+) = |\phi(\vec{k})) + G^+V|\phi_k). \tag{1-151}$$

From the Schrödinger equation

$$(H - E)|\psi^+) = 0, \quad H = H_o + V,$$

we see that G^+ is the resolvent of the <u>total</u> Hamiltonian H

$$G^{+}(E) = \lim_{\varepsilon \to 0^{+}} \frac{1}{E + i\varepsilon - H} . \tag{1-152}$$

The operator $(V + VG^{+}V)$ is known as the transition operator, $t(E)$,

$$t(E) \equiv V + VG^{+}(E)V, \tag{1-153a}$$

The transition matrix is given in terms of $t(E)$ by

$$T(\vec{k}',\vec{k},E) = (\phi(\vec{k}')\,|t(E)|\,\phi(\vec{k})). \tag{1-153b}$$

The transition matrix $T(\vec{k}',\vec{k},E)$ as defined by (1-153b) can be considered to be a function of the three variables $\vec{k}'$, $\vec{k}$ and E. For physical elastic scattering these kinematical variables are restricted by conservation of energy, which requires that $k'^2=k^2= 2mE/\hbar$. When the function $T(\vec{k}',\vec{k},E)$ satisfies this condition it is said to be'on the energy shell'.

The convergence of series such as (1-147) or (1-150) is by no means guaranteed. The conditions under which the series for the Green's function G^{+} converges has been investigated for a wide class of potentials by Klein and Zemach (1958), and the Born expansions of the partial wave amplitudes have been discussed by Kohn (1952), Jost and Pais (1951) and Manning (1965). In general terms (we refer the reader to the original papers for the precise conditions), it can be said that the Born series always converges at sufficiently high energies, provided the potential satisfies the conditions.

$$\int |\vec{r} - \vec{r}'|^{-1} V(r')dr' < C \text{ all } r,$$

$$\int |\vec{r} - \vec{r}'|^{-1} V(r')dr' \sim 0 \left(\frac{1}{r}\right) \text{ as } r \to \infty.$$

For the Born expansion to be convergent at all energies requires conditions to be satisfied that are equivalent to demanding that the potential possesses no bound states.

The momentum representation

It is often useful to represent the integral equation (1-145) in momentum space[9], rather than in configuration space, because the Green's function G_0 is diagonal in this representation. The unperturbed states are described by a wave function $\Phi(\vec{k},\vec{q})$, where

$$\Phi(\vec{k},\vec{q})=(\vec{q}|\phi(\vec{k})) = \left(\frac{1}{2\pi}\right)^{3/2} \int \exp(-i\vec{q}\cdot\vec{r})\phi(\vec{k},\vec{r})d^3r = (2\pi)^{3/2}\delta(\vec{k}-\vec{q}). \tag{1-154}$$

The wave functions $\Phi(\vec{k},\vec{q})$ satisfy the closure relation (compare 1-109)

$$(2\pi)^{-3}\int d^3k\Phi^*(\vec{k},\vec{q})\Phi(\vec{k},\vec{q}\,') = \delta(\vec{q}\,' - \vec{q}).$$

correspondingly the Green's function for the operator $(H_o - E)$ in the momentum representation $G_o(\vec{q},\vec{q}\,')$ is

$$G_o^{\pm}(q,q') = \frac{\hbar^2}{2m}(\vec{q}\,|G_o^{\pm}|\vec{q}\,') = \frac{\delta(\vec{q} - \vec{q}\,')}{k^2 \pm i\varepsilon - q^2}. \tag{1-155}$$

The integral equation for the momentum space wave function $\psi_{\pm}(\vec{q}) = (\vec{q}|\psi_{\pm})$ becomes

$$\psi^{\pm}(\vec{k},\vec{q})=\Phi(\vec{k},\vec{q}) + \frac{1}{k^2 \pm i\varepsilon - q^2}\int \tilde{U}(\vec{q}-\vec{q}\,')\psi^{\pm}(\vec{k},\vec{q}\,')d^3q', \tag{1-156}$$

where $\tilde{U}(q)$ is the Fourier transform of the potential $U(r)$

$$\tilde{U}(\vec{q}) = (2\pi)^{-3/2}\int d^3r \exp(-i\vec{q}\cdot\vec{r})U(r). \tag{1-157}$$

From (1-129) the scattering amplitude can be written as

$$-4\pi f^+(\vec{k},\theta)= \int d^3q \int d^3q' \, (\phi(k')|\vec{q})(\vec{q}|U|\vec{q}\,')(\vec{q}\,'|\psi^+(\vec{k})),$$

from which

$$-4\pi f^+(\vec{k},\theta) = \int d^3q'\tilde{U}(\vec{k}' - \vec{q}\,')\psi^+(\vec{k},\vec{q}\,'). \tag{1-158}$$

To recover the Born approximation, we substitute the incident wave $(2\pi)^{3/2}\delta(k-q)$ for $\psi^+(\vec{k},\vec{q}\,')$ in (1-155), giving

$$-4\pi f^B(k,\theta) = (2\pi)^{3/2}\,\tilde{U}(|\vec{k}' - \vec{k}|), \tag{1-159}$$

which agrees with (1-138).

1-7 SOME ANALYTIC PROPERTIES OF THE PARTIAL WAVE AMPLITUDES

Many results of interest have come from the study of scattering amplitudes as a function of complex k or E[10]. We shall study the partial wave amplitudes for the large class of potentials that can be represented by a superposition of exponentials,

$$U(r) = \int_{\mu}^{\infty} c(\alpha)\exp(-\alpha r)d\alpha. \tag{1-160}$$

where $\mu>0$ and where the weight function $c(\alpha)$ can be taken to satisfy $c(\alpha) = 0$ for $\alpha<\mu$.

The radial wave functions $f_\ell(r)$ are functions both of k and r and we shall display this by using in this section the notation $f_\ell(k,r)\equiv f_\ell(r)$. These functions satisfy equation (1-20) so that explicitly we have:-

$$\left(\frac{d^2}{dr^2} - \frac{\ell(\ell + 1)}{r^2} - U(r) + k^2\right) f_\ell(k,r) = 0.$$

From our earlier discussion in section (1-2), we know that an arbitrary solution of this equation is asymptotic, at large r, to a combination of the functions $s_\ell(kr)$ and $c_\ell(kr)$ or, alternatively, to a combination of the functions $e_\ell^{\pm}(kr)$. For large (kr) the functions $e_\ell^{\pm}(kr)$ have the form (equation 1-28) $\exp \pm i(kr - \ell\pi/2)$ and it is therefore possible to define solutions $f_\ell^{\pm}(k,r)$ of the radial equation that behave like $e_\ell^{\pm}(kr)$ at large r,

$$f_\ell^{\pm}(k,r) \underset{r\to\infty}{\sim} \exp[\pm i(kr - \ell\pi/2)] \tag{1-161}$$

We now introduce a new function $\phi_\ell(k,r)$ by requiring that

$$f_\ell^{+}(k,r) = \phi_\ell(-k,r)\exp[+i(kr - \ell\pi/2)], \tag{1-162a}$$

$$f_\ell^{-}(k,r) = \phi_\ell(+k,r)\exp[-i(kr - \ell\pi/2)], \tag{1-162b}$$

where, to satisfy the boundary condition (1-161) we must have that

$$\lim_{r\to\infty} \phi_\ell(\pm k,r)=1. \tag{1-163}$$

At the origin, the functions $f_\ell^{\pm}(k,r)$, which are linear combinations of the regular and irregular solutions of the equation, must be proportional to $(kr)^{-\ell}$. This fact allows us to define coefficients $\phi_\ell(\pm k)$, called Jost functions as

$$\phi_\ell(\pm k) = \lim_{r\to 0} \frac{(\pm kr)^\ell f_\ell^{\mp}(k,r)}{(2\ell + 1)!!} \qquad (1\text{-}164a)$$

In terms of the functions $\phi_\ell(k,r)$, we have that

$$\phi_\ell(\pm k) = \lim_{r\to 0} \frac{i^\ell (\pm kr)^\ell \phi_\ell(\pm k,r)}{(2\ell + 1)!!} \,. \qquad (1\text{-}164b)$$

It is now possible to find the particular combination of the functions $f_\ell^+(k,r)$ and $f_\ell^-(k,r)$ which is regular at the origin. Calling the regular solution $f_\ell^R(k,r)$ we find that

$$f_\ell^R(k,r) = \left((-1)^\ell \phi_\ell(-k) f_\ell^-(k,r) - \phi_\ell(+k) f_\ell^+(k,r)\right), \qquad (1\text{-}165)$$

and this will behave like r^ℓ at the origin.

On comparing the asymptotic form of this solution with (1-35a), it is seen that the S-matrix elements $S_\ell(k)$ can be written as

$$S_\ell(k) = (-1)^\ell \phi_\ell(k)/\phi_\ell(-k) \qquad (1\text{-}166)$$

In what follows, the case of $\ell=0$ will be treated, following the method of Martin (1965), but similar results for $\ell>0$ can be obtained. By inserting (1-162b) into the Schrödinger equation, an equation for $\phi_o(k,r)$ is obtained:-

$$\left(\frac{d^2}{dr^2} - 2ik\frac{d}{dr} - U(r)\right) \phi_o(k,r) = 0. \qquad (1\text{-}167)$$

As the potential is a superposition of exponentials, we attempt to write $\phi_o(k,r)$ in a similar form

$$\phi_o(k,r) = 1 + \int_0^\infty \rho_k(\alpha)\exp(-\alpha r)\,d\alpha. \tag{1-168}$$

The insertion of this expression for $\phi_o(k,r)$ into the equation (1-167), with the use of (1-160), leads to an integral equation for $\rho_k(\alpha)$

$$\alpha(\alpha + 2ik)\rho_k(\alpha) = c(\alpha) + \int_0^\alpha c(\alpha-\beta)\rho_k(\beta)\,d\beta. \tag{1-169}$$

As $c(\alpha)$ vanishes for $\alpha < \mu$ (see 1-160), the lower limit on the integral in this equation must be μ rather than zero, and the upper limit $(\alpha - \mu)$ rather than α, and

$$\alpha(\alpha + 2ik)\rho_k(\alpha) = c(\alpha) + \int_\mu^{\alpha-\mu} c(\alpha-\beta)\rho_k(\beta)\,d\beta. \tag{1-170}$$

We now see that $\rho_k(\alpha)$ must also vanish for $\alpha < \mu$ and the lower limit of integration in (1-168) is in fact μ. Equation (1-170) can now be solved by iteration, because if $\rho_k(\alpha)$ is known for $\alpha < n\mu$, it may be inserted on the right hand side of (1-170), giving, on the left hand side, $\rho_k(\alpha)$ in the range $\alpha < (n + 1)\mu$. For example

$$\rho_k(\alpha) = \frac{c(\alpha)}{\alpha(\alpha + 2ik)}, \mu \le \alpha < 2\mu$$

$$= \frac{1}{\alpha(\alpha + 2ik)}\left[c(\alpha) + \int_\mu^{\alpha-\mu} \frac{c(\alpha-\beta)c(\beta)}{\beta(\beta + 2ik)}\,d\beta\right], 2\mu < \alpha < 3\mu$$

$$= \ldots\ldots$$

This iterative procedure can be carried out for all complex values of k except for values of k which make $(\alpha + 2ik)$ vanish. That is except for values of k on the positive imaginary axis with $|k| > \mu/2$.

It is now necessary to check whether a finite $\rho_k(\alpha)$ exists. To do this we consider all values of k, except those on the line where $(\alpha + 2ik)$ vanishes, by requiring

$$|\alpha + 2ik| > \alpha \sin\varepsilon$$
$$|\alpha + 2ik| > 2|k| \sin\varepsilon, \tag{1-171}$$

where ε is as small as we please. Let us also introduce a positive increasing function $B(\alpha)$ such that

$$|c(\alpha)| < B(\alpha). \tag{1-172}$$

Then from (1-170)

$$|\rho_k(\alpha)| < \frac{B\ (\alpha)}{\alpha^2 \sin \varepsilon} \left(1 + \int_\mu^\alpha |\rho_k(\beta)|d\beta\right).$$

Differentiating we find that

$$\frac{d}{d\alpha} \frac{|\rho_k(\alpha)|}{y(\alpha)} < \frac{|\rho_k(\alpha)|}{y(\alpha)} \quad y(\alpha),$$

with $y(\alpha) \equiv B(\alpha)/\alpha^2 \sin \varepsilon$, from which we easily find that

$$|\rho_k(\alpha)| < \frac{B(\alpha)}{\alpha^2 \sin^2 \varepsilon} \exp\left(\int_\mu^\alpha \frac{B(\beta)}{\beta^2 \sin^2 \varepsilon} d\beta\right). \tag{1-173}$$

If we can find a function, $B(\alpha)$, such that

$$\int_\mu^\alpha (B(\beta)/\beta^2)d\beta \tag{1-174}$$

exists, it follows that $\rho_k(\alpha)$ exists everywhere except on the excluded line. Equation (1-170) then shows that $\rho_k(\alpha)$ and hence $\phi(k,r)$ are analytic functions of k, again with the exception of the excluded line. Further investigation shows that the excluded line is a branch cut, and that as $|k| \to \infty$ in any direction, $|\phi_0(k,r) - 1| \to 0$.

The condition (1-174) is satisfied with $B(\alpha) = \alpha^{1-n}, n>0$ and potentials for which $|c(\alpha)| < \alpha^{1-n}$ are those which are less singular than $1/r^2$ at the origin. For potentials which are not expressible in the form (1-160), Bargmann (1949) has shown that ϕ_0 remains analytic in the lower half k plane, and if

$$\int_0^\infty drU(r)\exp(\mu r) < \infty ,$$

$\phi_0(k,r)$ is also analytic in the upper half plane for $\mathrm{Im}k<\mu/2$.

For $\ell=0$, the Jost function $\phi_o(k) = \phi_o(k,0)$ so that $\phi_o(k)$ is analytic in the k plane except for the cut. Similar results have been obtained for $\ell>0$. From (1-169) it is seen that $\rho^*_{-k^*}(\alpha)$ satisfies the same equation as $\rho_k(\alpha)$ so that

$$\phi_o(k) = \phi_o^*(-k^*), \tag{1-175}$$

and

$$S(k) = \frac{\phi_o(k)}{\phi_o(k^*)} . \tag{1-176}$$

For real positive k, $S(k) = \exp(2i\delta_o(k))$ and equation (1-176) shows that in this interval $\phi_o(k)$ must have the phase $\delta_o(k)$,

$$\phi_o(k) = |\phi_o(k)\ \exp(i\delta_o(k)) \tag{1-177a}$$

and on the negative real axis, from (1-175)

$$\phi_o(-k) = |\phi_o(k)|\ \exp(-i\delta_o(k)) \tag{1-177b}$$

<u>Bound states and resonances</u>

As a function of k, S(k) is analytic apart from cuts along the imaginary axis in the intervals $+\ \mu/2 < \mathrm{Im}k < \infty$ and $-\ \mu/2 > \mathrm{Im}k > -\infty$, and with the exception of possible poles arising from the zeroes of the Jost function $\phi_o(-k)$. Let us first locate the position of the zeros of $\phi_o(-k)$ in the upper half k plane. Suppose these occur at $k = k_i = \lambda_i + i\mu_i$ with $\mu_i>0$, then near these points $f_o^R(k,r)$ will behave at large r (from (1-165) like

$$f_o^R(k,r) \sim \phi_o(+k_i)\ \exp(i\lambda_i r - \mu_i r)$$

These solutions are normalizable, and must therefore correspond to bound states, but as the eigenvalues of H are real (H is Hermitian), it follows that k_i^2 must be real and $\lambda_i=0$. The zeroes in the upper half plane of $\phi_o(-k)$ then all occur on the imaginary axis and correspond to bound states. These zeroes give rise to poles in S(k) also on the imaginary axis in the upper half k plane at $k_i=i\mu_i$ (see figure 1-4) with corresponding zeros in the lower half plane at $k_i = -i\mu_i$.

The zeros in the lower half plane of $\phi_o(-k)$ can occur at any point $k_i = \lambda_i - i\mu_i$ and, by (1-175), are symmetrically placed about the imaginary axis. They give rise to poles in S(k) in the lower half plane and zeros in the upper half plane, as shown in figure (1-4).

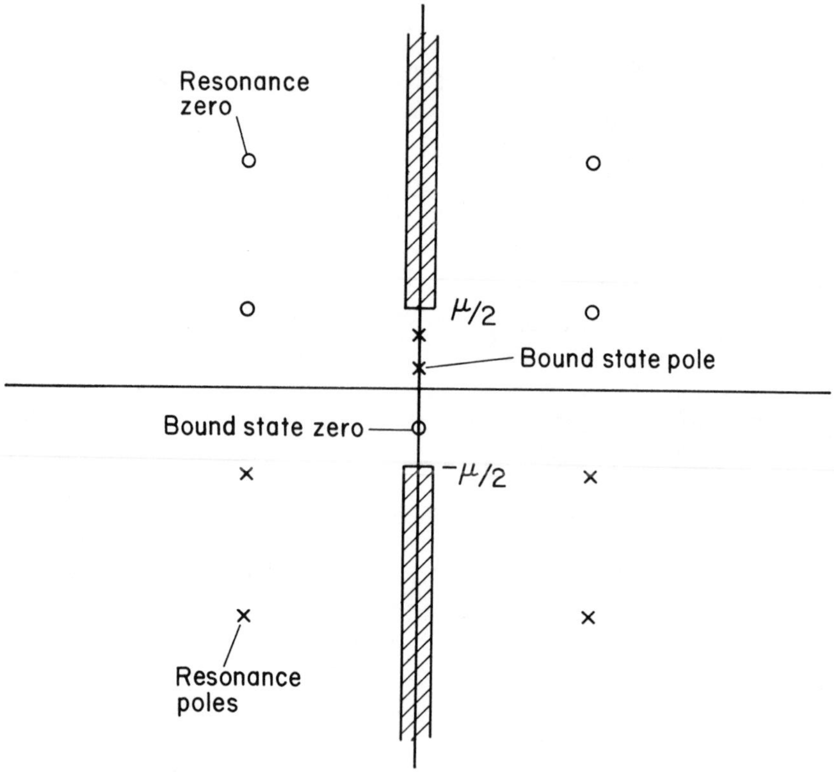

Figure 1-4 The structure of the S matrix element $S_o(k)$

Near one of the points $k = k_i - i\mu_i$, $\mu_i > 0$, $\phi_o(-k)$ will have the form

$$\phi_o(-k) = A(k - \lambda_i + i\mu_i)(k + \lambda_i + i\mu_i),$$

where A is a constant, showing the symmetrical disposition of the zeros about the imaginary axis. If k is real and the zero is near the real axis so that $\mu_i << \lambda_i$ we have, using (1-177b), that

$$\tan \delta_o(k) = \frac{2\mu_i k}{(k^2 - \lambda_i^2)} = \frac{\Gamma(E)}{2(E - E_R)}, \tag{1-178}$$

where $E = \hbar^2 k^2/2m$, $E_R = \hbar^2 \lambda_i^2/2m$ and $\Gamma(E) = \hbar^2(2\mu_i k)/m$. The scattering amplitude $T_\ell = \exp(i\delta_o) \sin \delta_o$ is then

$$T_\ell(E) = \frac{-\Gamma(E)/2}{(E - E_R) + i\Gamma(E)/2} \tag{1-179}$$

and the corresponding cross section is

$$\sigma_o(E) = \frac{\pi}{k^2} \quad \frac{\Gamma^2(E)}{(E - E_R)^2 + \Gamma^2(E)/4} \tag{1-180}$$

This is the famous Breit-Wigner formula for a narrow resonance. It is valid for values of E near E_R, if the width of the resonance $\Gamma(E_R)$ is small compared with the resonance position E_R. In general, the resonance will be superimposed on a slowly varying background.

In the vicinity of the pole the complete time dependent wave function of the system, which satisfies (1-3), will be of the form

$$\Psi(\vec{r},t) \sim r^{-1} f_o{}^R(k,r) \exp(-iEt/\hbar)$$

The asymptotic behavior for large r of $\Psi(\vec{r},t)$ is

$$\Psi(\vec{r},t) \underset{r\to\infty}{\sim} \exp(i\lambda_i r + \mu_i r) \exp(-iEt/\hbar) \tag{1-181}$$

where since at large r, Ψ satisfies the free particle equation with V=0, we have (neglecting $\mu_i^{\,2}$ in comparison with $\lambda_i^{\,2}$)

$$E = -\frac{\hbar^2}{2m} (-\lambda_i^{\,2} + 2\lambda_i \mu_i) = E_R - \Gamma(E_R)/2$$

It is seen that $\Psi(\vec{r},t)$ describes a state decaying in time with a mean life

$$T = 2\hbar/\Gamma(E_R) \tag{1-182}$$

A scattering resonance can thus be interpreted as being due to the formation of a semi-bound state, provided T is long compared with the natural collision time. Such a state is often known as a Siegert state.

As the poles in $S_o(k)$ occur in the lower half k plane, Γ is positive, which is consistent with the interpretation of the resonant state as a decaying state. The rate of change of the phase shift at the resonance is (using 1-178)

$$\frac{\partial \delta_o(E)}{\partial E} = \frac{2}{\Gamma(E_R)} \quad .$$

This shows that, near a resonance, $\delta_o(E)$ is a rapidly increasing function of E, in conformity with the discussion on page 23.

An exceptional case occurs when $\phi_o(-k)$ has a zero in the lower half plane on the imaginary axis. In this case the S-matrix has a pole at a negative real energy. This is not a bound state, however (this can be checked from looking at the asymptotic form of $f_o{}^R(k,r)$), but has been given the name 'anti-bound' state. The presence of such a state can have a pronounced influence on scattering at low energies if it is close enough to the physical threshold at $k^2 = 0$.

Levinson's theorem

The properties of the Jost function afford a simple proof of Levinson's theorem which was mentioned earlier (page 21). The integral I is formed where

$$I = \frac{1}{2\pi i} \int_C dk \left\{ \frac{d}{dk} \log \phi_o(+k) \right\} . \tag{1-183}$$

The contour is taken along the real axis and closed by an infinite semi-circle in the lower half plane. At each zero in $\phi_o(+k)$ the integrand possesses a pole with unit residue, so that, by Cauchy's theorem

$$I = -n, \tag{1-184}$$

where n is the number of zeros in $\phi_o(+k)$. Each zero in $\phi_o(+k)$ in the lower half plane corresponds to a bound state, so that n is equal to the number of bound states of the system.

The contribution to I from the infinite semi-circle is zero, since $\phi_0(k)\to 1$ as $|k| \to \infty$. Then using (1-177a)

$$I = \frac{1}{2\pi i} \int_{-\infty}^{\infty} dk \left(\frac{d}{dk} \log \{|\phi_0(k)|\exp(i\delta_0)\} \right) .$$

Using the symmetry property (1-177b)

$$I = \frac{1}{2\pi i} \int_{0}^{\infty} dk \frac{d}{dk} \left(\log |\exp(2i\delta_0(k))| \right) = \frac{1}{\pi} \left(\delta_0(\infty) - \delta_0(0) \right) . \tag{1-185}$$

Taking the phase shift at infinite energy to be zero, we have Levinson's theorem that

$$\delta_0(0) = n\pi, \tag{1-186a}$$

where n is the number of bound states. An exceptional case that we have not allowed for occurs when there is a pole at zero energy[11] and in this case it can be shown that Levinson's theorem holds in the form

$$\delta_0(0) = (2n + 1)\pi/2 \tag{1-186b}$$

It should be noted that the extra term of $\pi/2$ occurs only for $\ell=0$.

The effective range expansion

The scattering amplitude $T_\ell(k)$ is expressed in terms of the Jost function by

$$T_\ell(k) = \{(-1)^\ell \phi_\ell(k) - \phi_\ell(-k)\}/(2i\phi_\ell(-k)) \tag{1-187}$$

From the analytic properties of the Jost function, it can be shown, for potentials of the type (1-160), that $k^{2\ell+1} \mathrm{Re} T_\ell^{-1}$ is analytic in E about the threshold at E=0, within a circle of radius $(\mu^2\hbar^2/8m)$, where μ is the lower limit in the integral 1-160. It follows that the expansion in k^2,

$$k^{2\ell+1}\mathrm{Re}(T_\ell^{-1}) = k^{2\ell+1}\cot\delta_\ell = \frac{1}{a_s} + \frac{1}{r} r_o k^2 + \ldots., \tag{1-188}$$

converges near zero energy. For $\ell=0$ the parameter a_s is the scattering length (introduced on page 19), and r_o is called the effective range. The expansion (1-188), although of wide applicability, must be modified if the potential is not of 'short range' decreasing faster than any power of r as $r\to\infty$, and we shall return to this point in the next Chapter. The behavior of the phase shift near the threshold at k=0 is closely linked with the existence, or not, of a bound state of the system. We shall briefly discuss the case of an attractive potential with a bound state of zero angular momentum ($\ell=0$). The S-matrix for $\ell=0$ can be written as

$$S_o(k) = \frac{\mathrm{Re}(T_o^{-1}) + i}{\mathrm{Re}(T_o^{-1}) - i}\ .$$

The bound states occur at the poles of $S_o(k)$ on the positive imaginary axis at the points $k = i\lambda$, and at these points $\mathrm{Re}(T_o^{-1}) = i$. Using the effective range expansion for $(\mathrm{Re}T_o^{-1})$ we find

$$-\lambda = \frac{1}{a_s} - \frac{1}{2} r_o \lambda^2,$$

which is the required relation between the bound state energy $E_B = -h^2\lambda^2/2m$ and the low energy scattering parameters a_s and r_o.

The result is easily generalized to all ℓ. In particular, at the bound states

$$\mathrm{Re}(T_\ell^{-1}) = i \text{ for any } \ell. \tag{1-189}$$

The effective range expansion converges rapidly even for strong interactions and is a great help in analyzing experimental data at low energies. A generalization will be given later that is applicable in the case of inelastic many channel scattering.

1-8 CENTER OF MASS AND LABORATORY COORDINATES

To conclude this chapter, we shall show how the theory of potential scattering from a fixed center of force is related to the problem of two particles interacting via a potential that depends on their mutual separation. If the particles A and B are of mass m_A and m_B and possess momenta $\vec{q}_A$, $\vec{q}_B$ respectively, then the Hamiltonian in the momentum representation is

$$H = \frac{q_A{}^2}{2m_A} + \frac{q_B{}^2}{2m_B} + V. \tag{1-190}$$

Choosing a coordinate system in which the center of mass is at rest (called the center of mass system), it follows that

$$\vec{q}_A = -\vec{q}_B = \vec{q} \tag{1-191}$$

and

$$H = \frac{1}{2\mu} q^2 + V, \tag{1-192}$$

where

$$\mu = \frac{m_A m_B}{m_A = m_B}$$

The relative velocity of the particles is $\vec{q}/\mu = (\vec{r}_A - \vec{r}_B)$ so that the canonically conjugate coordinate to $\vec{q}$ is the relative position vector of the two particles $\vec{r}=\vec{r}_A - \vec{r}_B$. The Schrödinger equation is in the positive representation:

$$\left(- \frac{\hbar^2}{2\mu}\nabla^2 + V(r)\right) \Psi(r) = i\hbar \frac{\partial\Psi}{\partial t} ,$$

which is of the same form as the equation for scattering by a fixed center of force, with the reduced mass μ replacing m.

The probability that scattering has occurred cannot depend on the coordinate frame from which the event is viewed so that the total cross section

$$\sigma = 2\pi \int_{-1}^{1} d \cos \theta |f(\vec{k},\theta)|^2$$

is the same in all coordinate systems.

This fact may be used to connect the differential cross section in the center of mass system to that in the laboratory system in which the particle B is at rest. The invariance of σ requires that

$$\left.\frac{d\sigma}{d\Omega}\right|_{\text{Lab}} = \left.\frac{d\sigma}{d\Omega}\right|_{\text{c.m.}} \frac{d(\cos\theta')}{d(\cos\theta)}, \tag{1-193}$$

where θ is the scattering angle in the center of mass system and θ' in the laboratory system.

The velocity of the center of mass in the laboratory system is $\vec{V} = m_A\vec{U}_A/m_A + m_B)$, where $\vec{U}_A$ is the incident velocity of particle A. Suppose $\vec{V}_A$ is the final velocity of particle A in center of mass system and $\vec{V}'_A$ the same quality in the laboratory system.

Then $\vec{V}_A$ and $\vec{V}'_A$ are related by

$$\vec{V}_A = \vec{V}'_A - \vec{V},$$

from which on taking components at right angles

$$V_A \sin\theta = V'_A \sin\theta',$$

$$V_A \cos\theta = V'_A \cos\theta' - V.$$

On dividing we find

$$\tan\theta' = \frac{\sin\theta}{\cos\theta + V/V_A}.$$

The magnitude of the velocity of A in the center of mass system is the same before and after the collision. Before the collision it is $(U_A - V)$ so that

$$V_A = U_A - V \frac{m_B}{m_A} V,$$

giving

$$\tan\theta' = \frac{m_B \sin\theta}{m_B \cos\theta + m_A} \tag{1-194}$$

Finally, on differentiating, the required relationship is

$$\frac{d}{d\Omega}\bigg|_{\text{Lab}} = \frac{d}{d\Omega}\bigg|_{\text{c.m.}} \frac{\left(m_A^{\;2} + m_B^{\;2} + 2m_A m_B \cos\theta\right)^{3/2}}{m_B^{\;2}\left|m_B + m_A \cos\theta\right|} \qquad (1\text{-}195)$$

Although many experiments are carried out by scattering a beam of particles, from a stationary target, that is in the 'laboratory system', it is often more convenient to study the scattering of one beam of particles by another. These crossed beam experiments in which two beams, inclined at a certain angle, interact, are neither in the center of mass or the laboratory system, but the measured quantities are easily transformed to the center of mass system for comparison with theoretical calculations.

NOTES

1. A convenient summary of the necessary quantum mechanics may be found in the text by Bransden and Joachain (1982).

2. The theory of scattering by potentials which are more singular than $1/r^2$ at the origin has been developed. A good reference is Case (1950).

3. The following discussion of the asymptotic form of $f_\ell(r)$ applies to all potentials for which $r^{1-\varepsilon}V(r)\to 0$, $\varepsilon>0$ as $r\to\infty$. The Coulomb potential is excluded and will be treated separately.

4. The spherical Bessel and Neumann functions are defined as

$$j_\ell(x) = \left(\frac{\pi}{2x}\right)^{1/2} J_{\ell+\frac{1}{2}}(x) \qquad n_\ell(x) = (-1)^{\ell+1}\left(\frac{\pi}{2x}\right)^{1/2} J_{-\ell-\frac{1}{2}}(x)$$

These functions are discussed in the text by Morse and Feshbach (1953).

5. The form (1-29a) holds for values of r for which

$$U(r) \ll [k^2 - \ell(\ell+1)/r^2]$$

while (1-29b) holds for larger values of r for which

$\ell(\ell+1)/r^2 \ll k^2$

6. In some books the scattering length is defined with the opposite sign to the one used here.

7. The notation (ϕ,ψ) is employed to denote the inner product of two wave functions:

$$(\phi,\psi) \equiv \int d^3r\,\phi^*(\vec{r})\psi(\vec{r})$$

If $(\phi|$ and $|\psi)$ are the corresponding bra and ket vectors using Dirac's notation, we have

$$(\phi,\psi) = (\phi|\psi)$$

8. Since $U=(2m/\hbar^2)\bar{V}$ and $k=mv/\hbar$, the condition (1-139) can be put in the form $[2aV/\hbar v] \ll 1$, and it is seen that the domain of validity of Born's approximation depends only on the velocity v of the incident particle and not on its mass or energy.

9. The momentum space wave functions are the coefficients of the expansion of the configuration space wave functions in eigenfunctions of the momentum operator. These eigenfunctions are the plane waves $(2\pi)^{3/2}\exp(i\vec{q}\cdot\vec{r})$ so that the transformation to momentum space is equivalent to taking the Fourier transforms of the configuration space wave functions; see for example the discussion in Bransden and Joachain (1982) Chapter 2.

10. An excellent and extensive account of the analytic properties of scattering amplitudes can be found in the book by de Alfaro and Regge (1965).

11. A pole at zero energy does not necessarily imply the existence of a bound state of zero energy, although some potentials do support such bound states.

PROBLEMS

1.1 Show that in the asymptotic region ($r\to\infty$) any solution of (1-20) can be expressed as a linear combination of the functions $\exp(\pm ikr)$, provided $r|V(r)|\to 0$ as $r\to\infty$.

[Hint: Write solutions of (1-20) in the form

$$f_\ell(r) = g_\ell(r)\exp(\pm ikr)$$

where for large r, $g_\ell(r)$ is slowly varying. Find an equation for $g_\ell(r)$ and show that if $r|V(r)|\to 0$ then $g_\ell(r)\to C$ where C is a constant independent of r].

1.2 Verify by using the Wronskian relation (1-46), that $f_\ell(r)$ given by (1-48) satisfies (1-20). Repeat the verification using the Green's function g_ℓ^+, given by (1-53), in place of g_ℓ^P.

1.3 Solve the radial equation (1-20) numerically for the potential (1-63) to obtain the zero order phase shifts $\delta_0^\pm$ for k=0.2 and k=0.4, checking your answer against Table 1-1.

[Hint: A suitable method is that due to Fox and Goodwin. Writing the differential equation as

$$y''(x) = g(x)y(x)$$

it can be shown that, neglecting terms of order h^6,

$$(1-h^2g(x+h)/12)\ y(x+h) = (2+10h^2g(x)/12)y(x) - (1-h^2g(x-h)/12)y(x-h)$$

where h is a suitably small step length. Start the solution with $y(0)=0$, $y(h) = h$, and use the relation for $y(x+h)$ to generate the solution at $x=2h,3h,\ldots\ldots$ Find δ_0 by comparing the solution with the asymptotic form $f_0(r) = A\ [\sin kx + \tan\delta_0 \cos kx]$ at two successive values of x. which must be sufficiently large].

1.4 Determine the phase shifts for $\ell=0$ and $\ell=1$ for scattering by the square well (1-59) with the following parameters

(a) Attractive a=1 A=-1

(b) Attractive a=1 A=-10
(c) Repulsive a=1 A=1

In each case, plot δ_o, δ_1 and the partial cross sections σ_o, σ_1 for the range $0 \le k \le 2$.

1.5 Find the first Born approximation for $\tan\delta_o$ by using (1-57) for the potentials (a) $U(r)=A\exp(-\lambda r)$ (b) $U(r)=Ar^{-1}\exp(-\lambda r)$.

1.6 Find the first Born approximation for the scattering amplitudes by using (1-138) for the following potentials (a) $U(r) = A\exp(-\lambda r)$, (b) $U(r)=Ar^{-1}\exp(-\lambda r)$, (c) $U(r)=A\exp(-\lambda r^2)$, (d) $U(r)=A/(r^2+a^2)^2$. Verify the expression (1-143) for scattering by the potential (1-63), and obtain an expression for the total cross section, checking that $\sigma \propto 1/E$ for large E.

1.7 Using the effective range expansion (1-188), together with Table 1-1, find the scattering parameters a_s and r_o for the potentials U_+ and U_- for $\ell=0$, 1 and 2. Determine whether the potential U_- supports a bound state with $\ell=0$.

1.8 Verify that equation (1-169), follows from (1-167) and (1-160).
A Yukawa potential $V(r)=A\exp(-\mu r)/r$ can be obtained from (1-160) by setting $C(\alpha)=A$ for $\alpha>\mu$ $C(\alpha)=0$, $\alpha < \mu$. For this potential construct $\rho_k(\alpha)$ explicitly in the interval $\mu \le \alpha \le 3\mu$.

1.9 Plot the angle of scattering in the center of mass system against the angle of scattering in the laboratory system for an elastic collision between two particles of equal mass.

Chapter 2

SPECIAL METHODS IN POTENTIAL SCATTERING

In Chapter 1 we saw how the solution to the problem of scattering by a potential could be obtained to any degree of accuracy, by solving the radial Schrödinger equation numerically to calculate the phase shifts. In addition, in the course of a discussion of the integral equations satisfied by the scattering amplitude, the Born approximation was introduced, which however has a limited range of usefulness. In this chapter some other methods are described for evaluating the phase shifts, or the complete scattering amplitude, approximately. These methods are important because they can be generalized to solve many-body scattering problems for which exact numerical solutions cannot be found.

2-1 THE VARIATIONAL METHOD

The exact radial wave function $f_\ell(r)$ for scattering by a central potential $V(r)$ satisfies (see equation (1-20)):

$$\left(\frac{d^2}{dr^2} - \frac{\ell(\ell+1)}{r^2} - U(r) + k^2\right) f_\ell(r) = 0 \qquad (2\text{-}1)$$

where $U(r) = 2mV(r)/\hbar^2$. A real regular solution of this equation can be taken to satisfy the boundary conditions (see (1-29b)

$$f_\ell(0)=0; \quad f_\ell(r) \underset{r\to\infty}{\sim} \sin(kr-\tfrac{1}{2}\ell\pi) + K_\ell \cos(kr-\tfrac{1}{2}\ell\pi) \quad (2\text{-}2)$$

where $K_\ell = \tan \delta_\ell$ and δ_ℓ is the ℓth order phase shift and the normalization constant A_ℓ has been taken to be $A_\ell=1$.

We shall now consider the integral

$$I[\bar{f}_\ell] = \int_0^\infty \bar{f}_\ell(r) L\bar{f}_\ell(r)dr, \tag{2-3}$$

where L is the operator

$$L = \frac{-2m}{\hbar^2}(H_0 + V - E) = \left(\frac{d^2}{dr^2} - \frac{\ell(\ell+1)}{r^2} - U(r) + k^2\right) \tag{2-4}$$

and $\bar{f}_\ell(r)$ is a function that satisfies boundary conditions of the same form as (2-2) but with the constant K_ℓ replaced by some other value $\bar{K}_\ell$. That is

$$\bar{f}_\ell(0) = 0;\ \bar{f}_\ell(r) \sim \sin\left(kr - \frac{\ell\pi}{2}\right) + \bar{K}_\ell \cos\left(kr - \frac{\ell\pi}{2}\right) \tag{2-5}$$

If we set $\bar{f}_\ell = f_\ell$, where f_ℓ is the actual solution of the radial Schrödinger equation with these boundary conditions, then $\bar{K}_\ell \to K_\ell = \tan \delta_\ell$, and it is clear that $I[f_\ell] = 0$, since $Lf_\ell(r) = 0$.

Now suppose that $\bar{f}_\ell = f_\ell + \Delta f_\ell$, where Δf_ℓ is a function such that

$$\Delta f_\ell(0) = 0,\ \Delta f_\ell(r) \sim \Delta K_\ell \cos\left(kr - \frac{\ell\pi}{2}\right), \tag{2-6}$$

and where $\Delta K_\ell = \bar{K}_\ell - K_\ell$. Then we have

$$I[\bar{f}_\ell] = \int_0^\infty f_\ell L\Delta f_\ell dr + \int_0^\infty \Delta f_\ell L\Delta f_\ell dr$$

Writing

$$f_\ell L\Delta f_\ell = (f_\ell L\Delta f_\ell - \Delta f_\ell L f_\ell),$$

we find

$$I[\bar{f}_\ell] - I[\Delta f_\ell] = \int_0^\infty \{f_\ell(r) \frac{d^2}{dr^2} \Delta f_\ell(r) - \Delta f_\ell(r) \frac{d^2}{dr^2} f_\ell(r)\}dr$$

$$= \lim_{R\to\infty} \left[f_\ell(r) \frac{d}{dr} \Delta f_\ell - \Delta f_\ell \frac{d}{dr} f_\ell \right]_0^R = -k\Delta K_\ell, \tag{2-7}$$

where in the last line the asymptotic forms of $\Delta f_\ell(r)$ and $f_\ell(r)$ have been employed.

This is an identity, often called the Kato identity, satisfied by all functions $\bar{f}_\ell(r)$ of the required form. If we now take $\Delta f_\ell(r)$ to be a small quantity of the first order for all values of r, then the functional $I[\Delta f_\ell]$ is of the second order of smallness and can be neglected with respect to quantities like $I[\bar{f}_\ell]$ and ΔK_ℓ which are of first order. If $\Delta I = I[\bar{f}_\ell] - I[f_\ell]$ is defined as the change in I under the variation $f_\ell \to f_\ell + \Delta_\ell$, it is seen that the quantity $(I+kK_\ell)$ is stationary under the variation, that is:

$$\Delta(I + kK_\ell) = 0, \tag{2-8}$$

where quantities of the order $(\Delta f)^2$ have been neglected. Suppose we now have a parameterized form for $f_\ell(r)$ denoted by $f_\ell^t(r)$, which depends on parameters c_i, $i = 1, - - -n$, and suppose that, for certain values of the parameters, f_ℓ^t can be made to coincide with the exact function f_ℓ. Then a variation of the type we are considering is achieved by letting $c_i \to c_i + \Delta c_i$ and $K_\ell \to K_\ell + \Delta K_\ell$. Expanding $\Delta(I+kK_\ell)$ by Taylor's theorem and retaining first order terms, we have from (2-8)

$$\Delta(I + kK_\ell) = \sum_{i=1}^{n} \frac{\partial I}{\partial c_i} \Delta c_i + \frac{\partial I}{\partial K_\ell} \Delta K_\ell + k\Delta K_\ell = 0. \tag{2-9}$$

As the quantities Δc_i and ΔK_ℓ are independent, it follows that

$$\frac{\partial I}{\partial c_i} = 0, \quad i = 1,2,3 \ldots\ldots n \tag{2-10a}$$

and

$$\frac{\partial I}{\partial K_\ell} = - k. \qquad (2\text{-}10b)$$

These equations are sufficient to determine the parameters c_i and K_ℓ. A better value of K_ℓ, correct to the second order, can then be obtained by integrating (2-10b).

$$\tan \delta_\ell = K_\ell = K_\ell^{\ t} + \frac{1}{k} I[f_\ell^{\ t}], \qquad (2\text{-}11)$$

where $K_\ell^{\ t}$ is the value of K_ℓ obtained from equations (2-10) Equation (2-10) is, of course, the same as the Kato identity (2-7), and $k^{-1}I[f_\ell^{\ t}]$ is called the Kato correction. This procedure is due to Kohn (1948). An alternative procedure(Hulthén, 1944) is to determine K_ℓ by replacing equation (2-10b) by the equation

$$I(c_i, K_\ell) = 0. \qquad (2\text{-}12)$$

This again (by 2-8) ensures that $\Delta K_\ell=0$ and provides a value of $K_\ell = \tan \delta_\ell$ correct up to terms of the second order.

Many variants of the variational method can be obtained by imposing different boundary conditions on the trial functions $f_\ell^{\ t}(r)$. For example, a variational principle for the determination of $\cot \delta_\ell$ called the inverse Kohn method arises if $f_\ell^{\ t}(r)$ is taken to have the asymptotic form

$$f_\ell^{\ t}(r) \sim \cot \delta_\ell \sin(kr - \ell\pi/2) + \cos(kr - \ell\pi/2). \qquad (2\text{-}13)$$

All variational methods suffer from the severe disadvantage that if the difference between the trial functions and the exact function cannot be made small for any values of the parameters, entirely erroneous results may be obtained. Also as the value of K_ℓ obtained is stationary, but not necessarily a minimum, there is no theoretical test as to which of two trial functions is superior.

An example is given in Table 2-1, where s wave phase shifts (ℓ=0) are shown for scattering by the first order static potential between an electron and a hydrogen atom

$$U(r) = -2(1 + 1/r)\exp(-2r) \qquad (2\text{-}14)$$

where atomic units have been used. The results were obtained using the Kohn and Hulthén methods with the trial function (Massey and Moiseiwitsch, 1951)

$$f_o(r) = \sin(kr) + (c_1 + c_2 e^{-r})\ (1 - e^{-r})\cos(kr). \tag{2-15}$$

In this case the agreement with the exact phase shifts is good.

Table 2-1

Zero order phase shifts (ℓ=0) for scattering by the potential $U(r) = -2(1 + 1/r)\exp(-2r)$.

(Phase shifts in radians)

k(a.u.)	Exact	Kohn and Hulthén	Schwinger
0.1	0.730	0.721	0.695
0.2	0.973	0.972	0.950
0.3	1.046	1.045	-
0.4	1.057	1.057	1.045
0.5	1.045	1.044	-
1.0	0.906	0.904	0.901

Despite the attractive and useful nature of the Kohn variational method, it contains some inherent difficulties, which can impede specific applications. How these arise can be seen by choosing a trial function in which the parameters c_i enter linearly. Let us write

$$f_\ell^{t}(r) = u(r) + K_\ell w(r) + \sum_{i=1}^{n} c_i\phi_i(r) \tag{2-16}$$

where the functions u(r) and w(r) satisfy

$$u(o) = w(o) = 0; \quad u(r) \underset{r\to\infty}{\sim} s_\ell(kr), \quad w(r) \underset{r\to\infty}{\sim} c_\ell(kr)$$

and where the n functions $\phi_i(r)$ are square integrable with

$$\phi_i(r) \to 0\ , \qquad r \to \infty \tag{2-17}$$

From a given n basis functions ϕ_i, we can form the linear combinations that diagonalize the operator L, so there is no loss in generality in assuming that the ϕ_i satisfy

$$F_{ij} \equiv \int_0^\infty \phi_i \; L\phi_j \, dr = (k^2 - k_i^2) \; \delta_{ij} \qquad i,j = 1,2,.....n \tag{2-18}$$

We now substitute (2-16) into (2-1) to obtain:

$$I[f_\ell^t] = A + BK_\ell + CK_\ell^2 + \sum_{i=1}^n c_i D_i + K_\ell \sum_{i=1}^n c_i E_i + \sum_{i,j=k}^n c_i c_j F_{ij} \tag{2-19}$$

where

$$A = \int_0^\infty uLu \, dr \qquad B = \int_0^\infty (uLw + wLu) dr$$

$$C = \int_0^\infty wLw \, dr \qquad D_i = 2\int_0^\infty dr \; (uL\phi_i)$$

$$E_i = 2 \int_0^\infty dr \; wL\phi_i \tag{2-20}$$

Using (2-18), the variational equation (2-10) becomes:

$$\frac{\partial I}{\partial c_i} = 0 = D_i + K_\ell E_i + 2(k^2 - k_i^2) c_i \tag{2-21}$$

$$\frac{\partial I}{\partial K_\ell} = - k = B + 2CK_\ell + \sum_{i=1}^n c_i E_i \tag{2-22}$$

and solving for K_ℓ we find

$$K_\ell = \left(2C - \sum_{i=1}^n \frac{E_i^2}{2(k^2 - k_i^2)} \right)^{-1} \left(-(k+B) + \sum_{i=1}^n \frac{D_i E_i}{2(k^2 - k_i^2)} \right) \tag{2-23}$$

It is clear that at some value of k^2 close to each of the k_i^2 the denominator in (2-23) vanishes making K_ℓ infinite, unless, accidentally, the numerator is zero at the same value of k^2. Since the values of k_i^2 depend on the choice of the functions ϕ_i the singularities in K_ℓ at certain values of k are non-physical and have nothing to do with resonances. Well away from these particular values of k, accurate values of the phases can be obtained, so that the Kohn method does not lose its usefulness. Some interesting numerical examples showing the breakdown of the Kohn method at certain values of k have been given by Harris and Michels (1971) and by Rudge (1973).

Several methods have been developed to overcome this deficiency in the Kohn method. For example, the corresponding singularities in the variational method for cot δ_ℓ (the inverse Kohn method) arise at different values of k, so that if the Kohn method is singular at a particular value of k, the inverse Kohn method can be used and *vice versa*. For a complete discussion the reader is referred to the review by Callaway (1978) and the monograph by Nesbet (1980).

Schwinger's variational principle

A different variational principle is due to Schwinger. It can be applied both to the complete amplitude and to the partial wave amplitudes. From the integral equations for $\psi^{\pm}(\vec{k})$ which we write as (see 1-145)

$$|\psi^{\pm}(\vec{k})) = |\phi(\vec{k})) + G_o(E \pm i\varepsilon)\ V|\psi^{\pm}(k))$$

the scattering amplitude can be expressed in the following alternative forms:

$$\begin{aligned} -\frac{(2\pi)\hbar^2}{m} f(\vec{k},\theta) &= T(\vec{k}',\vec{k},E) \\ &= (\phi(k')|V|\psi^+(\vec{k})) \\ &= (\psi^-(\vec{k}')|V-V\ G_o(E+i\varepsilon)\ V|\psi^+(\vec{k})) \\ &= (\psi^-(\vec{k}'|V|\phi(\vec{k})) \end{aligned} \qquad (2\text{-}24)$$

where we have used $G_o\ (E + i\varepsilon) = G_o(E - i\varepsilon)$ and the limit $\varepsilon \to 0^+$ is understood. From these relations, we have the identity

$$T(\vec{k}',\vec{k},E) = \frac{(\psi^-(\vec{k}')|V|\phi(\vec{k}))(\phi(\vec{k})|V|\psi^+(k))}{(\psi^-(\vec{k}')|V-V\ G_o(E+i\varepsilon)V|\psi^+(\vec{k}))} \tag{2-25}$$

and it is easily checked that this is stationary under the arbitrary variations:

$$|\psi^\pm(\vec{k})) \rightarrow |\psi^\pm(\vec{k})) + \Delta|\psi^\pm(\vec{k}))$$

If plane waves are used as trial functions in (2-25)

$$\psi^+(\vec{k}) = \phi(\vec{k}) \ ; \quad \psi^-(\vec{k}') = \phi(k')$$

the term

$$(\phi(\vec{k}')|V\ G_o(E+i\varepsilon)\ V|\phi(\vec{k}))$$

is the second term in the Born expansion of $T(\vec{k}',\vec{k},E)$. However the results obtained from this variational expression may be accurate even if the second Born approximation is not.

To apply Schwinger's method to the calculation of a phase shift, consider the case $\ell=0$ (s-wave scattering). From equations (1-48) to (1-51), we can obtain the Schwinger identity

$$k \tan \delta_o = A/B$$

$$\text{where } A = [\int_0^\infty f_o(r) \sin(kr)\ U(r)\ dr]^2$$

and B =

$$\int_0^\infty [f_o(r)]^2 U(r)dr - \int_0^\infty dr \int_0^\infty dr' [f_o(r)U(r)g^P(r,r')U(r')f_o(r')] \tag{2-26}$$

which is stationary for the variations $f_o(r)$ $f_o(r)+\Delta f_o(r)$. The big advantages of this variational principle are that the trial function $f_o{}^t(r)$ need only be known in the region, where $U(r)$ is significant and that it is independent of the normalization of $f_o^t(r)$. Taking advantage of this Altshuler (1953) has used polynomial expressions as trial functions

$$f_o(r) = \sum_{n=1}^{N} c_n r^n , \qquad (2\text{-}27)$$

to compute tan δ_o from the equations

$$\frac{\partial(\tan\ \delta_o)}{\partial c_n} = 0 \quad n = 1, \ldots..N \qquad (2\text{-}28)$$

for the potential (2-14). His results for N = 3 are shown in Table 2-1. For the same number of parameters the results are not as accurate as those given by the Kohn and Hulthén methods, with this particular choice of trial function.

The [N,N] Padé approximant to the scattering amplitude is the ratio of two polynomials in the potential strength each of order N, which when expanded agrees with the first 2N terms in the Born series, (Nuttall, 1970). It is clear that when used with plane wave trial functions the Schwinger variational expression is the [1,1] Padé approximant to the scattering amplitude. Higher approximants can be generated by using as trial functions the higher Born approximations to the wave function.

Minimum principles

Although the variational methods we have discussed are of great value, in general the calculated phase shift is neither a maximum or a minimum value so that it is impossible to test which of two given trial functions is superior. This circumstance has led to an intensive search for methods that do provide a bound on the phase shifts[1]. For zero energy scattering Rosenberg and Spruch (1959) found a bound on the scattering length which could be applied in practice and which, most importantly, can be used in many particle scattering problems (provided that the target wave function is known).

The starting point of the discussion is the identity (2-7). We shall discuss the case ℓ=0. On dividing both sides by k^2 and taking the limit $k \to 0$, it is found that

$$I[\bar{u}] - I[\Delta u] = -\Delta a_s, \tag{2-29}$$

where

$$\bar{u}(r) = \lim_{k\to 0} k^{-1} f_o(r) \text{ and } a_s = \lim_{k\to 0} \delta_o/k. \tag{2-30}$$

Referring to the effective range expansion (1-188), it is seen that a_s is the scattering length. The boundary conditions satisfied by u(r) are

$$u(0) = 0,\ u(r) \sim (a_s + r). \tag{2-31}$$

The trial function $\bar{u}$ is equal to $(u + \Delta u)$ and satisfies

$$\bar{u}(0) = 0,\ \bar{u}(r) \sim (\bar{a}_s + r) \text{ with } \bar{a}_s = a_s + \Delta a_s. \tag{2-32}$$

With a given trial function $\bar{u}$, $I[\bar{u}]$ may be calculated, so that if we could bound or find the sign of $I[\Delta u]$, we would be able to bound the error in the scattering length a_s.

Suppose that the system has no bound state, then by the Raleigh-Ritz principle

$$\int \phi H \phi dr = -\frac{\hbar^2}{2m} \int \phi L_o \phi dr \geq 0, \tag{2-33}$$

where ϕ is any normalizable function and

$$L_o = \left(\frac{d^2}{dr^2} - U(r) \right) \tag{2-34}$$

The function $\Delta u(r)$ is not normalizable, but defining $I[\lambda, \Delta u]$ by

$$I[\lambda, \Delta u(r)] = \int_0^\infty [\Delta u(r) \exp(-\lambda r)]\ L_o\ [\Delta u(r) \exp(-\lambda r)]\ dr$$

we see that $I[\lambda, \Delta u] < 0$ because $\Delta u(r)\exp(-\lambda r)$ is a normalizable function. A short calculation shows that

$$I[\lambda, \Delta u(r)] - I[\Delta u]$$

$$= \int_0^\infty \Delta u(r)(\exp(-2\lambda r)-1) \left(\frac{d^2}{dr^2} \Delta u(r) - U(r)\Delta u(r) \right) dr +$$

$$+ \lambda^2 \int_0^\infty [\Delta u(r)]^2 \exp(-2\lambda r) dr - 2\lambda \int_0^\infty \exp(-2\lambda r) \Delta u(r) \frac{d}{dr} \Delta u(r)\ dr.$$

Each term on the right hand side vanishes as $\lambda \to 0$ so that as $I[\lambda, \Delta u] \leq 0$, it follows that $I[\Delta u] < 0$.

The required bound is then (from 2-29)

$$\Delta a_s \leq -I[\bar{u}], \tag{2-35a}$$

or

$$a_s \geq \bar{a}_s + I[\bar{u}]. \tag{2-35b}$$

The problem is then to determine $\bar{u}$ to make the right hand side of (2-35b) as large as possible. In this case this is achieved by the Kohn variational method we described earlier.

This maximum principle for a_s can be extended to the case in which the potential supports bound states (Rosenberg et al., 1960). To do this, some results from the Raleigh-Ritz variational method for bound states are needed. Suppose the functions ϕ_i are a normalizable set of linearly independent functions, then the function

$$\Psi = \Sigma_i \lambda_i \phi_i \tag{2-36}$$

where λ_i are constants, can be used as a trial function. Defining the integral I as

$$I = (\Psi, (H - E)\Psi) = \int \Psi^* (H - E)\Psi dr, \tag{2-37}$$

the Raleigh-Ritz principle requires that

$$\frac{\partial I}{\partial \lambda_i} = 0, \ i = 1, 2, \ \ldots\ldots \tag{2-28}$$

These equations reduce to linear equations for the parameters λ_i of the form

$$\sum_j (H_{ij} - EN_{ij})\lambda_j = 0, \tag{2-39}$$

where

$$H_{ij} = (\phi_i, H\phi_j), \tag{2-40a}$$

$$N_{ij} = (\phi_i, \phi_j). \tag{2-40b}$$

The eigenvalues E can then be determined from the condition that these equations are compatible:

$$\det|\mathcal{H} - E\mathcal{N}| = 0, \tag{2-41}$$

where $\mathcal{H}$ and $\mathcal{N}$ are the matrices with elements H_{ij} and N_{ij}. The Hyllerass-Undheim theorem states that if n of the roots of this equation $E_1, E_2 \ldots E_n$ are negative, then there are at least n bound states of the system. If we order the roots so that $E_1 < E_2 < E_3 \ldots$. then E_1 is an upper bound on the ground state energy, E_2 is an upper bound on the energy of the first excited state and so on. Consider a system for which it is known that one bound state exists and suppose ϕ_1 is a trial function, which provides a variational estimate $E_1^{(0)}$

$$E_1^{(0)} = H_{11}/N_{11}$$

Now consider trial function $\Psi=\lambda_1\phi_1 + \lambda_2\phi_2$ where ϕ_2 is some other normalizable function. The product of the roots of equation (2-39) is given by $\det|\mathcal{H}|/\det|\mathcal{N}|$, so that

$$E_1E_2 = \frac{H_{11}H_{22} - H_{12}^2}{N_{11}N_{22} - N_{12}^2} \tag{2-42}$$

By the Schwartz inequality the denominator on the right hand side of (2-42) is positive, E_1 is negative and, as there is only one bound state, E_2 must be positive. It follows that

$$H_{22} \geqslant H_{12}^2/H_{11}, \quad (H_{11} < 0). \tag{2-43}$$

This result is applied by taking for ϕ_2 the function $\Delta u(r)$ which, as we saw earlier, may be treated as a normalizable function in this context. Using (2-43), a bound on $I[\Delta u]$ is found immediately

$$I[\Delta u] \geq \frac{\hbar^2}{-2m} \frac{\left(\int_0^\infty \phi_1(r) L(\Delta u)\,dr\right)^2}{H_{11}}$$

As $L(\Delta u) = L(\bar{u}(r))$ the corresponding bound on the scattering length becomes

$$a_s > \bar{a}_s + I[\bar{u}] - \frac{\hbar^2}{2mH_{11}} \left(\int_0^\infty \phi_1 L(\bar{u})\,dr \right)^2 \tag{2-44}$$

If the Kohn variation method is carried through for a trial function of the form $(\bar{u} + \lambda\phi_1)$ where λ is a parameter, the value of a_s obtained is the same as the right hand side of (2-44). That is, the Kohn variational method provides a lower bound for a_s, if the trial function includes a term representing the bound state of the system. The result (2-44) is easily generalized to case where several bound states exist, by summing over a number of terms of the same form as the last term in (2-44).

The comparison potential method

The method described for the determination of scattering lengths can be extended to scattering at non-zero energies. It is necessary to subtract from the trial function those components that correspond to eigenfunctions of the Hamiltonian at all energies lower than the one considered. As the positive eigenenergies form a continuum, the spectrum is first rendered discrete by supposing the system to be placed in a large spherical box of radius R where R is much greater than the range of the potential. In practice this method, originally due to Risberg (1956) and Percival (1957) proves useful in conjunction with the R matrix method to be described later. In this section, we will consider a different approach based on the monotonic variation of the phase shift with potential strength discussed in Section 1-3.

The method of comparison potentials (Blankenbecler and Sugar, 1965) attempts to find a potential V_1 for which the phase shift can be found exactly and for which $V_1<V$, where V is the potential in which we are interested. It then follows from (1-62) that $\delta_\ell^1>\delta_\ell$, where δ_ℓ^1 and δ_ℓ are the phase shifts corresponding to the potentials V_1 and V respectively. The method is of particular interest, because the potential V can be a non-local (integral operator) potential like those that arise in the theory of scattering by complex systems.

Suppose that V is positive, and consider the inequality

$$I = \left(\left(\psi - \sum_{i=1}^{N} c_i\phi_i\right), V \left(\psi - \sum_{j=1}^{N} c_j\phi_j\right) \right) \geq 0, \quad (2\text{-}45)$$

where ψ is a scattering wave function (such as $f_\ell(r)$) and the ϕ_i are a discrete set of linearly independent functions.

To minimize the left-hand side of the inequality with respect to the parameters c_j, we require that

$$\frac{\partial I}{\partial c_i} = \Sigma_j c_j^*(\phi_j, V\phi_i) - (\psi, V\phi_i) = 0,$$

or

$$c_j^* = \sum_i (\psi, V\phi_i)(M^{-1})_{ij},$$

where M is the matrix with elements $M_{ij} = (\phi_i, V\phi_j)$. Inserting these values of c_j, in (2-45), we find

$$(\psi, V\psi) - \sum_{ij} (\psi, V\phi_i)(M^{-1})_{ij}(\phi_j, V\psi) \geq 0.$$

Since this is true for an arbitrary ψ, we may write

$$V \geq V_S^N, \tag{2-46}$$

where V_S^N is defined as the sum of separable potentials

$$V_S^N = \sum_{i,j=1}^{N} |V\phi_i) M^{-1}_{ij} (\phi_j V| \tag{2-47}$$

By expanding the set of independent functions ϕ_i, a sequence of potential

$$V_S^N, V_S^{N+1}, \ldots.$$

can be defined and it can be shown in a similar way that

$$V_S^{N+1} > V_S^N, \tag{2-48}$$

By the monotonicity theorem, the corresponding phase shifts δ^N, are lower bounds on the exact phase shift δ, $\delta^N < \delta$ and as N increases δ^N approaches δ.

<u>Separable potentials</u>

The comparison potential is separable and in configuration space is of the form (in the ℓth partial wave)

$$K_\ell(r,r') = \sum_{i,j} \alpha_{ij} U_i(r) U_j(r'), \tag{2-49}$$

where the α_{ij} are a set of coefficients. The corresponding Schrödinger equation for the partial wave is

$$\left(\frac{d^2}{dr^2} - \frac{\ell(\ell+1)}{r^2} + k^2\right) f_\ell(r) = \int_0^\infty K_\ell(r,r') f_\ell(r') dr'. \tag{2-50}$$

This equation has an exact solution which may be found as follows. Inserting the explicit form of the potential (2-49) into equation (2-50), we find

$$\left(\frac{d^2}{dr^2} - \frac{\ell(\ell+1)}{r^2} + k^2\right) f_\ell(r) = \sum_{ij} \alpha_{ij} U_i(r) N_j, \tag{2-51}$$

where

$$N_j = \int_0^\infty U_j(r) f_\ell(r) dr.$$

The solution of this equation can be obtained in terms of the standing wave Green's function $g_\ell^P(r,r')$. It is

$$f_\ell(r) = s_\ell(kr) + \sum_{ij} \alpha_{ij} \int_0^\infty g_\ell^P(r,r') U_i(r') dr' N_j, \tag{2-52}$$

and the phase shift is given by

$$\tan \delta_\ell = -\frac{1}{k} \int_0^\infty s_\ell(kr') \sum_{ij} \alpha_{ij} U_i(r') dr'. N_j. \tag{2-53}$$

It remains to find N_j and this may be done by multiplying (2-52) by $U_n(r)$ and integrating. We find

$$N_n = \int_0^\infty U_n(r) s_\ell(kr) dr + \sum_{ij} \alpha_{ij} \int_0^\infty dr \int_0^\infty dr' U_n(r) g_\ell^P(r,r') U_i(r') N_j. \tag{2-54}$$

This is a set of simultaneous linear equations for the N_j with the solution

$$N_j = \sum_n \left(\frac{1}{1 - M}\right)_{jn} \int_0^\infty U_n(r) s_\ell(kr) dr, \tag{2-55}$$

where M is the matrix with elements

$$M_{jn} = \sum_i \alpha_{in} \int_0^\infty dr \int_0^\infty dr' U_j(r) g_\ell{}^p(r,r') U_i(r'). \tag{2-56}$$

As an example, if the potential consists of the single term $K(r,r')=U(r)U(r')$, we have

$$k \tan \delta_\ell = - \frac{\left(\int_0^\infty s_\ell(kr) U(r) dr\right)^2}{1 - \int_0^\infty dr \int_0^\infty dr' U(r) g_\ell{}^p(r,r') U(r')} \tag{2-57}$$

This is an explicit expression for $\tan \delta_\ell$ in terms of the potential and does not involve the wave function $f_\ell(r)$. The method of comparison potentials, in common with the other methods described in this chapter, is not important for the solution of the single particle potential problem, because numerical solutions of the radial Schrödinger equations are easily obtained, but as we shall show later, the methods of this chapter can be used in the many particle problem, for which no exact numerical solution is feasible.

2-2 THE FREDHOLM METHOD

The Schrödinger equation for the radial wave function $f_\ell(r)$ for a particle scattered by a central potential $\lambda V(r)$ can be written in operator form as

$$(H_\ell + \lambda U - k^2) \, |f_\ell\,) = 0 \tag{2-58}$$

where in the position representation (see equation (2-1))

$$H_\ell = - \frac{d^2}{dr^2} + \frac{\ell(\ell+1)}{r^2}; \quad U(r) = 2mV(r)/\hbar^2$$

and

$$k^2 = 2mE/\hbar^2$$

We shall be concerned with the outgoing wave solutions of (2-58), so that we shall require the solution $f_\ell^+(r)$ where

$$f_\ell^+(r) \equiv (r|f_\ell^+) \sim s_\ell(kr) + T_\ell e^+_\ell(kr) \qquad (2\text{-}59)$$

and

$$T_\ell = \exp(i\delta_\ell) \sin \delta_\ell$$

Following the discussion in Section 1-6, the integral equation for $|f_\ell^+)$ can be written as

$$|f_\ell^+) = (1 + \lambda G_\ell^+ U)|\phi_\ell) \qquad (2\text{-}60)$$

where the outgoing wave Green's function G^+ is defined as

$$G_\ell^+ = (k^2+i\varepsilon - \lambda U - H_\ell)^{-1} \qquad (2\text{-}61)$$

and ε is a small positive quantity. The state vector $|\phi_\ell)$ represents the initial unperturbed state, so that

$$(r|\phi_\ell) = s_\ell(kr) \qquad (2\text{-}62)$$

The free particle Green's function (1-53) can be written in operator form as

$$g_\ell^+ = (k^2+i\varepsilon - H_\ell)^{-1} \qquad (2\text{-}63)$$

and in configuration space

$$g_\ell^+(r,r') = (r|g_\ell^+|r') = -k^{-1} s_\ell(kr_<)e_\ell^+(kr_>) \qquad (2\text{-}64)$$

From (2-61) and (2-63), we find immediately that

$$G_\ell^+ = R_\ell g_\ell^+ \qquad (2\text{-}65)$$

where the resolvant R_ℓ is defined by

$$R_\ell = (1 - \lambda g_\ell^+ U)^{-1} \qquad (2\text{-}66)$$

Since T_ℓ, the partial wave scattering amplitude, can be expressed as (using 2-60, 2-65 and 2-66):

$$T_\ell = -k^{-1}(\phi_\ell|U|f_\ell^+)$$

$$= -k^{-1}(\phi_\ell|U\mathcal{R}_\ell|\phi_\ell) \qquad (2\text{-}67)$$

a knowledge of $\mathcal{R}_\ell$ is sufficient to determine the phase shifts and hence the scattering cross section.

In the position representation, $g_\ell^+(r,r')$ can be looked upon as an 'infinite matrix' with rows and columns labeled by the continuous variables r and r′, and the same is true for the corresponding quantities $G^\ell(r,r')$, $\mathcal{R}_\ell(r,r')$. If these matrices were of finite dimension ($n \times n$) with rows and columns labeled by discrete indices i,j etc then the resolvant matrix $\mathcal{R}_\ell$ could be obtained at once as the solution of the simultaneous equations

$$\mathcal{R}_\ell\,(1 - \lambda g_\ell^+U) = 1 \qquad (2\text{-}68)$$

This solution can be written explicitly (Morse and Feshbach 1953)

$$(\mathcal{R}_\ell)_{ij} = \frac{A_{ji}}{D} \qquad (2\text{-}69)$$

where D is the determinant of the matrix $(1-\lambda g_\ell^+U)$

$$D = \det|1 - \lambda g_\ell^+U| \qquad (2\text{-}70)$$

and A_{ij} is the cofactor of $(1- \lambda g_\ell U)_{ij}$. Both A_{ij} and D can be expanded as polynomials in the parameter λ. As we shall see all the physical information can be extracted from the Fredholm determinant D, and this can be written as

$$D = 1 + \sum_{n=1}^{N}(-1)^n\lambda^n d_n \qquad (2\text{-}71)$$

The coefficients of the expansion d_n can be expressed in terms of the matrix elements K_{ij} of the kernel where

$$K = g_\ell^+U \qquad (2\text{-}72)$$

It is easy to verify that

$$d_1 = \sum_i K_{ii} = \mathrm{Tr}(K)$$

$$d_2 = \sum_{ij} \frac{1}{2!} \begin{vmatrix} K_{ii} & K_{ij} \\ K_{ji} & K_{jj} \end{vmatrix} \tag{2-73}$$

$$d_3 = \sum_{i,j,k} \frac{1}{3!} \begin{vmatrix} K_{ii} & K_{ij} & K_{ik} \\ K_{ji} & K_{jj} & K_{jk} \\ K_{ki} & K_{kj} & K_{kk} \end{vmatrix}$$

For matrices of infinite dimension, these polynomials become power series in λ and these series define the solution, which exists provided $\mathrm{Tr}(K^n)$ exists for n=1,2,...

In the position representation

$$K(r,r') = g_\ell^+(r,r')U(r') \tag{2-74}$$

so that

$$d_1 = \mathrm{Tr}(K) = \int_0^\infty dr\ g_\ell(r,r)U(r) \tag{2-75}$$

and this integral converges provided $U(r)$ is less singular than $1/r^2$ at the origin and vanishes faster than $1/r$ at large r. The coefficient d_2 is given by

$$d_2 = \frac{1}{2!} \int_0^\infty dr \int_0^\infty dr' \begin{vmatrix} K(r,r) & K(r,r') \\ K(r',r) & K(r',r') \end{vmatrix} \tag{2-76}$$

and the higher terms can be written down in the same way.

The determinant D is a function of $k^2+i\varepsilon$ and we shall display the dependence by writing it as $D(k^2+i\varepsilon)$. By using g_ℓ^- in place of g_ℓ^+, we can also construct $D(k^2-i\varepsilon)$ and we shall now show that the Jost functions (see section 1-7 equations (1-164)) $\phi_\ell(\mp k)$ are identical with the functions $D(k^2\pm i\varepsilon)$.

The Jost function

To show the identity of the Jost function $\phi_\ell(-k)$ and $D(E + i\varepsilon)$, an integral equation for $\phi_\ell(-k)$ is required. For simplicity consider the case of $\ell=0$. It can easily be verified by substitution that

$$F_0(\pm k,r) = e^{\pm ikr} + \lambda\int_0^\infty dr'\bar{g}(r,r')U(r')F_0(\pm k,r') \quad (2\text{-}77)$$

is a solution of the Schrodinger equation for the potential $\lambda V(r)$, with the boundary conditions (1-162), where $\bar{g}(r,r')$ is defined[2] by

$$\begin{aligned}\bar{g}(r,r') &= -k^{-1}(\sin kr \cos kr' - \cos kr \sin kr'), && r<r'\\ &= 0 && r>r'.\end{aligned} \quad (2\text{-}78)$$

From the definition (1-164), the Jost functions are

$$\begin{aligned}\phi_o(\mp k) &= \lim_{r\to 0} F_0(\pm k,r)\\ &= 1 + \frac{\lambda}{k}\int_0^\infty dr' \sin kr' U(r')F_0(\pm k,r')\end{aligned} \quad (2\text{-}79)$$

If the iterative solution of (2-77) is used for F_0, the resulting series is term by term the same as the expansion of $D(E \mp i\varepsilon)$ in powers of λ. The two functions are therefore the same.

A theorem of Poincaré states that if a parameter appears in a differential equation like the radial Schrödinger equation and if that parameter does not appear explicitly in the boundary conditions, then the solution of the equation is an entire function of the parameter. As the solution $F_0(\pm k,r)$ are defined by boundary conditions which are independent of λ, it follows that $D(k^2)$ and $\phi_0(\pm k)$ are entire functions of λ and that the power series expansion in λ converges for all values of λ.

Since $E=\hbar^2k^2/2m$, we can consider D as a function of E, D(E), and because of the double valued nature of the relation between E and k, D(E) has a branch point at E=0. We can take the branch cut along the real axis $0<E<\infty$, in which case the upper half k plane will map into the whole E plane, and $\phi(-k)$ for k real and positive may be identified with the boundary value of D just above the cut

$$\lim_{\varepsilon\to 0^+} D(E + i\varepsilon) = \phi(-k),$$

and in a similar way

$$\lim_{\varepsilon \to 0^+} D(E - i\varepsilon) = \phi(+k).$$

As the phase of $\phi(\pm k)$ is $\pm\delta_o$, (see equation 1-77) where δ_o is the phase shift, we have that

$$D(E \pm i\varepsilon) = |D(E)|\exp(\mp i\delta_o) \qquad (2\text{-}80)$$

showing that a knowledge of D is sufficient to solve the scattering problem. As D(E) is analytic in the entire E plane except for the cut along the real axis, a dispersion relation can be written for D(E) by integrating $(D(E')-1)/(E'-E)$ round the contour shown in figure 2-1.

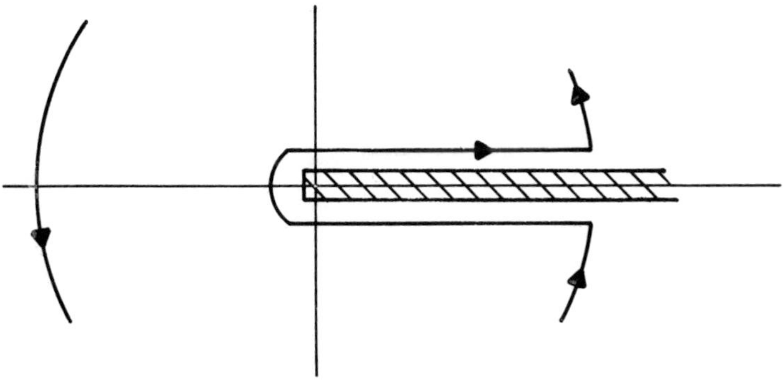

Figure 2-1 Contour for the integration leading to the dispersion relation for D(E).
Eq. (2-81)

Using Cauchy's theorem we have that

$$D(E + i\varepsilon) - 1 = \frac{1}{2\pi i}\int_C \frac{D(E') - 1}{E' - E - i\varepsilon}\, dE'$$

$$= \frac{1}{\pi}\int_0^\infty \frac{\mathrm{Im}D(E')}{E' - E - i\varepsilon}\, dE', \qquad (2\text{-}81)$$

where the fact that the discontinuity across the cut is 2iImD has been used in the last line. This follows from the relation

$$D^*(E^*) = D(E).$$

These equations can be made the basis of a practical

approximation (Baker, 1958; see also Nutt, 1964). For example, an approximation to ImD could be obtained from the lowest terms in the series (2-71), then ReD would be given by (2-81) and the phase shift by (2-80). This procedure is closely related to the "N/D" method frequently employed in high energy physics (Gasiorowicz, 1966).

The Fredholm series for $D(E+i\varepsilon)$ converges however large the potential strength parameter λ, in contrast to the Born series which often diverges. However, convergence may be slow and numerical examples (Moiseiwitsch and O'Brien 1970) show that for the potential (2-14) and similar potentials poor results are obtained if only one or two terms are retained in the expansion (2-71). A method of avoiding this expansion has been developed, by Reinhardt et al (1972), which has the advantage of being applicable to scattering by complex systems[3]. Looking back at (2-70) it is seen that the Fredholm determinant can be expressed at an arbitrary complex value of the energy, z, as

$$D(z) = \det \left| \frac{z - H}{z - H_o} \right| \tag{2-82}$$

where $H = H_o + V$ and

$$H_o = -\frac{\hbar^2}{2m}\left(\frac{d^2}{dr^2} - \frac{\ell(\ell+1)}{r^2}\right) \tag{2-83}$$

The Hamiltonian operators H and H_o are now approximated in terms of a discrete basis set of square integrable functions ϕ_i, truncated to a finite number of members N. That is the NxN matrices $\bar{H}_{ij}$ and $(\bar{H}_o)_{ij}$ are constructed where

$$\bar{H}_{ij} = (\phi_i|H|\phi_j),\ (\bar{H}_o)_{ij} = (\phi_i|H_o|\phi_j).$$

Since $\bar{H}$ and $\bar{H}_o$ are self-adjoint, these matrices can be diagonalized and the corresponding eigenvalues $\bar{E}_i$ and $(\bar{E}_o)_i$ are real. An approximation to D(z) is then:

$$D(z) \approx \det \left| \frac{z-\bar{H}}{z-\bar{H}_o} \right| = \prod_{i=1}^{N} \left(\frac{z - \bar{E}_i}{z - (\bar{E}_o)_i} \right) \tag{2-84}$$

The continuous spectrum of H_o which gives rise to the branch cut in D(z) along the real E axis, has been replaced in (2-84) by a series of poles at $z=(E_o)_i$. For this reason (2-84) will provide a good approximation to D(z) only for complex values of z well away from the real axis and not in the limit $z \to E+i\varepsilon$. To overcome this smooth extrapolation from a region of complex z to the real axis must be devised. One method is to fit D(z) to a rational function such as

$$R(z) = \frac{\Sigma p_i z^i}{1 + \Sigma q_i z^i} \qquad (2\text{-}85)$$

where the coefficients p_i, q_i are determined by fitting well away from the real axis. The phase shifts are then determined from the phase of $R(E+i\varepsilon)$ as $\varepsilon \to o^+$.

In practice, a stable extrapolation to the real axis can be achieved, and the method has the advantage (particularly apparent in many particle problems) of working only with square integrable functions and avoiding difficult numerical problems which arise when continuum functions are employed. Several different techniques, based on the idea of representing H in a discrete basis, have been developed in recent years and for a bibliography and review, reference may be made to the article by Reinhardt (1979).

<u>Three dimensional and multi-channel scattering</u>

The determinantal method will not work, as it stands, for the complete scattering amplitude because in this case

$$\mathrm{Tr}[K] = \int d^3r \int d^3r' G_0^+(\vec{r},\vec{r}\,')U(r')\delta(\vec{r} - \vec{r}\,') \qquad (2\text{-}86)$$

does not exist. It is possible to extend the method to avoid this difficulty, by subtracting the divergent parts of $\mathrm{Tr}[K]$. For instance if D(E) is defined as

$$D(E) = \exp \mathrm{Tr}[\log (1 - K) + K], \qquad (2\text{-}87)$$

no divergent integrals appear in the expansion in powers of λ. Details may be found in the paper by Baker (1958).

The extension of the determinantal theory to many channel scattering has been given by Blankenbecler (1963) and Blankenbecler and Sugar (1964).

2-3 THE R-MATRIX

We have already seen that when solving the radial equation (2-1) for potential scattering, provided the potential decreases sufficiently rapidly as the radial coordinate r increases, a value of r, r_o, can be chosen beyond which the solution $f_\ell(r)$ is represented accurately by its asymptotic form $f_\ell^a(r)$. We can write:

$$f_\ell(r) = f_\ell^a(r) \qquad r \geq r_o$$

where

$$f_\ell^a(r) = A_\ell \, [s_\ell(kr) + K_\ell c_\ell(kr)] \tag{2-88}$$

The phase shift f_ℓ is related to K_ℓ, by $K_\ell = \tan \delta_\ell$, and A_ℓ is a normalization constant. In the inner region where the potential is significant, the real regular solution satisfying the boundary condition $f_\ell(o) = o$ is denoted by $f_\ell^b(r)$

$$f_\ell(r) = f_\ell^b(r) \qquad r \leq r_o \tag{2-89}$$

To determine K_ℓ from a knowledge of $f_\ell^b(r)$, it is only necessary to equate the logarithmic derivative γ of f_ℓ (r) at the boundary of the inner and outer regions

$$\gamma \equiv \left(\frac{df_\ell^b}{dr} \Big/ f_\ell^b \right)_{r=r_o} = \left(\frac{df_\ell^a}{dr} \Big/ f_\ell^a \right)_{r=r_o} \tag{2-90}$$

From (2-90), we find immediately

$$K_\ell = \tan \delta_\ell = \frac{ks_\ell'(kr_o) - \gamma s_\ell(kr_o)}{\gamma c_\ell(kr_o) - kc_\ell'(kr_o)} \tag{2-91}$$

or, specializing to the case $\ell=0$ for which $s_o(x) = \sin x$, $c_o(x) = \cos x$

$$K_o = \tan \delta_o = \frac{k\cos kr_o - \gamma \sin kr_o}{\gamma \cos kr_o + k\sin kr_o} \tag{2-92}$$

Since $f_\ell^b(r)$ is only required in a region of limited extent $o<r<r_o$, we would expect to be able to approximate it accurately by a linear combination of a number of conveniently chosen functions $\phi_i(r)$

$$f_\ell^b(r) = \sum_{i=1}^{N} c_i \phi_i(r) \tag{2-93}$$

The coefficients c_i can be computed by demanding that $f_\ell^b(r)$ solves (2-1) in a least squares (or minimum norm[4]) sense. This is achieved by forming the quanity I, where

$$I = \int_0^{r_o} drW(r)\left[\left(\frac{d^2}{dr^2} - \frac{\ell(\ell+1)}{r^2} - U(r)+k^2\right)f_\ell^b(r)\right]^2 \times$$

$$\times \left[\int_0^{r_o} dr \left(f_\ell^b(r)\right)^2\right]^{-1} \tag{2-94}$$

and W(r) is a weight function. We then require I to be minimised with respect to the coefficients c_i, so that

$$\frac{\partial I}{\partial c_i} = 0 \qquad i = 1,2,\ldots\ldots N \tag{2-95}$$

Equations (2-95) are a linear set of equations for the c_i, the solution of which at each value of k^2, determines $f_\ell^b(r)$ and hence the phase shifts through (2-91). This method allows great flexibility in choice of the functions ϕ_i, which can, for example, be simple polynomials or Slater functions $r^n \exp(-\lambda_n r)$ and so on. In general convergence will be most rapid if r_o is taken to be as small as possible.

A different approach to the determination of $f_\ell^b(r)$, which has proved to be particularly useful in multi-channel scattering is the R-matrix method of Wigner and Eisenbud (1947). We shall describe this for the particular case $\ell=0$. Let us introduce a complete set of real eigenfunctions $Y_i(r)$ of the operator

$$\left(-\frac{d^2}{dr^2} + U(r)\right)$$

in the interval $o<r<r_o$, subject to the boundary conditions

$$Y_i(o)=0 \ , \qquad \left(\frac{dY_i}{dr}\Big/ Y_i\right)_{r=r_o} = b \tag{2-96}$$

where b is a fixed arbitrary number. Because of the boundary condition, the eigenvalue spectrum is discrete so that

$$\left(-\frac{d^2}{dr^2} + U(r)\right) Y_i(r) = k_i^{\,2} Y_i(r) \qquad i=1,2... \qquad (2\text{-}97)$$

The eigenfunctions are orthogonal and can be normalized to unity:

$$\int_0^{r_0} dr\, Y_i Y_j = \delta_{i\,j} \qquad i,j = 1,2,.... \qquad (2\text{-}98)$$

The radial function in the inner region can now be expanded in terms of the Y_i functions by

$$f_0^{\,b}(r) = \sum_{i=1}^{\infty} C_i Y_i(r) \qquad (2\text{-}99a)$$

with

$$C_i = \int_0^{r_0} dr\, Y_i(r)\, f_0^{\,b}(r) \qquad (2\text{-}99b)$$

By multiplying (2-97) by $f_0^{\,b}(r)$ and the radial equation for $f_0^{\,b}(r)$,

$$\left(-\frac{d^2}{dr^2} + U(r)\right) f_0^{\,b}(r) = k^2 f_0^{\,b}(r),$$

by $Y_i(r)$, subtracting and integrating over r, we obtain

$$\int_0^{r_0} dr \left(f_0^{\,b} \frac{d^2 Y_i}{dr^2} - Y_i \frac{d^2 f_0^{\,b}}{dr^2} \right) = (k^2 - k_i^2) \int_0^{r_0} dr\, Y_i\, f_0^{\,b}$$

or

$$\left(f_0^{\,b} \frac{dY_i}{dr} - Y_i \frac{df_0^{\,b}}{dr} \right)_{r=r_0} = (k^2 - k_i^{\,2})\, C_i \qquad (2\text{-}100)$$

which determines the coefficients C_i. At $r=r_0$ the function $f_0^{\,b}(r)$ is

$$f_o^{\,b}(r_o) = \sum_{i=1}^{\infty} C_i Y_i(r_o)$$

$$= \sum_{i=0}^{\infty} \frac{[Y_i(r_o)]}{k^2-k_i^{\,2}} \left(f_o^{\,b} \frac{dY_i}{dr} - Y_i \frac{df_o^{\,b}}{dr} \right)_{r=r_o}$$

from which the logarithmic derivative γ, which determines $\tan \delta_o$ can be calculated. It is given by

$$\gamma = b + \frac{1}{R} \tag{2-101}$$

where the boundary condition (2-96) has been used and R is defined as

$$R = - \sum_{i=1}^{\infty} \frac{[Y_i(r_o)]^2}{k^2-k_i^{\,2}} \tag{2-102}$$

A knowledge of R, which is called the R-matrix, determines the phase shift δ_o. The structure of R is particularly simple, being a series of poles along the real k^2 axis and if k^2 is near one of the poles k_i, $R(k^2)$ can be approximated by a single term

$$R(k^2) \sim [Y_i(r_o)]^2/(k^2-k_i^{\,2}).$$

In practice to determine the eigenfunctions Y_i and the eigenvalues $k_i^{\,2}$, is difficult and approximation schemes must be devised. One particular way of proceeding is to introduce as a basis, a known set of orthonomal functions, satisfying the boundary conditions (2-96). Truncating this set to N terms, the operator

$$\left(- \frac{d^2}{dr^2} + U(r) \right)$$

can be diagonalized in this finite basis, providing eigenvalues $\bar{k}_i^{\,2}$ and eigenfunctions $\bar{Y}_i(r)$ for i=1,...N. These eigenvalues and eigenfunctions can be employed as approximations to the first N eigenvalues and eigenfunctions $k_i^{\,2}$ and Y_i so we have, approximately

$$R = -\sum_{i=1}^{N} \frac{[\bar{Y}_i(r_o)]^2}{k^2-\bar{k}_i^2} \tag{2-103}$$

Because of the Raleigh-Ritz principle, the inequalities

$$\bar{k}_i^2 \geq k_i^2, \; i = 1,2,....N$$

are satisfied, and using this result a minimum principle for the phase shifts calculated at the energies $\bar{k}_i^2$ is found. In fact $\delta_o(\bar{k}_i)$ is a lower bound on the exact phase shift. In general, the approximate value of $R(k^2)$ given by (2-103) is not sufficiently accurate and a correction[5] must be made for the omission of the higher order eigenfunctions and eigenvalues $i = N+1, N+2 ....\infty$, but even when this is done the method retains the virtue that only one diagonalization on a finite basis is required to provide an approximation to $\tan \delta_o$ at all energies. There is no difficulty in extending the theory to $\ell \neq 0$ or to non-local potentials.

2-4 SEMI-CLASSICAL SCATTERING FORMULAE

It is well known from the theory of optics, that when the wave-length of light is small compared with the distance over which the refractive index changes appreciably, then rays can be defined which follow the laws of geometrical optics. In the same way, if the wave-length (h/p) of a particle is sufficiently short compared with the distance in which the potential changes appreciably, it is possible to define particle trajectories which obey the laws of classical mechanics. There is an important approximation, that is useful at high energies, termed the semi-classical approximation which is intermediate in character between a full classical and a full quantum treatment.

If the potential is of range a, the short wave-length condition amounts to requiring that $ka \gg 1$.

When classical conditions hold, the angle of scattering must be well defined, that is the uncertainty $\Delta\theta$ in the angle of scattering must be small compared with θ. The uncertainty in the transverse momentum imparted to the scattered particle, Δp, is by Heisenberg's uncertainty principle, of the order $(\hbar/a)$,

$$\Delta p \sim \hbar/a,$$

The corresponding uncertainty in the angle of scattering is

$$\Delta\theta = \frac{\Delta p}{p} \sim \left(\frac{1}{ka}\right),$$

and for classical conditions to apply, the angle of scattering θ must be greater than $(1/ka)$. If $\bar{V}$ is the average of the potential within the region $0<r<a$, the momentum transfer in the transverse direction, $\hbar K$, is of the order $(m\bar{V}/p)$, or in terms of $\bar{U}$ where $\bar{U} = 2m\,\bar{V}/\hbar^2$ and k, $(\hbar\bar{U}/2k)$. From this, it can be seen that the classical angle of scattering for large k is approximately given by

$$\theta = \frac{K}{k} = \left(\frac{\bar{U}}{2k^2}\right) \qquad (2\text{-}104)$$

and it follows that the inequality $\Delta\theta \ll \theta$ can be written as

$$\frac{a\bar{U}}{2k} \gg 1.$$

The Born approximation is also a high velocity approximation but it applies to angles of scattering within the cone $\theta < (\bar{U}/2k^2)$, whereas the classical scattering conditions apply when $\theta>(1/ka)$, and the two regions do not overlap.

Classical scattering cross-sections

Before exploring the classical and semi-classical limits of the Schrödinger equation, a brief discussion of classical scattering theory will be given. The starting point of the classical theory is the Lagrangian for a particle of mass m moving in the potential field $V(r)$. If the potential is central the motion takes place in a plane and if plane polar coordinates (r,ϕ) are introduced, with the center of force as origin, the Lagrangian is

$$\mathcal{L} = \frac{1}{2}m(\dot{r}^2 + r^2\dot{\phi}^2) - V(r). \qquad (2\text{-}105)$$

As ϕ is a cyclic coordinate, the angular momentum L where

$$L = \frac{\partial \mathcal{L}}{\partial \dot{\phi}} = mr^2\dot{\phi} \tag{2-106}$$

is a constant of the motion. The total energy E must also be conserved so that

$$E = \frac{1}{2}m(\dot{r}^2 + r^2\dot{\phi}^2) + V(r) = \frac{1}{2}m\dot{r}^2 + \frac{L^2}{2mr^2} + V(r)$$

is a constant. Solving the energy equation for $\dot{r} = dr/dt$, we find

$$\frac{dr}{dt} = \left(\frac{2}{m}(E - V(r)) - \frac{L^2}{m^2r^2}\right)^{\frac{1}{2}} \tag{2-107}$$

and integrating

$$t = \int dr \left[\frac{2}{m}(E - V(r)) - \frac{L^2}{m^2r^2}\right]^{-\frac{1}{2}} + t_o, \tag{2-108}$$

where t_o is a constant of integration. By writing $dt = mr^2d\phi/L$, the orbit equation can be deduced from (2-107):

$$\phi = \int_{r_o}^{r} dr \frac{L}{mr^2}\left(\frac{2}{m}(E - V(r)) - \frac{L^2}{m^2r^2}\right)^{-\frac{1}{2}}$$

$$= -\int_{r_o}^{r} dr \frac{\partial}{\partial L}\left(2m(E - V(r)) - \frac{L^2}{r^2}\right)^{\frac{1}{2}} \tag{2-109}$$

where the constant of integration has been determined by requiring that $\phi=0$ at $r=r_o$, where r_o is the distance of closest approach. The distance of closest approach is the largest root of the equation $\dot{r}=o$, which (from 2-107) can be written as

$$2m(E - V(r)) = \frac{L^2}{r^2} \tag{2-110}$$

If α is the angle between the asymptotes of the orbit, which is symmetrical about the point of closest approach, we have

$$\frac{\alpha}{2} = \phi(r = \infty) - \phi(r = r_o) = -\int_{r_o}^{\infty} dr \frac{\partial}{\partial L} \{2m[E-V(r)] - \frac{L^2}{r^2}\}^{\frac{1}{2}} \tag{2-111}$$

The angle of deflection Θ is defined as

$$\Theta = \pi - \alpha.$$

For repulsive potentials Θ is positive and for attractive potentials Θ is negative. If Θ lies in the interval $0 < \Theta < \pi$ and if Θ is a monotonic function of L, then can be identified with the angle of scattering θ.

In general the deflection angle can take any value in the interval $-\infty < \Theta < \pi$, and the scattering angle which is defined to lie in the interval of $0 < \theta < \pi$ is then

$$\theta = \pm\Theta + 2\pi m, \tag{2-112}$$

where m is an integer or zero.

The differential cross-section is calculated by considering the scattering of a uniform beam of particles each of velocity v. If N particles cross unit area normal to the beam per unit time, then the number per second with angular momentum between L and L + dL is equal to the number per second with impact parameters between b and b + db, where $b = L/mv$. This number is

$$2\pi N b db = 2\pi N L dL/(m^2v^2). \tag{2-113}$$

If the number of particles scattered per unit time between angles θ and $\theta + d\theta$ is I, we see that

$$I = \frac{2\pi NL}{m^2v^2} \left|\frac{dL}{d\theta}\right| d\theta, \tag{2-114}$$

where $L(\theta)$ is given by (2-111). The differential cross-section $d\sigma/d\Omega$ is therefore (using $d\theta = -d(\cos\theta)/\sin\theta$)

$$\frac{d\sigma}{d\Omega} = \frac{+L}{m^2v^2} \left|\frac{dL}{d\theta}\right| \frac{1}{\sin\theta}. \tag{2-115}$$

If there is more than one value of L satisfying equation (2-111) for a given θ, then the classical cross section is the sum of contributions from each trajectory

$$\frac{d\sigma}{d\Omega} = \sum_i \left(\frac{L_i}{m^2v^2} \left| \frac{dL}{d\theta} \right|_i \frac{1}{\sin\theta} \right) \tag{2-116}$$

Coulomb scattering

As an example, if V(r) is the Coulomb potential $Z_1Z_2e^2/r$ between two particles of charges Z_1e and Z_2e, then integration of (2-111) yields

$$\theta = \pi - 2\cot^{-1}\left(\frac{Z_1Z_2e^2\sqrt{m}}{L\sqrt{2E}} \right)$$

Inverting to obtain L, we find

$$L = \sqrt{\left(\frac{m}{2E}\right)}\; Z_1Z_2e^2 \cot(\theta/2),$$

and the differential cross-section is

$$\frac{d\sigma}{d\Omega} = \left(\frac{Z_1Z_2e^2}{4E} \right)^2 \frac{1}{(\sin\theta/2)^4}. \tag{2-117}$$

As $\theta \to 0$, the cross-section diverges. This is because some scattering occurs however far the particle is from the center of force, and large values of impact parameter b correspond to scattering through small angles. For this reason, the classical total cross section for Coulomb scattering, and for all potentials that do not vanish beyond a certain distance, is infinite.

The Eikonal approximation[6]

To investigate the classical limit of the Schrödinger equation the wave function $\psi(\vec{r})$ can be written as

$$\psi(\vec{r}) = e^{iS(\vec{r})/\hbar} \tag{2-118}$$

On substituting into the time independent Schrödinger equation,

$$\left(-\frac{\hbar^2}{2m}\nabla^2 + V(r) - E \right)\psi(\vec{r}) = 0\ , \tag{2-119}$$

we find that

$$\frac{1}{2m}\left(-i\hbar\nabla^2 S + (\vec{\nabla}S)^2\right) = E - V(r). \tag{2-120}$$

The classical limit is obtained when $\nabla^2 S \ll (\vec{\nabla} S)^2$ which is equivalent to taking the limit $h \to 0$. In this limit, $S = S_0(\vec{r})$, where

$$\frac{1}{2m} (\vec{\nabla} S_0)^2 = E - V(r), \tag{2-121}$$

which will be recognized as the classical Hamilton-Jacobi equation, if $S_0(\vec{r})$ is identified with Hamilton's characteristic function. In optics this equation, which determines the rays, is called the eikonal equation. The integration of this equation determines the orbits which are the normals to the surfaces over which $S_0(\vec{r})$ is constant. These normals are parallel to $\vec{\nabla} S$, and a formal solution of (2-102) can be written

$$S_0(\vec{r}) = \int ds \left[2m(E-V(r))\right]^{\frac{1}{2}} \tag{2-122}$$

where $\int ds$ denotes an integration along a trajectory (or orbit). The trajectories determined from the Hamilton-Jacobi equation are just those given by the Lagrangian method and determined from (2-109).

If $S_0(\vec{r})$ is substituted into (2-118) an approximation for the wave function is obtained which is termed the eikonal wave function. The use of this wave function in the integral equation for the scattering amplitude (1-129), forms the basis of the eikonal approximation. This approximation will be developed in a form suitable for use at high energies at which scattering is mainly confined to small angles. In this case, to lowest order, the classical trajectory can be approximated by a straight line parallel to the direction of incidence. Taking the center of force as the origin of the coordinate system, with the Z-axis in the direction of incidence, and defining $\vec{n}$ as a unit vector parallel to the Z-axis, and $\vec{b}$ as a vector perpendicular to $\vec{n}$ and of length equal to the classical impact parameter, the orbit is $\vec{r}(b)$ where

$$\begin{aligned} \vec{r} &= \vec{b} + z\vec{n}\ ; \\ \vec{b} \cdot \vec{n} &= 0. \end{aligned} \tag{2-123}$$

It is useful to note that z=vt, where v is the velocity of the particle and t=0 is the time of closest approach. With this approximation to the orbit, the eikonal equation (2-121) reduces to

$$\frac{1}{2m}\left(\frac{\partial S_o(z)}{\partial z}\right)^2 = E - V\,(\sqrt{b^2+z^2})$$

with the solution (see 2-122)

$$S_o(z) = \int \{2m\left[E - V(\sqrt{b^2+z^2})\right]\}^{\frac{1}{2}}\, dz + \text{constant.} \qquad (2\text{-}124)$$

The normalization required by the integral equation (1-129) is that the wave function approaches a plane wave of unit amplitude as $z \to -\infty$. This condition is satisfied by the approximate wave function provided

$$S_o(z) \to \hbar kz,$$

$$z \to -\infty.$$

The approximate wave function does not have the correct asymptotic form of a scattering wave function, in that it does not describe outgoing spherical waves at large r, but it can represent the wave function over the region in which V is large. Imposing the boundary condition to determine the integration constant,we have that

$$S_o(z) = \hbar kz + \int_{-\infty}^{z} \{\left(2m\ (E - V(\sqrt{b^2+ z^2})\right)^{\frac{1}{2}} - \hbar k\}dz \qquad (2\text{-}125)$$

For large values of the momentum $\hbar k$, since $E = \hbar\, k^2/2m$, $S_o(z)$ can be approximated by

$$S_o(z) \approx \hbar kz - \frac{m}{\hbar k}\int_{-\infty}^{z} V(\sqrt{b^2+z^2})\ dz \qquad (2\text{-}126)$$

The exact scattering amplitude satisfies (1-129)

$$f(\vec{k},\theta) = -\frac{1}{4\pi}\int d^3r\ \exp(-i\vec{k}'\cdot\vec{r})U(r)\psi(\vec{r})$$

From (2-118) and with the approximation (2-126) we have

$$f(\vec{k},\theta) = -\frac{1}{4\pi}\int d^3r\ \exp(-i\vec{k}'\cdot\vec{r})U(r) \times \qquad (2\text{-}127)$$

$$\times \quad \exp\{i\left[\vec{k}\cdot\vec{r} - \frac{1}{2k}\int_{-\infty}^{z} dz'U(\sqrt{b^2+z'^2})dz'\right]\}$$

where $\vec{r}$ is given by (2-123) and $U(r) = 2mV(r)/\hbar^2$, as usual.

Introducing the momentum transfer $\vec{K} = \vec{k} - \vec{k}'$, $|\vec{K}| = 2k \sin(\theta/2)$, we have that

$$\exp[i(\vec{k}\cdot\vec{r} - \vec{k}'\cdot\vec{r})] = \exp[i\vec{K}\cdot(\vec{b} + \vec{n}z)].$$

As $|\vec{k}'| = |\vec{k}|$, the momentum transfer, $\vec{K} = \vec{k} - \vec{k}'$, is nearly perpendicular to k for small angles of scattering θ,

$$\vec{K}\cdot\vec{k} = k^2(1 - \cos\theta) \cong \frac{1}{2}k^2\theta^2 \qquad (2\text{-}128)$$

This is not an additional approximation as the eikonal approximation is only reliable for small angles, because of the assumption of straight line trajectories. The maximum value of z of importance in the integration is ~a, where a is the range of the potential, so that the term $\exp(i\vec{K}\cdot\vec{n}z)$ may be replaced by 1 for angles such that $\theta^2 ka \ll 1$. Then setting

$$\int d^3r = \int_0^{2\pi} d\phi \int_0^{\infty} b\,db \int_{-\infty}^{\infty} dz,$$

(where $x = b\cos\phi, y = b\sin\phi$) we find

$$f(\vec{k},\theta) = -\frac{1}{4\pi}\int_0^{2\pi} d\phi \int_0^{\infty} b\,db \int_{-\infty}^{\infty} dz\, \exp(i\vec{K}\cdot\vec{b})\, U(\sqrt{b^2+z^2}) \times$$

$$\times \exp\left(-\frac{i}{2k}\int_{\infty}^{z} dz'\, U(\sqrt{b^2+z'^2})\right)$$

$$= \frac{k}{2\pi i}\int_0^{2\pi} d\phi \int_0^{\infty} b\,db\, \exp(i\vec{K}\cdot\vec{b})\left[\exp\left\{-\frac{i}{2k}\int_{\infty}^{\infty} dz U(\sqrt{b^2+z^2})\right\} - 1\right] \qquad (2\text{-}129)$$

The central potentials we are investigating do not depend on φ, so that the φ integration is (Morse and Feshbach (1953) p.620),

$$\int_0^{2\pi} d\phi \exp(iKb\cos\phi) = 2\pi J_0(Kb),$$

We have finally,

$$f(\vec{k},\theta) = \frac{k}{i}\int_0^\infty J_0(Kb)[\exp i\chi(b) - 1]b\,db, \qquad (2\text{-}130)$$

where the phase or eikonal $\chi(b)$ is defined by

$$\chi(b) = -\frac{1}{2k}\int_{-\infty}^{\infty} U(\sqrt{b^2+z^2})\,dz. \qquad (2\text{-}131)$$

The eikonal approximation has several important properties. For potentials of range $a, \chi(b)$ becomes small when $b>a$, so that $f(\vec{k},\theta)$ receives contributions only from the range $0<b<a$, which is what would be expected classically. Calculation (Glauber, 1959) shows that the optical theorem is satisfied by $f(\vec{k},\theta)$, implying conservation of probability. This is in contrast to the Born approximation, for which the scattering amplitude is real and which therefore can never satisfy the optical theorem. The total cross-section is (using $J_0(0) = 1$),

$$\sigma(\text{tot}) = \frac{4\pi}{k}\,\text{Im}\, f(\vec{k},\theta) = -4\pi\int_0^\infty b\,db\,\text{Re}[\exp i\chi(b)-1]. \qquad (2\text{-}132)$$

Impact parameter representations

It can be shown that the expression (2-130) is an exact representation of the scattering amplitude (however, the particular expression (2-131) for the phase is an approximation) for all energies and angles (Predazzi, 1966; Chadan, 1968).

To relate the eikonal phase $\chi(b)$ to the phase shifts introduced in Chapter 1, the following argument can be made. The partial wave expansion for the scattering amplitude $f(\vec{k},\theta)$ is (1-39)

$$f(\vec{k},\theta) = \sum_{\ell=0}^{\infty} (2\ell+1)\,\frac{1}{2ik}\,(\exp(2i\delta_\ell) - 1)\,P_\ell(\cos\theta) \qquad (2\text{-}133)$$

Under the conditions that (1) many partial waves are important (2) the variation of δ_ℓ with ℓ is smooth, the sum in (2-133) can be replaced by an integral, so that

$$f(\vec{k},\theta) = \frac{1}{ik} \int_0^\infty d\ell \ (\ell+\tfrac{1}{2}) \left[\exp(2i\delta_\ell) - 1 \right] \ P_\ell(\cos\theta) \qquad (2\text{-}134)$$

If we further specialize to small angles, the approximation

$$P_\ell(\cos\theta) \approx J_0(\ell\theta)$$

can be used, which is valid for $\theta<1/\ell$. Setting $b\approx\ell/k$ and $(\ell+\frac{1}{2})\approx \ell$, we immediately regain the impact parameter representation (2-130), if we identify

$$2\delta_\ell \approx \chi(b) \qquad (2\text{-}135)$$

Although we have assumed $V(r)$ to be real, the eikonal approximation is equally valid for real or absorptive complex potentials. In the latter case, χ becomes complex and

$$\begin{aligned} \text{Re}\chi &= 2\delta_\ell \\ \exp[-\text{Im}\chi] &= \eta_\ell . \end{aligned} \qquad (2\text{-}136)$$

Scattering by a black sphere

An example is given by scattering from a perfectly absorbing 'black' sphere of radius a. For $\ell<ka$, we may put $\eta_\ell=0$ which corresponds to complete absorption, while for $\ell>ka$, the partial wave scattering amplitude vanishes, so that, from (2-134) and (2-136)

$$\begin{aligned} f(\vec{k},\theta) &= -\frac{1}{ik} \int_0^{ka} \ell d\ell J_0(\ell\theta) \\ &= ia \frac{J_1(ka\theta)}{\theta} \end{aligned} \qquad (2\text{-}137)$$

The cross section has a typical diffraction shape, peaked in the forward direction, with subsidiary decreasing peaks as θ increases. The total cross section is

$$\sigma_{tot} = \frac{4\pi}{k} \text{Im} f(\vec{k},0) = 2\pi a^2 . \qquad (2\text{-}138)$$

As the sphere is completely absorbing, each partial

inelastic cross section $\sigma_\ell(\text{in})$ takes on its maximum value of $\pi(2\ell+1)/k^2$ and the complete inelastic cross section is

$$\sigma(\text{in}) = \sum_{\ell=0}^{ka} \frac{\pi(2\ell + 1)}{k^2} = \pi a^2 \tag{2-139}$$

As pointed out earlier (Section 1-5), when the cross section for inelastic scattering in a particular partial wave takes on its maximum value, the elastic scattering cross section $\sigma_\ell(\text{e}\ell)$ has an equal value. It follows that

$$\sigma(\text{e}\ell) = \pi a^2. \tag{2-140}$$

in conformity with (1-98a) and (1-98b). The elastic cross section can also be found by integrating $|f(\vec{k},\theta)|^2$ given by (2-137).

The Jeffreys or W.B.K. method

A more elaborate approximation not confined to high energies can be obtained if the phase shifts δ_ℓ are computed semi-classically from the radial Schrödinger equation (Jeffreys, 1923; Wentzel, 1926; Brillouin, 1926; Kramers, 1926). This has the advantage that the angular momentum eigenfunctions are treated exactly. The computed phase shifts may then be used in the partial wave series or, more conveniently, as under the conditions for which the semi-classical method is valid there are usually a very large number of important partial waves, the phase shifts may be used in an integral expression such as (2-134).

The treatment of the Jeffreys method that we shall follow is based on the work of Langer (1937; see also Morse and Feshbach, 1953, p. 1092). It is easiest to start from the one dimensional Schrödinger equation

$$\left(\frac{-\hbar^2}{2m}\frac{d^2}{dx^2} + V(x) - E\right)\psi(x) = 0, \tag{2-141}$$

where $\psi(x)$ is defined in the interval $-\infty < x < \infty$. A change of variable will be made to transform the radial Schrödinger equation into this one dimensional form at a later stage.

As in the eikonal method, we look for a solution in the form

$$\psi(x) = e^{iS(x)/\hbar}. \tag{2-142}$$

Substitution into the Schrödinger equation shows that S(x) satisfies

$$-i\hbar \frac{d^2S}{dx^2} + \left(\frac{dS}{dx}\right)^2 = F(x), \qquad (2\text{-}143)$$

where $F(x) = 2m[E - V(x)]$. Expanding S(x) in powers of h gives us

$$S = S_o(x) + \hbar S_1(x) + \hbar^2 S_2(x) + \ldots\ldots, \qquad (2\text{-}144)$$

On substituting into equation (2-143) and equating the coefficients of each power of ħ, we find

$$\left(\frac{dS_o}{dx}\right)^2 = F(x) \qquad (2\text{-}145a)$$

$$-i \frac{d^2S_o}{dx^2} + 2\frac{dS_o}{dx} \frac{dS_1}{dx} = 0 \qquad (2\text{-}145b)$$

$$-i \frac{d^2S_1}{dx^2} + \left(\frac{dS_1}{dx}\right)^2 + 2 \frac{dS}{dx} \frac{dS_2}{dx} = 0 \qquad (2\text{-}145c)$$

....

On integrating (2-145a), $S_o(x)$ is immediately found to be

$$S_o(x) = \pm \int F^{\frac{1}{2}}(x)dx. \qquad (2\text{-}146)$$

The next term $S_1(x)$ is found by using S_o in equation (2-145b) and integrating

$$S_1(x) = i \log |F(x)|^{+\frac{1}{4}} \qquad (2\text{-}147)$$

The equation for dS_2/dx, (2-145c), depends on the value of

$$\frac{dS_1}{dx} = \frac{i}{4F(x)} \frac{d|F(x)|}{dx}$$

$$= \frac{-im}{2F(x)} \frac{\partial V(x)}{\partial x} . \qquad (2\text{-}148)$$

The classical limit is applicable when the potential varies slowly compared with the variation of S(x). This requires that

$$\left|\frac{1}{F(x)} \frac{\partial V}{\partial x}\right|$$

is small, << 1. Under these circumstances S_2 and higher terms in the series for S can be neglected, as these are of the order

$$\left(\frac{1}{F(x)} \frac{\partial V}{\partial x}\right)^2$$

Provided this condition is satisfied, the most general solution for the case where $E>V(x)$, F(x) positive, is

$$\psi_+(x)=|F(x)|^{-\frac{1}{4}}\{A \exp\left(\frac{i}{\hbar}\int dx' F(x')^{\frac{1}{2}}\right)+ B \exp\left(-\frac{i}{\hbar}\int dx' F(x')^{\frac{1}{2}}\right)\} \tag{2-149}$$

and that for $E<V(x)$, F(x) negative, is

$$\psi_-(x)=|F(x)|^{-\frac{1}{4}} \; C \exp \frac{1}{\hbar}\int dx'|F(x')|^{\frac{1}{2}} + D \exp -\frac{1}{\hbar}\int dx'|F(x')|^{\frac{1}{2}}\} \tag{2-150}$$

where A, B, C and D are arbitrary constants.

Clearly the condition

$$\left|\frac{\partial V}{\partial x}\Big/F(x)\right| \ll 1$$

breaks down completely at the classical turning point at which $F(x) = 0$, and near such points the solution (2-149) and (2-150) are no longer valid. In general, there may be several turning points but the case that will be of interest to us is that in which F(x) has a zero at $x = x_0$, say, where $F(x)<0$ for $x<x_o$, $F(x)>0$ for $x>x_0$. Under these circumstances, for large negative x, the solution satisfying the boundary condition $\Psi(x)\to 0$ as $x\to -\infty$, is

$$\Psi_-(x) = |F(x)|^{-\frac{1}{4}} \; D \exp\left(-\int_x^{x_0} \frac{1}{\hbar}\, dx|F(x)|^{\frac{1}{2}}\right). \tag{2-151}$$

The problem is then to determine the corresponding solution in the region $x>x_0$.

Connecting formulae

To join the solutions to the left and right of the

turning point, a solution is required that is valid in the region where $|(x - x_o)|$ is small. This suggests that F(x) is expanded about the zero as

$$F(x) \approx A^2(x - x_o).$$

The Schrödinger equation is then for small $|x - x_o|$,

$$\left(\frac{d^2}{dx^2} + \frac{A^2}{\hbar^2}(x - x_o)\right)\psi(x) = 0.$$

This equation has a solution which is a linear combination of the Bessel functions

$$\sqrt{(x - x_o)}\; J_{\pm 1/3}\left[\frac{2}{3}\frac{A}{\hbar}(x - x_o)^{3/2}\right]. \qquad (2\text{-}152)$$

The solutions $\psi_{\pm}(x)$ depend on the integral

$$W(x) = \frac{1}{\hbar}\int_{x_o}^{x} F^{\frac{1}{2}}(x)dx. \qquad (2\text{-}153)$$

when $|x - x_o|$ is small, W(x) reduces to the argument of the Bessel function, that is to $2/3\, A/\hbar(x - x_o)^{3/2}$. It follows that the function

$$P = \frac{W}{|F(x)|}\,[EJ_{1/3}(W) + FJ_{-1/3}(W)], \qquad (2\text{-}154)$$

is an approximation to $\psi(x)$ near $x=x_o$. From the asymptotic form of the Bessel functions:-

$$J_{\nu}(z) \sim \left(\frac{2}{\pi z}\right)^{\frac{1}{2}} \cos\left(z - \frac{\pi\nu}{2} - \frac{\pi}{4}\right); -\pi<\text{Arg } z<\pi, \qquad (2\text{-}155)$$

it is seen that P(x) becomes a linear combination of the solutions ψ_- and ψ_+ for large $|x|$. The error in P (Morse and Feshbach, 1953) is of the order $\partial^2 V/\partial x^2$ which is small when the semi-classical approximation is valid.

It is now straightforward to verify that the particular solution $\psi_+(x)$ for $x >> x_o$ that joins the solution vanishing at $x = -\infty$, is

$$\psi_+(x) = \text{constant} \cdot F(x)^{-\frac{1}{4}} \cos\left(\int_{x_o}^{x}\frac{1}{\hbar}|F(x)|^{\frac{1}{2}}dx - \frac{\pi}{4}\right) \qquad (2\text{-}156)$$

The radial Schrödinger equation

The radial Schrödinger equation,

$$\left(\frac{d^2}{dr^2} - \frac{\ell(\ell+1)}{r^2} + k^2 - U(r)\right) f_\ell(r) = 0,$$

cannot be treated in the same way as the one-dimensional equation because of the singularity at r=0. It can, however, be brought into the form of the one dimensional equation by the substitutions

$$x = \log r; \ \psi = r^{-\frac{1}{2}} f_\ell(r), \qquad (2\text{-}157)$$

giving

$$\frac{d^2\psi}{dx^2} + e^{2x}\left(k^2 - U(e^x) - e^{-2x}(\ell+\tfrac{1}{2})^2\right)\psi = 0. \qquad (2\text{-}158)$$

Setting

$$F(x) = e^{2x}\left(k^2 - U(e^x) - e^{-2x}(\ell+\tfrac{1}{2})^2\right)$$

the required solution is given by equation (2-156) since the boundary condition $f_\ell(0) = 0$ corresponds to $\psi(x) \to 0$ at $x \to -\infty$.

Returning to the original variable r, the radial wave function is

$$f_\ell(r) = CF(r)^{-\frac{1}{4}} \cos\left(\int_{r_o}^{r} dr' F^{\frac{1}{2}}(r') - \frac{\pi}{4}\right), \qquad (2\text{-}159)$$

where $F(r) = k^2 - U(r) - (\ell + 1/2)^2/r^2$. For large r, $F(r) \to k^2$ so that

$$\int_{r_o}^{r} F^{\frac{1}{2}}(r')dr' \to \int_{r_o}^{\infty} [F^{\frac{1}{2}}(r') - k]dr' + k(r - r_o),$$

and comparing with the form $f_\ell(r) \sim \sin\left(kr - \frac{\ell\pi}{2} + \delta_\ell\right)$, the phase shift δ_ℓ may be identified as

$$\delta_\ell = \int_{r_o}^{\infty} [F^{\frac{1}{2}}(r') - k]dr' + \left(\ell + \frac{1}{2}\right)\frac{\pi}{2} - kr_o. \qquad (2\text{-}160)$$

This expression is accurate for large values of ℓ. Treating ℓ as a continuous variable, δ_ℓ defined by (2-160) can be used in (2-134). For large ℓ, the angular momentum L is

$$L = \hbar\sqrt{\ell(\ell+1)} \cong \hbar\left(\ell + \frac{1}{2}\right), \qquad (2\text{-}161)$$

and in terms of L, δ_ℓ can be written as

$$\delta_\ell = \frac{1}{\hbar}\int_{r_o}^{\infty}\left\{\left(2m(E - V(r)) - \frac{L^2}{r^2}\right)^{\frac{1}{2}} - k\hbar\right\}dr + \frac{L\pi}{2\hbar} - kr_o. \qquad (2\text{-}162)$$

Differentiating with respect to L

$$\hbar\frac{\partial\delta_\ell}{\partial L} = \frac{\pi}{2} + \int_{r_o}^{\infty}\frac{\partial}{\partial L}\{2m(E - V) - \frac{L^2}{r^2}\}^{\frac{1}{2}}dr, \qquad (2\text{-}163)$$

and comparing with (2-111) it is seen that twice the right hand side is identical with the classical deflection angle Θ

$$\hbar\frac{\partial\delta_\ell}{\partial L} = \frac{1}{2}\,\Theta, \quad L = \left(\ell + \frac{1}{2}\right)\hbar. \qquad (2\text{-}164)$$

The scattering amplitude

To determine the scattering amplitude, the approximation (2-162) for the phase shifts may be used in equation (2-134). For our present purpose, it is slightly more convenient to write the large ℓ approximation for P_ℓ(cos (θ)) in the form

$$P_\ell(\cos\ \theta) \sim \left(\frac{1}{2}\left(\ell + \frac{1}{2}\right)\pi\sin\ \theta\right)^{-\frac{1}{2}}\sin\left(\left(\ell + \frac{1}{2}\right)\theta + \frac{\pi}{4}\right), \qquad (2\text{-}165)$$

instead of in terms of $J_o(\ell\theta)$. This approximation is valid for $\ell > 1/\sin\theta$. As large ℓ values (of the order (ka)) are the most important, it follows that the approximation will be good for angles down to $\theta \cong 1/ka$, which is of course small since ka >> 1.

In the partial wave series for the scattering amplitude $f(\vec{k},\theta)$, the term not involving the phase shift can be summed, since

$$\frac{1}{2}\sum_{\ell=0}^{\infty}(2\ell + 1)P_\ell(\cos\ \theta)P_\ell(1) = \delta(\cos\ \theta - 1), \qquad (2\text{-}166)$$

using the closure relation for the Legendre polynomials.

This part of $f(\vec{k},\theta)$ contributes only in the forward direction and may therefore be omitted, as we have required that $\theta > 1/ka$. The remainder of the scattering amplitude is given by

$$f(\vec{k},\theta) = -\frac{1}{2k}\left(\frac{\pi \sin\theta}{2}\right)^{-\frac{1}{2}} \int_0^\infty \left(\ell + \frac{1}{2}\right)^{\frac{1}{2}} \left(e^{i\phi_+} - e^{i\phi_-}\right) d\ell, \tag{2-167}$$

where the asymptotic form (2-165) of the Legendre polynomials has been employed and

$$\phi_\pm = 2\delta_\ell \pm \left(\ell + \frac{1}{2}\right)\phi \pm \frac{\pi}{4}\,. \tag{2-168}$$

The integral can be evaluated by the method of stationary phase. Because of the oscillating nature of the integrand the only non-zero contributions to the integral arise from points $\ell=\ell_i$, where

$$\frac{d\phi^\pm}{d\ell} = 0. \tag{2-169}$$

If $\ell = \ell_o$ is such a point, then close to ℓ_o

$$\phi_\pm(\ell)=\phi_\pm(\ell_o) + \frac{1}{2}\phi_\pm''(\ell_o)(\ell - \ell_o)^2 \tag{2-170}$$

The condition $d\phi^\pm/d\ell = 0$ reduces to (using (2-168, 2-164)

$$\theta=\pm\Theta(\ell_o), \tag{2-171}$$

$$\phi_\pm''(\ell_o) = \left.\frac{d\Theta}{d\ell}\right|_{\ell=\ell_o} \tag{2-172}$$

The scattering angle θ must be positive, and this determines the sign to be used in (2-171). The deflection angle Θ is positive for a repulsion and negative for an attraction. Extending the integral from $-\infty$ to $+\infty$, we have

$$f(\vec{k},\theta) = -\frac{1}{2k}\left(\frac{\pi \sin\theta}{2}\right)^{-\frac{1}{2}} \left(\ell_o+\frac{1}{2}\right)^{\frac{1}{2}} \int_{-\infty}^{\infty} d\ell\, e^{i(\ell-\ell_o)^2\phi''/2} e^{i\phi_\pm(\ell_o)} \tag{2-173}$$

$$= -\frac{1}{2k}\left(\frac{\sin\theta}{2}\right)^{-\frac{1}{2}} \left(\frac{2}{i\phi_\pm''(\ell_o)}\right)^{\frac{1}{2}} e^{i\phi_\pm(\ell_o)} \left(\ell_o + \frac{1}{2}\right)^{\frac{1}{2}} \tag{2-174}$$

where in the last line we have used the result

$$\int_{-\infty}^{\infty} e^{i\alpha x^2}\,dx = \left(\frac{\pi}{i\alpha}\right)^{\frac{1}{2}}$$

In terms of $L = (\ell_o + 1/2)\hbar$, where ℓ_o is found from (2-171)

$$\frac{d\sigma}{d\Omega} = |f(\vec{k},\theta)|^2 = L\left|\frac{dL}{d\theta}\right| / (m^2v^2 \sin\theta), \tag{2-175}$$

which is identical with the classical result (2-115) and it is valid at a given angle θ, if ℓ_o found from (2-171) is large.

In evaluating the integral, it was assumed that only one stationary point existed. If this is so, the classical angular distribution is obtained, but if this is not so, very different distributions may be obtained, even though the semi-classical conditions are well satisfied. Some of the exceptional cases have been examined by Ford and Wheeler (1959), and we shall discuss their work briefly.

Interference effects

As in classical scattering, discussed on page 89, more than one value of the angular momentum may give rise to a given angle of scattering; in that case equation (2-169) or (2-171) is satisfied when ℓ is equal to ℓ_0, ℓ_1, ℓ_2 .... Each term in the scattering amplitude will then have the phase $\phi_\pm(\ell_i)=\beta_i$ and the 'semi-classical' differential cross section will be

$$\frac{d\sigma}{d\Omega} = \left|\sum_i \left|\frac{d\sigma}{d\Omega}\right|_i^{\frac{1}{2}} e^{i\beta_i}\right|^2 \tag{2-176}$$

where $(d\sigma/d\Omega)_i$ is the classical cross section arising from the ith branch of the deflection function. A situation in which this might occur is shown in figure 2-2, where $-\Theta(\ell)$ is plotted against ℓ.

The line $\theta=|\Theta(\ell)|$ intercepts the curve twice at the points $\ell=\ell_o$ and $\ell=\ell_1$. As θ changes, the differential cross section will oscillate between the values

$$\left(\frac{d\sigma}{d\Omega}\right)_\pm = \left|\left(\frac{d\sigma}{d\Omega}\right)_o^{\frac{1}{2}} \pm \left(\frac{d\sigma}{d\Omega}\right)_1^{\frac{1}{2}}\right|^2 \tag{2-177}$$

and the increment in θ in going from the maximum to the minimum is

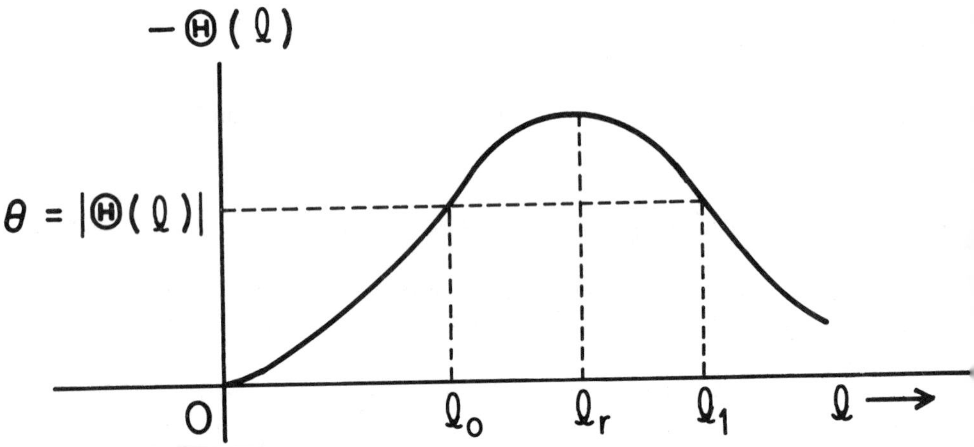

Figure 2-2 An example of the variation of the classical deflection function Θ with ℓ, for an attractive potential (Θ<o)

$$\delta\theta \cong \left|\frac{\pi}{|\ell_o - \ell_1|}\right|. \tag{2-178}$$

The angular difference $\delta\theta$ must be at least as large as the angle of resolution of the detecting system, or else the oscillations will not be observed.

The rainbow

When $\theta(\ell)$ is not a single valued function of ℓ, $\Theta(\ell)$ must possess either maxima or minima or singularities. In the example in figure 2, $d\Theta/d\ell = 0$ and $|\Theta|$ has a maximum at $\ell=\ell_r$ corresponding to a scattering angle θ_r. Any attractive monotonic potential, finite at the origin, will give rise to a curve with a minimum, because the deflection vanishes at $\ell=0$ and $\ell=\infty$ and is negative in between. At a maximum or a minimum in $\Theta(\ell)$, the calculation of the cross section that we have given breaks down, because $\phi_{\pm}''(\ell_r)$ which occurs in the integral (2-173) vanishes. When this happens in the corresponding optical situation a rainbow is produced, and the name rainbow scattering is also used to describe this phenomenon in the present context. The angle of scattering θ_r is called the rainbow angle.

Near the rainbow angle

$$\Theta(\ell) \cong \theta_r + q(\ell - \ell_r)^2 \tag{2-179}$$

where

$$q = \frac{1}{2}\frac{d^2\Theta}{d\ell^2}\bigg|_{\ell=\ell_r},$$

and the phase shift δ_ℓ may be expanded (using 2-164) as

$$\delta_\ell = \delta_{\ell_r} \pm \frac{1}{2}\theta_r(\ell - \ell_r) + \frac{q}{6}(\ell - \ell_r)^3$$

It follows that the functions $\phi_\pm$ are given by

$$\phi_\pm(\ell) = 2\delta_{\ell_r} \pm \theta_r(\ell - \ell_r) + \frac{q}{3}(\ell - \ell_r)^3 \pm \left(\ell + \frac{1}{2}\right)\theta \pm \frac{\pi}{4}.$$

Instead of the integral (2-173), we now have

$$f(\vec{k},\theta) \cong \left(\ell_r + \frac{1}{2}\right)^{\frac{1}{2}} \frac{1}{k}(2\pi \sin\theta)^{-\frac{1}{2}} e^{i\delta} \times$$

$$\times \int_{-\infty}^{\infty} e^{i[(\theta_r - \theta)(\ell - \ell_r) + (\ell - \ell_r)^3 q/3]} d(\ell - \ell_r),$$

where

$$\delta = 2\delta_{\ell_r} - \theta_r\left(\ell_r + \frac{1}{2}\right) \pm \frac{\pi}{4} \mp (\ell_r + \frac{1}{2})(\theta_r - \theta).$$

The integral,

$$\mathrm{Ai}(x) = \frac{1}{2\pi}\int_{-\infty}^{\infty} e^{iux + iu^3/3} du, \tag{2-180}$$

is known as the Airy integral. For $x > 0$ (the dark side of the rainbow) Ai(x) falls off rapidly, but for $x < 0$ (the bright side of the rainbow), Ai(x) oscillates:

$$\mathrm{Ai}(x) \sim \frac{3^{-1/3}}{2\sqrt{\pi}}\, x^{-\frac{1}{4}}\, e^{-(2/3)x^{3/2}}, \quad x \to +\infty$$

$$\sim \frac{3^{-1/3}}{\sqrt{\pi}} (-x)^{-\frac{1}{4}} \cos\left(\frac{2}{3}(-x)^{3/2} - \frac{\pi}{4}\right), \quad x \to -\infty \tag{2-181}$$

The final expression for the cross section is

$$\frac{d\sigma}{d\Omega}(\theta \cong \theta_r) = \frac{2\pi}{k^2}\left(\frac{\ell_r + 1/2}{\sin\theta}\right) q^{-\frac{2}{3}} \left|\mathrm{Ai}\left(\frac{\theta_r - \theta}{q^{\frac{1}{3}}}\right)\right|^2 \tag{2-182}$$

The glory

If $\Theta(\ell)$ passes smoothly through $\Theta=0$ or $\Theta=\pm\pi$, then $\sin\Theta(\ell)$ vanishes while $(d\Theta/d\ell)$ remains finite. The classical cross section then becomes infinite; this is termed a glory. In the evaluation of the semi-classical cross section, the approximation (2-165) for $P_\ell(\cos\theta)$ can no longer be used, because this is valid for $\sin > 1/\ell$. Instead, the approximation for small $(\sin\ \theta)$,

$$P_\ell(\cos\theta) \sim (\cos\theta)^\ell J_o\left(\left(\ell + \frac{1}{2}\right)\theta\right)$$

can be employed, which is valid for $\sin\theta < 1/\ell$. If the glory occurs at $\ell = \ell_g$ and δ_ℓ is expanded about this value of ℓ,

$$\delta_\ell = \frac{\pi}{2}(\ell - \ell_g) + \frac{a}{4}(\ell - \ell_g)^2 + \delta_g, \tag{2-183}$$

where

$a = \left.\frac{d\Theta}{d\ell}\right|_{\ell=\ell_g}$, and the stationary phase analysis can be extended to this case. If the glory occurs in the backward direction $\theta \cong \pi$ it is found that:

$$\frac{d\sigma}{d\Omega}(\theta) = \frac{1}{k^2}\left(\ell_g + \frac{1}{2}\right)^2 \left|\frac{2\pi}{a}\right| J_o^2(\ell_g \sin\theta). \tag{2-184}$$

The classical singularity is replaced by a finite peak at $\theta = \pi$ and as θ is decreased, the cross section oscillates rapidly.

Orbiting

Classically the scattered particle may be caught on an orbit that spirals infinitely, tending ultimately to a circular orbit. In this case, the deflection function exhibits a singularity at some value of ℓ. This is called orbiting and is well known in collisions between rare gas atoms and ions. As might be expected, the phenomenon is rather complicated and it will not be described here. The theory may be consulted in the original papers by Ford and Wheeler (1959), or in the monograph by Child (1974).

NOTES

1. Interesting reviews of variational and minimum principles with bibliographies of earlier work have been given by Spruch (1962, 1976).

2. Note that $\bar{g}(r,r') = g_0^{+}(r,r') + k^{-1}\, e_0(kr)s_0(kr')$

3. For applications to electron scattering by atoms see Murtaugh and Reinhardt (1972, 1973).

4. The least squares method can also be used without making a rigid decomposition into two regions. For details of a practical application see Levin et al (1977).

5. A full account of the development and applications of the R-matrix method has been given by Burke and Robb (1975).

6. The modern application of the eikonal approximation particularly to nuclear physics is due to Glauber (1959). An extensive review of subsequent developments in atomic physics has been given by Byron and Joachain (1977).

7. A detailed account of the semi-classical theory and its application to atomic scattering is given in the monograph by Child (1974), see also Child (1978).

PROBLEMS

2.1 If the $\ell=0$ partial wave function $f_o(r)$ is normalized so that $f_o(o)=o$, $f_o(r) \sim \sin(kr+\theta)+K\cos(kr+\theta)$ where $K = \tan(\delta_o-\theta)$, show that the Kato identity (2-7) holds for each value of the constant θ, and by setting $\theta=\pi/2$ find a variational method for $\cot\delta_o$ (the inverse Kohn method).

2.2 Calculate δ_o for the potential (2-14) using the Schwinger variational method with Altshuler's polynomial trial functions (2-27) for the case N=2, and for k=0.2. Compare your result with that given in Table 2-1 for N=3.

2.3 Using the truncated power series expansion of $D(k^2+i\varepsilon)$, given by (2-71) find expressions for $\tan\delta_o$ for the cases N=1 and N=2, compare your results with the expression for $\tan\delta_o$ in the first and second Born approximations.

2.4 Suppose that the effective interaction between an electron and a hydrogen atom is (in atomic units) $U(r)=2V(r)/\hbar^2 = -2(1+1/r)e^{-2r}$ and that the corresponding interaction between a proton and a hydrogen atom is $-U(r)$. Discuss whether the eikonal approximation will be accurate for scattering of electrons by atomic hydrogen of (a) 10eV, (b) 100keV, (c) 1keV and for scattering by protons with the same energies. If you decide the eikonal approximation can be used, state the angular range in which formulae (2-130) is expected to be accurate.

2.5 Consider scattering by a central potential for which the classical deflection function is of the form shown in Fig. 2-2. Show that if θ_r is the rainbow angle corresponding to $L=L_r$ that the classical differential cross section is of the form

$$\frac{d\sigma}{d\Omega} = \frac{1}{2m^2v^2}\,\frac{L_r}{\sin\theta_r}\left|\frac{1}{B(\theta-\theta_r)}\right|^{\frac{1}{2}} \qquad \theta < \theta_r$$

$$= 0 \qquad \theta > \theta_r$$

where B is a constant.

[Hint. Expand the deflection function Θ about the rainbow angle by

$\Theta = \Theta_r + B(L-L_r)^2$]

2.6 Show that if a non-local $V(r,r')$ potential is separable so that $V(r,r') = v(r)\,v(r')$, then an exact expression be found for the scattering amplitude $f(\vec{k},\theta)$, and prove that if $v(r)$ is spherically symmetrical scattering only occurs in the partial wave $\ell=0$.

Chapter 3

SCATTERING BY LONG RANGE POTENTIALS

Various aspects of the theory outlined in Chapters 1 and 2 must be modified when the potential decreases like an inverse power of r, for large r. In the important case of Coulomb scattering for which $V(r) = c/r$, the boundary conditions satisfied by the wave function at large r are different from those assumed in Chapter 1 and although potentials decreasing like r^{-1-n} with $n>0$, do satisfy the normal boundary conditions at infinity, the important effective range formulae for the phase shifts cease to apply.

3-1 COULOMB SCATTERING

When the target and scattered particles are charged, a Coulomb potential acts between them which, at small distances of separation, will be modified by other effective interactions, that in general decrease as some higher inverse power of r. In actual experiments, the Coulomb interaction will not extend to infinite distances, but will be shielded by the other atoms in the target. The shielding has the effect of cutting off the potential at some distance R, and to a good approximation the potential is of the form

$$V(r) = c/r, \quad r < R,$$

$$V(r) = 0, \quad r > R, \tag{3-1}$$

where R is of dimension comparable to the spacing of the atoms in the target. Since the problem of Coulomb scattering can be solved exactly, it is useful to ignore the shielding effects at the start, and subsequently it will be shown that they are not important in practice.

The Schrödinger equation for scattering by a pure Coulomb potential is

$$(\nabla^2 + k^2 - \alpha/r)\psi(\vec{r}) = 0, \qquad (3\text{-}2)$$

where if $(Z_1 e)$, $(Z_2 e)$ are the charges of the target and scattered particles, $\alpha = (2mZ_1Z_2e^2/\hbar^2)$. This equation is separable in parabolic coordinates (details can be found in Landau and Lifshitz, 1958, p.125, defined by

$$\xi = r + z,\ \eta = r - z,\ \phi = \tan^{-1}\left(\frac{y}{x}\right), \qquad (3\text{-}3)$$

where x, y and z are the usual Cartesian coordinates and $r^2 = x^2 + y^2 + z^2$. The coordinates ξ and η range from 0 to ∞ and ϕ ranges from 0 to (2π). The Schrödinger equation in parabolic coordinates is

$$\left(\frac{4}{\xi + \eta}\right)\left(\frac{\partial}{\partial\xi}\left(\xi\frac{\partial\psi}{\partial\xi}\right) + \frac{\partial}{\partial\eta}\left(\eta\frac{\partial\psi}{\partial\eta}\right)\right) + \frac{1}{\xi\eta}\,\frac{\partial^2\psi}{\partial\phi^2} + \left(k^2 - \frac{2\alpha}{\xi + \eta}\right)\psi=0 \qquad (3\text{-}4)$$

The equation may be separated by writing

$$\psi = f_1(\xi)f_2(\eta)e^{im\phi}, \qquad (3\text{-}5)$$

but because of the symmetry about the z axis (which is taken as the direction of incidence), the wave function must be independent of ϕ and only the case m=0 need be considered. Then $f_1(\xi)$ and $f_2(\eta)$ satisfy

$$\frac{d}{d\xi}\left(\xi\,\frac{df_1}{d\xi}\right) + \left(\frac{1}{4}k^2\xi + \beta\right)f_1 = 0,$$

$$\frac{d}{d\eta}\left(\eta\,\frac{df_2}{d\eta}\right) + \left(\frac{1}{4}k^2\eta - \beta - \frac{\alpha}{2}\right)f_2 = 0, \qquad (3\text{-}6)$$

where β is a constant of separation.

A solution is required that behaves like the plane wave exp(ikz), as $z \to -\infty$ and $r \to +\infty$. In terms of ξ and η, the incident plane wave looks like

$$\exp(ikz) = \exp(ik(\xi - \eta)/2, \qquad (3\text{-}7)$$

and ψ must behave like this as $\eta\to\infty$ (all ξ).

This condition can be satisfied by taking $\beta = -\frac{1}{2}ik$, in which case

$$f_1(\xi) = e^{ik\xi/2}. \tag{3-8}$$

The equation for $f_2(\eta)$ then becomes

$$\frac{d}{d\eta}\left(\eta\frac{df_2}{d\eta}\right) + \left(\frac{1}{4}k^2\eta - \frac{1}{2}\alpha + \frac{1}{2}ik\right) f_2 = 0. \tag{3-9}$$

To satisfy the boundary condition, we set

$$f_2(\eta) = e^{-\frac{1}{2}ik\eta}w(\eta), \tag{3-10}$$

and look for a solution such that $w(\eta)\to$ constant, as $\eta\to\infty$. The new function $w(\eta)$ satisfies

$$\eta\frac{d^2w}{d\eta^2} + (1 - ik\eta)\frac{dw}{d\eta} - \left(\frac{\alpha}{2}\right) w = 0. \tag{3-11}$$

This is the equation satisfied by the confluent hypergeometric function defined by the expansion (Morse and Feshbach, 1953, p.551; Landau and Lifshitz, 1958, p.600),

$$F(a,b,x) = \sum_{n=0}^{\infty} \frac{\Gamma(a+n)\Gamma(b)}{\Gamma(b+n)\Gamma(a)}\,\frac{x^n}{n!}. \tag{3-12}$$

This function is the solution, regular at the origin, of the equation

$$x\frac{d^2F}{dx^2} + (b - x)\frac{dF}{dx} - aF = 0, \tag{3-13}$$

so that the parameters a and b and the variable x must be identified by the relations

$$\alpha = -i\alpha/2k, \quad b = 1, \quad x = ik\eta. \tag{3-14}$$

In terms of spherical polar coordinates the solution of the original Schrödinger equation is

$$\psi_c^+(\vec{k},\vec{r}) = Ce^{ikz}F(-i\alpha/2k,1,ikr(1 - \cos\theta)), \tag{3-15}$$

where C is a constant. The asymptotic form of the confluent hypergeometric function is, for large x,

$$F(a,b,x) \sim \frac{\Gamma(b)}{\Gamma(b-a)} e^{-a \log(-x)} \left[1 + \frac{a(a+1-b)}{x} + \ldots\right] +$$

$$+ \frac{\Gamma(b)}{\Gamma(a)} e^{x+(a-b)\log x} \left[1 + \frac{(1-a)(b-a)}{x} + \ldots\right].$$

(3-16)

and hence the asymptotic form of the wave function is

$$\psi_c^+(\vec{k},\vec{r}) \sim C \frac{e^{\alpha\pi/4k}}{\Gamma(1+i\alpha/2k)} \left[\left\{1 - \frac{\alpha^2}{4ik^3 r(1-\cos\theta)}\right\} e^{i[kz + (\alpha/2k)\log kr(1-\cos\theta)]} + f_c(\vec{k},\theta) r^{-1} e^{i[kr-(\alpha/2k)\log 2kr]}\right]$$

(3-17)

where the scattering amplitude is

$$f_c(\vec{k},\theta) = -\frac{\alpha}{4k^2\sin^2\theta/2} \frac{\Gamma(1+i\alpha/2k)}{\Gamma(1-i\alpha/2k)} e^{-i(\alpha/2k)\log \sin^2\theta/2}.$$

(3-18)

It should be noticed that the asymptotic form is valid for sufficiently large r, except in the forward direction where $\cos\theta = 1$. Because of the slow decrease of the potential as r increases, the incident wave is distorted by logarithmic phase factors which, of course, do not alter the flux at large distances (to order $1/r^2$).

If $C = \Gamma(1 + i\alpha/2k)e^{-\alpha\pi/4k}$ the normalization is such that the flux of the incident wave is $F_+ = \hbar k/m$. The normalization of the wave function $\psi_c^+(\vec{k},\vec{r})$ is then

$$\int d^3r\, \psi_c^{+*}(\vec{k}',\vec{r})\psi_c^+(\vec{k},\vec{r}) = (2\pi)^3\, \delta(\vec{k}'-\vec{k})$$

and the closure relation is

$$(2\pi)^{-3}\int d^3k\psi_c^{+*}(\vec{k},\vec{r}')\psi_c^+(\vec{k},\vec{r})$$

$$+ \sum_i \phi_i^*(\vec{r}')\phi_i(\vec{r}) = \delta(\vec{r}-\vec{r}')$$

where the sum over i occurs only in the case of an attractive potential ($\alpha<0$) and the $\phi_i(\vec{r})$ are the bound state wave functions, normalized to unity.

It should be noted that alternative solutions of the Schrödinger equation for Coulomb scattering, can be defined, $\psi_c^-(\vec{k},\vec{r})$, which correspond to an incident (modified) plane wave and converging scattered waves. These functions are

$$\psi_c^-(\vec{k},\vec{r})=\exp(\pi\alpha/4k)\,\Gamma(1+i\alpha/2k)\exp(ikz)\ F\ (-i\alpha/2k,1,-ikr(1+\cos\theta$$

The differential cross section

$$\frac{d\sigma}{d\Omega} = |f_c(\vec{k},\theta)|^2 = \frac{\alpha^2}{16k^4\ \sin^4\ \theta/2} \qquad (3-19)$$

is identical with the classical expression obtained in Chapter 2, but the phase of the amplitude is naturally not given by classical mechanics and is important in several situations. For example, if the target and scattered particles are identical, the wave function must either be symmetric or anti-symmetric in the coordinates of the two particles and in the center of mass system, the wave function must be of the form

$$\Phi(r,\theta) = \psi(r,\theta) \pm \psi(r,\pi -\theta), \qquad (3-20)$$

where $\psi(r,\theta)$ is the solution of the Schrödinger equation with the usual boundary conditions for elastic scattering. The detector cannot distinguish between particles that have scattered and those which have recoiled, so that the cross section is

$$\frac{d\sigma}{d\Omega} = |f(\theta) \pm f(\pi - \theta)|^2 \qquad (3-21)$$

For Coulomb scattering between two spinless charged particles the total wave function must be symmetrical and the upper sign should be taken, giving the Mott formula

$$\frac{d\sigma}{d\Omega} = \frac{\alpha^2}{16k^4\ \sin^4\ \theta/2}\left[1+\tan^4\theta/2+2\tan^2\theta/2\ \cos\left(\frac{\alpha}{2k}\ \log\ \tan^2\theta/2\right)\right]$$

where the last term results from interference between the two amplitudes and depends directly on the phase.

Bound states

For an attractive potential, the scattering amplitude is expected to have poles at the energies of the bound states (Section 1-7). This immediately follows from the form (3-18), because the function $\Gamma(1-i\alpha/2k)$ has zeros located at the points where

$$k^2 = -\alpha^2/4n^2, \quad n = 1,2,3 \ldots., \tag{3-23}$$

and these coincide with the bound state energies of a particle in a Coulomb potential.

Shielding

Examining the asymptotic form of the wave function, it is seen that if the Coulomb potential is cut off as in equation (3-1) at a distance R then, provided $(\alpha^2/k^3 \ll R(1 - \cos\theta)$, the scattering amplitude will be altered only by a logarithmic phase factor

$$f(\vec{k},\theta) = f_c(\vec{k},\theta)e^{-i\alpha[\log(2kR)]/2k}$$

and the cross section is unaltered by the cut-off. Under experimental conditions the range of angles, $\theta<\alpha/(k^3R)^{\frac{1}{2}}$, for which terms in the wave function of order 1/R become significant, is small compared with angular acceptance of detectors and can be ignored. A complete discussion of the scattering amplitude for the screened Coulomb potential has been given by Ford (1964, 1966).

3-2 PARTIAL WAVE EXPANSION OF COULOMB AMPLITUDES

The Coulomb wave function can be expanded in a series of Legendre polynomials as in (1-19) and the radial wave functions satisfy the equation

$$\frac{d^2}{dr^2} + k^2 - \frac{\alpha}{r} - \frac{\ell(\ell+1)}{r^2}\; f^c{}_\ell(r) = 0. \tag{3-24}$$

This can be reduced to the equation satisfied by the confluent hypergeometric function by the substitution

$$f^c{}_\ell(r) = r^{\ell+1}e^{ikr}H_\ell(r), \tag{3-25}$$

we find

$$r\frac{d^2H_\ell}{dr} + 2(\ell+1+ikr)\frac{dH_\ell}{dr} + [2ik(\ell+1)-\alpha]H_\ell = 0. \tag{3-26}$$

A further change of variable to $\rho=-2ikr$ gives

$$\rho\frac{d^2H_\ell}{d\rho^2} + (2\ell + 2 - \rho)\frac{dH_\ell}{d\rho} + \left(\frac{\alpha}{2ik} - (\ell + 1)\right)H_\ell = 0, \tag{3-27}$$

and comparing (3-27) with (3-13), the solution regular at the origin is found to be

$$H_\ell(\rho) = F(i\alpha/2k + \ell + 1, 2\ell + 2, \rho). \tag{3-28}$$

The required solution for the radial function is

$$f^c{}_\ell(r) = A_\ell r^{\ell+1} e^{ikr} F(\ell + 1 + i\alpha/2k, 2\ell + 2, -2ikr), \tag{3-29}$$

where A_ℓ is a constant.

The asymptotic form of $f^c{}_\ell$ can be found from equation (3-16)

$$f_\ell{}^c(r) \sim A_\ell e^{\pi\alpha/4k} \frac{\Gamma(2\ell + 2)}{|\Gamma(\ell + 1 + i\alpha/2k)|} 2^{-\ell} k^{-(\ell+1)} \times$$

$$\times \sin(kr - \tfrac{1}{2}\ell\pi + \sigma_\ell - (\alpha/2k)\log 2kr), \tag{3-30}$$

where the Coulomb phase shifts σ_ℓ are defined as

$$\sigma_\ell = \arg\Gamma(\ell + 1 + i\alpha/2k). \tag{3-31}$$

A standard solution may be defined as $F_\ell(r)$, with the normalization

$$F_\ell(r) \sim \sin(kr - \tfrac{1}{2}\ell\pi + \sigma_\ell - \alpha/2k \log 2kr), \tag{3-32}$$

in which case

$$F_\ell(r) = e^{-\pi\alpha/(4k)} \frac{|\Gamma(\ell + 1 + i\ /2k)|}{(2\ell + 1)!} 2^\ell (kr)^{\ell+1} e^{ikr} \times$$

$$\times F(\ell + i\alpha/2k,\ 2\ell + 2,\ -2ikr). \tag{3-33}$$

The expansion of the complete Coulomb function in terms of the partial wave functions is

$$\psi_c{}^+(\vec{k},r) = \sum_{\ell=0}^{\infty} (2\ell + 1) i^\ell (kr)^{-1} e^{i\sigma_\ell} F_\ell(r) P_\ell(\cos\theta). \tag{3-34}$$

An independent solution of the radial equation is often required and it has been shown by Yost, Wheeler and Breit (1936) that a second solution $G_\ell(r)$ of equation (3-24), irregular at the origin, can be found that has the asymptotic form

$$G_\ell(r) \sim \cos\left[kr - \frac{1}{2}\ell\pi + \sigma_\ell - (\alpha/2k)\log(2kr)\right]. \qquad (3\text{-}35)$$

A very complete discussion of the many interesting properties of F_ℓ and G_ℓ may be consulted in the article by Hull and Breit (1959), where methods of numerical calculation of these functions are described and references are given to existing tabulations.

Scattering by a modified Coulomb potential

Consider the scattering by a potential $V(r)$ which is such that

$$U(r) = \frac{2m}{\hbar^2} V(r) = U_1(r) + \alpha/r, \qquad (3\text{-}36)$$

where $U_1(r)$ is of short range. The asymptotic solution of the radial wave equation regular at the origin must be a linear combination of F_ℓ and G_ℓ, and it is natural to define a phase shift δ_ℓ in a similar way to (1-50) by requiring that the solution of the radial wave equation has the asymptotic form

$$f_\ell(r) \sim F_\ell(r) + \tan\delta_\ell G_\ell(r). \qquad (3\text{-}37)$$

The phase shifts δ_ℓ will then characterize the short range potential $U_1(r)$, although it is important to notice that the δ_ℓ are not the same as phase shifts that would be obtained if α were set to zero.

To find the connection between the phase shifts δ_ℓ and the scattering amplitude, the solution $\psi(\vec{r})$ of the Schrödinger equation is introduced, where

$$\psi(\vec{r}) = \sum_{\ell=0}^{\infty} (2\ell+1) i^\ell (kr)^{-1} e^{i(\sigma_\ell+\delta_\ell)} \cos\delta_\ell f_\ell(r) P_\ell(\cos\theta). \qquad (3\text{-}38)$$

To find the asymptotic form of this solution, consider the difference $[\psi(\vec{r}) - \psi_c^+(\vec{k},\vec{r})]$ where $\psi_c^+(\vec{k},\vec{r})$ is the wave function for scattering by the Coulomb potential alone; we have

$$\left(\psi(\vec{r})-\psi_c^{+}(\vec{k},\vec{r})\right) \sim \sum_{\ell=0}^{\infty} \frac{(2\ell+1)i^{\ell}}{(kr)} \left(e^{i(\sigma_\ell+\delta_\ell)} \cos \delta_\ell \left[F_\ell + \tan \delta_\ell G_\ell\right] - e^{i\sigma_\ell} F_\ell(r) \right) P_\ell(\cos\theta). \tag{3-39}$$

From the asymptotic forms of F_ℓ and G_ℓ, we find that

$$\left(\psi(\vec{r}) - \psi_c^{+}(\vec{k},\vec{r})\right) \sim f_1(\theta) r^{-1} e^{i(kr - \alpha/2k \log 2kr)}$$

where

$$f_1(\theta) = \sum_{\ell=0}^{\infty} (2\ell+1) \frac{1}{2ik} e^{2i\sigma_\ell}(e^{2i\delta_\ell} - 1) P_\ell(\cos\theta). \tag{3-40}$$

Using the asymptotic form of $\psi_c^{+}(\vec{k},\vec{r})$, equation (3-17), we obtain

$$\psi(\vec{r}) \sim e^{i(kz+\alpha/2k \log kr(1-\cos\theta))} + \left(f_c(\vec{k},\theta) + f_1(\theta)\right) r^{-1} e^{i(kr-\alpha/2k \log 2kr)}, \tag{3-41}$$

where $f_c(\vec{k})$ is the Coulomb scattering amplitude. $\psi(\vec{r})$ represents an incident wave of unit amplitude and an outgoing wave of amplitude $[f_c(\vec{k},\theta) + f_1(\theta)]$ and the differential cross section is

$$\frac{d\sigma}{d\Omega} = |f_c(\vec{k},\theta) + f_1(\theta)|^2 \tag{3-42}$$

The partial wave series $f_1(\theta)$ converges rapidly, since the rate of convergence depends on the phase shifts δ_ℓ which relate to the short range potential. The partial wave series for $f_c(\vec{k},\theta)$ does not converge and the unexpanded form of $f_c(\vec{k},\theta)$, (3-18) must always be used.

The zero order Coulomb phase shift, which is given by

$$e^{2i\sigma_0} = \frac{\Gamma(1 + i\alpha/2k)}{\Gamma(1 - i\alpha/2k)}, \tag{3-43}$$

can be removed from both $f_c(\vec{k},\theta)$ and $f_1(\theta)$. If this is done

$$\frac{d\sigma}{d\Omega} = |\bar{f}_c(\theta) + \bar{f}_1(\theta)|^2 \tag{3-44}$$

where

$$\bar{f}_c(\theta) = -\frac{\alpha}{4k^2 \sin^2\theta/2} e^{-i(\alpha/2k)\log \sin^2 \theta/2}$$

and

$$\bar{f}_1(\theta) = \sum_\ell (2\ell + 1) \frac{1}{2ik} e^{2i(\sigma_\ell - \sigma_o)} \left(e^{2i\delta_\ell} - 1\right) P_\ell(\cos\theta). \tag{3-45}$$

The phase shift difference $(\sigma_\ell - \sigma_o)$ can easily be determined using the recurrence relation

$$\begin{aligned}(\sigma_{\ell+1} - \sigma_\ell) &= \arg \Gamma\left(\ell + 2 + \frac{i\alpha}{2k}\right) - \arg \Gamma\left(\ell + 1 + \frac{i\alpha}{2k}\right) \\ &= \arg\left(\ell + 1 + \frac{i\alpha}{2k}\right) = \tan^{-1}\left(\frac{\alpha}{2k(\ell + 1)}\right)\end{aligned} \tag{3-46}$$

3-3 GREEN'S FUNCTIONS FOR COULOMB SCATTERING

The equation for scattering by a modified Coulomb potential, such as (3-36), can be turned into an integral equation incorporating the required boundary conditions. The radial Schrödinger equation for scattering in the ℓth partial wave is

$$\left(\frac{d^2}{dr^2} - \frac{\ell(\ell + 1)}{r^2} - \frac{\alpha}{r} + k^2\right) f_\ell(r) = U_1(r) f_\ell(r), \tag{3-47}$$

and a solution is required with asymptotic form (3-37). The integral equation for $f_\ell(r)$ can be written as

$$f_\ell(r) = F_\ell(r) + \int_0^\infty dr' g^c{}_\ell(r,r') U_1(r') f_\ell(r'). \tag{3-48}$$

and it can be verified by substitution that $f_\ell(r)$ satisfies the radial Schrödinger equation (3-47), if $g_\ell{}^c(r,r')$ is

$$g_\ell{}^c(r,r') = -\frac{1}{k} F_\ell(r_<) G_\ell(r_>). \tag{3-49}$$

where $r_<$ and $r_>$ are the lesser and greater of r and r′ respectively. In obtaining this result it is necessary to use the Wronskian relation

$$\frac{dF_\ell}{dr} G_\ell - \frac{dG_\ell}{dr} F_\ell = k. \tag{3-50}$$

The asymptotic form of f (r) satisfies equation (3-37) and the phase shift δ_ℓ is determined by

$$\tan \delta_\ell = - \frac{1}{k}\int_0^\infty F_\ell(r) U_1(r) f_\ell(r) dr. \tag{3-51}$$

The analogue of the Born approximation, sometimes called the Coulomb-Born approximation, is obtained if $f_\ell(r)$ is replaced by $F_\ell(r)$ in (3-51),

$$\tan \delta_\ell^B = - \frac{1}{k} \int_0^\infty [F_\ell(r)]^2 U_1(r) dr. \tag{3-52}$$

Note that the Green's function g_ℓ^C satisfies the equation

$$\left(\frac{d^2}{dr^2} - \frac{\ell(\ell + 1)}{r^2} + k^2 - \frac{\alpha}{r}\right) g_\ell^C(r,r') = \delta(r-r').$$

Instead of imposing standing wave boundary conditions, Green's functions can be defined to satisfy outgoing wave boundary conditions

$$g_\ell^{C\pm}(r,r') = - \frac{1}{k} F_\ell(r_<) \left(G_\ell(r_>) \pm iF_\ell(r_>)\right) \tag{3-53}$$

from which it is easy to show that

$$T_\ell(k) = e^{i\delta_\ell} \sin \delta_\ell = - \frac{1}{k} \int_0^\infty F_\ell(r) U_1(r) f_\ell^+(r) dr, \tag{3-54}$$

where $f_\ell^+(r)$ is a solution of the radial Schrödinger equation satisfying the boundary condition

$$f_\ell^+(r) \sim F_\ell(r) + T_\ell[iF_\ell(r) + G_\ell(r)] \tag{3-55}$$

The Green's function for the operator $(\nabla^2+k^2-\alpha/r)$ can be obtained in closed form by summing a Legendre polynomial series with the coefficients g_ℓ^C, or otherwise (Schwinger, 1964; Hostler, 1964). The Green's function for a shielded Coulomb potential has also been obtained by Ford (1964, 1966). From these Green's functions an integral equation can be found for the scattering amplitude $f_1(\theta)$, appearing in (3-41). Rather than construct the Green's function explicitly, we shall derive a general expression for the scattering amplitude for scattering by the sum of two potentials.

Scattering by the sum of two potentials

A convenient expression can be obtained for the scattering amplitude when the potential V is the sum of two terms $(V_1 + V_2)$, for one of which the solution of the Schrödinger equation is known exactly. One of the potentials may be a screened Coulomb potential and the final result will also be true when one of the potentials is an unscreened Coulomb potential.

Let $|\chi^{\pm}(\vec{k}))$ be the solution of the Schrödinger equation

$$(H_o + V_1 - E)|\chi^{\pm}(\vec{k})) = 0, \qquad (3\text{-}56)$$

then the corresponding integral equation for $|\chi^{\pm}(\vec{k}))$ is

$$|\chi^{\pm}(\vec{k})) = |\phi(\vec{k})) + G_o^{\pm}V_1|\chi^{\pm}(\vec{k}) \qquad (3\text{-}57a)$$

$$=(1 + G_1^{\pm}V_1)|\phi(\vec{k})). \qquad (3\text{-}57b)$$

where in our usual notation $|\phi(\vec{k}))$ is the state vector for the incident unperturbed state, $G_o^{\pm}$ is the free particle Green's operator and G_1 is the complete Green's operator for the potential V_1.

$$G_1^{\pm} = (E \pm i\varepsilon - H_o - V_1)^{-1}. \qquad (3\text{-}58)$$

If $|\psi^{\pm}(\vec{k}))$ is the state vector for scattering from the potential $(V_1 + V_1)$, it satisfies

$$(H_o + V_1 + V_2 - E)|\psi^{\pm}(\vec{k})) = 0. \qquad (3\text{-}59)$$

The solution of this equation can now be written in terms of the Green's operator, G_1. A solution with the correct boundary conditions is

$$|\psi^{\pm}(\vec{k})) = |\chi^{\pm}(\vec{k})) + G_1^{\pm}V_2|\psi^{\pm}(\vec{k})). \qquad (3\text{-}60)$$

The scattering amplitude $f(\vec{k},\theta)$ for scattering by the combined potential is given by

$$f(\vec{k},\theta) = -\left(\frac{2m}{\hbar^2}\right)\frac{1}{4\pi}\ T(\vec{k}\to\vec{k}'), \tag{3-61}$$

where

$$T(\vec{k}\to\vec{k}') = (\phi(k')\ |V_1 + V_1|\psi^+(\vec{k})).$$

Using the integral equation for $\psi^+(\vec{k}))$ we find that

$$T(\vec{k}\to\vec{k}') = (\phi(\vec{k}')|V_1|\chi^+(\vec{k})) + (\phi(\vec{k}')|(V_1G_1{}^+ + 1)V_2|\psi^+(\vec{k}))$$

$$= (\phi(\vec{k}')|V_1|\chi^+(\vec{k})) + (\chi^-(\vec{k}')|V_2|\psi^+(\vec{k})) \tag{3-62}$$

where in the second line the adjoint of equation (3-57b) has been employed. The first term on the right hand side of (3-62) is the transition matrix element for scattering from the potential V_1 by itself. If V_1 is the Coulomb potential and V_2 a short range potential, then the result expressed in equations (3-41) and (3-42) is recovered

$$f\ (\theta) = f_c(\theta) + f_1(\theta),$$

where $f_c(\vec{k},\theta)$ is the Coulomb scattering amplitude. In this example $(\chi^-(\vec{k})|\vec{r})$ is the complex conjugate of the Coulomb wave function $\psi_c{}^-(\vec{k},\vec{r})$ where

$$\psi_c{}^-(\vec{k},\vec{r}) = e^{-\alpha\pi/4k}\Gamma\left(1 - \frac{i\alpha}{2k}\right)e^{ikz}F\left(\frac{i\alpha}{2k},1,-ikr(1 + \cos\theta)\right) \tag{3-63}$$

The asymptotic form of $\psi_c{}^-(\vec{k},\vec{r})$ is that of an incident plane wave and an incoming spherical wave, modified by the usual logarithmic phase factors. The scattering amplitude $f_1(\theta)$ is then

$$-(4\pi)f_1(\theta) = \int d^3r\ \psi_c{}^{-*}(\vec{k}',\vec{r})U_2(r)\psi^+(\vec{k},\vec{r}) \tag{3-64}$$

where $U_2(r) = 2mV_2/\hbar^2$.

3-4 SCATTERING AT VERY LOW ENERGIES AND LONG RANGE POTENTIALS

The effective range formulae must be modified when the potential varies like an inverse power of r for large r.

For short range potentials the variation of the phase shift with momentum was derived from equation (1-58). It is clear that the integral,

$$\int_0^\infty r^{2\ell+2} U(r)\,dr,$$

occurring in that equation will only converge if the potential decreases faster than

$$r^{-(2\ell+3)}$$

for large r. For a potential decreasing less fast than $1/r^3$, the limit $k\to 0$ of

$$(\delta_\ell / k^{2\ell+1})$$

does not exist for any ℓ and no scattering lengths can be defined. For a potential decreasing like $(1/r^4)$, the scattering length for $\ell=0$ exists, but the scattering lengths for higher ℓ do not. The condition for the existence of an effective range parameter is more restrictive, and it is necessary for the potential to decrease faster than

$$r^{-(2\ell+5)}$$

for this quantity to be defined.

The modified Coulomb potential

An effective range formulae for the phase shift δ_0 describing scattering from a short range potential in the presence of a Coulomb field can be obtained by using the Wronskian relations discussed in Chapter 1. Consider the solutions of the Schrödinger equation (3-47), $f_\ell(k,r)$, with the boundary conditions (for $\ell=0$),

$$f_0(k,0) = 0, \quad f_0(k,r) \sim F_0(r) \cot \delta_0 + G_0(r), \qquad (3\text{-}65)$$

where F_0 and G_0 are the regular and irregular Coulomb functions. By considering the radial Schrödinger equations for different energies k_1^2 and k_2^2, but the same potential, it is easy to follow an argument similar to that leading to (1-45), and to show that

$$\left[f_o(k_1,r)\frac{d}{dr}f_o(k_2,r) - f_o(k_2,r)\frac{d}{dr}f_o(k_1,r)\right]_o^r$$

$$= \left(k_1^2 - k_2^2\right)\int_o^r f_o(k_1,r)f_o(k_2,r)\,dr. \qquad \text{(3-66a)}$$

A similar equation can be written for the function

$$h_o(k,r) \equiv F_o(r)\cot\delta_o + G_o(r),$$

and on subtracting the equations for f_o and h_o, we find (remembering that $f_o(k,0) = 0$)

$$\lim_{r\to 0}\left(h_o(k_1,r)\frac{d}{dr}h_o(k_2,r) - h_o(k_2,r)\frac{d}{dr}h_o(k_1,r)\right)$$

$$= (k_1^2 - k_2^2)\int_o^\infty \left(f_o(k_1,r)f_o(k_2,r)-h_o(k_1,r)h_o(k_2,r)\right)dr. \qquad \text{(3-66b)}$$

To evaluate the left hand side, the expansions of G_o and F_o are required for small r. From the series expansion of the confluent hypergeometric function, it can easily be seen that for small r,

$$F_o(r) \to (kr)e^{-\pi\alpha/4k}\left|\Gamma\left(1 + \frac{i\alpha}{2k}\right)\right| = (kr)C(k), \qquad \text{(3-67)}$$

where

$$C^2(k) = \frac{\pi\alpha}{k(e^{\pi\alpha/k}-1)} .$$

Yost et al. (1936) have obtained the following form for $G_o(kr)$ at small r,

$$G_o(r) = \frac{1}{C(k)}\left(1 + \alpha r\left\{\log \alpha r - 1 + \gamma + \sum_{s=1}^{\infty} \frac{\alpha^2/4k^2}{s(s^2+\alpha^2/4k^2)} - \log\frac{\alpha}{2k}\right\}\right), \qquad \text{(3-68)}$$

where γ=0.5772157 is Euler's constant.

On using these expressions and multiplying by

$C(k_1)\ C(k_2)$ we obtain

$$-C^2(k_1)k_1 \cot \delta_o(k_1)-\alpha\phi(k_1) + C^2(k_2)k_2 \cot \delta_o(k_2) +\alpha\phi(k_2)$$
$$=(k_1{}^2-k_2{}^2)C(k_1)C(k_2)\int_0^\infty \left[f_o(k_1,r)f_o(k_2,r)-h_o(k_1,r)h_o(k_2,r)\right]dr, \tag{3-69a}$$

where

$$\phi(k) = +\gamma - \log\left(\frac{\alpha}{2k}\right)+ \sum_{s=1}^{\infty} \frac{\alpha^2/4k^2}{s(s^2+\alpha^2/4k^2)} \tag{3-69b}$$

Taking the limit $k_1 \to k_2$, we find

$$\frac{d}{d(k^2)}\{kC^2(k)\cot\delta_o+\alpha\phi(k)\}= C^2(k)\int_0^\infty\left[-f_o{}^2(k,r)+h_o{}^2(k,r)\right]dr.$$

Then expanding $\{C^2(k)\cot\delta_o+\alpha\phi(k)\}$ in a Taylor's series in k^2, about $k^2 = 0$, the effective range expansion is obtained as

$$C^2(k)\cot\delta_o + \alpha\phi(k) = \frac{1}{a_s} + \frac{1}{2} r_o k^2+ \ldots.., \tag{3-70}$$

where

$$r_o = \lim_{k\to 0} 2C^2(k)\int_0^\infty \left[-f_o{}^2(k,r) + h_o{}^2(k,r)\right] dr. \tag{3-71}$$

This effective range expansion can be generalized to all ℓ; it is found (Biberman and Norman, 1963),

$$\mathbf{N}_\ell{}^2\{kC^2(k)\cot\delta_\ell-\alpha\left(\phi(k) + \sum_{s=0}^{\ell} \frac{s}{s^2 + \alpha^2/4k^2}\right)\}$$
$$= \frac{1}{a_{s_\ell}} + \frac{1}{2}r_\ell k^2 + \ldots.., \tag{3-72}$$

where

$$N_\ell{}^2 = \prod_{s=1}^{\ell} \left(k^2 + \frac{\alpha^2}{4s^2}\right),\ N_o = 1.$$

Quantum defects

For an attractive Coulomb potential the S-matrix elements have poles at the bounds states, which occur at

$k = i\lambda$, with $\lambda^2 = (\alpha/2n)^2$, $n = 1,2....$ When a short range potential modifies the Coulomb potential, the energy levels are shifted. This can be taken into account by writing

$$E_{n,\ell} = -\frac{\hbar^2}{2m}\lambda^2, \quad \lambda^2 = \frac{\alpha^2}{4(n-\mu_{n,\ell})^2} \tag{3-73}$$

The constants $\mu_{n,\ell}$ are known as quantum defects. At the bound states, $\cot\delta_\ell = i$, (Section 1-7), and inserting $k_2{}^2 = -\lambda^2$ and $\cot\delta_0(k_2) = i$ in (3-69a), Seaton (1955) showed that

$$\cot\delta_0(k) = \left(1-\exp(-i\pi|\alpha|/k)\right)\cot\left(\pi\mu_0(k^2)\right) \tag{3-74}$$

where the quantum defect $\mu_0(k^2)$ is considered as a function of energy interpolating between the bound state positions (where it is defined by (3-73)) and extrapolated to positive energies.

This relation may be used to estimate, for example, the phase shifts for electron scattering by helium ions. The energy levels of the (1s, ns) series of He are known, and from these the interpolating function $\mu_0(k)$ can be computed. On extrapolating this function to positive energies, the phase shifts for electron scattering by the (1s) state of He^+ can be estimated (Seaton, 1957).

Inverse power potentials

The interaction between a charged particle and a neutral polarizable system, such as an atom or molecule, varies like $(1/r^4)$ at large distances. The Van der Waals interaction between two neutral polarizable systems varies as $(1/r^6)$ at large r and in certain circumstances interactions varying like $(1/r^2)$ can also be of importance in atomic physics. These long range interactions modify the threshold behavior of cross sections and, as we have already noted, the usual effective range formulae do not always hold.

It is important to note that in actual applications the inverse power law of the potential is not followed down to the origin, because if this were so, difficulties could arise in defining a solution of the Schrödinger equation. This may be seen as follows in the case of a potential varying as α/r^2. For small r, provided k^2 is finite, the radial Schrödinger equation is

$$\left(\frac{d^2}{dr^2} - \frac{\ell(\ell+1)}{r^2} - \frac{\alpha}{r^2}\right) f_\ell(r) = 0, \tag{3-75}$$

where α is the potential strength and where k^2 has been neglected compared with $1/r^2$. Expanding $f_\ell(r)$ as a power series

$$f_\ell(r) = \sum_{i=M}^{\infty} C_i r^{i+1}, \tag{3-76}$$

the indicial equation becomes

$$M(M + 1) = [\ell(\ell + 1) + \alpha], \tag{3-77}$$

with the solution

$$M_\pm = \frac{1}{2}\left(-1 \pm \{1 + 4\ell(\ell + 1) + 4\alpha)\}^{\frac{1}{2}}\right) \tag{3-78}$$

Consider the case $\ell=0$. If α is positive (repulsive potential), M_- is negative and the corresponding solution $f_0(r,-)$ is irregular and can be rejected. On the other hand M_+ is positive and the corresponding solution $f_0(r,+)$ is regular at the origin and can be accepted. For attractive potentials ($\alpha < 0$) the situation is quite different. If $4\alpha < 1$, both M_+ and M_- are complex for $\ell=0$. The two solutions $f_0(r,-)$ and $f_0(r,+)$ are complex conjugates of one another and there is no means of deciding which should be taken. For $0 > 4\alpha > -1$, both M_+ and M_-, are real and negative, so that in neither case is there an acceptable regular solution for $\ell=0$. Thus in general an acceptable regular solution for all ℓ exists for repulsive potentials which behave like α/r^2 at the origin, but no acceptable solution can be found for the corresponding attractive potentials[1].

If the potential satisfies the condition $r^2U(r) \to 0$ as $r \to 0$ but behaves like an inverse power of r for large r, there is no difficulty in defining a solution, because at small r the radial equation is dominated by the centrifugal barrier $\ell(\ell + 1)/r^2$. If the potential is exactly of the form α/r^2 for $r > r_0$, then at zero energy in this region the radial wave function will satisfy (3-75). The general solution is for the case $4\alpha < -[1 + 4\ell(\ell + 1)]$,

$$f_\ell(r) = Ar^{\frac{1}{2}}\cos[\gamma \log r + B], \tag{3-79}$$

where $\gamma^2 = (-\alpha - \ell(\ell + 1) - 1/4)$ and A and B are constants. This function has an infinite number of nodes and as the number of nodes in the wave function at zero energy is equal to the number of bound states[2] (Landau and Lifshitz, 1958), it follows that any potential which becomes equal to α/r^2 for r beyond a certain value r_0 supports an infinite number of bound states if α is sufficiently negative. It will be seen later that this observation has an important application in the theory of electron scattering by atoms with degenerate energy levels.

Effective range formulae

In the important case of a potential varying like an inverse fourth power for large r,

$$U(r) = -\left(\frac{\alpha}{r^4}\right),$$

effective range expansions have been obtained by O'Malley et al. (1961). It was shown that the Schrödinger equation had an exact solution in terms of Mathieu functions and the known properties of these functions were used to investigate the expansion of the phase shift about zero energy. The same results for $\ell=0$ have been found by Martynenko et al. (1963) in a different way, and the general problem for potentials varying like $1/r^n$ has been considered by Levy and Keller (1963). We will be content to quote the results for the inverse fourth power potential. These are

$$\tan \delta_0 = Ak - \frac{\pi}{3}\alpha k^2 + \frac{4}{3}\alpha A k^3 \log k + O(k^3),$$

$$\tan \delta_1 = \frac{\pi}{15}\alpha k^2 + A_1 k^3 + O(k^4), \qquad (3\text{-}80)$$

$$\tan \delta_\ell = \pi\alpha k^2/[(2\ell + 3)(2\ell + 1)(2\ell - 1)] + O(k^4), \quad \ell>1.$$

The low energy form of the elastic scattering cross section is then (O'Malley, 1963)

$$\sigma = 4\pi\left(A^2 - \frac{2}{3}\pi\alpha A k + \frac{8}{3}\alpha A^2 k^2 \log k + Bk^2 + \ldots\right), \qquad (3\text{-}81)$$

where B is a parameter depending on the effective range.

An interesting example of the use of these equations occurs in the work of O'Malley (1963), who determined the scattering length for electron scattering by the rare gases from the cross section measurements of Ramsauer and Kollath (1929, 1932). The polarizabilities α of the gases concerned, He, Ne, Ar, Kr and Xe are 1.36, 2.65, 11.0, 16.6 and 27.0 (in atomic units), respectively. The s wave scattering length A, can then be determined if δ_0 is known for a certain value of k close to threshold. When A is positive we have

$$\tan \delta_o = |A|k - \frac{\pi}{3}\alpha k^2 \tag{3-82}$$

and δ_o vanishes when $k = 3|A|/(\pi\alpha)$, giving rise to a dip in the cross section, provided that scattering in the higher partial waves is small. This is known as the Ramsauer-Townsend effect and it is observed in Ar, Kr and Xe at energies 0.37 ev, 0.60 ev and 0.65 ev above threshold respectively. From these figures the computed scattering lengths are Ar(+1.9), Kr(+3.7) and Xe(+6.2) in atomic units. The phase shift δ_1 also vanishes at an energy between 1 and 1.5 ev for all these gases, except helium, and this allows a similar calculation for A_1. If the zero occurs at $k = k_1$, then

$$A_1 = -\frac{\pi\alpha}{15k_1} .$$

The results are Ne(-1.66), Ar(-8.0), Kr(-12.8) and Xe(-23.2). More accurate results for the $\ell=0$ scattering length are obtained by detailed fitting of the cross section as a function of energy. These results are shown in Table 3-1.

Table 3-1

Scattering lengths ($\ell = 0$) for electron scattering by the rare gases

Gas	He	Ne	Ar	Kr	Xe
Scattering length (atomic units)	-1.19	-0.24	+1.70	+3.7	+6.5

The values shown in Table 3-1 agree rather well with similar calculations by Martynenko et al. (1963) for Ar, Kr and Xe and by Biberman and Norman (1964) for Ne and Ar.

NOTES

1. The case of an inverse fourth power potential has been discussed by Vogt and Wannier (1954).

2. This is the content of Levinson's theorem, which we proved for short range potentials in Chapter 1.

PROBLEMS

3.1 Obtain the Mott formula (3-22) from (3-21) and (3-18), and write down the differential cross section for this case that would be obtained from classical mechanics.

3.2 Verify that $f_\ell(r)$ given by the integral equation (3-48) is a solution of the radial Schrödinger equation (3-47).

3.3 Verify the formula (3-54) for the scattering amplitude T_ℓ.

3.4 Prove equations (3-66a) and (3-66b).

3.5 Using the data in the following Table show that the energies of the n ^{1}S excited state of helium can be fitted, approximately, to the quantum defect formula (3-73) by taking $\mu_0(k^2)$ to be a linear function of $\lambda^2 (= -k^2)$. Hence determine the $\ell=0$ partial cross section for elastic scattering of electrons by $He^+(1s)$ in the singlet state over an energy interval of 0-10 ev.

Ionisation potentials of He (ns, 1s) in eV.

	S = 1 (Triplet)	S = 0 (Singlet)
n = 2	4.7653	3.97244
n = 3	1.86965	1.66781
n = 4	0.994145	0.914550
n = 5	0.61614	0.576898
n = 6	0.41910	0.396950
n = 7	0.30351	0.289824

3.6 Consider scattering by the repulsive potential

$$V(r) = \frac{\hbar^2}{2m} U(r),$$

where $V(r) = \alpha/r^2$, $\alpha > 0$. Show that the radial function $f_\ell(r)$ is exactly equal to $s_\lambda(kr)$ where $\lambda(\lambda+1) = \ell(\ell+1)+\alpha$ and find an exact expression for the phase shifts δ_ℓ. Compare the exact phase shifts with those obtained by the W.K.B. approximation.

Chapter 4

GENERAL THEORY OF COLLISIONS

4-1 WAVE FUNCTIONS AND BOUNDARY CONDITIONS FOR MANY CHANNEL SCATTERING

Reaction channels

The theory so far developed is suitable for the description of scattering in which neither the target nor the projectile has internal structure. The theory must be extended to more realistic situations so that we can treat the scattering of electrons by atoms or atoms by atoms where both excitation and rearrangement are possible. For example, in proton-helium collisions, the reactions

$$p + He(1s^2) \to p + He(1s^2), \qquad (a)$$
$$p + He(1s^2) \to p + He(1s,2s), \qquad (b)$$
$$p + He(1s^2) \to H(1s) + He^+(1s), \qquad (c) \qquad (4\text{-}1)$$

are just three of the many possibilities. The first is elastic scattering, the second excitation and the third, in which an electron is transferred between the colliding systems, is known as charge exchange. Each different incident or final state defines a reaction channel. The three channels concerned in the reactions 4-1 are then

$$p + He(1s^2), \qquad (a)$$
$$p + He(1s,2s), \qquad (b)$$
$$H(1s) + He^+(1s) \qquad (c) \qquad (4\text{-}2)$$

The total energy E, which is the sum of the kinetic and internal energies of the colliding atoms, may not always be sufficient to excite a particular channel and in this case the channel is said to be closed. For example in the reactions

$$e^- + H(1s) \rightarrow e^- + H(1s), \qquad (a)$$

$$\rightarrow e^- + H(2s), \qquad (b) \qquad (4\text{-}3)$$

elastic scattering (a) is possible at all energies exceeding the ground state energy of hydrogen, while (b) is only possible when the total energy of the system exceeds -3.4 ev. Below this energy channel (a) is 'open' and (b) is 'closed'; above this energy both channels are open. Not all reactions are possible between a given set of particles, even if sufficient energy is available, because the appropriate quantum numbers (angular momentum, parity and so on) must be conserved.

The different reactions are of two types. Those for which the target and projectile contain the same particles before and after the collisions as in (4-1a) and (4-1b), and those for which particles are transferred between the colliding systems during the reaction, as in (4-1c). To avoid an elaborate notation, each channel will be labeled by an index m, which will be supposed to give all the information necessary to define the dynamical situation completely. It will be sometimes necessary to distinguish between different arrangements, and these will be labeled by a Greek letter $\alpha, \beta, \ldots$ For example, reactions (4-1a) and (4-1b) belong to the same arrangement, which might be labeled α, while (4-1c) belongs to a different arrangement and might be labeled β. We shall only discuss explicitly the case in which each channel contains two atoms, although much of the formalism can be extended to many-body situations.

At a given energy E, the state vector of the system satisfies the time-independent Schrödinger equation

$$(H - E)|\psi) = 0. \qquad (4\text{-}4)$$

The Hamiltonian H can be split in different ways corresponding to each arrangement as

$$
\begin{aligned}
H &= H_\alpha + V_\alpha \\
&= H_\beta + V_\beta \\
&\cdot\ \cdot\ \cdot\ \cdot\ \cdot \\
&= H_\gamma + V_\gamma \\
&\cdot\ \cdot\ \cdot\ \cdot\ \cdot
\end{aligned}
\tag{4-5}
$$

where V_α, V_β, V_γ are the interaction potentials acting between the colliding atoms in arrangements α, β, γ. The unperturbed state vectors $|\phi_m(\gamma, E))$ then satisfy the Schrödinger equations

$$(H_\gamma - E)|\phi_m(\gamma, E)) = 0. \tag{4-6}$$

For a given arrangement γ, the unperturbed state vectors are orthogonal and form a complete set. The state vectors for different arrangements are not necessarily orthogonal, and as we shall see this gives rise to some difficulties in the theory of rearrangement collisions, however if wave packets are formed, the overlap between the colliding packets will vanish as $t \to \pm\infty$, even in a rearrangement collision, and this is all that is necessary for the establishment of the theory.

As an example of an unperturbed wave function[1] in the position representation, we can consider the $\{H(1s) + He^+ (1s)\}$ system (4-2c). The unperturbed wave function is $\phi_m(\gamma)$ which can be expressed as

$$\phi_m(\gamma, \vec{x}_\gamma, \vec{r}_\gamma) = N_m X_m(\vec{x}_\gamma) \exp(i\vec{k}_m \cdot \vec{r}_\gamma) \tag{4-7}$$

where X_m is the product of the ground state wave functions of the hydrogen atom and the helium ion, and N_m is a normalization constant. The center of mass system is employed and $\vec{r}_\gamma$ is the vector joining the center of masses of the hydrogen atom and helium ion and $\vec{x}_\gamma$ stands collectively for the internal coordinates of the atoms. The relative motion of the atom and ion is described by a wave vector $\vec{k}_m$, such that $\hbar^2 k_m^{\ 2}/2\mu_m$ is the kinetic energy in the center of mass system, where μ_m is the reduced mass of the atom and ion, in the channel m. The total energy E can be expressed as

$$E_m = \varepsilon_m + \hbar^2 k_m^{\ 2}/2\mu_m, \tag{4-8}$$

where ε_m is the sum of the binding energies of the colliding atoms.

Integral equations

State vectors $|\psi_i^+)$, satisfying the Schrödinger equation (4-4), can be defined that correspond to the physical situation in which there is an incident wave in channel i only, with outgoing waves in all channels. The channel i will be taken to belong to the arrangement α. Following the discussion of potential scattering in Chapter 1, we expect $|\psi_i^+)$ to be expressible as $\lim_{\varepsilon\to 0}|\psi_i(E + i\varepsilon))$, where

$$|\psi_i(E + i\varepsilon)) = |\phi_i(\alpha,E)) + \frac{1}{E + i\varepsilon - H_\alpha} V_\alpha |\psi_i(E + i\varepsilon)) \tag{4-9}$$

The first term on the right hand side represents the incident wave, and the second contains outgoing waves only. The function $|\psi_i(E + i\varepsilon))$ satisfies the equation

$$(H - E - i\varepsilon)|\psi_i(E + i\varepsilon)) = -i\varepsilon|\phi_i(\alpha,E)) \tag{4-10a}$$

The source term on the right hand side of this equation serves to render the solution unique, and we notice that $|\psi_i(E + i\varepsilon))\to|\phi_i(\alpha,E))$ as $V_\alpha\to 0$. In the limit $\varepsilon\to 0$, $|\psi_i(E + i\varepsilon))$ reduces to $|\psi_i(E))$ which satisfies equation (4-4).

The verification that $|\psi_i(E + i\varepsilon))$ has the required boundary conditions, can proceed along the same lines as the discussion in Section 1-6, in which wave packets were constructed from the time independent solutions. In this way it can be shown that the wave packet

$$|\Psi_i^+(t)) = \int \rho(E''-E)|\psi_i(E'' + i\varepsilon))\exp(-iE''t/\hbar)dE'',$$

coincides with the incident wave packet

$$|\Phi_i(\alpha,t)) = \int \rho(E''-E)|\phi_i(\alpha,E''))\exp(-iE''t/\hbar)dE'',$$

at times in the remote past, $t\to-\infty$.

Just as in Chapter 1, we can also construct a solution $|\psi_i(E - i\varepsilon))$, which contains an incident wave in channel i and ingoing waves in all channels. The function $|\psi_i(E - i\varepsilon))$ satisfies the equation

$$(H - E + i\varepsilon))|\psi_i(E - i\varepsilon)) = + i\varepsilon|\phi_i(\alpha,E)) \qquad (4\text{-}10b)$$

and in this case, when wave packets are constructed, $|\Psi_i^-(t))$ is a solution that coincides with the unperturbed packet $|\phi_i(\alpha,E))$ at times in the distant future $t +\infty$.

We shall need time dependent wave functions when we come to calculate transition rates from the $\mathcal{S}$-matrix, but rather than construct wave packets explicitly, we shall indicate the finite duration of the wave train by writing

$$|\Psi_i^{\pm}(t)) = |\phi_i(\alpha,E))\exp(-iEt/\hbar) +$$

$$+ \frac{1}{E \pm i\varepsilon - H_\alpha} V_\alpha|\psi_i(E\pm i\varepsilon))\exp[-i(E\pm i\varepsilon)t/\hbar]. \qquad (4\text{-}11)$$

The factor $\exp(\pm\varepsilon t/\hbar)$, in the second term, ensures that $|\Psi_i^+(t))$ converges smoothly to $|\phi_i(\alpha,E))\exp(-iEt/\hbar)$ as $t\to -\infty$, and that $|\Psi_i^-(t))$ also converges smoothly to $|\phi_i(\alpha,E))\exp(-iEt/\hbar)$, but this time as $t\to+\infty$.

The operators $(E \pm i\varepsilon - H_\alpha)^{-1}$ are the resolvents or Green's operators appropriate to the division of the total Hamiltonian in channel α, in which we write H as $H = H_\alpha + V_\alpha$. Each division of the Hamiltonian gives rise to a Green's operator for the corresponding channel. We shall denote the Green's operator corresponding to arrangement γ as $G_\gamma^{\pm}(E)$, where

$$G_\gamma^{\pm}(E) = \lim_{\varepsilon\to 0^+} G_\gamma(E \pm i\varepsilon),$$

and

$$G_\gamma(E \pm i\varepsilon) = \left(\frac{1}{E \pm i\varepsilon - H_\gamma}\right) \qquad (4\text{-}12)$$

The Green's operator corresponding to the complete Hamiltonian H is defined in a similar way as $G^{\pm}(E)$, where

$$G^{\pm}(E) = \lim_{\varepsilon\to 0^+} G(E \pm i\varepsilon),$$

and

$$G(E \pm i\varepsilon) = \left(\frac{1}{E \pm i\varepsilon - H}\right) \qquad (4\text{-}13)$$

The integral equation (4-9) for $|\psi_i)$ is written in terms of

$G_\alpha = (E + i\varepsilon - H_\alpha)^{-1}$, which is the resolvent appropriate to the division of the Hamiltonian in the incident channel, $H = H_\alpha + V_\alpha$. From equations (4-10a,b) we can obtain an integral equation based on the Green's operator for an arrangement γ, which is not the arrangement in the incident channel. After a little algebra we find

$$|\psi_i(E \pm i\varepsilon)) = G_\gamma(E \pm i\varepsilon)\{\pm i\varepsilon|\phi_i(\alpha,E)) + V_\gamma|\psi_i(E \pm i\varepsilon))\} \tag{4-14}$$

and this is valid for all γ. In the particular case $\gamma=\alpha$, (4-14) can be shown to reduce to (4-9). It is important in this equation not to omit the term in $i\varepsilon|\phi_i(E))$, because in that case the equation becomes homogeneous in $|\psi_i)$ and the solution is no longer unique.

It is also useful to find expressions for $|\psi_i)$ in terms of the Green's operators $G^\pm(E)$ given by (4-13). Starting from equations (4-10a,b), it is straightforward to show that

$$\begin{aligned} |\psi_i(E \pm i\varepsilon)) &= \pm i\varepsilon G(E \pm i\varepsilon)|\phi_i(\alpha,E)) \\ &= |\phi_i(\alpha,E)) + G(E \pm i\varepsilon)V_\alpha|\phi_i(\alpha,E)). \end{aligned} \tag{4-15}$$

4-2 THE SCATTERING MATRIX AND CROSS SECTIONS

The probability P_{ji} of finding the system in a final unperturbed state j after scattering from an initial unperturbed state i, will be written as

$$P_{ji} = |\mathcal{S}_{ji}|^2 \tag{4-16}$$

where the probability amplitudes $\mathcal{S}_{ji}$ form the elements of the scattering or $\mathcal{S}$-matrix. It is convenient also to introduce a scattering operator $\mathcal{S}$, which is defined so that

$$\mathcal{S}_{ji} = (\phi_j(\beta,E_j)|\mathcal{S}|\phi_i(\alpha,E_i)) \tag{4-17}$$

where the channel i belongs to the arrangement α and the channel j to the arrangement β, which may or may not be the same as α.

The probability that <u>some</u> final state is reached must be unity, and it follows that

$$\sum_j P_{ji} = 1. \tag{4-18}$$

where the sum runs over all possible final states including the initial state i.

The state vector $|\psi_i^+)$ describes a state which evolved from the unperturbed state $|\phi_i(\alpha))$ at $t=-\infty$, and similarly $|\psi_j^-)$ is the state vector corresponding to the system being in the unperturbed state $|\phi_j(\beta))$ as $t\to+\infty$. The probability amplitude for finding the state j in the state i is $(\psi_j^-|\psi_i^+)$ and this is to be identified with S_{ji},

$$S_{ji} = (\psi_j^-(E_j)|\psi_i^+(E_i)). \tag{4-19}$$

In the center of mass system of coordinates that we are using, the sum of the momenta of the colliding particles is zero. If we had worked in an arbitrary system, each wave function would contain as a factor a term representing the motion of the center of mass of the system. In an exact treatment this term would be a localized wave packet, but for our purpose it is sufficient to use a plane wave, confined within a box of volume V. If $\vec{p}_i$ is the total momentum of the system and $\vec{R}$ the position of the center of mass, this plane wave, suitably normalized, is

$$V^{-\frac{1}{2}}\exp(i\vec{p}_i\cdot\vec{R}/\hbar)$$

Each matrix element such as S_{ji}, will contain as a factor the integral

$$V^{-1}\int_V d^3R\,\exp\{i(\vec{p}_i\cdot\vec{R} - \vec{p}_j\cdot\vec{R})/\hbar\} = \delta_{\vec{p}_i,\vec{p}_j}$$

which demonstrates that the operator S only causes transitions that conserve the total momentum of the system. By considering the evolution in time of the wave function, we shall later demonstrate in a similar way, that S only gives rise to transitions which conserve the total energy of the system.

The set of states $|\psi_i^+)$, together with any bound states $|\chi_n)$, of the system are complete. The states $|\psi_i^-)$ (together with the bound states) also form a complete set. In view of this we can write the following formal normalization and closure conditions

$$(\psi_i^+|\psi_j^+) = (\psi_i^-|\psi_j^-) = \delta_{ij}, \tag{4-20a}$$

$$(\chi_n|\chi_m) = \delta_{nm};\ (\psi_i^{\pm}|\chi_n) = 0, \tag{4-20b}$$

$$\sum_i|\psi_i^+)(\psi_i^+|+\sum_n|\chi_n)(\chi_n| = \sum_i|\psi_i^-)(\psi_i^-|+\sum_n|\chi_n)(\chi_n| = 1 \tag{4-20c}$$

Using these results the S matrix is easily shown to be unitary .

$$(S^\dagger S)_{ji} = \sum_q S^*_{qj}S_{qi} = \sum_q(\psi_j^+|\psi_q^-)(\psi_q^-|\psi_i^+)$$

$$= (\psi_j^+|\psi_i^+) = \delta_{ji}$$

Similarly we have that $(SS^\dagger)_{ji} = \delta_{ji}$. It should be noticed that the existence of bound states does not alter this relation, as the bound states are orthogonal to both the $|\psi_q^+)$ and the $|\psi_q^-)$. The unitarity of S expresses the conservation of probability given by equation (4-18). In the normalization equations (4-20), δ_{ji} is purely symbolic, j and i standing for all the variables defining the state, some of which, like the energy, are continuous.

If no interaction takes place, S must be the unit operator to ensure that the initial and final states are identical. It follows that the probability that the interaction causes a transaction, will be determined by a transition operator T, where

$$S = 1 + 2iT \tag{4-21a}$$

The factor 2i is introduced for later convenience. The matrix elements of S and T are related by

$$S_{ji} = \delta_{ji} + 2iT_{ji} \tag{4-21b}$$

where

$$T_{ji} \equiv (\phi_j|T|\phi_i)$$

In terms of T the unitary condition is

$$2T^\dagger T = i(T^\dagger - T) \tag{4-21c}$$

The transition rate

In order to discuss the transition rate from an initial state i to a final state j, we must display the time dependence of the state vectors, and we can use for this purpose the functions $|\Psi_i^{\pm}(t))$ defined by equation (4-11). The transition probability at a certain time, t, that the system which originated in the state $|\phi_i(\alpha))$ in the remote past will be found in a state which coincides with the state $|\phi_j(\beta))$ in the infinite future is determined by the S-matrix

$$S_{ji}(t) = (\Psi_j^{-}(E_j,t)|\Psi_i^{+}(E_i,t)).$$

If the observations are made at a time t (t>0) which is long compared with $(\hbar/\varepsilon)$, we see that $(\Psi_j^{-}(E_j,t)|$ can be replaced by $(\phi_j(\beta,E_j)|\exp(iE_jt/\hbar)$, as the second term in (4-11) is exponentially decreasing with t. We then have that, for large t, (t>0),

$$S_{ji}(t) = (\phi_j(\beta,E_j)|\phi_i(\alpha,E_i))\exp\{i(E_j-E_i)t/\hbar\} +$$

$$+ \exp\{i(E_j-E_i-i\varepsilon)t/\hbar\}(\phi_j(\beta,E_j)|\frac{1}{E_\alpha+i\varepsilon-H_\alpha}V_\alpha|\psi_i(E_i+i\varepsilon))$$

At this point, we shall assume that the channels j and i belong to the same arrangement, so that $H_\alpha = H_\beta$; $V_\alpha = V_\beta$, and hence

$$(E_i+i\varepsilon-H_\alpha)|\phi_j(\alpha,E_j)) = (E_i+i\varepsilon-E_j)|\phi_j(\alpha,E_j))$$

The second term in $S_{ji}(t)$ represents the transitions caused by the interaction, and corresponding to (4-21b) we write

$$S_{ji}(t) = \delta_{ji}+2iT_{ji}(t)$$

where

$$2iT_{ji}(t) = \left(\frac{\exp\{i(E_j-E_i-i\varepsilon)t/\hbar\}}{(E_i+i\varepsilon-E_j)}\right)T_{ji} \qquad (4\text{-}22)$$

The matrix elements T_{ji} are independent of time and are defined as

$$T_{ji} = (\phi_j(\alpha,E_j)|V_\alpha|\psi_i(E_i + i\varepsilon)) \tag{4-23}$$

We are interested in the transition probability for large values of t (t>0). In practise, (4-22) has to be integrated over a group of final states with energies E_j, and the resulting integral is similar to that given in (1-116). From the discussion of (1-116), we see that we can write:

$$\lim_{\varepsilon\to 0^+} \lim_{t\to\infty} \frac{\exp\{i(E_j-E_i-i\varepsilon)t/\hbar\}}{(E_i+i\varepsilon-E_j)} = -2\pi i\delta(E_j-E_i)$$

and accordingly:

$$\lim_{\varepsilon\to 0} \lim_{t\to\infty} \mathcal{T}_{ji}(t) = -\pi\delta(E_j - E_i)T_{ji}(E_i). \tag{4-24}$$

This demonstrates that transitions only occur between states of the same energy. In terms of the time independent $\mathcal{S}$-matrix defined by equations (4-19) and (4-21b) we can write

$$\mathcal{S}_{ji} = \delta_{ji} - 2\pi i\delta(E_j - E_i)T_{ji}(E_i). \tag{4-25}$$

This relation can be proved for rearrangement collisions as well as for direct collisions, and we shall show this explicitly below, in the argument leading from (4-34) to (4-36).

The transition rate from the state i to the state j, W_{ji} is determined by the equation

$$W_{ji} = \lim_{\varepsilon\to 0} \frac{\partial}{\partial t} |2i\mathcal{T}_{ji}(t)|^2$$

From the expression (4-22) we see that

$$W_{ji} = \lim_{\varepsilon\to 0} \left(\frac{\varepsilon \exp(2\varepsilon t/h)}{(E_i - E_j)^2 + \varepsilon^2}\right) \frac{2}{\hbar} |T_{ji}|^2$$

On taking the limit $\varepsilon\to 0$, and using the relation

$$\lim_{\varepsilon\to 0} \left(\frac{\varepsilon}{(E_i - E_j)^2 + \varepsilon^2}\right) = \pi\delta(E_j - E_i),$$

the transition rate is seen to be independent of time and to be given by the expression:

$$W_{ji} = \delta(E_i - E_j)\,\frac{2\pi}{\hbar}\,|T_{ji}|^2 \tag{4-26}$$

The transition rate vanishes unless energy is conserved, as we would expect.

The cross section σ_{ji}, for the transition $i\to j$, is

$$\sigma_{ji} = \frac{1}{F_i}\,\Sigma' W_{ji} \tag{4-27}$$

where the sum is over the group of final states, within the channel j, observed in the experiment, and F_i is the incident flux in channel i.

To proceed further, we must consider what the labels i and j represent. The unperturbed wave functions are given by (4-7), in which we see that the label m (and similarly for i and j) represents both a discrete index which defines the state of the bound systems and the vector $\vec{k}_m$ which describes the relative motion of the bound systems. To obtain the total cross section, σ_{ji}, a reaction starting from arrangement α, with the bound systems in level i and the relative motion described by $\vec{k}_i$ and ending in arrangement β, with the bound systems in level j, we must interpret the sum over final states as

$$\Sigma' \to \int d^3k_j\,\rho(k_j)$$

where $\rho(k_j)$ is a weight function, which depends on the normalization adopted for the unperturbed wave functions, that is what we take for the constants N_m in (4-7). The bound state wave functions X_m will always be normalized to unity and we shall normalize the plane waves to unit amplitude, $N_m=1$. In this case:

$$\int \phi_m{}^*(\gamma)\,\phi_n(\gamma)\,d^3r_\gamma d^3x_\gamma = \delta_{mn}\;(2\pi)^3\;\delta^3(\vec{k}_n-\vec{k}_m) \tag{4-28a}$$

with the same normalization for the unperturbed state vectors we have

$$(\phi_m(\gamma)\,|\,\phi_n(\gamma)) = \delta_{mn}\;(2\pi)^3\;\delta^3(\vec{k}_n-\vec{k}_m) \tag{4-28b}$$

$$= \delta_{mn}\,\frac{\hbar}{k_n\mu_\gamma}\,\delta(E_n - E_m)\,\delta(\Omega_n - \Omega_m)$$

where

$$\delta(\Omega_n - \Omega_m) \equiv \delta(\cos\theta_n - \cos\theta_m)\,\delta(\phi_n - \phi_m)$$

and (θ_n, ϕ_n), (θ_m, ϕ_m) are the polar angles of $\vec{k}_n$ and $\vec{k}_m$ respectively, and E_n, E_m are given by (4-8).
Note that because of the factor δ_{mn}, the internal energies ε_n and ε_m can be taken to be equal in defining E_n and E_m.

With this normalization to obtain the closure relation

$$\sum_m \int d^3k_m \rho(k_m)\,\phi_m(\gamma;\vec{r}_\gamma,\vec{x}_\gamma)\,\phi_m^*(\gamma,\vec{r}'_\gamma,\vec{x}'_\gamma)$$

$$= \delta^3(\vec{r}_\gamma - \vec{r}'_\gamma)\ \delta^3(\vec{x}_\gamma - \vec{x}'_\gamma)$$

the weight function $\rho(k_m)$ must be set equal to $(2\pi)^{-3}$. The total cross section σ_{ji} is therefore given by (from 4-27 and 4-26)

$$\sigma_{ji}\,(E_i) = \left(\frac{2\pi}{\hbar}\right)\ (2\pi)^{-3} \int d^3k_j \,\frac{1}{F_i}\ \delta(E_i - E_j)\ \left|T_{ji}(E_i)\right|^2$$

Since the incident plane wave is of unit amplitude, the incident flux is (see 1-12)

$$F_i = \hbar k_i/\mu_i$$

The integration over d^3k_j can be performed since

$$d^3k_j = k_j^{\,2}dk_j\ d\cos\theta_j d\phi_j \equiv k_j^{\,2}dk_j d\Omega_j$$

where (θ_j, ϕ_j) are the polar angles of $\vec{k}_j$ with respect to $\vec{k}_i$ as axis.

Using

$$\delta(E_i - E_j) = \delta\left(\frac{\hbar^2 k_i^{\,2}}{2\mu_i} + \varepsilon_i - \frac{\hbar^2 k_j^{\,2}}{2\mu_j} - \varepsilon_j\right)$$

we find[3]

$$\sigma_{ji}(E_i) = \frac{\mu_i \mu_j}{4\pi^2\hbar^4}\,\frac{k_j}{k_i} \int d\Omega_j\ \left|T_{ji}(E_i)\right|^2 \qquad (4\text{-}29)$$

where

$$k_j^{\,2} = \frac{\mu_j}{\mu_i} k_i^{\,2} + \frac{2\mu_j}{\hbar^2}\left(\varepsilon_i - \varepsilon_j\right)$$

It is usual to define a scattering amplitude $f_{ji}(\theta_j,\phi_j)$ such that the differential cross section $d\sigma_{ji}/d\Omega_j$ is given by

$$\frac{d\sigma_{ji}}{d\Omega_j} = \frac{v_j}{v_i}\left|f_{ji}(\theta_j,\phi_j)\right|^2 \tag{4-30}$$

where v_j and v_i are the relative velocities in the channels j and i

$$v_j = \hbar k_j/\mu_j\ , \qquad v_i = \hbar k_i/\mu_i$$

Adopting the sign to agree with that chosen for the scattering amplitude in Chapter 1, we have

$$f_{ji}(\theta_j,\phi_j) = -\frac{\mu_j}{2\pi\hbar^2}\ T_{ji} \tag{4-31}$$

The optical theorem

The optical theorem, proved in Chapter 1 for scattering by a central potential, is always valid, as we shall now demonstrate. From (4-21c), the unitarity condition is

$$\sum_j \mathcal{T}^*_{ji}\mathcal{T}_{ji} = \mathrm{Im}\mathcal{T}_{ii}. \tag{4-32a}$$

As $\mathcal{T}$ only connects states of the same energy, the sum over j is a sum over all states energetically accessible from the state i. On extracting the energy conserving delta function, with the help of equation (4-24), equation (4-32a) becomes

$$\sum_j (\pi)\delta(E_i - E\ )\left|T_{ji}\right|^2 = -\mathrm{Im}T_{ii}. \tag{4-32b}$$

From (4-26) and (4-27), the left hand side of this equation is seen to be related to the total cross section for scattering from state i. We have

$$\hbar F_i(\Sigma_j\sigma_{ji}) = -2\mathrm{Im}T_{ii}.$$

On the right hand side T_{ii} is the amplitude for a transition in which the final and initial states are identical. If i is a two particle state (the state j can contain any number of particles), the flux factor F_i is $(\hbar k_i/\mu_i)$, and we find

$$\sigma = \sum_j \sigma_{ji} = -\left(\frac{2\,\mathrm{Im}T_{ii}}{hF_i}\right) = \left(\frac{4\pi}{k_i}\right)\,\mathrm{Im}f_{ii}(\theta_i = 0). \qquad (4\text{-}33)$$

This is the general form of the optical theorem. It should be emphasized that $\mathrm{Im}f_{ii}(\theta_i=0)$, the imaginary part of the forward elastic scattering amplitude, refers to scattering without change in spin or other variable.

Calculation of S_{ji} and T_{ji}

We will now rederive equations (4-25) and (4-23), in a form applicable to both direct and rearrangement collisions. Once again we take channel i to belong to arrangement α and channel j to arrangement β, where β may be equal to α. Substituting $|\psi_j^-)$, as given by (4-15), into (4-19), we obtain

$$S_{ji} = (\phi_j\,|1 + V_\beta G(E_j + i\varepsilon)|\psi_i^+), \qquad (4\text{-}34)$$

where we have used the result

$$G^\dagger(E_j - i\varepsilon) = G(E_j + i\varepsilon).$$

Since the total Hamiltonian H can be decomposed as in (4-5), we can express equation (4-10a) as

$$(H_\beta - E_i - i\varepsilon)|\psi_i(E_i + i\varepsilon)) = -i\varepsilon|\phi_i(E_i)) - V_\beta|\psi_i(E_i + i\varepsilon))$$

where β is an arrangement of channel j. Using this relation the first term in (4-34) can be expressed as

$$(\phi_j|\psi_i^+) = -\frac{i\varepsilon}{E_j - E_i - i\varepsilon}(\phi_j|\phi_i) - \frac{1}{E_j - E_i - i\varepsilon}(\phi_j|V_\beta|\psi_i(E_i + i\varepsilon)) \qquad (4\text{-}35)$$

Taking the limit $\varepsilon \to 0^+$ we find from (4-34) and (4-35)

$$S_{ji} = \delta_{ji} - 2\pi i\delta(E_i - E_j)(\phi_j|V_\beta|\psi_i^+) \tag{4-36}$$

where we have used the relation

$$\underset{\varepsilon\to 0}{\ell t}\left(\frac{1}{E_i - E_j + i\varepsilon} - \frac{1}{E_i - E_j - i\varepsilon}\right) = \underset{\varepsilon\to 0}{\ell t}\frac{-2i\varepsilon}{(E_i - E_j)^2 + \varepsilon^2}$$

$$= -2\pi i\delta(E_i - E_j).$$

The derivation of (4-36) is correct both for direct collisions and for those involving rearrangement. Consistently with equation (4-25), the definition of T_{ji} is in all cases taken to be

$$T_{ji}(E) = (\phi_j|V_\beta|\psi_i^+), \tag{4-37}$$

where both ϕ_j and ψ_i^+ are determined at the same energy E; that is T_{ji} is 'on the energy shell'.

The Born expansion and the Born approximation

From (4-15) and (4-37), the transition matrix can be written in terms of $G^+(E)$

$$T_{ji}(E) = (\phi_j|T|\phi_i) = (\phi_j|V_\beta(1 + G^+V_\alpha)|\phi_i). \tag{4-38}$$

where j belongs to the arrangement β and i to the arrangement α.

By expanding G^+ in terms of one of the Green's functions G_γ^+, various Born expansions can be obtained. To do this, we find an equation for G^+ in terms of G_γ^+, by operating from the left on both sides of (4-13) with $(H_\gamma - E - i\varepsilon)$, giving

$$(H_\gamma - E - i\varepsilon)G^+ = -1 - V_\gamma G^+,$$

or

$$G^+ = \frac{1}{H_\gamma - E - i\varepsilon}(-1 - V_\gamma G^+) = G_\gamma(1 + V_\gamma G^+). \tag{4-39}$$

This equation can be iterated by substituting for G^+ on the right hand side, obtaining

$$G^{+} = G_{\gamma} + G_{\gamma}V_{\gamma}G_{\gamma} + G_{\gamma}V_{\gamma}G_{\gamma}V_{\gamma}G^{+}.$$

By repeating this procedure, we find an infinite series for G^{+}:

$$G^{+} = G_{\gamma} + G_{\gamma}V_{\gamma}G_{\gamma} + G_{\gamma}V_{\gamma}G_{\gamma}V_{\gamma}G_{\gamma} + \ldots..$$

By using such a series expansion, it is clear that many different Born expansions for the transition matrix can be found corresponding to different choices of G_{γ}. For elastic scattering or excitation it is natural to choose $\gamma=\alpha$, where α is the arrangement in the incident channel and for such collisions $V_{\alpha}=V_{\beta}$ so that

$$T_{ji}(E) = (\phi_j|V_{\alpha} + V_{\alpha}G_{\alpha}V_{\alpha} + \ldots..|\phi_i). \tag{4-40}$$

In the first Born approximation the first term of this expansion is retained; if two terms are retained, we have the second Born approximation and so on. The conditions ensuring the accuracy of the first Born approximation,

$$T^{B}_{ji} = (\phi_j|V_{\alpha}|\phi_i), \tag{4-41}$$

are not always similar to those discussed in potential scattering and each case requires special discussion.

The transition matrix in configuration space

In discussing the position representation, we take the case in which each channel contains just two atoms and three body collisions will not be treated explicitly. The Green's functions G_{γ} belonging to an arrangement γ can be expanded in terms of the eigenfunctions of the Hamiltonian H_{γ}. In the arrangement γ, the internal coordinates of the colliding atoms are denoted collectively by $\vec{x}_{\gamma}$ and the vector joining the center of masses of the two atoms is denoted by $\vec{r}_{\gamma}$. To simplify the notation the subscripts γ on $\vec{x}$ and $\vec{r}$ will be omitted, except where there is any danger of confusion. The eigenfunctions of H_{γ} will be written as in (4-7) as $\phi_m(\gamma,\vec{x},\vec{r})$. These functions satisfy the Schrödinger equation

$$(H_{\gamma} - E_m)\phi_m(\gamma,\vec{x},\vec{r}) = 0 \tag{4-42}$$

where E_m is given by (4-8). The internal wave functions

$X_m(x)$ will be assumed to form a complete orthonormal set:

$$\int d^3\vec{x}\; X_m^*(\vec{x})X_n(\vec{x}) = \delta_{mn} \tag{4-43}$$

and the normalization of ϕ_m is defined, as above, by taking $N_m = 1$.

The Green's functions $G_\gamma^\pm$ in configuration space, satisfy the equation

$$(E \pm i\varepsilon - H_\gamma(\vec{x},\vec{r}))G_\gamma^\pm(\vec{x},\vec{r};\vec{x}',\vec{r}') = \delta(\vec{x}-\vec{x}')\delta(\vec{r}-\vec{r}') \tag{4-44}$$

where the limit $\varepsilon \to 0^+$ is understood. On expanding $G_\gamma^\pm$ in terms of the functions $\phi_m(\gamma)$, we obtain

$$G_\gamma^\pm(\vec{x},\vec{r};\vec{x}',\vec{r}') = (2\pi)^{-3}\sum_m \int d^3k'(E \pm i\varepsilon - E_m)^{-1} \times$$

$$\times X_m(\vec{x})X_m(\vec{x}')\exp i\vec{k}'\cdot(\vec{r}-\vec{r}')$$

where

$$E'_m \equiv \varepsilon_m + \hbar^2k'^2/2\mu_\gamma$$

We now write $G_\gamma^\pm$ in the form

$$G_\gamma^\pm(\vec{x},\vec{r};\vec{x}',\vec{r}') = \sum_m \frac{2\mu_\gamma}{\hbar^2} X_m(\vec{x})X_m^*(\vec{x}') \times$$

$$\times \left(\frac{1}{2\pi}\right)^3 \int d^3k' \frac{\exp i\vec{k}'\cdot(\vec{r}-\vec{r}')}{k_m^2 - k'^2 \pm i\varepsilon} \tag{4-45}$$

where k_m^2 is defined by the equation

$$k_m^2 = \frac{2\mu_\gamma}{\hbar^2}(E - \varepsilon_m)$$

By referring to equation (1-125), the last factor in (4-45) is seen to be equal to the free particle Green's function $G_0^\pm$, and $G_\gamma^\pm$ can be written finally as

$$G^\pm(\vec{x},\vec{r};\vec{x}',\vec{r}') = \sum_m \frac{2\mu_\gamma}{\hbar^2} X_m(\vec{x})X_m^*(\vec{x}')G_0^\pm(k_m;\vec{r},\vec{r}') \tag{4-46}$$

where the free particle Green's functions are

$$G_o^{\pm}(k_m,\vec{r},\vec{r}') = -\frac{1}{4\pi}\frac{1}{|\vec{r}-\vec{r}'|}\exp \pm ik_m|\vec{r}-\vec{r}'|$$

We are now in a position to examine the asymptotic form of the wave function as we let r, the mutual separation of the colliding atoms in arrangement γ, become large. The integral equation for the complete wave function, when the incident state is i, is (from 4-14).

$$\psi_i^+(\vec{x},\vec{r}) = \phi_i(\alpha,\vec{x},\vec{r})\,\delta_{\alpha,\gamma} + \\ + \int d^3x'\int d^3r' G_\gamma^{\pm}(\vec{x},\vec{r};\vec{x}',\vec{r}')V_\gamma(\vec{x}',\vec{r}')\psi_i^+(\vec{x}',\vec{r}') \qquad (4\text{-}47)$$

If we are interested in elastic scattering or in excitation without rearrangement, the Green's function appropriate to the arrangement in the incident channel is used and we set $\gamma=\alpha$. In this case, the unperturbed initial wave function appears on the right hand side of (4-47), which arises from the term in $(i\varepsilon)$ on the right hand side of (4-41) (see also 4-9). In this case, the function $\psi_i^+(\vec{x},\vec{r})$ on the left hand side of (4-47) automatically satisfies the boundary conditions. On the other hand, if we are concerned with a rearrangement collision, $\gamma\neq\alpha$, the term in $\phi_i(\alpha,\vec{x},\vec{r})$ does not appear. In this case the equation is homogeneous and the boundary conditions are not automatically satisfied but must be imposed. It should also be noted that the position vectors $\vec{x},\vec{r}$, differ in each arrangement.

Using the asymptotic form of $G_o^{\pm}$ for large r, obtained in Chapter 1, we have that

$$\psi_i^+(\vec{x},\vec{r}) \underset{r\to\infty}{\sim} \phi_i(\alpha,\vec{x},\vec{r})\delta_{\alpha,\gamma} + \\ +\sum_m(-\mu_m/(2\pi h^2))X_m(\vec{x})\; T_{mi}r^{-1}\exp(ik_m r) \qquad (4\text{-}48a)$$

where we have set $\mu_\gamma\equiv\mu_m$, since the channel m belongs to the arrangement γ and T_{mi} is defined by

$$T_{mi} = \int d^3x\int d^3r\left(X_m(\vec{x})\exp(i\vec{k}_m\cdot\vec{r})\right)^* V_\gamma(\vec{x},\vec{r})\psi_i^+(\vec{x},\vec{r}) \qquad (4\text{-}48b)$$

The amplitude of the outgoing wave in the state m, is the scattering amplitude, $f_{mi}(\theta)$, connected to the cross section by (4-29), and

$$f_{mi}(\theta) = -\frac{\mu_m}{2\pi\hbar^2} T_{mi} \tag{4-49}$$

and this is in agreement with the expressions that we obtained earlier, for example (4-31).

The function $\psi_i^+(\vec{r},\vec{x})$ contains in the channel i the incident plane wave ϕ_i, and has outgoing waves in all channels that are open at a given energy. If the number of open channels is N, we can obtain N independent solutions of the Schrödinger equation, by placing the incident wave in each of the N channels in turn. From the asymptotic form of the N solutions the complete N×N transition matrix can be calculated using (4-48).

4-3 THE REDUCTION OF THE S-MATRIX

No matter what the reaction, several quantities must be conserved in addition to the energy and momentum. For instance, charge is always conserved and it follows that the matrix elements of $\mathcal{S}$ connecting states of different charge must vanish, that is, $\mathcal{S}$ is diagonal in the charge. The total angular momentum is a constant of the motion and for reactions involving light atoms, the total spin and the total orbital angular momentum are conserved separately (to a high degree of approximation). The $\mathcal{S}$-matrix can correspondingly be diagonalized in these quantities. The problem of reducing the $\mathcal{S}$-matrix to diagonal form has been discussed by Blatt and Biedenharn (1952) for the case in which each channel contains two particles. Rather than pursue this problem in full generality, one of the simpler cases will be treated.

Let us start by supposing that in each channel the total spin and total internal orbital angular momentum of each of the colliding particles is zero. The total angular momentum, $\vec{L}$, of the system then coincides with the orbital angular momentum of relative motion and a representation can be found in which L^2 and L_z are diagonal with quantum numbers ℓ and m

$$L^2 = \ell(\ell + 1)\hbar^2,$$

$$L_z = m\hbar.$$

In what follows the unperturbed state vectors $|\phi_m(\gamma))$ corresponding to the unperturbed wave functions (4-7) will be labeled by the wave vector $\vec{k}_m$ of relative motion and, to avoid an over elaborate notation, the label γ of the arrangement will be omitted; we write

$$|\phi_m(\vec{k}_m)) \equiv |\phi_m(\gamma))$$

The eigenvectors of L^2 and L_z, describing the unperturbed state in channel i, will be labeled $|\ell,m,i)$, and these may be formed by projecting the states $|\phi_i(k_i))$ on the spherical harmonics $Y_{\ell,m}(\theta_i,\phi_i)$, where (θ_i,ϕ_i) are the polar angles of $\vec{k}_i$ since the spherical harmonics are the simultaneous eigenfunctions of L^2 and L_z with quantum numbers ℓ,m.

It is only necessary to consider states of the same energy so that the factor $\delta(E_n - E_m)$ can be omitted in the normalization of the unperturbed state vectors and we can write the normalization condition as

$$(\phi_i(\vec{k}_i)|\phi_j(\vec{k}_j))=(2\pi)^3\delta_{ij}\delta(\Omega_i-\Omega_j)\omega_i^2 \tag{4-50a}$$

where

$$\omega_i^2 = (\hbar^2/\mu_i k_i) \tag{4-50b}$$

With this normalization, the states $|\ell,m,i)$ are defined as

$$|\ell,m,i)=(2\pi)^{-3/2}\left(\frac{1}{\omega_i}\right)\int d\Omega_i Y^*_{\ell,m}(\theta_i,\phi_i)|\phi_i(\vec{k}_i)) \tag{4-51}$$

where

$$(\ell',m',j|\ell,m,i) = \delta_{\ell\ell'}\delta_{mm'}\delta_{ij} \tag{4-52a}$$

and the closure relation is

$$\sum_{\ell,m,i} |\ell,m,i)(\ell,m,i| = 1 \tag{4-52b}$$

Another way of expressing (4-51) is

$$(\phi_i(\vec{k}_i)|\ell,m,j) = \delta_{ij}Y^*_{\ell,m}(\theta_i,\phi_i)(2\pi)^{3/2}\omega_i$$

Omitting the energy conserving delta function from (4-24), since we are working only with states of equal energy, we see that, from (4-21b)

$$T_{ji}(E) = -\frac{1}{\pi}(\phi_j(\vec{k}_j)|T|\phi_i(\vec{k}_i))$$

Making use of (4-51), (4-53) and the completeness relation (4-52b), the transition matrix $T_{ji}(E)$ can be expanded as

$$-\pi T_{ji}(E) = (\phi_j(\vec{k}_j)|T|\phi_i(\vec{k}_i))$$

$$= \sum_{\ell,\ell'} \sum_{m,m'} \sum_{q,q'} (\phi_j(\vec{k}_j)|\ell,m,q) \times$$

$$\times(\ell,m,q|T|\ell',m',q')(\ell',m',q'|\phi_i(\vec{k}_i)) \tag{4-54}$$

As pointed out above, the transition matrix is diagonal in ℓ and m, and since the transition probability cannot depend on the orientation of the complete system, the transition matrix must be independent of m; and can be written in the form

$$(\ell,m,q|T|\ell',m',q') = T^{\ell}_{qq'}\,\delta_{\ell\ell'}\,\delta_{mm'} \tag{4-55}$$

The diagonal elements T^{ℓ}_{qq} have the same normalization as the transition matrix elements T_{ℓ} introduced in Chapter 1.

Using (4-55), the transition matrix element (4-54) reduces to

$$T_{ji}(E) = -8\pi^2\omega_i\omega_j \sum_{\ell,m} T^{\ell}{}_{ji}\, Y_{\ell,m}(\theta_j,\phi_j)Y^*_{\ell,m}(\theta_i,\phi_i)$$

$$= -2\pi\omega_i\omega_j \sum_{\ell} T_{ji}{}^{\ell}\,(2\ell+1)P_{\ell}(\cos\theta) \tag{4-56}$$

where in the second line the addition theorem for the spherical harmonics has been used (see Appendix B). The angle of scattering θ is the angle between the vectors $\vec{k}_i$ and $\vec{k}_j$.

The diagonal elements of $T^{\ell}{}_{ji}(E)$, $T^{\ell}{}_{jj}$, describe elastic scattering and, as in Chapter 1, these elements may be written in terms of real phase shifts $\delta_{\ell}(j)$ and an inelasticity paramater $\eta_{\ell}(j)$. Taking into account the relation between S_{ji} and T_{ji}, we find that

$$T^{\ell}_{jj}(E) = \frac{1}{2i}\left(S^{\ell}_{jj} - 1\right), \tag{4-57a}$$

where

$$S^{\ell}_{jj} = \eta_{\ell}(j)\ \exp\left[2i\delta_{\ell}(j)\right] \tag{4-57b}$$

The partial cross sections of order ℓ are (using 4-56 in 4-29)

$$\sigma_{ji}(\ell) = \frac{4\pi(2\ell + 1)}{k_i^{\,2}}\left|T^{\ell}_{ji}\right|^2 \tag{4-58}$$

If N channels are open at a certain energy, T^{ℓ}_{ji} is a square N×N matrix. Not all the elements are independent, because invariance under time reversal links the amplitude for the reaction $j\to i$ with that for $i\to j$ by

$$(\phi_i(\vec{k}_i)|\mathcal{T}|\phi_j(\vec{k}_j)) = (\phi_j(-\vec{k}_j)|\mathcal{T}|\phi_i(-\vec{k}_i)) \tag{4-59}$$

In the angular momentum representation the relation is satisfied provided that

$$T^{\ell}_{ji} = T^{\ell}_{ij} \tag{4-60}$$

which reduces the number of independent elements of $\mathcal{T}$ or $\mathcal{S}$ to $N(N + 1)/2$. As $\mathcal{S}^{\ell}$ is a unitary matrix it may be diagonalized by a real orthogonal matrix $\mathcal{R}^{\ell}$, where

$$\Sigma_j R^{\ell}_{ji} R^{\ell}_{jq} = \delta_{iq}$$

If $\mathcal{R}^{T}$ is the transpose of $\mathcal{R}$, we may write

$$\mathcal{S}^{\ell} = \mathcal{R}^{T}\bar{\mathcal{S}}^{\ell}\mathcal{R}$$

where $\bar{\mathcal{S}}^{\ell}$ is diagonal

$$(\bar{\mathcal{S}}^{\ell})_{ij} = \delta_{ij}\exp(2i\Delta^{\ell}_{i}). \tag{4-61}$$

The parameters Δ^{ℓ}_i are called eigenphase shifts, and, if only one channel is open, Δ^{ℓ}_i is equal to the ordinary phase shift δ_{ℓ}. For two channel scattering the matrix elements of $\mathcal{R}$ depend on one parameter ε, called the mixing parameter, and $\mathcal{R}$ can be written as

$$\mathcal{R} = \begin{pmatrix} \cos\varepsilon & \sin\varepsilon \\ -\sin\varepsilon & \cos\varepsilon \end{pmatrix} \tag{4-62}$$

Target with non-zero angular momentum

A more realistic case is that in which the target in channel α is in an eigenstate of orbital angular momentum of magnitude $\{\ell_i(\ell_i + 1)\hbar^2\}^{\frac{1}{2}}$ with Z component $m_i\hbar$, while we shall suppose that the scattered particles in each channel are structureless (such as electrons or protons). As we are considering the case in which the total orbital angular momentum $\vec{L}$ and the total spin $\vec{S}$ are separately conserved, we can reduce the transition matrix to diagonal form in $\vec{L}$ and $\vec{S}$ separately, and, to start with, we shall only deal with the orbital angular momentum.

If the orbital angular momentum of relative motion in the channel i is of magnitude $\{L_i(L_i + 1)\hbar^2\}^{\frac{1}{2}}$ with Z component $M_i\hbar$ and the total orbital angular momentum of the whole system is $\{L(L + 1)\hbar^2\}^{\frac{1}{2}}$ with Z component $M\hbar$, the ordinary rules of addition of angular momenta[4] require that

$$|L_i - \ell_i| \leq L \leq (L_i + \ell_i),$$
$$M = M_i + m_i. \tag{4-63}$$

The unperturbed wave functions $\phi_i(\alpha,\vec{x},\vec{r})$ can be labeled by the angular momentum of the target and are of the form

$$\phi_i(\alpha,\vec{x},\vec{r}) \equiv \phi_i(\ell_i,m_i,\vec{k}_i) = \exp(i\vec{k}_i\cdot\vec{r})X_i(\ell_i,m_i,\vec{x}) \tag{4-64}$$

where $X_i(\ell_i,m_i,\vec{x})$ is the target wave function. The state vector corresponding to ϕ_i will be written as

$$|\phi_i(\ell_i,m_i,\vec{k}_i))$$

If the eigenstates of total orbital angular momentum are labeled as $|L_i,\ell_i,L,M)$ with the normalization

$$(L_j,\ell_j,L',M'|L_i,\ell_i,L,M) = \delta_{ij} \ \delta_{L'L} \ \delta_{M'M} \tag{4-65}$$

then in place of (4-51), we have

$$|L_i,\ell_i,L,M) = \sum_{m_iM_i} (2\pi)^{-3/2} \left(\frac{1}{\omega_i}\right) \int d\Omega_i \ Y_{L_i,M_i}(\theta_i,\phi_i) \ \times$$
$$\times \ |\phi_i(\ell_i,m_i,\vec{k}_i))(L_i,\ell_i, M_i,m_i|L,M)$$

and

$$(\phi_i(\ell_i, m_i\vec{k}_i)|L_i, \ell_i, L, M) = (2\pi)^{3/2}\ \omega_i Y_{L_i, M_i}(\theta_i, \phi_i)(L_i \ell_i, M_i, m_i|L, M) \tag{4-66}$$

where $(L_i, \ell_i, M_i, m_i|LM)$ is the Clebsch-Gordan coefficient[5] relating the representation in which L_i, ℓ_i, L, M are diagonal to that in which L_i, ℓ_i, M_i, m_i are diagonal.

Similarly to (4-55), the matrix elements of T can be expressed as in the L_i, ℓ_i, L, M basis as

$$(L_j, \ell_j, L', M'|T|L_i, \ell_i, L, M)$$

$$= T^L{}_{ji}(L_j, \ell_j, L_i, \ell_i)\ \delta_{LL'}\ \delta_{MM'} \tag{4-67}$$

Because of conservation of angular momentum, T can only connect states having the same value of L and M and further since there is no preferred direction in space (rotational invariance), $T^L{}_{ji}$ must be independent of M.

The expansion of $T_{ji}(E)$ is, using (4-66) and (4-67),

$$T_{ji}(E) = -\frac{1}{\pi} \sum_{L, L_i, L_j} \sum_{M_i M_j} (2\pi)^3 \omega_i \omega_j\ Y_{L_j M_j}(\theta_j, \phi_j) Y^*{}_{L_i, M_i}(\theta_i, \phi_i)\ \times$$

$$\times\ (L_i, \ell_i, M_i, m_i|L, M)(L_j, \ell_j, M_j, m_j|L, M)\ T^L_{ji}(L_j, \ell_j, L_i, \ell_i) \tag{4-68a}$$

The direction of incidence which is parallel to $\vec{k}_i$ can be taken as the Z axis, and setting

$$Y^*{}_{L_i, M_i}(o, o) = \left(\frac{2L_i+1}{4\pi}\right)^{\frac{1}{2}}$$ we have

$$T_{ji}(E)\quad 8\pi^2 \sum_{\substack{L, L_i, L_j \\ M_i, M_j}} \omega_i \omega_j\ Y_{L_j, M_j}(\theta, \phi)\ T^L{}_{ji}(L_j, \ell_j, L_i, \ell_i)\ \times$$

$$\times \left(\frac{2L_i+1}{4\pi}\right)^{\frac{1}{2}} (L_i, \ell_i, M_i, m_i|L, M)(L_j, \ell_j, M_j, m_j|L, M) \tag{4-68b}$$

The sum over L_j and L_i for given values of ℓ_j, ℓ_i and L is restricted by the conditions (4-63). In addition, there are restrictions due to the conservation of parity. The parity of an angular momentum eigenfunction $Y_{\ell,m}$ is $(-1)^{\ell}$. Combining the parity of the continuum states with that of the initial bound state (Π_i) and the final bound state (Π_j), conservation of parity requires:

$$\Pi_i(-1)^{L_i} = \Pi_j(-1)^{L_j}.$$

General expressions can be obtained from (4-66) for the differential cross section and have been given by Blatt and Biedenharn (1952), and the particular case of electron-hydrogen atom scattering has been developed by Percival and Seaton (1957). The total cross section has the simple form (making no allowance for spin)

$$\sigma_{ji}(E) = \frac{4\pi}{k_i^2} \sum_{L,L_i,L_j} \frac{(2L+1)}{(2\ell_i+1)} \left| T^L{}_{ji}(L_j,\ell_j,L_i,\ell_i) \right|^2 \tag{4-69}$$

In (4-69) each term, of the sum over L, has been weighted by the degeneracy (2L+1) of a state specified by the quantum numbers L and Π (the parity), and divided by the degeneracy $(2\ell_i+1)$ of the target in the initial state.

Although in diagonalizing the T-matrix, we have supposed the target to be an eigenstate of orbital angular momentum, specified by integer (or zero) quantum numbers, ℓ_i, ℓ_j, the discussion is quite general and also applies to the case in which spin dependent interactions are important and the target is specified by the total (orbital plus spin) angular momentum. In such cases, ℓ_i, and ℓ_j can take half-integral values in addition to integral values. The case in which both partners in the collision have non-zero internal angular momentum is a straightforward, if complicated generalization.

Elastic scattering of spin one-half by a spin-zero target.

A particular case of importance is the elastic scattering of spin one-half particles by a spin-zero target when the interaction includes a spin dependent term. For example, electrons scattered by a heavy spin-zero atom, such as Hg, experience an effective interaction which includes a spin-orbit potential of relativistic origin[6]. Equation (4-68b) can be used for the decomposition of the T-matrix. Since we are interested in elastic scattering the magnitudes of $\vec{k}_i$ and $\vec{k}_j$ are equal, $|\vec{k}_i| = |\vec{k}_j| = k$ and $\omega_i = \omega_j = \omega$. We then set $\ell_i = \ell_j = \frac{1}{2}$, so that from (4-63) the orbital angular momentum of relative motion in the initial and final channels L_i and L_j are restricted to the values $L_i = L \pm \frac{1}{2}$ $L_j = L \pm \frac{1}{2}$ for each value of the total angular momentum quantum number L. A further restriction arises from conservation of parity. Equating the parities of the initial and final channels we have

$$(-1)^{L_i} = (-1)^{L_j}$$

and it follows that only $L_i = L_j$ is allowed, and we define $\ell = L_i = L_j$, so that $L = \ell \pm \frac{1}{2}$. For each value of ℓ (or L) there are just two partial wave amplitudes f_+, f_- defined so that

$$f_{\ell\pm} = T^{\ell\pm\frac{1}{2}}(\ell,\ \tfrac{1}{2},\ell,\ \tfrac{1}{2}) = \frac{1}{2i}\left(\exp(2i\delta_{\ell\pm})-1\right) \tag{4-70}$$

The Z components of the spin, for spin one-half particles can take the values $\pm\hbar/z$, so that $m_i = \pm\frac{1}{2}$, $m_j = \pm\frac{1}{2}$. The scattering amplitude can be written as

$$f_{m_j,m_i}(\theta,\phi),$$

forming a 2 x 2 matrix F where

$$F_{ji} \equiv f_{m_i,m_j}$$

but of the four elements of F only two are independent. There are two cases to consider, first if $m_i = m_j$, the spin one-half particles are scattered without a change in spin direction. Using (4-49) and (4-68b) together with the explicit values of the Clebsch-Gordan coefficients, the corresponding scattering amplitude is $f(\theta)$ where

$$f(\theta) = k^{-1} \sum_{\ell=0}^{\infty} \left(\frac{4}{2L+1}\right)^{\frac{1}{2}} Y_{\ell,0}(\theta,\phi)\ \{(\ell+1)f_{\ell+} + f_{\ell-}\} \tag{4-71}$$

In the second case, the spin direction of the scattered particles changes, and the amplitude for scattering with 'spin-flip', $g(\theta,\phi)$ is

$$g(\theta,\phi) = k^{-1} \sum_{\ell=0}^{\infty} \left(\frac{4\pi}{2\ell+1}\right)^{\frac{1}{2}} Y_{\ell,2m_i}(\theta,\phi)\ (f_{\ell+}-f_{\ell-})$$

$$= (-1)^{(m_i+\frac{1}{2})}\bar{g}(\theta)\exp(i2m_i\phi) \qquad (4\text{-}72)$$

where

$$\bar{g}(\theta) = k^{-1}\sum_{\ell=0}^{\infty} (f_{\ell+} - f_{\ell-}) \sin\theta\ P'_{\ell}(\cos\theta) \qquad (4\text{-}73)$$

Written in matrix form the scattering amplitude F is

$$F(\theta,\phi) = \begin{pmatrix} f(\theta), & -\bar{g}(\theta)\exp(i\phi) \\ \bar{g}(\theta)\exp(-i\phi), & f(\theta) \end{pmatrix} \qquad (4\text{-}74)$$

If the incident beam of spin one-half is unpolarized, that is if there are equal numbers of particles with $m_i = \frac{1}{2}$ and $m_i = -\frac{1}{2}$, the differential cross section is found by summing over the final spin states and averaging over the initial spin states

$$\frac{d\sigma}{d\Omega} = \frac{1}{2}\sum_{i,j} |F_{ji}(\theta,\phi)|^2 = |f(\theta)|^2 + |\bar{g}(\theta)|^2 \qquad (4\text{-}75a)$$

In a matrix notation, we have the alternative useful form

$$\frac{d\sigma}{d\Omega} = \frac{1}{2}\,\mathrm{Tr}(FF^{+}) \qquad (4\text{-}75b)$$

Polarization and the density matrix

The plane wave states $|\phi_j(\ell_j,m_j,\vec{k}_j))$ representing the motion of a spinless particle with respect to a target with angular momentum quantum numbers ℓ_j,m_j, are eigenstates of the Z-component of the total angular momentum[7]. For spin one-half particles, $\ell_j=\frac{1}{2}$ and

$$J_z|\phi(\pm\tfrac{1}{2})) = \pm\frac{1}{2}\hbar\ |\phi(\pm\tfrac{1}{2})) \qquad (4\text{-}76)$$

where only the dependence of $|\phi_j)$ on m_j is exhibited. New states $|\psi(\pm))$ can be constructed from $|\phi(\pm\frac{1}{2}))$ by a rotation into a direction $\vec{d}$ with polar angles (θ,ϕ) with respect to the Z axis.

$$|\psi(+1)) = a|\phi(\tfrac{1}{2})) + b|\phi(-\tfrac{1}{2}))$$
$$|\psi(-1)) = c|\phi(\tfrac{1}{2})) + d|\phi(-\tfrac{1}{2})) \qquad (4\text{-}77a)$$

where

$$a = d^{*} = \cos\,(\theta/2)$$
$$b = -c^{*} = \exp(i\phi)\,\sin\,(\theta/2) \qquad (4\text{-}77b)$$

The new states $|\psi(\pm))$ are eigenstates of the component of the total angular momentum in the direction $\vec{d}$,

$$J_d|\psi(\pm)) = \pm\,\frac{1}{2}\hbar\;|\psi(\pm)) \qquad (4\text{-}78)$$

The states $|\psi(\pm 1))$ are the most general that can be formed the basis of the states $|\phi(\pm\tfrac{1}{2}))$, they are completely specified by the two coefficients a and b (or c and d). The coefficients of $|\phi(\tfrac{1}{2}))$ and $|\phi(-\tfrac{1}{2}))$ can be written as a 2-dimensional column vector, and in this basis a general state can be written as

$$\Psi = \begin{pmatrix} a \\ b \end{pmatrix}$$

To calculate the differential cross section for scattering from one such state Ψ_i, specified by coefficients a_i,b_i to another Ψ_j specified by coefficients a_j,b_j, we calculate the scattering amplitude f_{ji} from the 2 x 2 matrix F given by (4-74)

$$f_{ji} = (\Psi_j,\, F\Psi_i) \qquad (4\text{-}79)$$

In general, the particles in a beam, or atoms in a target, are not all in the same pure state, but are in an incoherent mixture of pure states. Let $|\psi_a)$ be a normalized state vector describing a pure state a, and suppose a fraction p_a of the particles in a beam are in the state a, then the average value of an observable O in the beam is

$$\mathrm{Av}(O) = \sum_a p_a(\psi_a|O|\psi_a) \qquad (4\text{-}80)$$

where the sum is over a complete set of pure states and

$$\sum_a p_a = 1$$

An alternative expression for Av(O) is

$$\begin{aligned} Av(O) &= T_r\,(\rho O) \\ &= \sum_c (\psi_c|\rho O|\psi_c) \end{aligned} \tag{4-81}$$

where ρ is the density operator defined as

$$\rho = \sum_a p_a|\psi_a)(\psi_a| \tag{4-82}$$

From (4-82), it immediately follows that

$$\rho^+ = \rho \text{ and } T_r(\rho) = 1 \tag{4-83}$$

Both mixed and pure states are completely specified by the density operator. In the special case of a pure state b, $p_a = \delta_{ab}$ and

$$\begin{aligned} \rho &= \sum_a p_a|\psi_a)(\psi_a| \\ &= |\psi_b)(\psi_b| \end{aligned}$$

In this case ρ reduces to a projection operator onto the state b.

The matrix elements of ρ with respect to some orthonormal basis $|\omega_m)$, ρ_{nm}, form the density matrix. We have

$$\rho_{nm} = \sum_a p_a(\omega_n|\psi_a)(\psi_a|\omega_m) \tag{4-84}$$

and

$$\begin{aligned} Av(O) &= Tr\,(\rho O) \\ &= \sum_{nm} \rho_{nm}\,(\omega_n|O|\omega_m) \end{aligned} \tag{4-85}$$

Spin one-half particles

To apply the density matrix formalism to a beam of spin one-half particles, we can identify the pure states $|\psi_a)$ with the $|\psi(\pm))$ of equations (4-77) and take as the basis vectors $|\omega_m)$ the state vectors $|\phi(\pm\frac{1}{2}))$. The density matrix is then a 2 x 2 matrix with unit trace. Thus, if a beam is travelling in the direction $\vec{d}$ specified by the cycles (θ,ϕ) and a fraction p of the beam is in the state $|\psi(+1))$ so that a fraction (1-p) is in the state $|\psi(-1)$, we find

$$\rho = p \begin{pmatrix} aa^* & ab^* \\ ba^* & bb^* \end{pmatrix} + (1-p) \begin{pmatrix} cc^* & cd^* \\ dc^* & dd^* \end{pmatrix} \tag{4-86}$$

where (a,b) and (c,d) are given in terms of (θ,ϕ) by (4-77b). The most general 2 x 2 matrix with unit trace can be written in terms of the three Pauli spin matrices[8] σ_x, σ_y, σ_z where

$$\sigma_x = \begin{pmatrix} 0 & 1 \\ 1 & 0 \end{pmatrix} \quad \sigma_y = \begin{pmatrix} 0 & -i \\ i & 0 \end{pmatrix} \quad \sigma_z = \begin{pmatrix} 1 & 0 \\ 0 & -1 \end{pmatrix}$$

We have

$$\rho = \frac{1}{2} (1 + \vec{P}\cdot\vec{\sigma}) \tag{4-87}$$

where $\vec{P}$ is called a polarization vector. Since the spin $\vec{S}$ is equal to $\hbar\vec{\sigma}/2$ and since from (4-85)

$$\begin{aligned} Av(S) &= Tr\ (\rho\vec{S}) \\ &= \hbar\ \vec{P}/2 \end{aligned} \tag{4-88}$$

we see that $\vec{P}$ specifies the average of the spin in a beam.

Now consider scattering from an incident beam specified by a density matrix ρ_i, into a direction (θ,ϕ). To determine the state of polarization of the scattered beam, we need to calculate the density matrix ρ_j of the final state. For an initial pure state specified by the 2-dimensional column vector Ψ_i, the final state is given by the column vector Ψ_j where

$$\Psi_j = N\ (F\Psi_i), \tag{4-89}$$

N is a normalization factor, and F is found from (4-74). If p_i is the fraction of the initial beam in each of the states i, the density matrix of the final state ρ_j is

$$\rho_j = \sum_i p_i\ |N|^2\ (F\Psi_i)\ (F\Psi_i)^+ = |N|^2\ F\ \rho_i\ F^+$$

To determine $|N|^2$, we use the fact that $Tr(\rho_j)=1$ so that

$$|N|^{-2} = Tr\ (F\rho_i F^+)$$

and finally

$$\rho_j = \frac{F\rho_i F^+}{Tr(F\rho_i F^+)} \tag{4-90}$$

This is clearly a general result which will apply to particles of higher spin than one-half, in which case F will have a higher dimensionality than 2 x 2. In the case of a spin one-half beam, if the incident beam is unpolarized $\vec{P}_i = 0$ and $2\rho_i = 1$, the unit matrix. In this case

$$Tr(F\rho_i F^+) = \frac{1}{2}Tr(FF^+) = d\sigma/d\Omega$$

where $d\sigma/d\Omega$ is the differential cross section for an unpolarized beam. The polarization vector for the scattered beam $\vec{P}_j$ is then

$$\vec{P}_j = Av(\vec{\sigma}) = Tr(\rho_j\vec{\sigma})$$

$$= \frac{Tr(\vec{\sigma}FF^+)}{2d\sigma/d\Omega} \tag{4-91}$$

and we find using (4-74)

$$|P_j| = 2Im\left(f(\theta)\bar{g}^*(\theta)\right) / (d\sigma/d\Omega) \tag{4-92}$$

The direction of $\vec{P}_j$ is parallel to the vector $\vec{k}_j x\vec{k}_i$, and is at right angles to the plane of scattering. This polarization produced in the scattered beam can be detected by scattering the beam a second time again from a spin zero target. Because of the asymmetry with respect to the plane P, of the first collision, the intensity of scattering at a certain angle in the second collision is different on either side of P_i. If the spin zero targets in each of the two collisions are of the same species, the measurement of the asymmetry allows the magnitude, but not the sign of $\vec{P}_j$ to be determined.

4-4 THE RADIAL WAVE FUNCTIONS

It is important to determine the T-matrix, which we expressed in the previous Section in an angular momentum representation, in terms of a radial wave function as we did for potential scattering in Chapter 1. In this Section, we will assume for simplicity that we are dealing with direct collisions with all channels belonging to the same arrangement α, and that there are no rearrangement channels. However the results obtained are quite general and can be used for both direct and rearrangement collisions.

As before let us take the case where in each channel there are two colliding atoms. The product of the internal wave functions of the bound systems in channel m is $X_m(\vec{x})$ where $\vec{x}$ denotes the internal coordinates of these atoms collectively. The exact wave function corresponding to an incident plane wave in channel i and outgoing waves in all open channels is $\psi_i^+(\vec{x},\vec{r})$ where $\vec{r}$ is the relative position vector of the two atoms. Expanding ψ_i^+ in terms of the complete set of orthonormal functions X_m, we have

$$\psi_i^+(\vec{x},\vec{r}) = \sum_m X_m(\vec{x})\ F_{mi}(\vec{r}) \tag{4-93}$$

The coefficients of the expansion $F_{mi}(\vec{r})$ describe the relative motion of the two atoms in channel m and are called channel wave functions. In the channel α, we have

$$H = H_\alpha + V_\alpha = H_o - \frac{\hbar^2}{2\mu} \nabla_r^{\ 2} + V_\alpha \tag{4-94}$$

where H_o is the internal Hamiltonian of the bound systems such that

$$(H_o - \varepsilon_m)\ X_m(\vec{x}) = 0 \tag{4-95}$$

Inserting the expansion (4-93) into the Schrödinger equation

$$(H_o - \frac{\hbar^2}{2\mu}\nabla_r^2 + V_\alpha - E)\psi_i^+(\vec{x},\vec{r}) = 0$$

and projecting with the wave functions $X_m(\vec{x})$, we find the following system of coupled equations satisfied by the channel functions $F_{mi}(\vec{r})$:

$$\left(- \frac{\hbar^2}{2\mu}\nabla^2{}_r - E + \varepsilon_m\right) F_{mi}(\vec{r}) = - \sum_n V_{mn}(\vec{r})\ F_{ni}(\vec{r}) \tag{4-96}$$

The matrix potentials $V_{nm}(\vec{r})$ are defined as

$$V_{mn}(\vec{r}) = \int d^3x\ X_m^*(\vec{x})\ V_\alpha(\vec{x},\vec{r})\ X_n(\vec{x}) \tag{4-97}$$

and will be assumed to vanish at large r faster than 1/r. Since $k_m^2 = 2\mu(E - \varepsilon_m)/\hbar^2$ we can write (4-96) more conveniently as

$$\left(\nabla^2_r + k_m^2\right) F_{mi}(\vec{r}) = \sum_n U_{mn}(\vec{r})\ F_{ni}(\vec{r}) \tag{4-98}$$

where $k_m^2>0$ for open channels, $k_m^2<0$ for closed channels and

$$U_{mn}(\vec{r}) = 2\mu\ V_{mn}(\vec{r})/\hbar^2 \tag{4-99}$$

Comparing (4-93) with (4-48a,b), we see that in the open channels $F_{mi}(\vec{r})$ has the asymptotic form for large r,

$$F_{mi}(\vec{r}) \sim \delta_{mi} \exp(i\underset{\sim}{k}_i \cdot \underset{\sim}{r}) - \left(\frac{\mu}{2\pi\hbar^2}\right) T_{mi}(E) r^{-1} \exp(ik_m r) \tag{4-100}$$

where the transition matrix $T_{mi}(E)$ is

$$T_{mi}(E) = \sum_n \int d^3r \exp(-i\underset{\sim}{k}_m \cdot \underset{\sim}{r})\ V_{mn}(\vec{r})\ F_{ni}(\vec{r}) \tag{4-101}$$

In the closed channels $F_{ni}(\vec{r})$ vanishes as $r \to \infty$ at least as fast as 1/r, so that it does not contribute to outgoing radial flux of scattered particles.

The channel functions $F_{ni}(\vec{r})$ can be expanded in eigenfunctions of orbital angular momentum. In the case where $V_{mn}(\vec{r})$ is a function of $|\vec{r}|$ only, the system is axially symmetric, and the expansion is

$$F_{mi}(\vec{r}) = \sum_{\ell=0}^{\infty} A_\ell r^{-1} f_{mi}(\ell,r) P_\ell(\cos\theta) \tag{4-102}$$

where the A_ℓ are constants.

The boundary conditions satisfied by $f_{mi}(\ell,r)$ are then for M<N, where N is the number of open channels

$$f_{mi}(\ell,0) = 0$$

$$f_{mi}(\ell,r) \sim k_m^{-1}\left(s_\ell(k_m r)\ \delta_{mi} + \frac{\omega_i}{\omega_m} \exp i(k_m r - \ell\pi/2) T_{mi}^{\ell}(E)\right) \tag{4-103}$$

where ω_i, ω_m are defined by (4-50b). In the closed channels with M>N, the boundary conditions are

$$f_{mi}(\ell,0) = 0 \text{ and } f_{mi}(\ell,0) \sim 0 \text{ as } r \to \infty.$$

In equation (4-103), T^{ℓ}_{mi} is related to T_{mi} by (4-56) and $s_\ell(x)$ is defined in Section 1-2.

The solution to the many channel scattering problem then amounts to solving the set of coupled radial Schrödinger equations

$$\left(\frac{d^2}{dr^2} - \frac{\ell(\ell+1)}{r^2} + k_m^{\ 2}\right) f_{mi}(\ell,r) = \sum_n U_{mn}(r)\ f_{ni}(\ell,r) \tag{4-104}$$

with the boundary conditions (4-103). The indices m and n run over all the channels, both open and closed. There will be N independent solutions of the coupled equations, which are conveniently defined by taking the incident wave in each open channel in turn, that is, we let i range from 1 to N.

Integral equations for the radial functions can be obtained by straightforward generalizations of the methods employed for single channel scattering and described in Chapter 1. The variational methods of Kohn, Hulthén and Schwinger are easily adapted to deal with coupled channels, and so is the determinantal method of Baker. In a more general situation in which different arrangements are allowd, the potential matrix V_{nm} becomes a non-local integral operator, but this causes no essential difficulty.

The reaction matrix

In practice it is easier, when numerical solutions are required, to define real solutions of the coupled equations, by imposing the boundary conditions,

$$f_{mi}(\ell,0) = 0$$

$$f_{mi}(\ell,r) \sim k_m^{-1}\left(s_\ell(k_m r)\delta_{mi} + \frac{\omega_i}{\omega_m} C_\ell(k_m r) K_{mi}^{\ \ell}(E)\right) \qquad M \leqslant N$$

$$f_{mi}(\ell,r) \sim 0,\ r \to \infty,\ M > N \tag{4-105}$$

Comparing the solutions (4-103) and (4-105) it is seen that the reaction matrix K^{ℓ} is given in terms of T^{ℓ} by

$$K^{\ell} = \frac{T^{\ell}}{1 + iT^{\ell}} = \frac{1}{i}\left(\frac{S - 1}{S + 1}\right) \tag{4-106}$$

As S is unitary and symmetric, it follows that K is real and symmetric. An important property of the K matrix is that if it is calculated in any approximation, the S matrix elements calculated from (4-106) will be automatically unitary. The real orthogonal matrix R, that diagonalizes the S matrix, will also diagonalize T and K:

$$K_{mi}^{\ell} = \sum_n R_{nm} R_{ni} \tan \Delta_n^{\ell}$$

$$T_{mi}^{\ell} = \sum_n R_{nm} R_{ni} \left(\frac{1}{2i}\right)\left(\exp(2i\Delta_n^{\ell}) - 1\right) \tag{4-107}$$

An illustrative example

A simple approximation, that describes the excitation of the (2s) state of hydrogen by electron impact on the ground state, is obtained if just two terms are retained in the expansion of the wave function in terms of the target eigenfunctions. For scattering in the $\ell=0$ partial wave, we have

$$\psi^{+}(\vec{x},\vec{r}) = \phi_{1s}(x) r^{-1} f_1(r) + \phi_{2s}(x) r^{-1} f_2(r), \tag{4-108}$$

where ϕ_{1s} and ϕ_{2s} are the (1s) and (2s) eigenfunctions of the hydrogen atom and the label i defining the incident channel has been omitted. No allowance for electron exchange has been made, and because of this the model is not very realistic, but it serves to illustrate the methods employed. The coupled radial Schrödinger equations are (in atomic units)

$$\frac{1}{2}\left(\frac{d^2}{dr^2} + k_i^2\right) f_i(r) = \sum_{j=1}^{2} V_{ij}(r) f_j(r), \quad i = 1,2, \tag{4-109}$$

where

$$k_2^2 = k_1^2 + 2\left(\varepsilon_{1s} - \varepsilon_{2s}\right) = k_1^2 - 0.75.$$

The perturbation between the incident electron and the atom is

$$V(\vec{r},\vec{x}) = \frac{1}{|\vec{r}-\vec{x}|} - \frac{1}{r} \tag{4-110}$$

so that the matrix potential $V_{ij}(r)$ is

$$V_{ij}(r) = \int d^3x \phi_i(x)\phi_j(x)V(\vec{r},\vec{x}). \tag{4-111}$$

With

$$\phi(r) = \pi^{-\frac{1}{2}}\exp(-r)$$

and

$$\phi_{2s}(r) = \frac{1}{2}(2\pi)^{-\frac{1}{2}}(1-r/2)\exp(-r/2)$$

it is easily found that

$$V_{11} = -\left(1 + \frac{1}{r}\right)\exp(-2r)$$

$$V_{22} = \frac{1}{2}\left(\frac{1}{4}r^2 + 5r + \frac{2}{r} - 3\right)\exp(-r) \tag{4-112}$$

$$V_{12} = V_{21} = \frac{\sqrt{8}}{27}(6 - 3r - 8)\exp(-3r/2)$$

The partial cross sections obtained from accurate numerical solutions of equations (4-109) are shown in Tables 4-1 and 4-2. Because all the elements of the scattering matrix are calculated, the elastic cross section ϕ_{1s-1s} can be found as well as ϕ_{1s-2s}, the inelastic cross section. The same equations have been solved in variational and distorted wave approximations.

The distorted wave approximation

The distorted wave approximation is useful under conditions for which the coupling between the channels is small. If electrons are incident on the hydrogen ground state, it may be a good approximation to neglect the influence of the second channel in the elastic scattering channel, and to drop the term V_{12} in the coupled equations. We then have

Table 4-1

Zero order partial cross sections for the 1s - 2s excitation of hydrogen by electron impact (without exchange)

Energy of incident electron		σ_{1s-2s} (units of πa_o^2)				Phase of T_{12}	
(ev)	E	DW	V_1	V_2	V_3	$\pi + \theta$	$\delta_1+\delta_2$
11.5	0.286	-	-	-		3.947	-
13.5	0.204	0.198	0.110	0.164	0.189	3.643	3.66
19.4	0.102	0.127	0.055	0.081	0.094	3.060	3.08
30.4	0.045	0.058	0.027	0.035	0.040	2.636	2.61
54.0	0.0155	0.019	0.003	0.012	0.014	2.124	2.10

E: From numerical solution of equation (4-109) (Bransden and McKee, 1956).
DW: Distorted wave method (Erskine and Massey, 1952).
V_1,V_2,V_3: Variational method with 1,2 and 3 polynomial terms in the wave functions (Bransden and McKee, 1957).
θ,δ_1,δ_2 : See text

Table 4-2

Zero order partial cross sections for elastic scattering of electrons by the ground state of hydrogen

Energy of incident electron	σ_{1s-1s} (Units of πa_o^2)	
(ev)	(a)	(b)
11.5	-	2.52
13.5	2.47	2.12
19.4	1.57	1.42
30.4	0.885	0.828
54.0	0.411	0.394

(a): From the single channel equation using the phase shifts of Table 1-1.
(b): From the coupled equation (4-109).

$$\frac{1}{2}\left(\frac{d^2}{dr^2} + k_1{}^2\right) f_1(r) = V_{11}f_1(r) \qquad \text{(a)}$$

$$\frac{1}{2}\left(\frac{d^2}{dr^2} + k_2{}^2\right) f_2(r) = V_{22}f_2(r) + V_{21}f_1(r) \qquad \text{(b)} \tag{4-113}$$

The solution of equation (4-113a) with the elastic scattering boundary condition,

$$f_1(r) \sim k_1{}^{-1}e^{i\delta_1}\sin(k_1r + \delta_1), \tag{4-114}$$

is easily found, and this solution may be substituted into equation (4-113b). The boundary condition satisfied by $f_2(r)$ is that outgoing waves only should appear in the second channel

$$f_2(r) \sim (k_1k_2)^{-\frac{1}{2}}T_{12}\exp(ik_2r) \tag{4-115}$$

To construct a solution with this boundary condition, a Green's function $g_2(r,r')$ is required that satisfies

$$\left(\frac{d^2}{dr^2} + k_2{}^2\right) - 2V_{22}g_2(r,r') = \delta(r - r'),$$

in which case

$$f_2(r) = 2\int_0^\infty g_2(r,r')V_{21}(r')f_1(r')dr'. \tag{4-116}$$

The Green's function g_2 is given by

$$g_2(r,r') = -L(r_<)H(r_>), \tag{4-117}$$

where $r_<$ and $r_>$ are the lesser and greater of r and r' respectively and where H and L are solutions of the equation

$$\left(\frac{d^2}{dr^2} + k_2{}^2 - 2V_{22}\right)F = 0, \tag{4-118}$$

with the boundary conditions

$$L(r) \sim \sin(k_2r + \delta_2)$$

$$H(r) \sim k_2^{-1}\exp[i(k_2r + \delta_2)]. \tag{4-119}$$

It is easy to check that (4-116) is the solution of (4-113b) using the Wronskian relation,

$$\left(\frac{dL}{dr}H - \frac{dH}{dr}L\right) = 1. \tag{4-120}$$

For large r we have from (4-116) that

$$f_2(r) \sim -2k_2^{-1}e^{ik_2r}e^{i\delta_2}\int_0^\infty L(r')V_{21}(r')f_1(r')dr' \tag{4-121}$$

so that

$$T_{12} = -2\sqrt{\frac{k_1}{k_2}}\, e^{i\delta_2}\int_0^\infty L(r)V_{21}(r)f_1(r)dr. \tag{4-122}$$

The partial cross section σ_{1s-2s} in this approximation is included in Table 4-1. The distorted wave method predicts that the phase of the amplitude θ, where

$$T_{12} = |T_{12}|e^{i\theta} \tag{4-123}$$

should be $(\delta_1 + \delta_2)$, where δ_1 and δ_2 are the elastic scattering phase shifts in each channel. In Table 4-1, $(\delta_1 + \delta_2)$ is seen to be close to $(\pi + \theta)$, where θ is the exact phase. The quoted results (from Erskine and Massey, 1952) were determined using variational rather than exact functions for L(r) and H(r) so that they may misrepresent the distorted wave method to some extent, and, except at the lowest energies, the agreement between the approximate and exact results is not very close.

A variational method

It is also interesting to see how effective the Schwinger variational method is for an inelastic collision with a polynomial wave function of the kind that was used in the single channel example in Section 2-1. In the Schwinger method the coupled equations are written as integral equations. Two solutions $F_i^{A,B}(r)$ are defined as

$$\begin{aligned} F_i^A(r) &= \phi_i^A + \sum_{j=1}^{2}\int_0^\infty G_i(r,r')V_{ij}(r')F_j^A(r')dr', \quad i = 1,2 \\ F_i^B(r) &= \phi_i^B + \sum_{j=1}^{2}\int_0^\infty G_i^*(r,r')V_{ij}(r')F_j^B(r')dr', \quad i = 1,2 \end{aligned} \tag{4-124}$$

where

$$\Phi_i^A = \delta_{i1} k_i^{-1} \sin k_i r, \qquad i = 1,2$$

$$\Phi_i^B = \delta_{i2} k_i^{-1} \sin k_i r \qquad i = 1,2$$

and

$$G_i(r,r') = -k_i^{-1} \sin k_i r_< \exp(ik_i r_>)$$

The solution F_i^A has an incident plane wave in channel 1 and outgoing spherical waves in both channels and F_i^B has an incident plane wave in channel 2, and incoming spherical waves in both channels.

It is straightforward to show that

$$\left(\frac{k_1}{k_2{}^3}\right)^{\frac{1}{2}} T_{12} = R = S = Y, \tag{4-125}$$

where

$$R \equiv \sum_{ij} \int_0^\infty \phi_i^{B^*}(r) V_{ij}(r) F_j^A(r)\, dr,$$

$$S \equiv \sum_{ij} \int_0^\infty F_i^{B^*}(r) V_{ij}(r) \phi_j^A(r)\, dr, \tag{4-126}$$

$$Y \equiv \sum_{ijk} \int_0^\infty \int_0^\infty F_i^{B^*}(r) V_{ij}(r) [\delta(r-r')\delta_{jk} - G_j(r,r') V_{jk}(r')] \times$$

$$\times F_k^A(r')\, dr\, dr'.$$

The expression

$$\left(\frac{k_1}{k_2{}^3}\right)^{\frac{1}{2}} T_{12} = RSY^{-1}$$

is stationary with respect to variations in the functions F_i^A and F_i^B, if trial functions are taken of the form

$$F_i^A(r) = \sum_{n=1}^{N} c_{i,n}^A r^n, \qquad i = 1,2 \tag{4-127a}$$

$$F_i^B(r) = \sum_{n=1}^{N} C_{i,n}^B r^n, \qquad i = 1,2 \tag{4-127b}$$

The constants $C_{i,n}^{A,B}$ are found from the equations

$$\frac{\partial R}{\partial C^A_{i,n}} + \frac{\partial S}{\partial C^A_{i,n}} = \frac{\partial Y}{\partial C^A_{i,n}} \qquad i = 1,2;\ n = 1,2,..N. \tag{4-128}$$

and similar equations for $C_{i,n}^B$. The calculated cross sections are shown in Table 4-1 for the cases with N = 1,2,3. The convergence is rather good in this particular case. Another variational method due to Massey and Moiseiwitsch (1953) with trial functions similar to those of the one channel case given in equation (2-15) is less successful in this example.

4-5 MANY CHANNEL SCATTERING, RESONANT STATES AND EFFECTIVE RANGE EXPANSIONS

Should one of the eigenphase shifts increase rapidly through $\pi/2$ as the energy increases, each matrix element of the K matrix, and also of the T matrix, will possess a pole which will induce a peak in the partial cross sections. As for single channel scattering, discussed earlier, this behavior can be interpreted as being due to the formation of a metastable or resonant state. If the pole in the T matrix is near the real energy axis, the width of the resonance is small and the mean life of the resonant state is long compared with the natural collision time.

If E_R is an energy for which $\Delta_n^\ell = \pi/2$, then for E in the neighbourhood of E_R,

$$\tan \Delta_n^\ell = \frac{\Gamma}{E_R - E} + A(E), \tag{4-129}$$

where

$$\Gamma^{-1} = \left.\frac{\partial \Delta_n^\ell}{\partial E}\right|_{E=E_R}$$

and A(E) is a slowly varying function of E. At $E = E_R$,

all the elements of the reaction matrix possess a pole on the real energy axis. The corresponding pole in the transition matrix is at a complex value of E. If just one eigenphase, Δ_n^ℓ, is resonant and if the elements R_{mi} of the orthogonal matrix R are slowly varying with energy, then near $E = E_R$, $\mathcal{T}$ can be expressed as

$$T_{mi}^{\ell}(E) = R_{nm}R_{ni}\exp(2i\phi)\frac{\gamma}{(E_R' - E) - i\gamma/2}+\mathcal{T}_{mi}^{\ell}(E), \quad (4\text{-}130)$$

where $\mathcal{T}_{mi}^{\ell}(E)$ is a slowly varying background, and E_R' differs from E_R by a level shift ε. The background amplitude is given by:

$$\mathcal{T}_{mi}^{\ell} = \left[R_{nm}R_{ni}\sin\phi + \sum_{q\neq n} R_{qm}R_{qi}e^{i\Delta_q^{\ell}}\sin\Delta_q^{\ell}\right] \quad (4\text{-}131)$$

The width γ, the level shift $\varepsilon \equiv E_R' - E_R$, and the phase are related to Γ and $A(E)$ by the equations,

$$\gamma(E) = \frac{2\Gamma}{1 + A^2}, \quad \varepsilon = \frac{A\Gamma}{1 + A^2}, \exp(2i\phi) = \frac{(1 + iA)^2}{1 + A^2} \quad (4\text{-}132)$$

It is customary to introduce, instead of the matrix elements R_{nm} and R_{ni} partial widths γ_m and γ_i through the definitions,

$$\frac{\gamma_m}{\gamma} = \left(R_{nm}\right)^2$$
$$\frac{\gamma_i}{\gamma} = \left(R_{ni}\right)^2 \quad (4\text{-}133)$$

Because of the orthogonality of R, the partial widths have the property

$$\Sigma_m \gamma_m = \gamma, \quad (4\text{-}134)$$

where the sum extends over all the open channels. Following the discussion in Chapter 1, $\tau=(\hbar/\gamma)$ is the mean lifetime of the metastable state and the quantities $\tau_m=(\hbar/\gamma_m)$ are the lifetimes for decay into the channel m. All the partial widths must be positive.

Since the eigenphases Δ_q do not cross each other as a function of energy, near a resonance several or all the eigenphases may increase sharply through an angle π[9], a suitable parameterization of the T-matrix is then

$$T^{\ell}_{mi}(E) = \mathcal{T}^{\ell}_{mi}(E) + \sum_{jk}\left[\mathcal{S}^{\ell}(E)^{\frac{1}{2}}\right]_{mj} \gamma_j^{\frac{1}{2}}\left[\frac{1}{(E_R{}'-E)-i\gamma/2}\right]\gamma_k^{\frac{1}{2}}\left[\mathcal{S}^{\ell}(E)^{\frac{1}{2}}\right]_{ki}$$

where, as before, $\mathcal{T}^{\ell}(E)$ is the background T-matrix in the absence of the resonance and $\mathcal{S}^{\ell}(E)$ is the corresponding background S-matrix

$$\mathcal{S}^{\ell}(E)_{ij} = 2i\ \mathcal{T}^{\ell}(E)_{ij} + \delta_{ij}.$$

The partial widths γ_j satisfy the property (4-134) and determine the strength of the coupling between the resonant state and each of the open channels j.

Threshold behavior and effective range formulae

By introducing the free particle Green's functions $g^{\ell+}(r,r')$, see (1-53) equations (4-104) can be expressed as integral equations, from which it is easy, following the methods outlined in Chapter 1 to show that

$$T^{\ell}_{mi} = -\left(\frac{\omega_m}{\omega_i}\right)\sum_n \int_0^{\infty} s_{\ell}(k_m r)U_{mn}(r)f_{ni}(\ell,r)dr \qquad (4\text{-}136)$$

where $f_{ni}(\ell,r)$ satisfies the boundary condition (4-103), and that

$$K^{\ell}_{mi} = -\left(\frac{\omega_m}{\omega_i}\right)\sum_n \int_0^{\infty} s_{\ell}(k_m r)U_{mn}(r)f_{ni}(\ell,r)dr \qquad (4\text{-}137)$$

where $f_{ni}(\ell,r)$ now satisfies the boundary condition (4-105). In the realistic case, in which the target has structure, the angular momentum ℓ is different in each channel. In this case the coupled equations take the same form as (4-104) with ℓ_m the angular momentum in channel m, replacing ℓ on the left hand side. The $\mathcal{T}$ or $\mathcal{K}$ matrices are diagonal in the total angular momentum L, and the generalization of (4-137) is

$$K^{L}_{mi} = -\left(\frac{\omega_m}{\omega_i}\right)\sum_n \int_0^{\infty} s_{\ell_m}(k_m r)U_{mn}(r)f_{ni}(\ell_n,r)dr \qquad (4\text{-}138)$$

To discuss the behavior of K^L_{mi} near the threshold for the reaction $i \to m$, as we argued in the case of single channel scattering, it is sufficient to examine the Born approximation. This consists of replacing $f_{mi}(\ell_m, r)$ by the unperturbed wave function

$$\delta_{im} k^{-1} s_{\ell_i}(k_i r).$$

Then

$$K^L_{mi} = -\frac{1}{k_i}\left(\frac{\omega_m}{\omega_i}\right)\int_0^\infty s_{\ell_m}(k_m r)\, s_{\ell i}(k_i r) V_{mi}(r)\,dr$$

$$= -\left(\frac{\mu_i}{\mu_j k_i k_j}\right)^{\frac{1}{2}}\int_0^\infty s_{\ell_m}(k_m r)\, s_{\ell_i}(k_i r) V_{mi}(r)\,dr \qquad (4\text{-}139)$$

Since $k^{-\ell} s_\ell(kr)$ is an entire analytic function of k^2, it follows that K^L_{mi} and T^L_{mi} possess square root branch points at each threshold. If the potentials V_{mi} are of short range, K^L_{mi} will possess the cuts along the negative real E axis due to the potential (discussed in Chapter 1 for the single channel case), and poles on the real axis due to the bound states and resonances[10]. The branch cut at each threshold can be removed by introducing a new matrix, M, by the relation (Ross and Shaw, 1961)

$$M(E) = \kappa^{\ell+\frac{1}{2}}(K^L)^{-1}\kappa^{\ell+\frac{1}{2}} \qquad (4\text{-}140)$$

where $\kappa^{\ell+\frac{1}{2}}$ represents a diagonal matrix with elements

$$\left(\kappa^{\ell+\frac{1}{2}}\right)_{mi} = \delta_{mi} k_i^{\ell_i + \frac{1}{2}} \qquad (4\text{-}141)$$

The M matrix is analytic about each threshold and so may be expanded as a power series in E about a threshold at $E = E_o$.

$$M(E) = M(E_o) + \frac{1}{2} R_o (E - E_o) + \dots\dots \qquad (4\text{-}142)$$

This is the analogue of the single channel effective range series and R_o is an effective range matrix. When only a single channel is open this reduces to the usual effective range formula for $M = k^{2\ell+1} \cot \delta_\ell$.

The branch points in the amplitude at the thresholds induce cusps into the partial cross sections, which in practice are usually not sufficiently large to be observed. There is a considerable literature on the threshold behavior of the cross sections which may be traced from the papers of Newton (1959), Baz (1959), Fonda (1961a,b) and Delves (1958a,

Continuation of the reaction matrix below open threshold

Using the analyticity of $M(E)$, the reaction matrix may b continued below one or more of the open thresholds. We shall treat the case of s-waves ($\ell=0$), although the theory is easil generalized to any ℓ. Suppose that at a certain energy N channels are open and the $N \times N$ K matrix is defined by imposi the boundary conditions (4-105) on the radial wave functions. If the energy is now set to a value below the threshold of channel m,the highest of the N thresholds, the wave function in channel m becomes in the asymptotic region

$$f_{mi}(r) \sim |k_m|^{-1}\left(\sinh(|k_m|r) + K_{mi}\left(\frac{\omega_i}{\omega_m}\right)\cosh(|k_m|r)\right) \quad (4\text{-}143)$$

This form may be contrasted with that applying in all the closed channels (with $M > N$). In that case the closed channel wave functions decrease exponentially like $\exp(-|k_m|r$ and are not smooth continuations of open channel functions. The continued matrix K_{mi} is still of dimension $N \times N$ although there are now only $(N - 1)$ channels open. It is a Hermitian matrix, but the matrix elements are no longer real.

The continuation below the thresholds can be carried out until one of the branch points associated with the potent is encountered. For example, if the interaction V_{mi} is proportional to $\exp(-\lambda r)$ then terms like $\exp\{|k|r - \lambda r\}$ occur in the wave function, and when $|k|$ is reduced to the value $(\lambda/2)$, the asymptotic wave function will cease to have the form (4-143) and at this energy K_{mi} will possess a branch point. If we continue below n of the original N open channel a new matrix of dimension $M = N - n$ may be defined by equatio (4-105). This matrix will be denoted by K^M and called the reduced K-matrix. The original K matrix, of dimensions $N \times N$ continued into the same region will be denoted by K^N. To relate the two matrices, we partition K^N by

$$K^N = \begin{pmatrix} K^{MM}, K^{Mn} \\ K^{nM}, K^{nn} \end{pmatrix} \quad (4\text{-}144)$$

where $\mathcal{K}^{RS}$ denotes a matrix of dimensions R x S. The connection is obtained by observing that the transition matrix for the M open channels must have the same value whether computed from $\mathcal{K}^{N}$ or $\bar{\mathcal{K}}^{M}$. It follows that

$$\bar{\mathcal{K}}^{M} = \mathcal{K}^{MM} + i\mathcal{K}^{Mn} \frac{1}{1 - i\mathcal{K}^{nn}} \mathcal{K}^{nM} \tag{4-145}$$

This relation is obvious for two channels, and a general proof may be given by expanding the transition matrix in powers of $\mathcal{K}$ (Dalitz, 1961).

Poles in the reduced matrix $\bar{\mathcal{K}}^{M}$ on the real axis give rise to poles in $\mathcal{T}$ which are observed, as we have seen, as resonances in the cross section. A pole in $\bar{\mathcal{K}}^{M}$ may be due to a pole in the original reaction matrix $\mathcal{K}^{N}$, in which case each element of $\mathcal{K}^{N}$ is a rapidly varying function of energy. Alternatively, if the condition

$$\det\left|1 - i\mathcal{K}^{nn}\right| = 0, \tag{4-146}$$

is satisfied at a particular energy, a pole will appear in $\bar{\mathcal{K}}^{M}$ without any element of the original matrix $\mathcal{K}^{N}$ exhibiting a rapid variation with energy. If there were no coupling to other channels, the energies for which (4-146) is satisfied would be the energies of the real bound states of the n closed channel system, since at these energies the exponentially increasing part of the wave function vanishes and the wave function for the n coupled closed channels is normalizable. When the coupling is switched on, the poles in the transition matrix move off the real energy axis and the resonances produced are said to be due to 'virtual bound states'.

It is interesting to examine the analytic structure of the $\mathcal{S}$ matrix as a function of k rather than of E. If there are just two channels labeled 1 and 2, then

$$k_1^{\,2} = k_2^{\,2} + \alpha \quad (\alpha > 0), \tag{4-147}$$

where α is a constant. Each matrix element of $\mathcal{S}$ can be considered either as a function of k_1 or of k_2. As a function of k_1, there will be branch points on the real axis at $k_1 = \pm\sqrt{\alpha}$, which may be joined by a branch cut as shown in Fig. 4-1. As a function of k_2, the branch points will be on the imaginary axis from $-i\sqrt{\alpha}$ to $+i\sqrt{\alpha}$. If the two channels were decoupled ($S_{12} = S_{21} = 0$), the bound state poles in $S_{22}(k_2)$ would lie on the imaginary k_2 axis ($\mathrm{Im}\,k_2 > 0$),

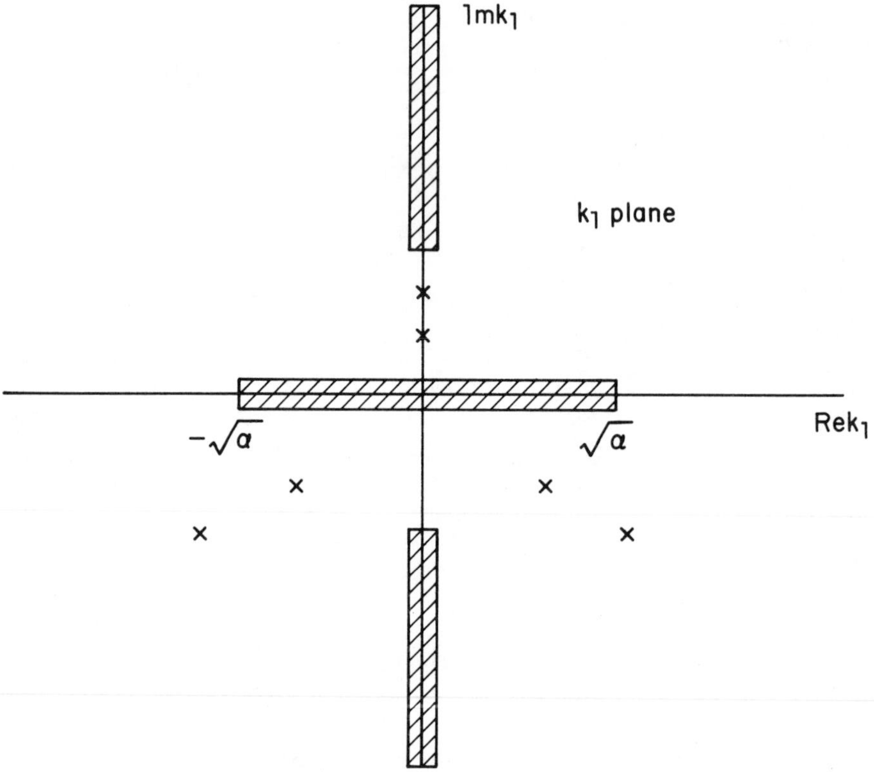

Figure 4-1 The structure of the S matrix when there are two open channels.

or correspondingly as a function of k_1 on the real k_1 axis between $\pm\sqrt{\alpha}$, on the cut. When the coupling is switched on, these poles will migrate from the real k_1 axis into the lower half k_1 plane, giving rise to resonances. This phenomena is of great importance in the theory of electron atom collisions and we shall encounter several examples in the following chapters. Ross and Shaw (1961) have made an interesting numerical study of the case of two coupled channels with square well potentials, and they have shown in detail how the various effects we have discussed vary with potential range and strength and they have discussed the limits of usefulness of the effective range expansion of the M matrix. In particular they have given arguments that suggest that the diagonal elements of R_0 the effective range matrix are much more important than the off-diagonal elements, which may often be neglected.

4-6 THE THREE BODY PROBLEM AND THE FADDEEV EQUATIONS

In the following chapters it will be shown that many practical approximations for treating many-body scattering problems can be based on the variational method, or on the truncation of infinite sets of coupled equations, such as equations (4-104). For many purposes, it would be desirable to attempt to solve the integral equations for the transition matrix or for the Green's functions directly, and we saw in Chapters 1 and 2 that this could be done rather easily in the case of potential scattering, because the equations were of Fredholm form, which implies, among other things, that numerical solutions can be obtained by approximating the integration by a sum, and solving the resulting simultaneous linear equations by matrix inversion. As we shall see, in the many-body case the situation is not straightforward, because the kernels of the integral equations are highly singular, and not of Fredholm form. These difficulties appear first in the three-body system, which we shall study as the prototype of many-body scattering. Among the scattering processes that can occur between three particles are those in which two particles interact together, while the third particle passes undisturbed. In momentum space, this physical situation is represented by the presence of delta functions in the kernel of the equation, showing that the momentum of the unscattered particle is conserved. These terms are illustrated by Fig. 4-2, which represents a kernel of the form $\delta(\vec{k}_1 - \vec{k}_1')K(\vec{k}_2,\vec{k}_3;\ \vec{k}'_2,\ \vec{k}'_3)$. In the diagram the blob represents the interaction between the pair of particles

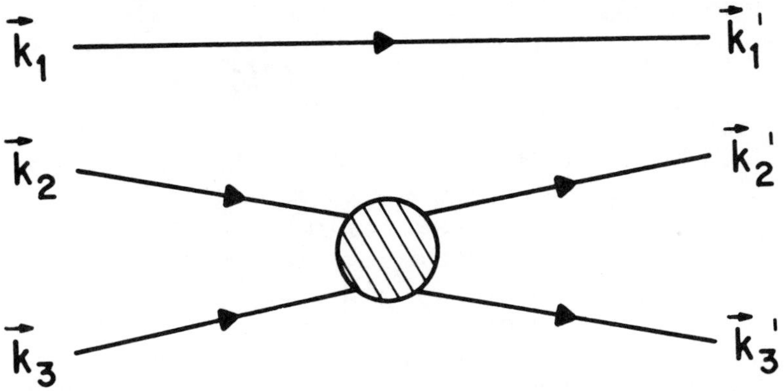

Figure 4-2.

(2 + 3), while the straight line with no blob represents the non-interacting particle 1. A kernel, for which the corresponding diagram contains lines that have no blobs representing interactions, is said to be disconnected.

Before we can see how disconnected terms arise and the difficulties associated with them, it is necessary to introduce some notation. We shall consider a system of three spinless particles, 1, 2 and 3, with masses m_1, m_2 and m_3 and position vectors $\vec{r}_1$, $\vec{r}_2$ and $\vec{r}_3$ respectively, and the interaction between particles i and j will be denoted by V_{ij}. The momentum of particle i will be denoted by $\hbar\vec{k}_i$, and we shall work in the center of mass system in which

$$\vec{k}_1 + \vec{k}_2 + \vec{k}_3 = 0 \tag{4-148}$$

As only two of the momenta $\vec{k}_1$, $\vec{k}_2$ and $\vec{k}_3$ are independent, it is more convenient to introduce momentum coordinates $(\vec{p}_1, \vec{q}_1)$ defined by

$$\vec{p}_1 = \frac{1}{(m_2 + m_3)} (m_3\vec{k}_2 - m_2\vec{k}_3),$$

$$q_1 = \frac{1}{(m_1 + m_2 + m_3)} \{m_1(\vec{k}_2 + \vec{k}_3) - (m_2 + m_3)\vec{k}_1\} \tag{4-149a}$$

The momentum $\vec{p}_1$ is the center of mass momentum in the two particle sub-system (2 + 3), while $\vec{q}_1$ is the momentum of particle 1 relative to the center of mass of the (2 + 3) sub-system. The momenta $\vec{p}_1$ and $\vec{q}_1$ are conjugate to the center of mass coordinates $\vec{S}_1$ and $\vec{R}_1$, where

$$\vec{S}_1 = \vec{r}_2 - \vec{r}_3,$$

$$\vec{R}_1 = -\vec{r}_1 + \frac{1}{(m_2 + m_3)} (m_2\vec{r}_2 + m_3\vec{r}_3). \tag{4-149b}$$

The vector $\vec{S}_1$ is the relative position vector of the particles in the sub-system (2 + 3), while $\vec{R}_1$ is the position vector of 1 with respect to the center of mass of (2 + 3).

Plainly, alternative sets of momenta can be introduced, $(\vec{p}_2,\vec{q}_2)$ or $(\vec{p}_3,\vec{q}_3)$, in which $\vec{p}_2$ is the center of mass momentum in the sub-system (1 + 3), and $\vec{q}_2$ is the relative momentum of 2 with respect to the center of mass of (1 + 3), while $\vec{p}_3$ is the center of mass momentum in the sub-system (1 + 2) and $\vec{q}_3$ is the relative momentum of particle 3 with respect to this sub-system. In the same way, corresponding center of mass coordinates $(\vec{S}_2, \vec{R}_2)$, $(\vec{S}_3, \vec{R}_3)$, can be defined.

Expressions for $(\vec{p}_i, \vec{q}_i), (\vec{S}_i, \vec{R}_i)$ can be obtained from equations (4-149a,b) by cyclic permutation of the suffices 1, 2 and 3.

The three sets of momenta are linearly dependent and we can transform from one set to another using the equations

$$\vec{p}_i = \lambda_{ij}\vec{p}_j + \eta_{ij}\vec{q}_j,$$

$$\vec{q}_i = \bar{\lambda}_{ij}\vec{p}_j + \bar{\eta}_{ij}\vec{q}_j. \tag{4-150}$$

We shall not stop to tabulate the coefficients λ_{ij}, $\bar{\lambda}_{ij}$, $\bar{\eta}_{ij}$ and η_{ij} which depend only on the masses m_i and which can be obtained easily by the reader.

In forming integral equations, we shall often require several independent sets of momenta. We shall use the convention that sets of momenta with different numbers of primes attached will be independent of one another. That is to say that the three sets of momenta $(\vec{p}_i, \vec{q}_i)$, $i = 1,2,3$ will be linearly dependent, but will be independent of the three sets $(\vec{q}'_i, \vec{p}'_i)$, and so on.

Having disposed of these somewhat lengthy notational problems, we can examine the matrix elements of the kinetic and potential energy operators in the basis of the plane wave states $|\vec{p}_i, \vec{q}_i)$. We shall adopt the normalization

$$(\vec{p}_i{}', \vec{q}_i{}' | \vec{p}_i, \vec{q}_i) = \delta(\vec{p}_i{}' - \vec{p}_i)\, \delta(\vec{q}_i{}' - \vec{q}_i) \tag{4-151}$$

The kinetic energy operator K is diagonal in each of the three sets of momenta and we have

$$(\vec{p}_i, \vec{q}_i | K | \vec{p}_i{}', \vec{q}_i{}') = \left(\frac{\hbar^2}{2M_i} p_i{}^2 + \frac{\hbar^2}{2\mu_i} q_i{}^2\right) \delta(\vec{p}_i - \vec{p}_i{}')\, \delta(\vec{q}_i - \vec{q}_i{}'), \tag{4-152}$$

where the reduced masses M_i and μ_i are defined by

$$M_i = \frac{m_j m_k}{(m_j + m_k)},$$

$$\mu_i = \frac{m_i(m_j + m_k)}{m_i + m_j + m_k}, \qquad i = 1,2,3;\ i \neq j \neq k \tag{4-153}$$

The two body potential $V_{ij}(\vec{S}_k)$, $i \neq j \neq k$, is diagonal in the momentum $\vec{q}_k$, and the matrix element of V_{ij} in the basis $|\vec{p}_k,\vec{q}_k)$ is given by

$$(\vec{p}_k,\vec{q}_k|V_{ij}|\vec{p}_k{}',\vec{q}_k{}')$$

$$= (2\pi)^{-6}\int d^3R_k \int d^3S_k \exp\left(-i(\vec{p}_k\cdot\vec{S}_k + \vec{q}_k\cdot\vec{R}_k)\right) \times$$

$$\times V_{ij}(\vec{S}_k)\exp\left(i(\vec{p}_k{}'\cdot\vec{S}_k + \vec{q}_k{}'\cdot\vec{R}_k)\right)$$

$$= \delta(\vec{q}_k-\vec{q}_k{}')\ v_{ij}\ (\vec{p}_k{}' - \vec{p}_k) \tag{4-154}$$

where v_{ij} is the Fourier transform of the potential

$$v_{ij}(\vec{p}) = (2\pi)^{-3}\int d^3\vec{x}V_{ij}(\vec{x})\exp(i\vec{k}\cdot\vec{x}). \tag{4-155}$$

The Green's function

The complete Green's function for the system, G^+, defined by

$$G^+(E) = (E + i\varepsilon - K - V_{12} - V_{23} - V_{31})^{-1} \tag{4-156}$$

satisfies integral equations of the general form (4-39). In particular, if in (4-39) we set V_γ equal to the complete interaction, and G^+_γ equal to $G_0{}^+$, the free particle Green's function, it is found that G^+ satisfies the equation

$$G^+ = G_0{}^+ + G_0{}^+(V_{12} + V_{23} + V_{31})G^+, \tag{4-157}$$

where $G_0{}^+$ is, as usual, defined as

$$G_0{}^+(E) = (E + i\varepsilon - K)^{-1}. \tag{4-158}$$

The formal solution of equation (4-157) is

$$G^+(E) = RG_0(E), \tag{4-159}$$

where the resolvent R is the operator

$$R = [1 - G_o^+(V_{12} + V_{23} + V_{31})]^{-1}. \tag{4-160}$$

If we wished to construct R using Fredholm's theory, we would have to consider the determinant

$$D(E) = \det|1 - G_o^+(V_{12} + V_{23} + V_{31})|, \tag{4-161}$$

and for this to exist $\mathrm{Tr}\{G_o^+(V_{12} + V_{23} + V_{31})\}$ must be finite. The matrix element of $(G_o^+V_{23})$ is, using (4-152) and (4-154),

$$(\vec{p}_1,\vec{q}_1|G_o^+V_{23}|\vec{p}'_1,\vec{q}'_1) = \left(E + i\varepsilon - \frac{p_1^2}{2M_1} - \frac{q_1^2}{2\mu_1}\right)^{-1} V_{23}(\vec{p}_1 - \vec{p}'_1) \times$$

$$\times\ \delta(\vec{q}_1 - \vec{q}'_1). \tag{4-162}$$

Because of the presence of the delta function $\delta(\vec{q}_1 - \vec{q}'_1)$ the trace of this term does not exist. In the same way the traces of each of the terms $(G_o^+V_{12})$ and $(G_o^+V_{13})$, are also divergent, and it follows that Fredholm's theory cannot be applied directly to the kernel $\{G_o^+(V_{12} + V_{23} + V_{31})\}$.

The Born series

The presence of disconnected terms in the kernel also causes difficulties in the discussion of the Born series for rearrangement collisions[11]. If we consider a transition between an initial state ϕ_1 in which free particle 1 moves with respect to a bound state of the sub-system (2 + 3) and a final state ϕ_3, in which particle 3 moves with respect to a bound state of the sub-system (1 + 2), the transition matrix T_{31} is given, using (4-38), by

$$T_{31} = B_{31} + (\phi_3|(V_{31} + V_{32})G^+(V_{12} + V_{13})|\phi_1), \tag{4-163}$$

where B_{31} is the first Born approximation to the transition matrix

$$B_{31} = (\phi_3|(V_{31} + V_{32})|\phi_1). \tag{4-164}$$

By introducing a complete set of plane wave intermediate states, T_{31} can be written as

$$T_{31} = B_{31} + \int d^3\vec{p}_1 \int d^3\vec{p}'_1 \int d^3\vec{q}_1 \int d^3\vec{q}'_1 (\phi_3|(V_{31} + V_{32})|\vec{p}_1,\vec{q}_1)$$

$$\times (\vec{p}_1,\vec{q}_1|G^+|\vec{p}'_1,\vec{q}'_1)(\vec{p}'_1,\vec{q}'_1|(V_{12} + V_{13})|\phi_1). \qquad (4\text{-}165)$$

Because ϕ_3 and ϕ_1 contain bound states of the (1 + 2) and (2 + 3) sub-systems respectively, there is no restriction on the values of the momenta in the intermediate states and the integrations in (4-165) are over all values of $\vec{p}_1$, $\vec{p}'_1$, $\vec{q}_1$ and $\vec{q}'_1$.

Now the Born series for G^+ is obtained by iterating the integral equation (4-157). It is

$$G^+ = G_o^+ + G_o^+(V_{12} + V_{23} + V_{31})G_o^+ +$$
$$+G_o^+(V_{12} + V_{23} + V_{31})G_o^+(V_{12} + V_{23} + V_{31})G_o^+ + \ldots, \qquad (4\text{-}166)$$

and by inserting this series into (4-163) the Born series for the transition matrix is obtained.

As a consequence of the disconnected nature of the kernel of the integral equation for G^+, among the various sub-series in (4-166) are those that represent successive scattering by one potential only. For example the sub-series containing V_{23} is

$$\{G_o^+ + G_o^+V_{23}G_o^+ + G_o^+V_{23}G_o^+V_{23}G_o^+ + \ldots\ldots\}$$

This series can be summed formally, and denoting the sum by $G_1^+(E)$, we have

$$G_1^+(E) = (E + i\varepsilon - K - V_{23})^{-1}. \qquad (4\text{-}168)$$

This is a three-body Green's operator for a system in which the only potential acting is that between particles (2 + 3).

The matrix element of G_1^+ in the basis $|\vec{p}_1, \vec{q}_1)$ is diagonal in $\vec{q}_1$ and we can write, using (4-152) and (4-154),

$$(\vec{p}_1,\vec{q}_1|G_1^+|\vec{p}'_1,\vec{q}'_1) = \delta(\vec{q}_1-\vec{q}'_1)(\vec{p}_1|g_1^+\left(E - \frac{q'^2_1}{2\mu_1}\right)|\vec{p}'_1) \qquad (4\text{-}169)$$

where $g_1^+(z)$ is defined as

$$g_1^+(z) = (z + i\varepsilon - K_{23} - V_{23})^{-1}, \qquad (4\text{-}170)$$

and where K_{23} is the kinetic energy operator associated with the particles 2 and 3 in their center of mass system. The matrix element of K_{23} is

$$(\vec{p}_1|K_{23}|\vec{p}'_1) = \delta(\vec{p}_1 - \vec{p}'_1)\left(\frac{p_1^2}{2M_1}\right)$$

The Green's function $g_1^+(z)$ operates in the two particle sub-space (2 + 3) only, and is the Green's function appropriate to the scattering of a single particle by the potential V_{23}, which was discussed extensively in Chapter 1. In particular, we know that $g_1^+(z)$ has a pole at $z = E_B$ where E_B is the binding energy of the bound system (2 + 3). Because of this pole the Born expansion of $g_1^+(z)$ certainly diverges for z in the range $|z| < |E_B|$. As the $|\vec{q}'|$ integration in (4-165) is over the range $0 \leq |\vec{q}'_1| \leq \infty$, for each energy E there will be a range of $|\vec{q}'_1|$ for which $0 < |E - (\vec{q}'_1)^2/2\mu_1| < |E_B|$ and it follows that in this interval the expansion of $g^+(z)$ diverges and that the sub-series (4-167) in G^+ also diverges.

As all the remaining terms in the expansion of G^+ involve V_{12} or V_{31} these terms cannot compensate, in general, for the divergence in the sub-series in V_{23}. It follows that the expansion of G^+ necessarily diverges at all energies E, for some ranges of the variables $\vec{p}_1$, $\vec{q}_1$, $\vec{p}'_1$, $\vec{q}'_1$. The divergence of the expansion of G^+ makes the convergence of the series for the transition matrix doubtful. Little is known about the convergence of the Born series for the transition matrix, but Dettmann and Leibfried (1969) and subsequently Shakeshaft and Spruch (1979), in an important paper, were able to demonstrate in the case of a wide class of potentials that the energy variation of T_{31} is given correctly at sufficiently large energies, by the first two terms of the Born series. It is not clear whether the series itself converges at high energies, or whether it is an asymptotic (semi-convergent) series, but it is clear that except for special values of the masses the use of the first Born approximation is unjustified in the case of rearrangement collision at any energy.

Removal of disconnected terms

The poor properties of the integral equation (4-157) for G^+ arise from terms in an expansion, such as (4-166) in which only one potential operates. These sub-series can be formally summed as in the expression for G_1^+ (4-168). The Green's function G_1^+ and the corresponding operators

G_2^+ and G_2^+ can be defined as

$$G_i^+(E) = (E + i\varepsilon - K - V_{jk})^{-1}, \quad i \neq j \neq k. \tag{4-171}$$

In the three-body system, these operators are identical with those introduced earlier in this chapter, by equation (4-12). It is straightforward to verify that G_i^+ satisfies integral equations of the standard type:

$$G_i^+ = G_o^+(1 + V_{jk}G_i^+) = (1 + G_i^+V_{jk})G_o^+, \quad i \neq j \neq k. \tag{4-172}$$

The general method for finding an integral equation for the three-body problem that has a connected kernel, is to make use of the fact that the operators G_i^+ can be constructed exactly, by the methods developed for potential scattering and described in Chapters 1 and 2, to eliminate all the divergent sub-series in expansions like (4-166).

Let us first examine in more detail the problem of scattering in which a potential acts between one pair of particles only. The Green's function $g_1^+(z)$, for potential scattering between particles 2 and 3 in their center of mass system, has been introduced in (4-170). In the same way $g_2^+(z)$ and $g_3^+(z)$ describing the interaction of particles (1 + 3) and (1 + 2) can be defined, by

$$g_i^+(z) = (z + i\varepsilon - K_{jk} - V_{jk})^{-1}, \quad i \neq j \neq k. \tag{4-173}$$

The corresponding two-body transition operators $t_i(z)$ can be introduced as

$$t_i(z) = V_{jk} + V_{jk}g_i^+(z)V_{jk}, \qquad i \neq j \neq k. \tag{4-174}$$

We shall suppose the three two-body problems have been solved and that the $t_i(z)$ and their matrix elements $(\vec{p}_i|t_i(z)|\vec{p}'_i)$ are known exactly.

To calculate the scattering amplitude for potential scattering, we must satisfy the conservation of energy condition

$$\frac{p_i^2}{2M_i} = \frac{p'^2_i}{2M_i} = z$$

When this condition is satisfied $(\vec{p}_i|t_i(z)|\vec{p}'_i)$ is said to be 'on the energy shell'. In the applications that follow, we require this matrix element for independent values $\vec{p}_i, \vec{p}'_i$ and z is not constrained by the conservation of energy condition, and in this case $(\vec{p}_i|t_i(z)|\vec{p}'_i)$ is said to be 'off the energy shell'.

The Green's functions G_i^+, which relate to a three-body system in which only one potential is acting, are now determined by equations typified by (4-169). In general we have

$$(\vec{p}_i,\vec{q}_i|G_i^+(e)|\vec{p}'_i,\vec{q}'_i) = \delta(\vec{q}_i-\vec{q}'_i)(\vec{p}_i|g_i^+(E-q_i^2/2\mu_i)|\vec{p}'_i). \tag{4-175}$$

It is important to notice that the analytic structure of G_i^+ is different from that of g_i^+. At a bound state of the two particle system $g_i^+(z)$ must have a pole, at $z = E_B$, say, but G_i^+ will possess a line of singularities (a branch cut) because the argument of g_i^+ in (4-173) depends on $(E-q_i^2/2\mu_i)$, which is a function of q_i^2. This cut runs over the real energy axis in the interval $E_B \leq E < \infty$, and represents the physical cut associated with the scattering of the third particle by the two-body bound sub-system.

Three transition operators T_i can be associated with the Green's functions G_i by the definitions

$$T_i = V_{jk} + V_{jk}G_i^+(E)V_{jk}, \quad i \neq j \neq k. \tag{4-176}$$

For future reference we note that a slight manipulation of this equation leads to the results

$$\begin{aligned} G_o^+T_i &= G_i^+V_{jk}, \\ T_iG_o^+ &= V_{jk}G_i^+, \end{aligned} \qquad i \neq j \neq k, \tag{4-177}$$

where we have made use of the integral equations (4-172).

The matrix elements of the T_i can be expressed in terms of the two-body transition operators t_i, since

$$(\vec{p}_i,\vec{q}_i|T_i(e)|\vec{p}'_i,\vec{q}'_i) = \delta(\vec{q}_i-\vec{q}'_i)(\vec{p}_i|t_i(E-q_i^2/2\mu_i)|\vec{p}'_i) \tag{4-178}$$

The resolvents R_i of the integral equations satisfied by G_i^+ and T_i^+ are defined as

$$R_i(E) = (1 - G_o^+(E)V_{jk})^{-1}, \; i \neq j \neq k, \tag{4-179}$$

and we have that

$$G_i^+ = G_o^+(1 + V_{jk}G_i^+) = R_iG_o^+,$$
$$i \neq j \neq k \qquad (4\text{-}180)$$
$$T_i = V_{jk} + V_{jk}G_i^+V_{jk} = V_{jk}R_i.$$

These resolvents clearly exist and can be constructed in principle. The Fredholm determinants of the resolvents are non-singular in the two particle sub-spaces in which the potentials V_{jk} act. It should be noted that because the resolvents contain delta functions in $\vec{q}_i$ the Fredholm determinants are not defined in the complete space of the three particles.

The determinantal method

The first method[12] to be discussed is the extension of the determinantal method discussed in Chapter 2. The idea is to introduce two arbitrary operators L and M and to write the resolvent of the three-body system (4-160) as

$$R = L\,[M\{1-G_o^+(V_{12} + V_{23} + V_{31})\}L]^{-1}M \qquad (4\text{-}181)$$

we can then try to choose L and M so that M^{-1} and the determinant D(E) exist, where

$$D(E) \equiv \det(M\{1 - G_o^+(V_{12} + V_{23} + V_{31})\}L). \qquad (4\text{-}182)$$

These conditions ensure that the inverse of the operator $(M\{1 - G_o^+(V_{12} + V_{23} + V_{31}\}L)$ can be constructed, which in turn allows us to construct R through equations (4-181). There are many possible ways in which M and L can be chosen. One possibility is to set

$$L = 1,\ M = (1 + C)(R_1 + R_2 + R_3 - 2), \qquad (4\text{-}183)$$

where C will be chosen in a moment, and the R_i are the resolvents defined by (4-179), which can be calculated in terms of two-body scattering. We then find after a little algebra that

$$M\{1 - G_o^+(V_{12} + V_{23} + V_{31})\}L = (1 + C)(1 - C_o), \qquad (4\text{-}184)$$

where

$$C_0 = G_0^+\{V_{23}R_1G_0^+(V_{12} + V_{31})$$

$$+ V_{31}R_2G_0^+(V_{32} + V_{21}) \qquad (4\text{-}185)$$

$$+ V_{12}R_3G_0^+(V_{23} + V_{31})\}$$

This operator contains no disconnected parts, since different potentials occupy adjacent positions in the kernel, and in a series expansion of C_0 we find no sub-series in which one potential acts alone. These sub-series have in fact already been summed and are represented in the known resolvents R_i. The operator C can now be chosen so that the trace of $(1 + C)(1 - C_0)$ exists. A possible choice is $C = C_0$, and the leading term in the trace is then $Tr(C_0^2)$. As this contains the product of four potentials, it will exist given reasonable behavior at the origin and at infinity.

An application of this method has been made to electron hydrogen atom scattering (Nutt, 1964), and for practical details reference may be made to the original paper.

The Faddeev equations

We shall discuss the approach of Faddeev (1958, 1963), in the form developed by Lovelace (1964). To start we must define transition operators for all the possible reactions that can occur between three particles. The transition operators will be written as $U_{\beta\alpha}(E)$, where the suffix α is 1, when the initial state is in the arrangement in which particle 1 moves with respect to a bound state of sub-system (2 + 3), 2 when particle 2 moves with respect to a bound state of (3 + 1), and 3 when particle 3 moves with respect to a bound state (2 + 1). The suffix β can also take the values 1, 2 or 3 and describes the possible final states in which particles 1, 2 or 3 are free. Reactions can also occur in which all three particles are unbound in either the initial or final state, or both, and these channels will be denoted by setting α or β equal to 0.

The interaction potential in channel γ (cf.4-4,4-5) is denoted by V_γ and is equal to the difference of the complete interaction, $(V_{12} + V_{13} + V_{23})$, and the potential between the pair of bound particles. In channel 0 where no particles are bound the interaction V_0 is equal to the complete interaction.

$$
\begin{aligned}
V_o &= V_{12} + V_{23} + V_{31} \\
V_1 &= V_{12} + V_{13} \\
V_2 &= V_{23} + V_{21} \\
V_3 &= V_{31} + V_{32}
\end{aligned}
\tag{4-186}
$$

The transition operators then satisfy the equations[13] (see 4-38)

$$U_{\beta\alpha}(E) = V_\alpha + V_\beta G^+(E) V_\alpha, \quad \alpha,\beta = 0,1,2,3 \tag{4-187}$$

where $G^+(E)$ can be determined by the integral equations (4-39)

$$G^+ = G_\gamma^{\ +}(1 + V_\gamma G^+) \tag{4-188}$$

and the $G_\gamma^{\ +}$ are defined by (4-171) (see also 4-12). The matrix elements of all these operators are to be taken with respect to sets of plane wave states $|\vec{p}_i,\vec{q}_i)$ as before. To compute the physical transition matrix $T_{12}(E)$ for a reaction in which the initial state is in channel 2 and the final state in channel 1, we need the momentum space wave functions ϕ_{13} and ϕ_{23} of the initial and final bound states of the (2 + 3) and (1 + 3) sub-systems. We then have

$$T_{12}(\vec{q}_1,\vec{q}'_2) = \int d^3p_1 \int d^3\vec{p}'_2 \phi_{23}(\vec{p}_1)(\vec{p}_1,\vec{q}_1|U_{12}(E)|\vec{p}'_2,\vec{q}'_2)\phi_{13}(\vec{p}'_2). \tag{4-189}$$

The primed and unprimed momenta are independent, but for physical scattering the conservation of energy relation must be satisfied,

$$\varepsilon_{23} + \frac{\hbar^2}{2\mu_1} q_1^{\ 2} = \varepsilon_{13} + \frac{\hbar^2}{2\mu_2} q'_2{}^2$$

where ε_{23} and ε_{13} are the binding energies in the (2 + 3) and (3 + 1) sub-systems. The scattering amplitude for any other reaction can be written down in a similar way.

The important step in the Faddeev method is the elimination of the potentials in the kernel of equation (4-187). Taking the equation for $U_{12}(E)$ and writing it in full, we have

$$U_{12} = (V_{23} + V_{21}) + (V_{12} + V_{13})G^+(V_{23} + V_{21}). \qquad (4\text{-}190)$$

In the term containing $V_{12}G^+$, we use the integral equation (4-188) for G^+ with γ set equal to 3 and in the term containing $V_{13}G^+$ we use the same equation, but with γ set equal to 2. We then obtain

$$U_{12} = (V_{23} + V_{21}) + [V_{12}G_3^+ + V_{12}G_3^+(V_{31} + V_{32})G^+ + $$
$$+ V_{13}G_2^+ + V_{13}G_2^+(V_{23} + V_{21})G^+](V_{23} + V_{21}). \qquad (4\text{-}191)$$

On using equations (4-187) we then find that

$$U_{12} = (V_{23} + V_{21}) + V_{12}G_3^+U_{32} + V_{13}G_2^+U_{22}.$$

Looking back at equation (4-177), it is seen that the operators $V_{12}G_3^+$ and $V_{13}G_2^+$ are equal to $T_3G_o^+$ and $T_2G_o^+$ respectively, so we may write finally

$$U_{12} = (V_{23} + V_{21}) + T_3G_o^+U_{32} + T_2G_o^+U_{22}$$
$$= V_2 + \sum_{\gamma=1}^{3}\left(1 - \delta_{1\gamma}\right) T_\gamma G_o^+ U_{\gamma 2}. \qquad (4\text{-}192)$$

Proceeding in the same way, we find generally,

$$U_{\beta\alpha} = V_\alpha + \sum_{\gamma=1}^{3}\left(1 - \delta_{\beta\gamma}\right) T_\gamma G_o^+ U_{\gamma\alpha}. \qquad (4\text{-}193)$$

To include the channels in which all three particles are unbound we write

$$T_o = 0, \qquad (4\text{-}194)$$

and then the suffices α, β and γ can be allowed to take values from 0 to 3, rather than from 1 to 3.

The equations (4-193) are in a form due to Lovelace (1964) and are equivalent to the original equations of Faddeev. It is immediately evident that the kernel of the equations is connected, because on iterating the equation we always obtain terms such as

$$. \; . \; . \; T_\alpha G_o^+ T_\delta G_o^+ \; . \; . \; . \; . \; , \tag{4-195}$$

where $\alpha \neq \delta$ always, and no sub-series exist in which each term contains a momentum conserving delta function. This is because we have solved all the individual two-body scattering problems first, and we do not attempt to expand the operators T_γ, which would reintroduce the disconnected terms.

It is possible to write equations in which the inhomogeneous terms contain the two-body transition operators T_γ rather than the potentials V_γ. To see how this is done, let us concentrate on the three transition matrices $U_{\alpha 2}$ that describe processes in which the initial state is in channel 2, which is the arrangement in which particle 2 moves with respect to a bound state of (1 + 3). Three auxiliary operators $W_{\alpha 2}(E)$ are introduced through the definitions

$$\begin{aligned} W_{12}(E) &= V_{32} + V_{32}G^+(E)(V_{23} + V_{21}) \\ W_{22}(E) &= V_{13}G^+(E)(V_{23} + V_{21}) \\ W_{32}(E) &= V_{12} + V_{12}G^+(E)(V_{23} + V_{21}). \end{aligned} \tag{4-196}$$

From equation (4-190) it is seen that $U_{12}(E)$ can be expressed in terms of the $W_{\beta 2}$ by

$$U_{12}(E) = (V_{23} + V_{12}) + (W_{22} + W_{32} - V_{12}) = V_{23} + W_{22} + W_{32}.$$

Similarly U_{22}, U_{32} and U_{02} are expressed as

$$\begin{aligned} U_{22} &= W_{12} + W_{32} \\ U_{32} &= V_{12} + W_{12} + W_{22} \\ U_{02} &= W_{12} + W_{22} + W_{32} \end{aligned} \tag{4-197}$$

To obtain integral equations for the new quantities $W_{\beta\alpha}$, we have again to use the integral equation (4-188) for G^+, with V_γ defined by (4-186). We have that

$$\begin{aligned} W_{12} &= V_{23} + V_{23}G^+(V_{23} + V_{21}) \\ &= V_{23} + V_{23}\{G_1^+ + G_1^+(V_{12} + V_{13})G^+\}(V_{23} + V_{21}) \\ &= V_{23} + V_{23}G_1^+V_{23} + V_{23}G_1^+(W_{32} + W_{22}). \end{aligned} \tag{4-198}$$

Since, (4-176), (4-177)

$$V_{23} + V_{23}G_1^+V_{23} = T_1. \tag{4-199}$$

and

$$V_{23}G_1^+ = T_1G_o,$$

we find that

$$W_{12} = T_1 + T_1G_o^+(W_{32} + W_{22}). \tag{4-200a}$$

In an exactly similar manner, we find

$$W_{22} = T_2G_o^+(W_{12} + W_{32}), \tag{4-200b}$$

$$W_{32} = T_3 + T_3G_o^+(W_{22} + W_{12}). \tag{4-200c}$$

In general, if the incident channel is channel β, we find

$$W_{\alpha\beta} = T_\alpha\left(1 - \delta_{\alpha\beta}\right) + T_\alpha G_o^+ \sum_{\gamma=1}^{3} \left(1 - \delta_{\alpha\gamma}\right) W_{\gamma\beta}, \tag{4-201}$$

$$\alpha, \beta = 1,2,3.$$

The kernel of these equations is similar to that of equations (4-193) and the iterative solution contains no successive scatterings by the same two-body potential. In principle, the solution of these equations enables us to calculate the transition matrix for all excitation, rearrangement or break-up processes, however the equations are of considerable complexity and in practice some simplifications must be made.

Short range potentials, which support a finite number of bound states, can be represented accurately as the sum of a number of separable potentials. In this case it is possible to construct the off-shell T-matrix for the two-body scatterings explicitly and finally to reduce the Lovelace-Faddeev equations to coupled integral equations in one momentum variable. Numerical solutions can then be obtained. Proceeding in this way, the three-body problem in nuclear physics can be solved from some assumed set of two-body potentials. Unfortunately, this procedure has not been so successful in atomic collisions because of the long range nature of the Coulomb interaction, which spoils the convergence properties of the iterative solution of the equations[14].

NOTES

1. Except where mentioned, the center of mass of coordinates will be used. This implies that the sum of the momentum of the colliding particles with respect to the origin of coordinates (the center of mass) is zero. If a transformation to some other coordinate system were made, an extra factor of exp $(i\,\vec{p}\cdot\vec{R}/\hbar)$ would appear in the wave function where $\vec{R}$ is the position of the center of mass and $\vec{p}$ is the total momentum of the system.

2. A rigorous proof of the unitarity of the S-matrix has been given by Jauch and Marchland (1966).

3. Provided a consistent choice is made, the cross section is independent of the normalization of the wave function. For example, if the continuum wave functions are normalized to unity in a box of volume V, the constant N_m in (4-7) becomes

$$N_m = (V)^{-\frac{1}{2}} \text{ and } (\phi'_m(\gamma)|\phi'_n(\gamma)) = \delta_{mn}\delta_{\vec{k}_n,\vec{k}_m}$$

where the prime denotes claims normalized in this way. The incident flux becomes $F_i = \hbar k_i/(\mu_i V)$ and the sum over final states can be achieved by composing periodic boundary conditions, so if $\rho(\vec{k})$ is the density of states

$$\sum_j{}' \rho(k) \rightarrow (V/(2\pi)^3) \int d^3k_j \text{ and from (4-26, 4-27)}$$

$$\sigma_{ji}(E_i) = \left(\frac{2\pi}{\hbar}\right) (2\pi)^{-3} \int d^3k_j \frac{1}{F_i} \delta(E_i - E_j) |VT'_{ji}(E_i)|^2$$

where T'_{ji} is the transition matrix with wave functions normalized to unity in the box. Since each $\phi'_j = V^{-\frac{1}{2}}\phi_j$ and $\psi_i'^{+} = V^{-\frac{1}{2}}\psi_L^{+}$, we have $VT'_{ji} = T_{ji}$ and the same result (4-28) is obtained as with the normalization adopted in the text.

4. For an introduction to the quantum theory of angular momentum see Merzbacher (1970). More advanced material can be found in the monograph of Edmonds (1960).

5. Some useful relations satisfied by Clebsch-Gordan

coefficients are given in Appendix B.

6. The spin-orbit interaction and its influence on the structure of atoms is discussed in the text of Bransden and Joachain (1982). The relativistic theory of electron scattering by atoms has been reviewed by Walker (1971).

7. Note that the component of the orbital angular momentum in the direction of motion $\vec{k}$ of a plane wave is zero.

8. See Merzbacher (1970) or Bransden and Joachain (1982).

9. See Macek (1970).

10. The angular structure of T^L or K^L can be investigated most easily by examining the Fredholm determinant associated with the set of coupled equations (Newton, 1961).

11. The Born series for rearrangement collisions have been discussed by Shakeshaft and Spruch (1979).

12. This section is based on the work of Sugar and Blankenbecler (1964).

13. We have arbitrarily chosen to work with the operators $U_{\beta\alpha}$ rather than $\bar{U}_{\beta\alpha}$ where $\bar{U}_{\beta\alpha} = V_\beta + V_\beta G^+(E)V_\alpha$. The matrix elements of $U_{\beta\alpha}$ and $\bar{U}_{\beta\alpha}$ are not the same off the energy shell, but the same physical on-shell scattering amplitude is derived from both operators.

14. For an application of the Faddeev method to electron scattering by atomic hydrogen see Ball et al (1968).

PROBLEMS

4.1 Prove equations (4-14) and (4-15), starting from (4-10a) and (4-10b).

4.2 Show that (4-34) follows from (4-15) and (4-19).

4.3 Starting from (4-44) go through the steps that lead to the expression for the Green's function $G_\gamma^\pm$, (4-45).

4.4 Using the properties of the Clebsch-Gordan coefficients given in Appendix B, prove the formula (4-69) for the total cross section starting from the expansion (4-68b).

4.5 Obtain expressions (4-71) and (4-72) for $f(\theta)$ and $g(\theta,\phi)$.

4.6 Show that the amplitude matrix F_{ji} (4-74) can be written as

$$F_{ji} = f(\theta)\delta_{mj,mi} + i\,\bar{g}(\theta)\,(m_j|\vec{\sigma}|m_i)\cdot\vec{n}$$

where σ_i are the Pauli spin matrices and $\vec{n}$ is a unit vector defined as

$$\vec{n} = \vec{k}_i \times \vec{k}_j \,/\, |\vec{k}_i \times \vec{k}_j|$$

4.7 Determine the components p_x, p_y, p_z of the polarization vector (4-87) in terms of the coefficients a and b defined in (4-77).

4.8 Show that if a non-local potential is separable and of the form $V = -\,U(r)U(r')$ then the two-body T-matrix is given by

$$(\vec{p}|t(E)|\vec{p}\,') = J(E)v(p)v(p')$$

where $v(p)$ is the Fourier transform of $v(r)$ and

$$[J(E)]^{-1} = 1 - 2M\int d^3p''\,\frac{[v(p'')]^2}{(p^2-2ME-i\varepsilon)}$$

Chapter 5

SCATTERING OF ELECTRONS BY ATOMS AT LOW ENERGIES

5-1 THE ELASTIC SCATTERING OF ELECTRONS BY HYDROGEN ATOMS

In this chapter, the scattering of electrons which are of energy such that the target atom, assumed to be in the ground state, cannot be excited, will be discussed. Rather than develop the general theory of elastic scattering of electrons by atoms the simple example of electron scattering by the ground state of hydrogen will be studied at first, and the results for some other atoms considered later.

The mass of the electron can be neglected in comparison with the mass of the nucleus of the atom. In this approximation, the laboratory and center of mass systems coincide and the nucleus can be taken as the origin of the coordinate system. In atomic units, (see Appendix A) the Schrödinger equation of a system of two electrons and a proton is

$$L\psi = \left(-\frac{1}{2}\nabla_1{}^2 - \frac{1}{2}\nabla_2{}^2 + V(r_1)+V(r_2)+v(|\vec{r}_1-\vec{r}_2|)-E\right)\psi(\vec{r}_1,\vec{r}_2)=0, \tag{5-1a}$$

where $\vec{r}_1$ and $\vec{r}_2$ are the position vectors of electrons 1 and 2, with respect to the proton. The interactions are purely coulombic since for light atoms spin dependent potentials, such as the spin orbit potential $(\vec{L} \cdot \vec{S})$ are very small and may be neglected.

$$V(r_i) = -1/r_i, \quad v|\vec{r}_1-\vec{r}_2| = 1/|\vec{r}_1-\vec{r}_2| \tag{5-1b}$$

The total spin of the system is conserved, and in the present case, as each electron has spin one-half, the total spin S of the two electron system is given by $S^2 = s(s + 1)\hbar^2$ with s = 0 or s = 1. The state with s = 0 is a singlet state and the corresponding spin wave function, $\chi_{s,m}$ where mh is the Z component of the spin, is

$$\chi_{0,0} = \frac{1}{\sqrt{2}}[\alpha(1)\beta(2) - \alpha(2)\beta(1)], \tag{5-2}$$

where $\alpha(i)$ is the spin wave function of electron i, quantized parallel to the Z axis, (m=1/2) and $\beta(i)$ is the spin wave function quantized anti-parallel to the Z axis, (m= - 1/2).

The state with s=1 is a triplet state and

$$\chi_{1,1} = \alpha(1)\alpha(2),$$

$$\chi_{1,0} = \frac{1}{\sqrt{2}}[\alpha(1)\beta(2) + \beta(1)\alpha(2)],$$

$$\chi_{1,-1} = \beta(1)\beta(2). \tag{5-3}$$

The singlet state is antisymmetrical under the interchange of electrons 1 and 2, while the triplet state is symmetrical.

The Pauli exclusion principle[1] states that the wave function of a system of identical particles of spin one-half must be completely antisymmetrical, and it follows that the spatial part of the wave function $\psi^s(\vec{r}_1,\vec{r}_2)$ must be symmetrical for the singlet state s = 0 and anti-symmetrical for the triplet states s = 1

$$\psi^s(\vec{r}_1,\vec{r}_2) = (-1)^s\psi^s(\vec{r}_2,\vec{r}_1). \tag{5-4}$$

Because the Schrödinger equation (5-1) is symmetrical in 1 and 2, the solutions divide into a symmetrical and an antisymmetrical class and this would remain true even in the absence of the Pauli principle. The symmetry is a constant of the motion and the symmetrical and anti-symmetrical wave functions are orthogonal.

Boundary conditions

If the incident electron has a kinetic energy less than 10.2 ev the hydrogen atom cannot be excited, and at large distances of separation the wave function must become equal to the product of a free electron wave function and the target atom wave function. If electron 1 is incident on the atom we have

$$\psi^s(\vec{r}_1,\vec{r}_2) \xrightarrow[r_1 \to \infty]{} F^s(\vec{r}_1)\phi_0(r_2), \tag{5-5}$$

where $\phi_0(r_2)$ is the normalized ground state wave function of hydrogen. The hydrogenic wave functions $\phi_n(\vec{r}_2)$ satisfy

$$(-1/2\nabla_2^{\,2} - 1/r_2 - \varepsilon_n)\phi_n(\vec{r}_2) = 0, \tag{5-6}$$

where ε_0 is the ground state energy.

The free electron wave function must satisfy the incoming plane wave and outgoing spherical wave boundary conditions discussed in Chapter 1, so we can take $F^s(\vec{r}_1)$ to be

$$F^s(\vec{r}_1) = \exp(i\vec{k}_0 \cdot \vec{r}_1) + r_1^{-1}\, f^s(\theta)\exp(ik_0 r) \tag{5-7}$$

where $f^s(\theta)$ is the scattering amplitude and $\vec{k}_0$ is the momentum of the incident electron. We have (in atomic units)

$$E = \frac{1}{2}k_0^{\,2} + \varepsilon_0 = \frac{1}{2}(k_0^{\,2} - 1).$$

Because of the symmetry properties of the solution, the boundary conditions for large r_2 must be

$$\psi^s(\vec{r}_1,\vec{r}_2) \xrightarrow[r_2 \to \infty]{} (-1)^s F^s(\vec{r}_2)\phi_0(r_1). \tag{5-8}$$

It is of course perfectly possible to define solutions which are not symmetrical and which are linear combinations of ψ^0 and ψ^1, but the possibility of electron "exchange", in which electron 1 is captured and electron 2 becomes free, must be included in the boundary conditions.

The differential cross sections for scattering when the electron-hydrogen atom system is in an eigenstate of spin is $|f^s(\theta)|^2$. In an unpolarised beam of electrons there will be three times as many electrons in the triplet state (s = 1) as in the singlet state (s = 0), and the differential cross section for scattering of an unpolarised beam is obtained by summing over the final and averaging over the initial spin states.

$$\frac{d\sigma}{d\Omega} = \frac{3}{4}|f^1(\theta)|^2 + \frac{1}{4}|f^0(\theta)|^2 \tag{5-9a}$$

The total cross section is then

$$\sigma = \frac{\pi}{2} \int_{-1}^{+1} d(\cos\theta)\,[3|f^1(\theta)|^2 + |f^0(\theta)|^2]. \qquad (5\text{-}9b)$$

The variational method

A stationary expression for the scattering amplitude, akin to those discussed for tan δ_ℓ in Chapter 2, can be found as follows. For each value of the spin, two solutions $\psi_1{}^s$ and $\psi_2{}^s$ of the Schrödinger equation (5-1) are defined satisfying the boundary conditions

$$\psi_1(\vec{r}_1,\vec{r}_2) \underset{r_1\to\infty}{\sim} \left[\exp(i\vec{k}_o\cdot\vec{r}_1) + r_1^{-1} f^+(k_o,\theta)\exp(ik_o r_1)\right]\phi_o(r_2) \qquad (5\text{-}10a)$$

$$\psi_2(\vec{r}_1,\vec{r}_2) \underset{r_1\to\infty}{\sim} \left[\exp(i\vec{k}\cdot\vec{r}_1) + r_1^{-1} f^-(k_o,\theta)\exp(-ik_o r_1)\right]\phi_o(r_2) \qquad (5\text{-}10b)$$

where for simplicity the superscripts s are omitted, and $|\vec{k}| = k_o$. Two trial functions $\bar{\psi}_1$, $\bar{\psi}_2$ are introduced which satisfy the same boundary conditions as ψ_1 and ψ_2, but with scattering amplitudes $(f^+ + \Delta f^+)$ and $(f^- + \Delta f^-)$ in place of f^+ and f^-. We easily obtain the result

$$I[\bar{\psi}_2,\bar{\psi}_1] - I[\Delta\psi_2,\Delta\psi_1] = -\frac{1}{2}\int d^3r_1 \int d^3r_1 \sum_{i=1}^{2} \{\psi_2{}^*\nabla_i{}^2\Delta\psi_1 - \Delta\psi_1\nabla_i{}^2\psi_2{}^*\} \qquad (5\text{-}11)$$

$$= -\int d^3r_1 \int d^3r_2 \{\psi_2{}^*\nabla_1{}^2\Delta\psi_1 - \Delta\psi_1\nabla_1{}^2\psi_2{}^*\}$$

where

$$\Delta\psi_i \equiv \bar{\psi}_i - \psi_i \text{ and,}$$

$$I\,[\phi,\psi] = \int d^3r_1 \int d^3r_2\ \phi^* L\psi \qquad (5\text{-}12)$$

where L is defined by (5-1). Denoting the right hand side of (5-11) by J, and using Green's theorem to transform the volume integral over $\vec{r}_1$, to an integral over the surface of a large sphere of radius R, we find

$$J = -\lim_{R\to\infty} \int d^3r_2\ R^2 \int d\Omega(\theta_1,\phi_1) \left[\psi_2{}^*\nabla_1{}^2\Delta\psi_1 - \Delta\psi_1\nabla_1{}^2\psi_2{}^*\right]_{r_1=R}$$

On using the asymptotic form of $\Delta\psi_1$ and ψ_2 and remembering that $\phi_o(r_2)$ is normalized to unity, we find

$$J = -\lim_{R\to\infty} R^2 \int d\Omega(\theta_1,\phi_1) \left(\exp(-i\vec{k}\cdot\vec{r}_1) \frac{\partial}{\partial r_1} (r_1^{-1} \exp ik_o r_1) \right.$$

$$\left. - r_1^{-1}\exp(ik_o r_1) \frac{\partial}{\partial r_1} \exp(-i\vec{k}\cdot\vec{r}_1) \right)_{r_1=R} \Delta f^+(k_o,\theta_1)$$

where terms proportional to $f^-(k,\theta)$ which vanish in the limit $R\to\infty$ have been dropped. Evaluating the large curved bracket, we have

$$J = -i \lim_{R\to\infty} \int d\Omega(\theta_1,\phi_1)(k_oR+\vec{k}\cdot\vec{R})\exp i(k_oR-\vec{k}\cdot\vec{R})\Delta f^+(k_o,\theta_1)$$

In the limit $R\to\infty$, the integral must vanish unless $\vec{k}\cdot\vec{R} = k_oR$. This implies $\vec{R}$ is in the direction of $\vec{k}$ and that θ_1 becomes equal to the angle of scattering for the transition $\vec{k}_o\to\vec{k}$. As $\Delta f^+(k,\theta)$ is a slowly varying function of θ, it can be taken outside the integral and setting $\vec{k}\cdot\vec{R} = k_oR\mu$, J becomes

$$J = -i\ (2\pi k_oR)\Delta f(k_o,\theta)\int_{-1}^{+1} d\mu(1+x)\exp ik_oR(1-x)$$

The integral is elementary and approaches $2i/(k_oR)$ for large R, and finally from (5-11)

$$I[\psi_2,\psi_1] - I\ [\Delta\psi_2,\Delta\psi_1] = 4\pi\Delta f^+(k_o,\theta) \qquad (5\text{-}13)$$

This identity shows that the error in $f^+(k_o,\theta)$ is of second order if the condition that $I[\bar{\psi}_2,\bar{\psi}_1]=0$ is satisfied with suitable trial functions.

A simple trial function for ψ_i^s is

$$\bar{\psi}_i^s(\vec{r}_1,\vec{r}_2)=F_i^s(\vec{r}_1)\phi_o(r_2) + (-1)^sF_i^s(\vec{r}_2)\phi_o(r_1),$$

$$i = 1,\ 2. \qquad (5\text{-}14)$$

The asymptotic forms of the functions F_i^s are then

$$F_1^s(\vec{r}) \sim \exp(i\vec{k}_o\cdot\vec{r}) + r^{-1}f_1^s(\theta)\exp(ik_or)$$

$$F_2^s(\vec{r}) \sim \exp(i\vec{k}\cdot\vec{r}) + r^{-1}f_2^s(\theta)\exp(-ikr).$$

Using the symmetry of the wave function, it is found that

$$I[\bar{\psi}_1,\bar{\psi}_2] = 2\int d^3r_1\int d^3r_2 F_2^{S*}(\vec{r}_1)\phi_o(r_2)L\Big\{F_1^S(\vec{r}_1)\phi_o(r_2) + (-1)^S F_1^S(\vec{r}_2)\phi_o(r_1)\Big\}$$

Keeping in mind that F_2^S differs from the exact function (if the wave function is capable of being represented in this form) by a first order quantity which is arbitrary, the condition I = 0 implies that

$$\int d^3r_2\phi_o(r_2)L\Big\{F^S(\vec{r}_1)\phi_o(r_2) + (-1)^S F^S(\vec{r}_2)\phi_o(r_1)\Big\} = 0 \tag{5-15}$$

where the subscript on F^S is now unnecessary and has been omitted.

The Schrödinger equation (5-6) satisfied by the wave function $\phi_o(r)$ can be employed to reduce this equation for $F^S(\vec{r})$ to the form

$$(\nabla_1^2 + k_o^2)F^S(\vec{r}_1) = U(r)F^S(\vec{r}_1)+(-1)^S\int K(\vec{r}_1,\vec{r}_2)F^S(\vec{r}_2)d^3r_2. \tag{5-16}$$

The potential U(r) is defined by the equation

$$U(r) = -2\int\phi_o^*(r_2)\left(\frac{1}{r_1} - \frac{1}{|\vec{r}_1 - \vec{r}_2|}\right)\phi_o(r_2)d^3r_2, \tag{5-17}$$

The non-local potential operator $K(\vec{r}_1,\vec{r}_2)$ is defined as

$$K(\vec{r}_1,\vec{r}_2) = 2\phi_o(r_2)L\phi_o(r_1)$$

Using Green's theorem it is straightforward to show that

$$\int d^3r_2\phi_o(r_2)L\phi_o(r_1)F^S(\vec{r}_2) = \int d^3r_2F^S(\vec{r}_2)L\Big\{\phi_o(r_1)\phi_o(r_2)\Big\}$$

From this result the non-local potential K can be expressed as:

$$\begin{aligned} K(\vec{r}_1,\vec{r}_2) &= 2L\{\phi_o(r_1)\phi_o(r_2)\} \\ &= -2\phi(r_1)\phi(r_2)\left(-\frac{1}{|\vec{r}_1-\vec{r}_2|} + (E - 2\varepsilon_o)\right) \end{aligned} \tag{5-18}$$

The potential U(r) is the electron-atom interaction averaged over the ground state wave function, and the non-local potential K describes electron exchange, in which the two electrons interchange. With this form of trial function, no allowance is made for the possible distortion of the hydrogen wave function during the collision and no explicit terms depending on $|\vec{r}_1 - \vec{r}_2|$ describing correlations between the two electrons appear in the wave function. The importance of both these effects is expected to be enhanced at low energies, and we will see later how they may be taken into account.

To evaluate the integral in (5-17), it is convenient to use the expansion (Morse and Feshbach, 1953, p.1274)

$$\frac{1}{|\vec{r}_1 - \vec{r}_2|} = \sum_{n=0}^{\infty} \gamma_n(r_1,r_2)P_n(\cos\theta_{12}), \tag{5-19}$$

where θ_{12} is the angle between $\vec{r}_1$ and $\vec{r}_2$, and

$$\gamma_n = \frac{1}{r_>}\left(\frac{r_<}{r_>}\right)^n, \tag{5-20}$$

$r_<, r_>$ being the lesser and greater of r_1 and r_2 respectively. The hydrogen ground state function is

$$\phi_o(r) = \pi^{-\frac{1}{2}}\exp(-r)$$

and performing the integral over r_2, we find

$$U(r) = -2(1 + 1/r)\exp(-2r) \tag{5-21}$$

To calculate the partial wave amplitudes and the corresponding phase shifts, the wave function $F^S(\vec{r})$ can be expanded as in Section 1-2

$$F^S(\vec{r}) = \sum_{\ell} A_\ell r^{-1} f_\ell^{\,S}(r)P_\ell(\cos\theta),$$

where the A_ℓ are normalization constants.

In obtaining the radial equations, the Legendre polynomial expansion of K is required. Using (5-19) we find

$$K(\vec{r}_1,\vec{r}_2) = \sum_{\ell=0}^{\infty} (r_1r_2)^{-1}K_\ell(r_1,r_2)\left(\frac{2\ell+1}{4\pi}\right)P_\ell(\cos\theta_{12}) \tag{5-22a}$$

with

$$K_\ell(r_1,r_2) = -\left(\frac{8r_1r_2}{2\ell+1}\right) e^{-(r_1+r_2)}\left[(E-2\varepsilon_o)\delta_{\ell,0}-\gamma_\ell(r_1,r_2)\right] \tag{5-22b}$$

Expressing $P_\ell(\cos\theta_{12})$ in terms of θ_1 and θ_2 by the addition theorem (Morse and Feshbach, 1953, p.1274)

$$\frac{2\ell+1}{4\pi}P_\ell(\cos\theta_{12}) = \sum_m Y_{\ell,m}(\theta_1,\phi_1)Y_{\ell,-m}(\theta_2,\phi_2), \tag{5-23}$$

the integration over angles in the kernel is effected. The required radial equation is then found to be

$$\left(\frac{d^2}{dr_1^2} - \frac{\ell(\ell+1)}{r_1^2} + k_o^2\right)f_\ell^s(r_1) = U(r)f_\ell^s(r_1) +$$

$$+ (-1)^s\int_0^\infty K_\ell(r_1,r_2)f_\ell^s(r_2)\,dr_2, \tag{5-24}$$

which may be solved numerically with the boundary conditions

$$f_\ell^s(o) = 0,$$

$$f_\ell^s(r) \sim s_\ell(k_or) + \tan\delta_\ell^s c_\ell(k_or). \tag{5-25}$$

The s wave phase shifts ($\ell = 0$) in this approximation, which we shall call the static exchange approximation, are shown in Fig. 5-1, together with the phase shifts when the exchange kernel K_o is neglected. It can be seen at once that exchange is of great significance at low energies, the phase shifts δ_o^1 and δ_o^0 both tending to π as $k \to 0$, while the non-exchange phase shift $\delta_o \to 0$ as $k \to 0$. These results illustrate the breakdown of Levinson's theorem for non-local potentials. For singlet scattering ($s = 0$) there exists one bound state with zero angular momentum of the system of two electrons and a proton. This is the hydrogen negative ion, with a binding energy of $\varepsilon_{H^-} = -0.75$ ev. Levinson's theorem therefore applies in this case. For triplet scattering no such state exists and according to Levinson's theorem the phase shift δ_o^1 should tend to zero as $k_o \to 0$. The failure of Levinson's theorem is due to the existence of a bounded solution of equation (5-24), which vanishes for large r and yet does not correspond to a bound state. That such a solution exists can be seen from equation (5-15), which is

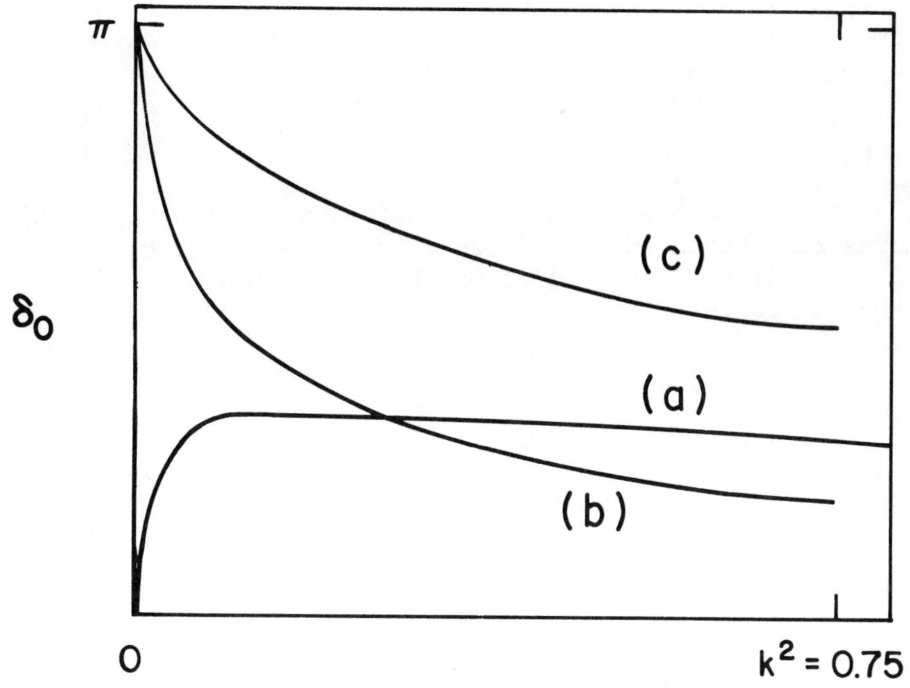

Figure 5-1. Phase shifts for the elastic scattering of electrons by hydrogen atoms, calculated (a) with no allowance made for exchange, (b) singlet phase shifts in the static exchange approximation, (c) triplet phase shifts in the static exchange approximation.

satisfied identically if we take

$$F^1(\vec{r}) = \phi_o(r). \tag{5-26}$$

Correspondingly equation (5-24) is solved, for $\ell = 0$, by setting

$$f^1_o(r) = r\phi_o(r). \tag{5-27}$$

If $f^1_o(r)$ is any solution of (5-24) satisfying the boundary condition for scattering (5-25), then

$$f^1_o(r,\lambda) = f^1_o(r) + \lambda r\phi_o(r), \tag{5-28}$$

is also an acceptable solution having the same phase shift,

where λ is an arbitrary constant. This degeneracy can be removed, if desired, by requiring $f^1{}_0(r,\lambda)$ to be orthogonal to the ground state of hydrogen:

$$\int_0^\infty r\phi_0(r)f^1{}_0(r,\lambda)dr = 0. \tag{5-29}$$

The existence of such a solution, vanishing at infinity, gives rise to an additional zero in the Jost function, $\phi_0(-k)$, which in turn modifies the derivation of Levinson's theorem, so that now

$$\delta^1{}_0(0) - \delta^1{}_0(\infty) = \pi \tag{5-30}$$

The location of the zero can be determined as follows. Using the orthogonality condition (5-29), equation (5-24) for $f^1{}_0(r)$ is modified by the omission of the part of the kernel K that contains $(E - 2\varepsilon_0)$ as a factor (see 5-22b). It can then be verified that $r\phi_0(r)$ is an eigenfunction of the modified equation belonging to the eigenvalue $k^2 = -1$. The corresponding zero in the Jost function occurs at $k = i$.

Martin (1955) (see also Swan, 1954) has shown, for kernels that vanish when r or r′ exceeds a certain value r_0, that Levinson's theorem takes the form

$$\delta_\ell(0) - \delta_\ell(\infty) = (n + m)\pi, \tag{5-31}$$

where n is the number of bound states and m is the number of families of degenerate solutions vanishing at infinity. Physically these solutions are connected with bound states that could exist if they were not excluded by the Pauli principle.

The phase shifts for $\ell = 1$ and $\ell = 2$ in the static approximation are much smaller than those for $\ell = 0$. The total cross section does not depend significantly on either the $\ell = 1$ or $\ell = 2$ terms, but the angular distributions are modified by the $\ell = 1$ phase shifts and to a small extent by the $\ell = 2$ phase shifts, and show a departure from isotropy. Some results are shown in Table 5-1 for the $\ell = 0$, $\ell = 1$ and $\ell = 2$ phase shifts.

TABLE 5-1

Phase shifts for the scattering of electrons by hydrogen atoms in the static exchange approximation

	Phase shifts in radians					
k^2 (a.u.)	Singlet (s = 0)			Triplet (s = 1)		
	$\ell = 0$	$\ell = 1$	$\ell = 2$	$\ell = 0$	$\ell = 1$	$\ell = 2$
0.0*	8.098	-	-	2.350	-	-
0.1	2.396	-0.0012	-	2.908	0.0022	-
0.3	0.9488	-0.0811	-	1.987	0.2000	-
0.5	0.7370	-0.1084	-0.0108	1.739	0.2866	0.0230
0.76	0.6087	-0.1159	-0.0155	1.541	0.3362	0.0395

*Scattering lengths are shown for $k^2=0$, in units of a_o.

5-2 ALTERNATIVE BOUNDARY CONDITIONS

The exact wave function $\psi(\vec{r}_1,\vec{r}_2)$ may be expanded in a complete orthonormal set of hydrogen atom eigenfunctions

$$\psi(\vec{r}_1,\vec{r}_2) = \sum_n \phi_n(\vec{r}_2)F_n(\vec{r}_1) + \int d^3K\phi^-(\vec{K},\vec{r}_2)F(\vec{K},\vec{r}_1) \quad (5\text{-}32)$$

where we have distinguished the bound hydrogenic functions ϕ_n from the continuum functions $\phi^-(\vec{K},\vec{r}_2)$. The functions $\phi^-(\vec{K},\vec{r}_2)$ are Coulomb functions of the kind discussed in Chapter 3 and are eigenfunctions of energy with $\varepsilon(K) = K^2/2$. The normalization of the functions $\phi^\pm(\vec{k},\vec{r})$ will be chosen so that

$$\int d^3r \left[\phi^\pm(\vec{k},\vec{r})\right]^* \left[\phi^\pm(\vec{k}',\vec{r})\right] = \delta(\vec{k}-\vec{k}') \quad (5\text{-}33)$$

On comparing with the normalization of the Coulomb functions introduced in Section 3-1, we see that

$$\phi^\pm(\vec{k},\vec{r}) = (2\pi)^{-3/2}\psi_C^\pm(\vec{k},\vec{r})$$

The boundary conditions satisfied by the functions $F_n(\vec{r}_1)$ and $F(\vec{K},\vec{r}_1)$, when the incident energy is less than the first excitation threshold, are

$$F_0(\vec{r}_1) \sim \exp(i\vec{k}_0 \cdot \vec{r}_1) + r_1^{-1} f_0(\theta)\exp(ik_0 r_1) \tag{5-34a}$$

and

$$r_1 F_n(\vec{r}_1) \xrightarrow[r_1\to\infty]{} 0 \qquad n \neq 0$$

$$r_1 F(\vec{K},\vec{r}_1) \xrightarrow[r_1\to\infty]{} 0. \tag{5-34b}$$

The functions F_n describe the motion of an electron moving relative to a hydrogen atom in the state n, and the conditions (5-34) follow from the requirement that the flux of particles must vanish at large distances for all n, except n = 0. The solution ψ is neither symmetrical nor antisymmetrical like the solutions ψ^S but, having obtained ψ, solutions of the correct symmetry $\psi^S = [\psi(\vec{r}_1,\vec{r}_2) + (-1)^S\psi(\vec{r}_2,\vec{r}_1)]$ may be constructed. The possibility of rearrangement exists, independently of the symmetry of the solution, so that $\psi(\vec{r}_1,\vec{r}_2)$ must obey the additional (and independent) boundary conditions

$$\int \phi_n^*(\vec{r}_1)\psi(\vec{r}_1,\vec{r}_2)dr_1 = G_n(\vec{r}_2),$$

$$\int \phi^{-*}(\vec{K},\vec{r}_1)\psi(\vec{r}_1,\vec{r}_2)dr_1 = G(\vec{K},\vec{r}_2) \tag{5-35a}$$

where

$$G_0(\vec{r}_2) \xrightarrow[r_2\to\infty]{} r_2^{-1} g_0(\theta)\exp(ik_0 r_2)$$

$$r_2 G_n(\vec{r}_2) \xrightarrow[r_2\to\infty]{} 0, \qquad n \neq 0 \tag{5-35b}$$

$$r_2 G(\vec{K},\vec{r}_2) \xrightarrow[r_2\to\infty]{} 0.$$

It has been assumed that electron 1 is incident on the atom and therefore only outgoing waves are present in the wave function $G_0(\vec{r}_2)$.

It is not immediately obvious how the boundary conditions (5-35) can be satisfied by the expansion (5-32). Clearly, each of the bound state terms $\phi_n(\vec{r}_2)$ in the sum (5-32) vanishes for large $|\vec{r}_2|$, and any non-zero contributions to $\psi(\vec{r}_1,\vec{r}_2)$ at large $|\vec{r}_2|$ must come from the continuum terms in the expansion[2]. To avoid logarithmic phase factors we shall consider the case in which the potentials $V(r_i)$ and

$v(|\vec{r}_1-\vec{r}_2|)$ which appear in (5-1a) are screened, in which case the functions $\phi^-(\vec{K},\vec{r}_2)$ have the asymptotic form

$$\phi^-(\vec{K},\vec{r}_2) \sim \exp(i\vec{K}\cdot\vec{r}_2) + r_2^{-1}h^*(\vec{K},\pi-\theta)\exp(-iKr_2),$$

where $h(\vec{K},\theta)$ is the scattering amplitude for scattering by the potential $V(r_2)$. For large r_2, we have

$$\psi(\vec{r}_1,\vec{r}_2) \underset{r_2\to\infty}{\sim} \int d^3K\ \phi^-(K,r\ )F(K,r\ ) \tag{5-36}$$

and in view of the oscillating character of the functions $\phi^-(\vec{K},\vec{r}_1)$, $\psi(\vec{r}_1,\vec{r}_2)$ must vanish for large r_2, unless $F(\vec{K},\vec{r}_1)$ is a singular function of $\vec{K}$. To discuss this possibility, $F(\vec{K},\vec{r}_1)$ can be expanded in the set of eigenfunctions $\{\phi_n(\vec{r}_1),\phi^-(\vec{K},\vec{r}_1)\}$:-

$$F(\vec{K},\vec{r}_1) = \sum_n a(\vec{K},n)\phi_n(\vec{r}_1) + \int d^3K'a(\vec{K},\vec{K}')\phi^-(\vec{K}',\vec{r}\ ). \tag{5-37}$$

The coefficients $a(\vec{K},n)$ can be obtained from the equation

$$\int d^3r_1\int d^3r_2[\phi^{-*}(\vec{K},\vec{r}_2)\phi_n{}^*(\vec{r}_1)L\psi(\vec{r}_1,\vec{r}_2)] = 0$$

using expansions (5-32) and (5-37) for $\psi(\vec{r}_1,\vec{r}_2)$. The coefficients $a(\vec{K},\vec{K}')$ can be found in the same way. On using the Schrödinger equations satisfied by the orthonormal hydrogenic functions, (5-6), it is easy to show that

$$a(\vec{K},n) = \left(E - \varepsilon_n - \frac{1}{2}K^2\right)^{-1} A(\vec{K},n), \tag{5-38}$$

where

$$A(\vec{K},n) = \int d^3r_1'\int d^3r_2'\left(\phi(\vec{K},\vec{r}_2{}')\phi_n(\vec{r}_1{}')\right)^* v(|\vec{r}_1{}'-\vec{r}_2{}'|)\psi(\vec{r}_1{}',\vec{r}_2{}') \tag{5-39}$$

Since $v(r)$ is a screened Coulomb potential, $A(\vec{K},n)$ is a well behaved function of $\vec{K}$. Similar expressions can be written down for $A(\vec{K},\vec{K}')$.

The coefficient $A(\vec{K},n)$ and hence $F(\vec{K},r_1)$ is singular at the values of K^2 for which the denominator in (5-38) vanishes, which occurs when

$$E = \varepsilon_n + \frac{1}{2}K^2.$$

If the total energy $E = (\varepsilon_o + k_o^2/2)$ is below the first excitation threshold, this can happen only for $n = 0$, and $K^2 = k_o^2$. The coefficient $a(\vec{K},\vec{K}')$ is non-singular, in this energy region.

The non-vanishing part of $\psi(\vec{r}_1,\vec{r}_2)$ at large r_2, is obtained from the term $a(\vec{K},0)$, and using (5-39) and (5-36), we find

$$\psi(\vec{r}_1,\vec{r}_2) \underset{r_2\to\infty}{\sim} \int d^3K\phi^-(\vec{K},\vec{r}_2) \frac{A(\vec{K},0)}{(E - \varepsilon_o - K^2/2)} \phi_o(\vec{r}_1) \qquad (5\text{-}40)$$

To obtain an outgoing wave solution, we follow the prescription introduced in Chapter 1 and add a small positive imaginary term to E. The integral over $\vec{K}$ is then of the form (with $k_o^2 = 2(E-\varepsilon_o)$)

$$I = \ell t_{\eta\to 0+}\ 2\int d^3K \frac{\phi^-(\vec{K},\vec{r}_2)A(\vec{K},0)}{k_o^2+i\eta - K^2)}$$

By using Cauchy's theorem, it can be shown that, for large r_2 $(k_o^2+i\eta-K^2)^{-1}$ applied to a diverging wave acts like $-2\pi i\ \delta(k_o^2-K^2)$ and applied to a coverging wave produces zero. It follows using the asymptotic form of $\phi^-(\vec{K},\vec{r}_2)$ that in the limit of large r_2

$$I = -\sqrt{2\pi}\ A(\vec{k},0)r_2^{-1}\exp(ik_o r_2) \qquad (5\text{-}41)$$

where $|\vec{k}| = k_o$ and $\vec{k}$ is in the direction of $\vec{r}_2$, which establishes the asymptotic form (5-35) with

$$g_o(\theta) = -\sqrt{2\pi}\int d^3r_1'\int d^3r_2'\left(\phi^-(\vec{k},\vec{r}_2')\phi_o(\vec{r}_1')\right)^* v(|\vec{r}_1'-\vec{r}_2'|) \times$$
$$\times\ \psi(\vec{r}_1',\vec{r}_2')$$

If the functions $\phi^+(\vec{K},\vec{r}_2)$ had been employed in the expansion (5-32), we would not have obtained the outgoing wave asymptotic form given by (5-41), and this is the reason for using the expansion in terms of the functions ϕ^-.

The expansion (5-32) with the boundary conditions (5-33, 5-34) is unique, but alternative expansions such as

$$\psi(\vec{r}_1,\vec{r}_2) = \sum_n \phi_n(\vec{r}_2)F_n(\vec{r}_1) + \sum_m \phi_m(\vec{r}_1)G_m(\vec{r}_2), \tag{5-43}$$

are clearly not so. (Here we have reverted to our usual practice, in which the sum over n includes an integration over the continuum.) This freedom allows us to choose the F_n and G_m functions to be non-singular in n or m, so that for large r_1, only the first sum contributes to the boundary conditions (5-34) and for large r_2 only the second sum contributes to the rearranged boundary conditions (5-35). These remarks are not confined to low energies below the excitation threshold, but can be generalised appropriately.

To calculate the cross sections from the amplitudes $f_o(\theta)$ and $g_o(\theta)$ introduced in (5-34) and (5-35b) the solutions of definite symmetry ψ^s are formed. Using the asymptotic forms of these solutions, we find at once that

$$f^s(\theta) = f_o(\theta) + (-1)^s g_o(\theta), \tag{5-44a}$$

and the differential cross section for an unpolarized beam becomes

$$\frac{d\sigma}{d\Omega} = |f_o(\theta)|^2 + |g_o(\theta)|^2 - \mathrm{Re}[f_o(\theta)g_o^*(\theta)]. \tag{5-44b}$$

The first two terms may be considered as giving the intensities of direct and rearranged scattering, while the last term represents interference which is specifically related to the identity of the electrons and is due to the Pauli exclusion principle.

Yet another form of expansion for the wave function in which solutions of the required symmetry are formed from the beginning are very useful. To achieve this the singlet and triplet wave functions are expanded separately as

$$\psi^s(\vec{r}_1,\vec{r}_2) = \sum_n \left[\phi_n(\vec{r}_2)F_n^s(\vec{r}_1) + (-1)^s\phi_n(\vec{r}_1)F_n^s(\vec{r}_2)\right] \tag{5-45}$$

As for the expansion (5-43), the functions F_n^s can be chosen to be non-singular in n, so that the continuum terms in the expansion do not contribute to the elastic channel (or any discrete excitation channel) boundary conditions.

5-3 THE LONG RANGE INTERACTION AND THE POLARIZED ORBITAL METHOD

The trial function (5-13) in the static exchange method does not include terms representing the distortion or polarization of the target atom by the field of the incident electron. This distortion gives rise to an interaction between the electron and the atom which, at energies below the first inelastic threshold, varies like $(1/r^4)$ and is characteristic of the interaction between a charged particle and a neutral polarizable system. To identify the long range potential the expansion of the total wave function (5-32) is inserted in the Schrödinger equation to obtain an infinite set of coupled equations for the functions $F_n(\vec{r}_1)$

$$\int \phi_n^*(\vec{r}_2) L \left(\sum_m \phi_m(\vec{r}_2) F_m(\vec{r}_1) \right) d^3 r_2 = 0, \quad n = 0,1,2....$$

where, as usual, the continuum states in the expansion have not been indicated explicitly. Using the wave equation (5-6) for the hydrogenic functions $\phi_m(\vec{r}_2)$, we find

$$(\nabla^2 + k_n^2) F_n(\vec{r}_1) = \sum_{m=0}^{\infty} U_{nm}(\vec{r}_1) F_m(\vec{r}_1), \tag{5-46}$$

where

$$k_n^2 = k_o^2 + 2\varepsilon_o - 2\varepsilon_n,$$

and

$$U_{nm} = 2 \int \phi_n^*(\vec{r}_2) \left(\frac{1}{r_{12}} - \frac{1}{r_1} \right) \phi_m(\vec{r}_2) d^3 r_2. \tag{5-47}$$

For $n \neq 0$, k_n^2 is negative since we have supposed that only the elastic scattering channel is open, and all channels with $n \neq 0$ are closed. Using the expansion (5-19) for $1/r_{12}$, the form of U_{nm} for large r_1 may be determined.

Consider the potential U_{0m} which connects the equation for F_0 (the wave function in the open channel) with the closed channel wave functions. The bound hydrogenic functions $\phi_m(\vec{r}_2)$ are eigenfunctions of angular momentum of the form

$$\phi_m(\vec{r}_2) = r_2^{-1} R_{n\ell}(r_2) Y_{\ell,q}(\theta_2, \phi_2). \tag{5-48}$$

since m stands collectively for the set of quantum numbers n, ℓ, q defining the hydrogenic state; $R_{n\ell}$ being the radial function and $Y_{\ell,q}$ a spherical harmonic. Only the ℓth term in the Legendre polynomial expansion of $1/r_{12}$ contributes to U_{0m}, from which we see that

$$U_{0m}(\vec{r}_1) \propto 1/r_1^{\ell+1} \text{ for large } r_1 \ (\ell \neq 0); \qquad (5\text{-}49)$$

when $\ell = 0$, $U_{0m}(\vec{r}_1)$ vanishes exponentially as $r_1 \to \infty$. It follows that the dominant terms for large r_1 arise from p states ($\ell = 1$) and for these $U_{0m} \propto 1/r_1^2$. It can be shown that for all states n and m (including continuum states) $U_{nm}(\vec{r}_1)$ decreases at least as fast as $1/r_1^2$ as $r_1 \to \infty$. In view of the boundary condition (5-34), for large r_1 and $n \neq 0$ the only term of importance on the right hand side of each of the equations (5-46) is that connecting the channel n with the open channel 0; hence ($n \neq 0$)

$$(\nabla^2 - \lambda_n^2)F_n(\vec{r}_1) \cong U_{n0}(\vec{r}_1)F_0(\vec{r}_1), \ r_1 \text{ large}, \qquad (5\text{-}50)$$

where

$$\lambda_n^2 = |k_n^2|$$

For large r_1, we must have that

$$\nabla^2 F_0(\vec{r}_1) = -k_0^2 F_0(\vec{r}_1) + 0\left(\frac{1}{r_1^4}\right), \qquad (5\text{-}51)$$

and if $U_{n0}(\vec{r}_1) \propto (1/r_1)^p$, with $p \geq 2$, we have

$$\nabla^2\left(U_{n0}(\vec{r}_1)F_0(\vec{r}_1)\right) = -k_0^2\left(U_{n0}(\vec{r}_1)F_0(\vec{r}_1)\right) + 0\left(\frac{1}{r_1^{p+1}}\right) \qquad (5\text{-}52)$$

Comparing this relation with equation (5-50), we see that the functions $F_n(\vec{r}_1)$ have the form, for large r_1,

$$F_n(\vec{r}_1) \sim \frac{-1}{\lambda_n^2 + k_0^2} U_{n0}(\vec{r}_1)F_0(\vec{r}_1); \quad n \neq 0. \qquad (5\text{-}53)$$

By substituting this expression for F_n into equation (5-46), the equation satisfied by $F_0(\vec{r})$ for large r, is found to be

$$(\nabla^2 + k_o^{\ 2})F_o(\vec{r}) = U(r)F_o(\vec{r}) + U_p(r)F_o(\vec{r}), \qquad (5\text{-}54)$$

where

$$U_p(r) = \sum_{n=o} \frac{-|U_{on}(\vec{r}_1)|^2}{(\lambda_n^{\ 2} + k_o^{\ 2})} \qquad (5\text{-}55)$$

and $U(r) \equiv U_{oo}(r)$ is defined by (5-21). As the dominant (p wave) terms in U_{on} vary as $1/r^2$ for large r, the polarization potential $U_p(r)$ varies as $1/r^4$ as $r \to \infty$ and this is the exact long range potential, up to terms of $O(1/r^6)$. The polarization is attractive because the denominator in (5-55) is always positive.

Adiabatic polarization

When a hydrogen atom is placed in the field of a fixed charge, it is distorted or 'polarized' and the energy levels are shifted. The new energy and wave function can be calculated by using perturbation theory. The approximation in which it is assumed that the electron is moving so slowly that its kinetic energy may be neglected is known as the adiabatic approximation and we shall now show that the potential $U_p(r)$ is identical with the polarization energy calculated to second order in the adiabatic approximation. The Schrödinger equation for a hydrogen atom in the field of an electron fixed at position $\vec{r}$ is

$$[H_o + \lambda V]\Phi(\vec{r},\vec{x}) = E(\vec{r})\Phi(\vec{r},\vec{x}), \qquad (5\text{-}56)$$

where

$$H_o = -\frac{1}{2}\nabla_x^{\ 2} - \frac{1}{x}; \quad V = \frac{1}{|\vec{r} - \vec{x}|} - \frac{1}{r} \qquad (5\text{-}57)$$

and $\lambda = 1$. Applying the Rayleigh-Schrödinger perturbation theory (see, for example, Bransden and Joachain, 1982, Chapter 2), E and Φ are expanded in powers of λ:-

$$\begin{aligned} \Phi &= \phi_o(x) + \lambda\phi_{pol} + O(\lambda^2), \\ E &= E_o^{\ o} + \lambda E_o^{\ 1} + \lambda^2 E_o^{\ 2} + \ldots\ldots. \end{aligned} \qquad (5\text{-}58)$$

If the perturbation is removed by letting $\lambda \to o$ the solution coincides with the hydrogenic ground state $\phi_o(x)$ with energy $E_o^{\ o} = \varepsilon_o$. The first order energy $E_o^{\ 1}$ is $(\lambda = 1)$,

$$E_o^{1}(r) = \int \phi_o(x) V \phi_o(x) d^3x. \tag{5-59}$$

It is seen that $2E_o^{1} = U(r)$, where $U(r)$ is the static interaction occurring in the scattering equation (5-16). The first order wave function $\phi_{pol}(\vec{r},\vec{x})$ is given by ($\lambda = 1$)

$$\phi_{pol}(r,x) = \sum_{n \neq o} \frac{\int \phi_o(\vec{x}') V \phi_n^{*}(\vec{x}') d^3x'}{(\varepsilon_o - \varepsilon_n)} \phi_n(\vec{x}). \tag{5-60a}$$

and is the solution of the equation

$$(H_o - \varepsilon_o)\phi_{pol} = E_o^{1}\phi_o(x) - V\phi_o(x). \tag{5-60b}$$

The second order energy E_o^{2} can be calculated from ϕ_{pol} and is given by

$$E_o^{2} = \int \phi_o(x)[V - E_o^{1}]\phi_{pol}(\vec{r},\vec{x}) d^3x$$

$$= \sum_{n \neq o} \frac{\left| \int \phi_o(x) V \phi_n(\vec{x}) d^3x \right|^2}{(\varepsilon_o - \varepsilon_n)} \tag{5-61}$$

Comparing (5-61) with (5-55) it is seen that $U_p(r) = 2E_o^{2}(r)$.

The interaction potential can be expanded in a multipole expansion

$$V(\vec{r},\vec{x}) = \sum_{\ell=0}^{\infty} V_\ell(r,x) P_\ell(\cos\theta), \tag{5-62a}$$

where

$$V_\ell(r,x) = \left(\gamma_\ell(r,x) - \delta_{\ell,o} \frac{1}{r} \right)$$

and θ is the angle between $\vec{x}$ and $\vec{r}$. The polarization potential U_p can also be expanded

$$U_p(r) = \sum_{\ell=0}^{\infty} U_p(\ell,r), \tag{5-62b}$$

where $U_p(\ell,r)$ is determined by the multipole of order ℓ.

$$U_p(\ell,r) = \sum_{n=o} \frac{2\left|\int \phi_o(x) V_\ell(r,x) P_\ell(\cos\theta)\phi_n(\vec{x})d^3x\right|^2}{(\varepsilon_o - \varepsilon_n)} \quad (5\text{-}62c)$$

As we noted earlier the multipole of longest range is the dipole term. This arises from the p states of hydrogen and

$$U_p \sim -\frac{\alpha_1}{r^4}$$

where α_1 is the dipole polarizability of the atom; for hydrogen $\alpha_1 = 4.5$. The monopole contribution to U_p vanishes exponentially, while for $\ell \neq o$

$$U_p(\ell,r) \sim \alpha_\ell / r^{2\ell+2}, \text{ as } r \to \infty \quad (5\text{-}63a)$$

where

$$\alpha_\ell = \sum_{n=o} \frac{2\left|\int \phi_o(x)\phi_n(\vec{x}) x^\ell P_\ell(\cos\theta) d^3x\right|^2}{(\varepsilon_o - \varepsilon_n)} \quad (5\text{-}63b)$$

In the case of hydrogen, exact solutions of (5-60b) and (5-61) have been obtained (Dalgarno and Lynn, 1957), and the multipole contributions to U_p and ϕ_{pol} for $\ell = 0,1,2$, have been calculated by Reeh (1960).

Corrections to the effective potential U_p, to be employed in equation (5-54) for $F_o(\vec{r})$, arise both from higher order terms in the perturbation series (5-58), and also by avoiding the adiabatic approximation, in which the kinetic energy of the electron is neglected. The leading non-adiabatic terms for large r, have been investigated by Kleinman et al. (1968) and by Dalgarno et al. (1968). Working to the lowest order in the kinetic energy, the correction of the effective potential is easily seen to be of the form

$$\bar{U}(r) = \int d^3x \Phi(\vec{r},\vec{x}) \nabla_r^{\,2} \Phi(\vec{r},\vec{x}),$$

where Φ is the solution of equation (5-56). For large r, the leading term in $\bar{U}(r)$ is proportional to $(1/r^6)$. The only other term of this order arises from the quadrupole term $U_p(2,r)$ in the expansion of the adiabatic potential, and the exact asymptotic form of the effective potential up to terms of order $(1/r^7)$ is

$$U_p(r) \sim -\frac{\alpha_1}{r^4} - (\alpha_2 - 6\beta_1)\frac{1}{r^6} + O\left(\frac{1}{r^7}\right) \tag{5-64}$$

where α_2 is the quadrupole polarizability. The coefficient β_1 is obtained from the expansion of $\bar{U}(r)$, and can be expressed in the form

$$\beta_1 = \sum_{n\neq o} \frac{\left|\int \phi_o(x) x \cos\theta \phi_n(\vec{x}) d^3x\right|^2}{(\varepsilon_o - \varepsilon_n)^2} \tag{5-65}$$

In the case of hydrogen $\alpha_2 = 15$ and $\beta_1 = 5.375$, so that the non-adiabatic term has a significant effect in decreasing the effective attraction from that derived from the adiabatic approximation.

The method of polarized orbitals

The method of polarized orbitals[3] attempts to include both the effect of polarization and that of exchange, in a relatively simple approximation. The trial function ψ_t is written in the form

$$\psi_t^S(\vec{r},\vec{x}) = [1 + (-1)^S P_{12}][\phi_o(x) + \phi_{pol}(\vec{x},\vec{r})]F^S(\vec{r}). \tag{5-66}$$

where P_{12} is an operator interchanging the coordinates of the two electrons. An equation for $F^S(\vec{r})$ is obtained by requiring

$$\int \phi_o(x)[H-E]\psi_t^S(\vec{r},\vec{x}) d^3x = o. \tag{5-67}$$

The equation for $F^S(\vec{r})$ is similar in form to (5-16):-

$$[\nabla^2 + k^2 - U(r) - U_p(r)]F^S(\vec{r}) = \int \{K(\vec{r},\vec{r}\,') + K_p(\vec{r},\vec{r}\,')\}F^S(\vec{r}\,')d^3r'. \tag{5-68}$$

where K_p is an additional kernel arising from the rearranged or exchange part of the wave function

$$K_p(\vec{r},\vec{r}\,') = (-1)^S 2\phi_o(r')[H - E]\phi_{pol}(\vec{r},\vec{r}\,'). \tag{5-69}$$

The equation for $F^S(\vec{r})$ can be reduced to a set of radial equations by expanding in eigenfunctions of angular momentum in the usual way.

Since the wave function $\phi_{pol}(\vec{r},\vec{x})$ given by (5-60b) is certainly in error for small r, Temkin and Lamkin (1961) employed a simplified form, in which only the dipole contribution was retained. In addition they required $\phi_{pol}(\vec{r},\vec{x})$ to vanish when $r < x$. Thus ϕ_{pol} was of the form

$$\phi_{pol}(\vec{r},\vec{x}) = \theta(r - x)r^{-1}f_p(r,x) \cos \alpha, \qquad (5\text{-}70)$$

where $\cos \alpha = \vec{r} \cdot \vec{x}/rx$ and $\theta(y) = 1$, $y > o$, $\theta = o$ otherwise. By substituting this form into equation (5-60b), f_p is found to satisfy

$$\left(\frac{d^2}{dx^2} - \frac{2}{x^2} + \frac{2}{x} - 1\right) f_p(r,x) = \left(\frac{4}{\pi}\right)^{\frac{1}{2}} \frac{x^2}{r^2}\exp(-x) \qquad (5\text{-}71)$$

with the solution (Sternheimer, 1954)

$$f_p(r,x) = -\left(\frac{1}{\pi}\right)^{\frac{1}{2}} \frac{x^2}{r^2}\left(1 + \frac{x}{2}\right)\exp(-x) \qquad (5\text{-}72)$$

This gives the terms of longest range (which are proportional to $(1/r^2)$) correctly, and the corresponding form for U_p is

$$U_p(r) = -r^{-4}\left(\frac{9}{2} - \frac{2}{3}e^{-2r}\left(r^5 + \frac{9}{2}r^4 + 9r^3 + \frac{27}{2}r^2 + \frac{27}{2}r + \frac{27}{4}\right)\right) \qquad (5\text{-}73)$$

This approximation for U_p is quite close to the exact dipole contribution $U_p(1,r)$. It vanishes at the origin and behaves like $(-\alpha_1/r^4)$ for large r. In forming the exchange kernel some care has to be taken with terms involving the derivatives of the step function θ in (5-70). This has been investigated by Sloan (1964). The modification of the phase shifts produced by the exchange kernel K_p is quite small. If K_p is omitted, a variation of the method is obtained that is known as the 'exchange-adiabatic' approximation.

The phase shifts found from the polarized orbital method are shown in Tables 5-2 and 5-3. The relative change in higher order phase shifts from the values given by the exchange equations is greater than for the $\ell = o$ phase shift, as would be expected. Also included in the tables are the phase shifts given by Schwartz (1961) and Armstead (1968), which, as we shall see, may be considered to be 'exact', and comparison shows that the agreement in the case of the s-wave is good, but the method is less successful for $\ell = 1$, particularly in the singlet $(S = o)$ state.

Table 5-2

Singlet (S=0) phase shifts for the elastic scattering of electrons by hydrogen atoms in the ground state

k(a.u.)	Phase shifts in radians								
	$\ell = 0$			$\ell = 1$			$\ell = 2$		
	Ex.	P.O.	V	Ex.	P.O.	V	Ex.	P.O.	V
0*	8.10	5.7	5.95	-	-	-	-	-	-
0.1	2.396	2.853	2.553	-0.0012	0.0048	0.0070	-	-	0.0012
0.2	1.870	2.114	2.067	-	-	0.0147	-	-	0.0052
0.3	1.568	1.750	1.696	-0.0241	0.0322	0.0170	0.0006	0.0113	0.0108
0.4	1.239	1.469	1.415	-	-	0.0100	-	-	0.0183
0.5	1.031	1.251	1.202	-0.0713	0.0392	-0.0007	-0.00397	0.266	0.0274
0.75	0.694	0.904	-	-0.1126	0.0347	-	-0.0123	0.0456	-
0.80	-	-	0.886	-	-	-0.004	-	-	0.0745

*Scattering lengths.

Ex. = static exchange; P.O. = polarized orbital; V = Schwartz ($\ell = 0$); Armstead ($\ell = 1$); Register and Poe ($\ell = 2$)

Table 5-3

Triplet (S=1) phase shifts for the elastic scattering of electrons by hydrogen atoms in the ground state

	Phase shifts in radians								
k(a.u.)	$\ell = 0$			$\ell = 1$			$\ell = 2$		
	Ex.	P.O.	V	Ex.	P.O.	V	Ex.	P.O.	V
0*	2.35	1.7	1.77	-	-	-	-	-	-
0.1	2.907	2.946	2.939	0.0021	0.0090	0.1140	-	-	0.0013
0.2	2.679	2.732	2.717	-	-	0.0450	-	-	0.0052
0.3	2.461	2.519	2.500	0.0511	0.098	0.1063	0.0008	0.0118	0.0114
0.4	2.257	2.320	2.294	-	-	0.1873	-	-	0.0198
0.5	2.070	2.133	2.105	0.169	0.245	0.2699	0.0070	0.0350	0.0304
0.75	1.679	1.745	-	0.304	0.390	-	0.0274	0.0746	-
0.80	-	-	1.643	-	-	0.427	-	-	0.0697

*Scattering lengths.

Ex. = static exchange; P.O. = polarized orbital; V = Schwartz ($\ell = 0$); Armstead ($\ell = 1$); Register and Poe ($\ell = 2$).

5-4 FURTHER VARIATIONAL CALCULATIONS AND THE CLOSE COUPLING METHOD

Much more elaborate trial functions than the simple function (5-13), which gave the static exchange approximation, may be devised. These may be classified as purely algebraical, of close coupling (or eigenfunction expansion) form or as a mixture of the two. Each case will be considered in turn.

Algebraic trial functions

The Kohn or Hulthén variational method may be employed with trial functions that depend on a number of parameters including the phase shifts. For example, if the trial function for s-wave scattering is written in the form

$$\psi_t(r_1,r_2) = \phi_o(r_1)r_2^{-1}f_t(r_2), \tag{5-74}$$

where $f_t(r_2)$ is the Massey-Moiseiwitsch trial function given in equation (2-15), the results given in Table 2-1 would be obtained. These results are an approximation to the exact phase shift for scattering by the static potential U alone. To include exchange effects, the function

$$\psi_t^s(r_1,r_2) = [1 + (-1)^s P_{12}]\phi_o(r_1)r_2^{-1}f_t(r_2), \tag{5-75}$$

can be employed where f_t again has the form (2-15) and in this case the results are approximations to the static exchange phase shifts. The most elaborate investigation of this kind have been carried out by Schwartz (1961) for s-waves (ℓ = o) and later extended by Armstead (1968) for p-waves (ℓ = 1) and by Register and Poe (1975) for d-waves (ℓ = 2). The trial wave functions of Schwartz were constructed using the fact, exploited in Rayleigh-Ritz calculations on the bound states of the two electron system by Hylleraas, that a trial function of the form $f(r_1,r_2,r_{12})$ where $r_{12} = |\vec{r}_1 - \vec{r}_2|$ is an eigenfunction of total orbital angular momentum, belonging to the eigenvalue zero. A general form of the s-wave function is

$$\psi_t^s(\vec{r}_1,\vec{r}_2) = [1 + (-1)^s P_{12}]\left(\phi_o(r_2)r_1^{-1}\left\{\sin kr_1 + \tan\delta_o^s\left(1-e^{-\lambda r_1/2}\right)\cos kr_1\right\} + \sum_{\ell mn} C_{\ell mn}e^{-\lambda/2(r_1+r_2)}r_{12}^{\ell}r_1^{m}r_2^{n}\right) \tag{5-76}$$

The first term in the smaller curved brackets has the correct asymptotic form for large r_1, and the remainder of the wave function vanishes at infinity; the exponential factors in the second term providing the necessary cut-off for large r_1 or r_2. The parameters $C_{\ell,m,n}$ and $\tan \delta_o^s$ can be found by the Kohn procedure. Schwartz included as many terms in the trial function as was necessary to secure convergence, using up to 50 parameters. Although the expansion in powers or r_1, r_2 and r_{12} is capable of representing any kind of behavior, the exponential cut-off makes the convergence slow, because the wave function contains terms which decrease like $1/r_1^2$ at large r_1, convergence is greatly improved when additional terms having this property are added.

The phases obtained, which are included in Tables 5-2 and 5-3, represent the exact phases accurately. This conclusion is supported by the results of the non-adiabatic method of Temkin described in (5-5) below, and the method of variational bounds developed by Gailitis (1965a,b). These conclusions receive further support from experiment. The differential cross section for elastic scattering by an unpolarized beam of electrons has been measured at a number of energies between 0.5 and 8.7 ev by Williams (1975). For angles greater than 30°, the data is consistent with the differential cross sections computed from the accurate phase shifts for $\ell = 0$, 1 and 2. At smaller angles, at the higher energies, phase shifts for $\ell > 2$ have an important influence on the cross section although each phase shift is small. For $\ell > 2$, exchange can be neglected and both the singlet and triplet phase shift are given accurately by treating the long range polarization potential by the effective range formulae (3-80), where for hydrogen $\alpha = 4.5$ in atomic units. At the highest energy (8.7 ev) and in the forward direction ($\theta = 0^o$) phase shifts of up to $\ell = 50$ are required for the differential cross section to be obtained to an accuracy of a few percent. The data and the theoretical prediction for E = 4.89 ev (k = 0.6 ev) are shown in Fig. 5-2.

The close coupling method

The complete wave functions can be exactly represented by an expansion into a complete set of hydrogen atom eigenfunctions. By taking a finite number of terms in the expansion, the truncated sum

$$\psi_t^s(\vec{r}_1, \vec{r}_2) = [1 + (-1)^s P_{12}] \sum_{n=0}^{N} \phi_n(\vec{r}_1) F_n(\vec{r}_2), \qquad (5\text{-}77)$$

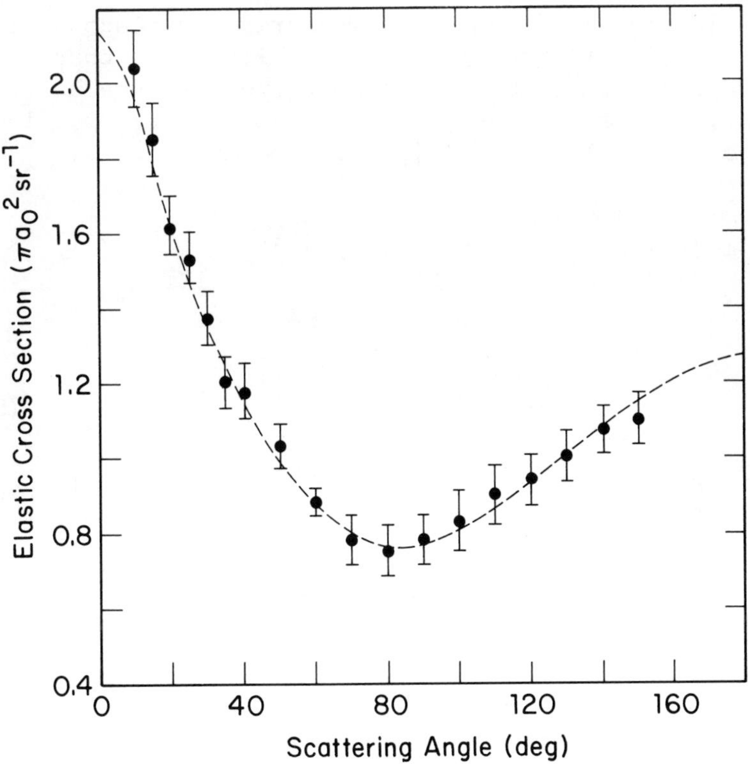

Figure 5-2. The differential cross section for the elastic scattering of electrons by atomic hydrogen at 4.89 ev. The line of dashes represents the theoretical prediction obtained as described in the text.

can be used as a trial function in the variational integral (5-12). On varying each of the unknown functions $F_n(\vec{r})$, in place of the single equation (5-15), we find a set of coupled integro-differential equations

$$\int \phi_n^*(\vec{r}_1)(H - E)\psi_t^S(\vec{r}_1,\vec{r}_2)d^3r_1 = o, \quad n = o,1,..N \quad (5-78)$$

The boundary conditions satisfied by the unknown functions F_n are (5-7) for n = o and $F_n(\vec{r}_1) \to 0$, as $r_1 \to \infty$ for $n \neq o$. In numerical applications, an expansion in eigenstates of the angular momentum is used to reduce (5-78) to sets of coupled equations in one radial variable. Using the notation introduced in Section 4-3, the total orbital angular momentum quantum number is L, with Z component M, the angular momentum quantum numbers of the hydrogenic target in channel i are ℓ_i, m_i and of the scattered electron are L_i, M_i.

The Hamiltonian (and hence the T-matrix) is diagonal in L and M, and also in the spin S and parity Π, so that each eigenfunction $\psi_{LM}{}^{S\Pi}$ corresponding to the eigenvalues L,M, S and Π, can be considered separately. Corresponding to (5-77) each trial function $\psi_{LM}{}^{S\Pi}$ can be expanded as

$$\psi_{LM}{}^{S\Pi} = \left(1+(-1)^{S}P_{12}\right) \sum_{n_i \ell_i L_i} R_{n_i \ell_i}(r_1) r_2{}^{-1} F_{n_i \ell_i L_i}{}^{LS\Pi}(r_2) \quad \times$$

$$\times \quad \mathcal{Y}_{\ell_i L_i}{}^{LM}(\theta_1, \phi_1, \theta_2, \phi_2) \qquad (5\text{-}79)$$

where $R_{n_i \ell_i}(r)$ is a radial hydrogenic wave function,

$F_{n_i \ell_i L_i}{}^{LS\Pi}$ is a radial partial wave scattering function

and

$\mathcal{Y}_{\ell_i L_i}{}^{LM}$ is a simultaneous eigenfunction of the total

orbital angular momentum, its Z component and the orbital angular momentum, its Z component and the orbital angular momentum of the target and scattered particles. The explicit form of

$$\mathcal{Y}_{\ell_i L_i}{}^{LM}$$

is given in Appendix B. By the rules of addition of angular momenta, for given values of L and ℓ_i, the angular momentum of the partial wave is restricted to the range

$$|L - \ell_i| \le L_i \le (L + \ell_i).$$

In addition conservation of parity

$$\Pi = (-1)^{L_i + \ell_i}$$

imposes a further restriction.

The coupled radial equations for the functions

$$F_{n_i \ell_i L_i}{}^{LS\Pi}$$

can be found from equations similar to (5-78). Using a simplified notation in which i denotes the set of quantum numbers $n_i \ell_i L_i$, the radial equations for each set of conserved quantities $LS\Pi$ take the form:

$$\left(\frac{d^2}{dr^2} - \frac{L_i(L_i+1)}{r^2} + k_i^2\right)F_i(r) = \sum_j \left(W_{ij}(r)F_j(r) + (-1)^S \int_0^\infty dr' K_{ij}(r,r')F_j(r')\right), i=o,1,2.. \tag{5-80}$$

where the $W_{ij}(r)$ are direct (local) potential matrix elements and the $K_{ij}(r,r')$ are exchange (non-local) potential matrix elements. Details of the calculation of the potential matrices are given by Percival and Seaton (1957). Below the first inelastic threshold, there is only one open channel labeled i = o and the boundary condition is ($\ell_o = o$, $L_o = L$)

$$F_{1,0,L}^{LS\Pi}(r) \sim \sin(k_o r - L\Pi/2) + \tan \delta_L^S \cos(k_o r - L\Pi/2) \tag{5-81}$$

and in all other channels $i \neq o$

$$F_j(r) \sim 0, \quad r \to \infty \tag{5-82}$$

The direct numerical solution of the sets of coupled equations (5-80) has been discussed by Burke and Seaton (1971) (see also Crees et al 1978, Rowntree et al 1976). Alternatively the R-matrix or Fredholm methods discussed in Chapter 2 can be extended to coupled equations (see for example Burke and Robb 1975) or a variational method employing algebraic trial functions can be used (Callaway 1978a,1980)

Dipole polarization effects arise from the p states of the hydrogen atom retained in the expansion (5-79). About 66% of the polarizability arises from the 2p state, but only 82% arises from all discrete p states, leaving 18% from the continuum, and this suggests that the results may converge rather slowly as more discrete states are included in the expansion. However, as will be shown later, the phase shifts obtained in this way satisfy a minimum principle. Below the first excitation threshold, if the 1s - 2s - 2p states of hydrogen are included in the expansion the resulting phase shifts lie between half and three-quarters of the way between those of the static exchange method and the exact phase shifts The inclusion of the 3s and 3p states only improves the result slightly, illustrating the slow rate of convergence.

Despite the poor convergence rate, results of outstanding importance have been obtained within the close coupling method A narrow resonance in the singlet s phase shift, superimposed on a smooth background was first discovered in the 1s - 2s state approximation (Smith et al., 1962) and later confirmed in the 1s - 2s - 2p approximation (Burke and Schey, 1962) at an energy (9.61 ev) just below the excitation threshold (10.2 ev). The width of the resonance was about 0.11 ev. A further resonance occurs in the 1s - 2s - 2p approximation in the triplet p wave at 9.78 ev with a width ~0.009 ev, and possibly there are also resonances in the singlet p and triplet d waves. These resonances will be discussed in Chapter 7. The close coupling method is also well adapted for use above the first inelastic threshold when the channels in which the electron moves relatively to the 2s and 2p states of hydrogen are open, and this circumstance is, as we shall see, connected with the success of the method in the description of resonances. To overcome the defect of the close coupling method that it cannot represent the long range potential fully, Damburg and Karule (1967) suggested that the sum over radial hydrogenic functions in (5-79) should be extended over one or more radial functions $\bar{R}_{n\ell}(r)$ of non-hydrogenic form chosen so that the full dipole polarizability calculated from (5-63b) is obtained from the set of functions $R_{n\ell}$, $\bar{R}_{n\ell}$ included in the trial function. To obtain the dipole polarizability such functions, called pseudofunctions, have to correspond to p states (ℓ = 1). The pseudostate suggested by Damburg and Karule, assumed no other p states were retained in the trial function and was of the form

$$\bar{R}_{21} = \left(\frac{32}{129}\right)^{\frac{1}{2}} r\ (1 + r/2)\exp(-r) \qquad (5\text{-}83)$$

If the true hydrogenic 2p level (and no other p level) is represented in the expansion, the full polarizability can be obtained by adding the function $\bar{R}_{31}$ which is orthogonal to R_{21} where

$$\bar{R}_{31} = 0.340\ r\ \exp(-r/2) - 0.966\ r(1+r/2)\exp(-r) \qquad (5\text{-}84)$$

Using a trial function in which the 1s and 2s hydrogenic

functions were retained in addition to the 2p and $\bar{3}$p functions (we shall mark pseudofunctions by a bar over the configuration), Burke et al (1969) were able to obtain accurate values for the elastic differential cross section in the forward direction, where the long range potential is particularly important.

By adding one or more pseudostate functions in other angular momentum states, the effect of the omitted terms, and in particular the continuum terms, in the expression (5-79) can be simulated. There is no unique prescription for determining pseudofunctions, but it is convenient to impose the condition that for a given target angular momentum ℓ, the set of functions $R_{n\ell}$, $\bar{R}_{n'\ell}$ retained in the trial function diagonalize the target Hamiltonian. This is easily achieved if the functions $\bar{R}_{n'\ell}$ are linear combinations of Slater orbitals of the form $r^p \exp(-\lambda r)$. The $\bar{R}_{n'\ell}$ are orthogonal to the true hydrogenic state retained in the expansion and we have

$$\int_0^\infty \left(r\bar{R}_{n'\ell}(r)\right)\left(-\frac{d^2}{dr^2}+\frac{\ell(\ell+1)}{r^2}-\frac{2}{r}\right)\left(r\bar{R}_{n''\ell}(r)\right)dr=\delta_{n'n''}\left(2\bar{\varepsilon}_{n'\ell}\right) \tag{5-85}$$

By the Rayleigh-Ritz principle, the energies $\bar{\varepsilon}_{n'}$ must be greater than the true hydrogenic energies corresponding to the same configuration ($\bar{\varepsilon}_{n'\ell}>\varepsilon_n$) and can be either positive or negative.

Retaining a relatively small number of pseudofunctions in addition to the 1s, 2s and 2p hydrogenic orbitals, in the basis set the computed phase shifts at low energies are very close to those of the most elaborate variational calculations (Callaway 1978a,b).

Mixed trial functions

A more general trial function is obtained if a trial function of algebraic type is added to the truncated eigenfunction expansion. Writing the trial function as

$$\psi_t^S(\vec{r}_1,\vec{r}_2)=[1+(-1)^S P_{12}]\left(\sum_{n=0}^{N}\phi_n(\vec{r}_1)F_n(\vec{r}_2)+\sum_{i=1}^{M}C_i\phi_i(\vec{r}_1,\vec{r}_2)\right) \tag{5-86}$$

where C_i are the variational parameters. The Kohn variation principle leads to the set of mixed integro-differential and algebraic equations (Gailitis, 1965a,b;

Burke and Taylor, 1966).

$$\int \phi_n^*(\vec{r}_1)(H - E)\psi_t^S(\vec{r}_1,\vec{r}_2)d^3r_1 = 0, \quad n = 0,1,2...N$$

$$\int \phi_i(\vec{r}_1,\vec{r}_2)(H - E)\psi_t^S(\vec{r}_1,\vec{r}_2)d^3r_1d^3r_2 = 0, \; i = 1,...M. \tag{5-87}$$

As we shall see this method retains the minimum property of the phase shifts and the results necessarily improve as further algebraic terms or close coupling terms are added. If algebraic terms similar in form to those used by Schwartz (the second term in curved brackets in (5-76) are added to the 1s - 2s - 2p close coupling wave function, convergence is reached using about sixteen parameters and agreement with the accurate results is obtained.

5-5 THE NON-ADIABATIC SOLUTION OF TEMKIN

An alternative to the variational method that allows the calculation of phase shifts for = 0 for the elastic scattering of electrons by hydrogen to arbitrary accuracy, has been introduced by Temkin (1962). If the total orbital angular momentum of the electron-hydrogen atom system is zero, the wave function is a function of r_1, r_2, and θ only, where $\cos\theta = \vec{r}_1 \cdot \vec{r}_2/(r_1r_2)$, and can be expanded in the Legendre polynomial series,

$$\psi^S(r_1,r_2,\theta) = r_1^{-1}r_2^{-1}\sum_{\ell=0}^{\infty}(2\ell + 1)^{\frac{1}{2}}\phi_\ell^S(r_1,r_2)P_\ell(\cos\theta). \tag{5-88}$$

If this expression is inserted in the Schrodinger equation, a set of coupled equations for the functions ϕ_ℓ^S is obtained. The boundary conditions are

$$\phi_\ell^S(r_1,0)=0; \quad \phi_o^S(r_1,r_2)\underset{r_1\to\infty}{\sim} r_2\phi_o(r_2)\sin(kr_1 + \delta_o^S), \tag{5-89}$$

and

$$\phi_\ell^S(r_1,r_2)\sim 0 \text{ as } r_1 \to \infty, \; \ell\neq 0$$

To ensure the correct symmetry of the wave function, we must have that

$$\phi_\ell^S(r_1,r_2) = (-1)^S\phi_\ell^S(r_2,r_1). \tag{5-90}$$

Because of this symmetry condition a solution is required only for $r_2 > r_1$ provided that the additional boundary conditions

$$\phi_\ell^{\,1}(r_1,r_1) = 0, \quad \left.\frac{\partial\phi_\ell^{\,o}(r_2,r_1)}{\partial n}\right|_{r_1=r_2} = 0 \tag{5-91}$$

are satisfied, where the differentiation, $\partial/\partial n$, is carried out in a direction in the r_1,r_2 plane perpendicular to the line $r_1=r_2$. Temkin has discussed various perturbative and non-perturbative methods for solving the truncated set of partial differential equations. In the lowest approximation, in which all the ϕ_ℓ are set equal to zero except for ϕ_o, it is found that ϕ_o satisfies

$$\left(\frac{\partial^2}{\partial r_1{}^2} + \frac{\partial^2}{\partial r_2{}^2} + \frac{2}{r_2} + 2E\right) \phi_o(r_1,r_2) = 0, \tag{5-92}$$

and this equation may be solved numerically. The solution is equivalent to that given by the close coupling equation in the approximation in which all s-states of the hydrogen atom are retained (both discrete and continuous). From the previous discussion of polarization, it is clear that to allow for dipole and quadrupole polarization the coupled equations for ϕ_o, ϕ_1 and ϕ_2 must be solved, in a sufficient approximation. The results of this calculational program (Temkin, 1962; Temkin and Sullivan, 1963) agree very well with those of Schwartz and Gailitis. For example, the scattering lengths computed by

Temkin and Sullivan are $a_o^{\,o} = -5.6$, $a_o^{\,1} = -1.767$ and those given by Schwartz are $a_o^{\,o} = -5.965$, $a_o^{\,1} = -1.769$.

The resonances discovered below the first excitation threshold in the close coupling approximations can also be found by the non-adiabatic method and an additional singlet resonance is found in this way (Temkin, 1964). The formalism may be generalized for total angular momentum L greater than zero (Temkin and Bhatia, 1964), but unlike the other methods we have discussed, extension to systems of more than two electrons is hardly practicable, the importance of the work lying in the establishment of effectively exact results in the electron-hydrogen atom problem.

5-6 THE ESTABLISHMENT OF BOUNDS AND THE OPTICAL POTENTIAL

In Chapter 2, the Kohn variational method was shown to provide a lower bound to the scattering length in the case of potential scattering, provided that the trial function was of the form

$$\psi_t = \psi + \sum_{i=1}^{N} \lambda_i \phi_i, \tag{5-93}$$

where, if there are N bound states, the ϕ_i are approximate bound state eigenfunctions and the λ_i are parameters. The analysis can be generalized to many particle systems (Spruch and Rosenberg, 1960; Rosenberg et al., 1960) but it is necessary that the trial function should have the correct asymptotic form, which is for $\ell = 0$:

$$\psi_t(\vec{r},\vec{x}) = \phi_o(x)\left(A_t + \frac{1}{r}\right) \tag{5-94}$$

where ϕ_o is the target wave function. Unless the target wave function is known exactly, the scattering length obtained by the variational method will not obey a strict bound. It follows that strict bounds can only be obtained in this way for collisions in which the target is a hydrogen atom, although in practice, if the target wave function is known to a good approximation, quite accurate variational calculations can be made[4].

In the triplet state no bound state of the electron-hydrogen atom system exists, and the Kohn variational method for electron-hydrogen atom scattering immediately provides a lower bound on the scattering length, but in the singlet state a single state of the negative hydrogen H^- exists with $\varepsilon = -0.75$ ev and the trial function must contain a term describing this state. When comparing different trial functions the one giving the largest value of the scattering length is the best, and the results (quoted in Table 5-2) of the variational calculations of Schwartz represent the best lower bounds on the scattering length at present[5].

Projection operators and the optical potential

Above the threshold, it is possible to place a lower bound on the phase shift[6]. To do this we shall first describe a projection operator formalism due to Feshbach (1958, 1962), by which the scattering is described by an equivalent or 'optical' non-local potential. The method can be generalized to deal with systems with several open channels, but we shall continue to confine our attention at this point to energies below the first excitation threshold.

A projection operator P is introduced that projects the component of the wave function containing the open channel out of the complete wave function. For the scattering of electrons by hydrogen atoms, P is defined by the properties

$$P\psi^s(\vec{r}_1,\vec{r}_2) \xrightarrow[r_1\to\infty]{} F^s(\vec{r}_1)\phi_o(r_2), \tag{5-95a}$$

$$\xrightarrow[r_2\to\infty]{} (-1)^s F^s(\vec{r}_2)\phi_o(r_1), \tag{5-95b}$$

where F^s is given by (5-7).

It is clear that P defined in this way is highly non-unique, because it amounts to projecting <u>any</u> subspace containing the open channel out of the total Hilbert space for the problem. A particular choice is obtained by defining

$$P = P_1 + P_2 - P_1P_2, \tag{5-96}$$

where

$$P_1\psi^s(\vec{r}_1,\vec{r}_2) = \phi_o(r_1)\int_0^\infty \phi_o^*(r_1')\psi^s(\vec{r}_1{}',\vec{r}_2)d^3r_1'. \tag{5-97a}$$

$$P_2\psi^s(\vec{r}_1,\vec{r}_2) = \phi_o(r_2)\int_0^\infty \phi_o^*(r_2')\psi^s(\vec{r}_1,\vec{r}_2{}')d^3r_2'. \tag{5-97b}$$

In this equation ϕ_o is, as usual, the normalized ground state wave function of hydrogen. $(P_1\psi^s)$ has the asymptotic form of (5-95b) for large r_2) and vanishes for large r_1, while $(P_2\psi^s)$ satisfies condition (5-95a) for large r_1, and vanishes for large r_2. It is necessary to include the term P_1P_2 in the definition (5-96) so that P satisfies $P^2 = P$, since although $P_1{}^2 = P_1$ and $P_2{}^2 = P_2$, P_1P_2 is not zero. Using the expansion (5-43), the action of P is to project out a term of the same form as the first term in the series representing direct and exchange scattering in the elastic scattering channel

$$P\psi(\vec{r}_1,\vec{r}_2) = \phi_o(r_2)\bar{F}_o(\vec{r}_1) + \phi_o(r_1)\bar{G}_o(\vec{r}_2), \tag{5-98}$$

or if the symmetrized expansion (5-45) is used, a term of the same form as the first term is again projected out

$$\mathcal{P}\psi^s = \phi_o(r_2)\bar{F}_o^{\,s}(\vec{r}_1) + (-1)^s\phi_o(r_1)\bar{F}_o^{\,s}(\vec{r}_2). \tag{5-99}$$

The functions $\bar{F}_o(\vec{r})$ and $\bar{G}_o(\vec{r})$ coincide with $F_o(\vec{r})$ and $G_o(\vec{r})$ respectively at large r, but differ at small values of r, and in the same way the functions $\bar{F}_o^{\,s}(\vec{r})$ and $F_o^{\,s}(\vec{r})$ become identical at large r and define the same scattering amplitudes $f^s(\theta)$.

The complexity of the projection operator arises from the identity of the target and scattered electrons, which ensures that the rearranged channel is always open. For positron-hydrogen atom scattering, at energies below the threshold for positronium formation[7], the boundary conditions on the wave functions are just those of equations (5-32, 5-33 and 5-34), where $\vec{r}_1$ is the coordinate at the positron, and a satisfactory projection operator would be given by $\mathcal{P}_2$ of equation (5-97).

If $\mathcal{Q}$ is defined by

$$\mathcal{Q} = 1 - \mathcal{P}, \tag{5-100}$$

$\mathcal{Q}$, is the operator that projects out the part of the wave functions not included in $\mathcal{P}\psi$. We have that

$$\mathcal{Q} = \mathcal{Q}, \quad \mathcal{QP} = \mathcal{PQ} = 0 \tag{5-101}$$

and

$$\psi = (\mathcal{P} + \mathcal{Q})\psi. \tag{5-102}$$

By operating from the left on the Schrödinger equation, first with $\mathcal{P}$ and then with $\mathcal{Q}$, the coupled equations

$$\mathcal{P}(H - E)\mathcal{P}\psi = -\mathcal{P}H\mathcal{Q}\psi \tag{5-103}$$

$$\mathcal{Q}(H - E)\mathcal{Q}\psi = -\mathcal{Q}H\mathcal{P}\psi \tag{5-104}$$

are found, which are rigorously equivalent to the original Schrödinger equation. Equation (5-104) can be solved formally, since

$$\mathcal{Q}\psi = \frac{-1}{\mathcal{Q}(H - E)\mathcal{Q}}\,\mathcal{Q}H\mathcal{P}\psi \tag{5-105}$$

where no problems arise in the specification of the Green's function, since the continuum spectrum of the wave operator $\mathcal{Q}H\mathcal{Q}$ starts at the first excitation threshold. The wave function $\mathcal{Q}\psi$ represents some or all of the closed channels, so that

$$\mathcal{Q}\psi \to 0 \quad \text{as} \quad |\vec{r}_1| \to \infty \quad \text{or} \quad |\vec{r}_2| \to 0 \tag{5-106}$$

Substituting $\mathcal{Q}\psi$ into the equation for $\mathcal{P}\psi$, we find

$$[\mathcal{P}H\mathcal{P} + V_p - E]\mathcal{P}\psi = 0, \tag{5-107}$$

where V_p is the optical potential:

$$V_p = -\mathcal{P}H\mathcal{Q}\frac{1}{\mathcal{Q}(H - E)\mathcal{Q}}\mathcal{Q}H\mathcal{P} \tag{5-108}$$

To investigate the form of V_p, the Green's function $[\mathcal{Q}(H - E)\mathcal{Q}]^{-1}$ can be constructed from the eigenfunctions of $\mathcal{Q}H\mathcal{Q}$, denoted by Φ_n, where

$$[\mathcal{Q}H\mathcal{Q} - \eta_n]\Phi_n(\vec{r}_1,\vec{r}_2) = 0 \tag{5-109}$$

The Φ_n span the closed channel subspace, so that the normalization and closure conditions are

$$(\Phi_n,\Phi_m) = \delta_{nm}; \quad \sum_n |\phi_n)(\Phi_n| = \mathcal{Q}, \tag{5-110}$$

while $\mathcal{Q}\Phi_n = \Phi_n$; $\mathcal{P}\Phi_n = 0$. The optical potential is then

$$V_p = -\sum_n \mathcal{P}H\,|\,\Phi_n)\frac{1}{(\eta_n - E)}(\Phi_n\,|H\mathcal{P}. \tag{5-111}$$

The spectrum of $\mathcal{Q}H\mathcal{Q}$ becomes continuous at the threshold for excitation of the 2s and 2p levels of hydrogen, that is η_n is continuous above $\eta_n = \varepsilon_2$ where ε_2 is the energy of the 2s and 2p levels. Below the energy ε_2, $\mathcal{Q}H\mathcal{Q}$ may have (and in the case of electron-hydrogen scattering does have) a discrete spectrum at energies η_0, η_1,η_2,.... When E the total energy is less than the lowest discrete energy η_0, V_p is a negative definite operator and represents an effective attraction. From the arguments given in Chapters 1 and 2, it follows that a phase shift computed from equation (5-107) with V_p set equal to zero must be less than the true phase shift. When $\mathcal{P}$ is given by (5-96, 5-97) and $V_p = 0$, we obtain the static exchange approximation, which therefore provides a lower bound to the phase shifts. Further, if V_p is approximated by taking a finite number of terms in the sum in (5-111), then as the number of terms is increased, so that the set of functions Φ_n spans more and more of the closed sub-space, the phase shift will steadily increase. This argument will hold, not only for the set of functions Φ_n, but for any set of functions spanning the Q space or part of the Q space.

If $\mathcal{Q}\psi$ is expanded in terms of a symmetrized set of hydrogen atom eigenfunctions, the phase shift for a given ℓ must increase steadily as the number of terms in the set increases and at each stage of the calculation a lower bound is obtained. This expansion is identical with the close coupling expansion, which therefore always provides a bound on the phase shift. The same is true for the solution of the variational equation with the mixed algebraic and close coupling trial function referred to earlier (Gailitis, 1965a,b). The Kohn variational procedure will provide a bound even if the trial function for $\mathcal{Q}\psi$ is not orthogonal to $\mathcal{P}\psi$, as required by the relation $\mathcal{P}\mathcal{Q} = 0$. This is because (Burke and Taylor, 1966) any part of a trial function for $\mathcal{Q}\psi$ which is orthogonal to $\mathcal{P}\psi$ can be added to $\mathcal{P}\psi$ without altering the asymptotic form of $\mathcal{P}\psi$.

The discrete eigenvalue spectrum of $\mathcal{Q}H\mathcal{Q}$ gives rise to singularities in the optical potential, which, as we shall see, lead to resonances in elastic scattering of the kind discussed in Chapter 4. Following similar arguments to those given in Chapter 2, it can be shown that for all energies below the continuum of $\mathcal{Q}H\mathcal{Q}$ the lower bound on the phase shift is retained, provided the trial function contains the same number of discrete states of $\mathcal{Q}H\mathcal{Q}$ as the exact wave function. Care has to be taken under these circumstances to define the phase shift in a consistent manner. For example, when $\mathcal{Q}\psi_t$ is set equal to zero, the phase shift is determined by applying the modified Levinson's theorem to the static-exchange equation. If $\mathcal{Q}\psi_t$ is gradually extended, then the phase shift will increase until, when sufficient of the Q-space is spanned by $\mathcal{Q}\psi_t$, a resonance will appear at the first excitation energy of the system. As $\mathcal{Q}\psi_t$ is further improved the resonance will move to lower energies and when it reaches a particular energy, the phase shift at that energy will increase by π. If there are N resonances below the energy under consideration, and if in the absence of V_p the phase shift satisfies $0 < \delta < \pi$, then the true phase shift will satisfy $N\pi < \delta < (N + 1)\pi$.

Another way of using the bound property is to construct inequalities of the kind (such as 2-35b) that we discussed in connection with bounds on the scattering length. If the wave function is expanded in eigenfunctions of angular momentum, denoted by ψ^ℓ, then $\mathcal{P}\psi^\ell$ can be defined by

$$\psi^{\ell} \underset{r_1\to\infty}{\to} \phi_o(r_2) r_1^{-1}\left(\cos\left(kr - \frac{\ell\pi}{2}\right) + \tan\delta_\ell \sin\left(kr_1 - \frac{\ell\pi}{2}\right)\right) P_\ell(\cos\theta_1).$$

At energies below the discrete spectrum of $\mathcal{Q}H\mathcal{Q}$ the following inequality can be shown to hold (Hahn, 1965)

$$\tan\delta_\ell \geq \tan\delta_\ell^{A} - (2\pi k)^{-1}\left(\mathcal{Q}\psi_t^{\ell},\ (H - E)\psi_t^{\ell}\right) \qquad (5\text{-}112)$$

where δ_ℓ^A is the phase shift computed from the equation

$$\mathcal{P}(H - E)\mathcal{P}\psi^{\ell} = -\mathcal{P}H\mathcal{Q}\psi^{\ell} \qquad (5\text{-}113)$$

Approximations to the optical potential

The exact optical potential V_p can be approximated in several ways. For example, it will be immediately apparent that $\phi_{pol}(\vec{r},\vec{x})$ defined by (5-60a) belongs to Q space, and that the potentials U_p and K_p appearing in (5-68) are approximations to the direct and exchange parts of the optical potential. In obtaining U_p (or K_p) from the exact expression (5-108), two steps are necessary; first, an expansion to second order in the matrix potentials V_{nm}, second, the neglect of the kinetic energy of the scattered electron in an intermediate state (the adiabatic approximation). To obtain the direct part of the optical potential to second order the potential V_{nm}, without the adiabatic approximation, we return to equations (5-50), which have the exact solution

$$F_n(\vec{r}_1) = \int d^3r_2 G_o^{c}(\lambda_n^{2};\vec{r}_1,\vec{r}_2)V_{no}(\vec{r}_2)F_o(\vec{r}_2) \qquad (5\text{-}114)$$

where G_o^c is the free particle Green's function for negative energies satisfying

$$(\nabla^2 - \lambda_n^{2})G_o^{c}(\vec{r}_1,\vec{r}_2) = \delta(\vec{r}_1-\vec{r}_2) \qquad (5\text{-}115)$$

Substituting (5-114) into the first equation of the set (5-46), we find

$$(\nabla^2 + k_o^{2})F_o(\vec{r}_1) = U_{oo}(r_1)F_o(\vec{r}_1)$$

$$+ \int d^3r_2 W_{oo}(\vec{r}_1,\vec{r}_2)F_o(\vec{r}_2) \qquad (5\text{-}116)$$

where $W_{oo}(\vec{r}_1,\vec{r}_2)$ is the second order term in the expansion of the optical potential

$$W_{oo}(\vec{r}_1,\vec{r}_2) = \sum_{n\neq 0} G_o^{\,c}(\lambda_n^{\,2};\vec{r}_1,\vec{r}_2)U_{on}(\vec{r}_1)U_{no}(\vec{r}_2) \tag{5-117}$$

No allowance for exchange has been made in equation (5-116), but this can be included by using symmetrized wave functions. To lowest order in the exchange potential we find

$$(\nabla^2 + k_o^{\,2})F_o^{\,s}(\vec{r}_1) = U_{oo}(r_1)F_o(\vec{r}_1) + \int d^3r_2 W_{oo}(\vec{r}_1,\vec{r}_2)F_o(\vec{r}_2) + (-1)^s \int d^3r_2 K(\vec{r}_1,\vec{r}_2)F_o(\vec{r}_2) \tag{5-118}$$

where K is given by (5-18). Like K, W is non-local but it is much more difficult to evaluate since it contains a sum over an infinite number of intermediate states, both discrete and continuous. Fortunately only a limited number of intermediate states turnout to be of importance and W_{oo} has been calculated numerically by Coulter and Garrett (1978). A slightly different evaluation of W_{oo} has been made by Scott and Bransden (1981), who replaced the continuum intermediate wave functions by pseudofunctions of the type we have already discussed. The phase shifts obtained by the solution (5-118) cannot compete in accuracy with some of the other methods we have discussed, but as we shall see in the next Chapter, the second order optical potential method can be extended to higher energies, above the inelastic thresholds, where the accurate variational methods cannot be employed.

5-7 ELASTIC SCATTERING OF ELECTRONS BY COMPLEX ATOMS

The general methods outlined in the earlier parts of this Chapter can be applied in principle to the scattering of electrons by complex atoms containing N electrons. The complete wave function for the (N + 1) electron system can be written as (cf.5-102)

$$\psi = \mathcal{P}\psi + \mathcal{Q}\psi \tag{5-119}$$

where $\mathcal{P}\psi$ contains the open elastic scattering channel and $\mathcal{Q}\psi$ vanishes as $r_i \to \infty$ for $i = 1,2,\ldots.(N + 1)$. The projection operators $\mathcal{P}$ and $\mathcal{Q}$ satisfy, as before

$$\mathcal{P}^2 = \mathcal{P}, \quad \mathcal{Q}^2 = \mathcal{Q}, \quad \mathcal{P}\mathcal{Q} = \mathcal{Q}\mathcal{P} = 0$$

$$\mathcal{P}+\mathcal{Q} = 1 \qquad (5\text{-}120)$$

If the antisymmetrized target eigenfunctions (including the spin functions) are denoted by $\Phi_n(1,2,...N)$, where $n = 0$ represents the ground state $\mathcal{P}\psi$ can be expressed as

$$\mathcal{P}\psi = \mathcal{A}\ \Phi_0(1,2,...N)\ F_0(N+1) \qquad (5\text{-}121)$$

where $F_0(m_s,\vec{r}_{N+1})$ is the wave function of the scattered electron (including a dependance on the spin m_s) and $\mathcal{A}$ is an antisymmetrization operator. The asymptotic form of F_0 determines the scattering amplitude and is given by (5-34a)

By setting $\mathcal{Q}\psi = 0$ and satisfying the equation

$$\Phi_0|H-E|\mathcal{P}\psi) = 0$$

where H is the total Hamiltonian of the (N + 1) electron system and E is the total energy, the static exchange approximation is obtained. Similarly by replacing Φ_0 in (5-121) by the target wave function perturbed by the field of the incident electron in the adiabatic approximation, we obtained the polarized orbital approximation.

The closed channel wave function $\mathcal{Q}\psi$ can be expanded as

$$\mathcal{Q}\psi = \sum_{n\neq 0} \mathcal{A}\Phi_n(1,2,.....N)F_n\ (N+1) \qquad (5\text{-}122)$$

In the close coupling method a finite number of terms is retained in this expansion, and coupled equations for functions F_n are found as in the case of electron-hydrogen scattering. The functions Φ_n can be augmented by pseudo-functions to represent the continuum states of the target, as before. The coupled equations for the functions F_n can be solved directly, or by the R-matrix method or by various variational procedures. An alternative method is to express $\mathcal{Q}\psi$ by the linear combination

$$\mathcal{Q}\psi = \sum_{i=1}^{M} c_i\chi_i(1,2,.....N+1) \qquad (5\text{-}123)$$

where the functions χ_i are predetermined fully antisymmetrical (N + 1) electron wave functions, orthogonal to $\mathcal{P}\psi$ and bounded, and the C_i are coefficients. The functions $\mathcal{P}\psi$ and $\mathcal{Q}\psi$ satisfy the coupled equations (5-103), (5-104) from which we saw that $\mathcal{P}\psi$ satisfies the Schrödinger equation (5-107) with the optical potential (5-108). With a trial function of the form (5-123), the coefficients C_i can be found by satisfying (5-104) in the sub-space spanned by the functions χ_i, which requires

$$\left(\chi_i \middle| H - E \middle| \sum_{j=1}^{m} C_j \chi_j\right) = - \left(\chi_i \middle| H \middle| \mathcal{P}\psi\right) \quad i = 1,2,\ldots N \qquad (5\text{-}124)$$

It follows that

$$C_i = \sum_{k=1}^{m} \left(Z^{-1}\right)_{ik} \left(\chi_k \middle| H \middle| \mathcal{P}\psi\right) \qquad (5\text{-}125)$$

where Z is the matrix with elements

$$Z_{ik} = (\chi_i | H - E | \chi_j) \qquad (5\text{-}126)$$

The optical potential (5-108) is given in this approximation by

$$V_p = - \sum_{i,k} \mathcal{P}H|\chi_i)\left(Z^{-1}\right)_{ik} \left(\chi_k \middle| H \middle| \mathcal{P}\psi\right) \qquad (5\text{-}127)$$

The basis function χ_i can be expressed as combinations of Slater determinants of one particle orbitals. A systematic procedure for determining the χ_i which allows for the distortion, or response, of the target to the perturbating field of the scattered electron, based on the Bethe-Goldstone equations has been described by Mittleman (1966) and developed particularly by Nesbet and his collaborators (Nesbet, 1975, 1980).

Various other methods for calculating the optical potential have been devised. For example perturbation expansions can be made in terms of a basis of Hartree-Fock orbitals (Kelly, 1967; Pu and Cheng, 1966; Knowles and McDowell, 1973) or Schwinger's formulation of many-body theory can be applied (Csanak et al. 1971; Thomas et al. 1973).

We shall now discuss some particular cases briefly to illustrate typical applications of the low energy theoretical models.

Helium

After atomic hydrogen, the simplest atom is that of helium, for which the Hartree-Fock wave function[8] for the ground state can be written as

$$\Phi_0 = \phi_0(r_1)\phi_0(r_2)\chi_{0,0}(1,2) \tag{5-129}$$

where $\chi_{0,0}(1,2)$ is the singlet spin function (5-2). The exact Hartree-Fock orbitals are well represented by the form

$$\phi_0(r) = N\,(e^{-ar} + be^{-cr}) \tag{5-130}$$

where N is a normalization constant and a,b and c can be determined by the Rayleigh-Ritz variational method. It is found that (Byron and Joachain 1966), in atomic units

$$a = 1.41 \qquad b = 0.799 \qquad c = 2.61 \qquad N = 0.73485$$

Much of the earlier work was based on the even simpler function

$$\phi_0(r) = \left(\frac{\pi}{\lambda}\right)^{3/2} e^{-\lambda r}, \tag{5-131}$$

The constant λ which represents the effective charge seen by one electron moving in the Coulomb field of the nucleus, screened by the second electron. In atomic units λ has the value 1.6875.

The static exchange approximation for elastic scattering is based on the trial function

$$\mathcal{P}\psi(1,2,3) = (1 - P_{12} - P_{13}) \times$$

$$\times\ \phi_0(r_2)\phi_0(r_3)F_0(\vec{r}_1)\chi_{\frac{1}{2},\pm\frac{1}{2}}(1,2,3) \tag{5-132}$$

where P_{ij} is the operator that exchanges all the coordinates (including spin) of particles i and j and $\chi_{\frac{1}{2},\pm\frac{1}{2}}$ is the doublet spin function:

$$\chi_{\frac{1}{2},\pm\frac{1}{2}}(1,2,3) = \frac{1}{\sqrt{2}} \left.\begin{matrix}\alpha(1)\\ \beta(1)\end{matrix}\right\} [\alpha(2)\beta(3) - \beta(2)\alpha(3)]. \tag{5-133}$$

With this wave function an integro-differential equation for $F_0(r)$ is obtained which is similar to equation (5-16), for electron-hydrogen atom scattering. The radial equations have been solved by Morse and Allis (1933) for the partial waves $\ell = 0$ and $\ell = 1$, and for $\ell = 2$ (d-wave) by Massey et al. (1966). Morse and Allis found that if the exchange kernel was neglected it was impossible to obtain reasonable agreement with the measured cross section, particularly at the lowest energies. The results of the static exchange approximation agree rather well with the measured total cross sections and reasonably well with the differential cross sections.

To include the effects due to the distortion of the atom, the polarized orbital method has been used. The polarized wave function is again written in the Hartree-Fock form (5-129) but the orbitals $\phi(r_i)$ are modified by

$$\phi_o(r_i) \to \phi_o(r_i) + \phi_o^{P}(\vec{r}_i, \vec{x})$$

where $\vec{x}$ is the position vector of the scattered electron. ϕ^P can be calculated to first order in perturbation theory using the adiabatic approximation. The polarization potential is not as important as in the case of atomic hydrogen, because of the small polarizability of helium (see Table 5-4) and the results of polarized orbital calculations[9] agree rather well with both the measured angular distributions[10] (see Fig. 5-3) and the total cross section data[11] (see Fig. 5-4). For $\ell \geq 2$, the phase shifts are determined largely by the tail of the potential and can be calculated accurately from equation (3-80).

Since about half of the polarizability of helium derives from continuum intermediate states, the ordinary close coupling method is not satisfactory, but accurate results have been obtained by adding pseudostates which allow for both dipole and quadruple long range potentials (O'Malley et al 1979). Phase shifts of high accuracy have also been calculated by Nesbet (1979) from the optical potential (5-127) using basis functions determined from the Bethe-Goldstone scheme.

In addition to the total and differential cross sections measurements have also been made of the momentum transfer cross section, which is a measure of the average forward momentum of the projectile lost in a collision. In the center of mass system, the change in the forward momentum of the projectile is $\mu v(1 - \cos\theta)$ where μ is the reduced mass, v the relative velocity and θ is the scattering angle.

Table 5-4

Parameters in the long range part of the effective potential between an electron and atom in the ground state

(see equation 5-64)

	Atomic units								
	H	He	Ne	A	Kr	Xe	Li	Na	K
α_1	4.5	1.39	2.67	11.1	16.8	27.1	164	159	293
α_2	15	2.41	9.0	72.9	-	-	-	-	-
β_1	5.375	0.706	1.27	8.33	14.50	29.15	1.18×10^3	1.1×10^3	2.4×10^3

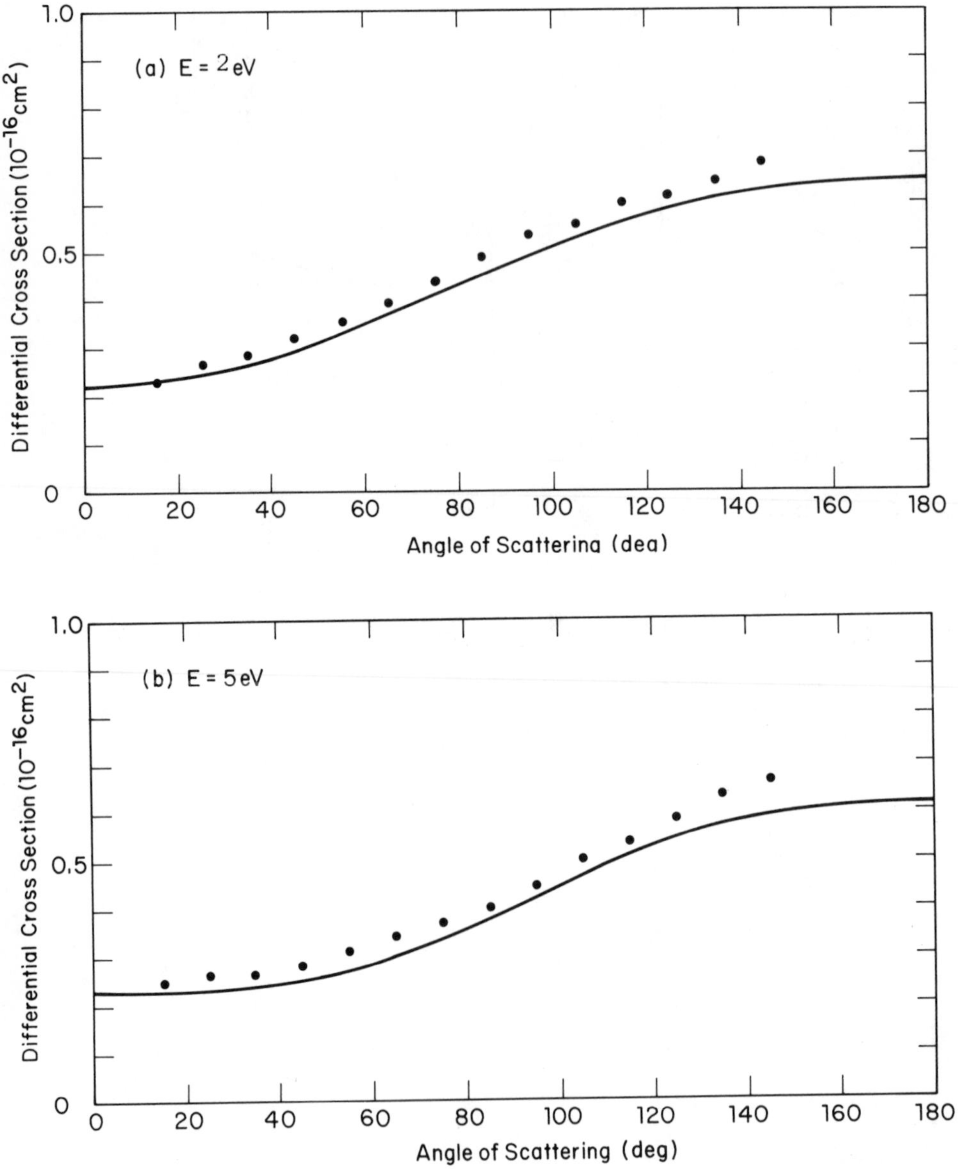

Figure 5-3 Angular distributions for the elastic scattering of electrons by helium.

• • • • • • Experimental data of Andrick and Bitsch (1975)

——————— Calculated cross section from the phase shifts of Yau et al (1978)

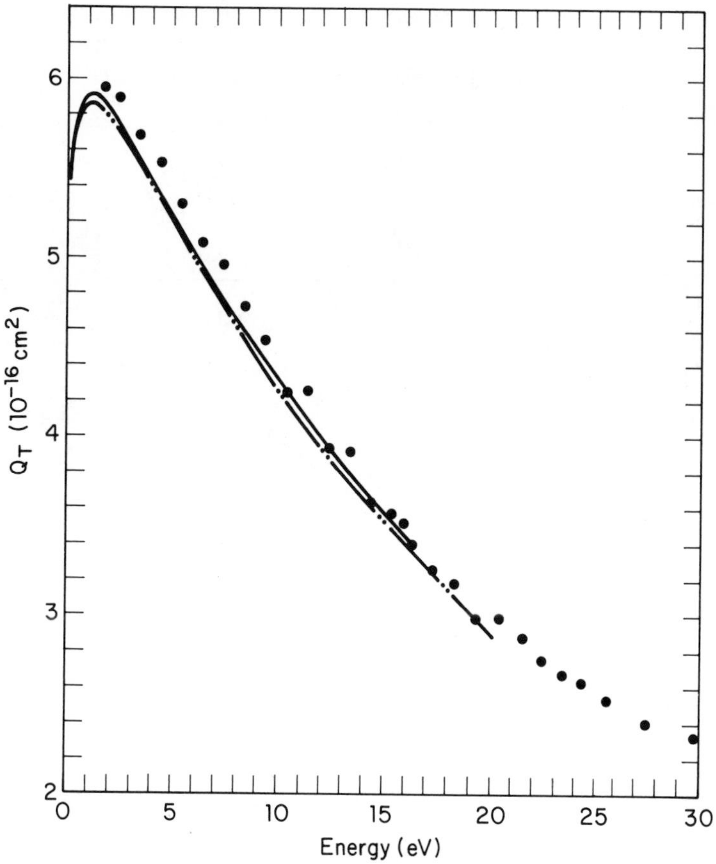

Figure 5-4 The total elastic cross section for electron helium scattering

—··—··— ·· Polarised orbital model (Callaway et al. 1968)

———— Variational method of Nesbet (1979)

• • • • • • Experimental data Stein et al (1978)

The momentum transfer cross section is then defined as

$$\sigma_D = \int (1 - \cos \theta) \left(\frac{d\sigma}{d\Omega}\right) d\Omega, \qquad (5\text{-}134)$$

where $(d\sigma/d\Omega)$ is the usual differential cross section. If the scattering is isotropic, it is clear that $\sigma_D = \sigma$, where σ is the total cross section; but if the scattering is concentrated in the forward direction $\sigma_D < \sigma$ while if it is concentrated in the backward direction $\sigma_D > \sigma$.

For electron-helium collisions the measurements of the momentum transfer cross section agree rather well with the best theoretical predictions (see Fig. 5-5).

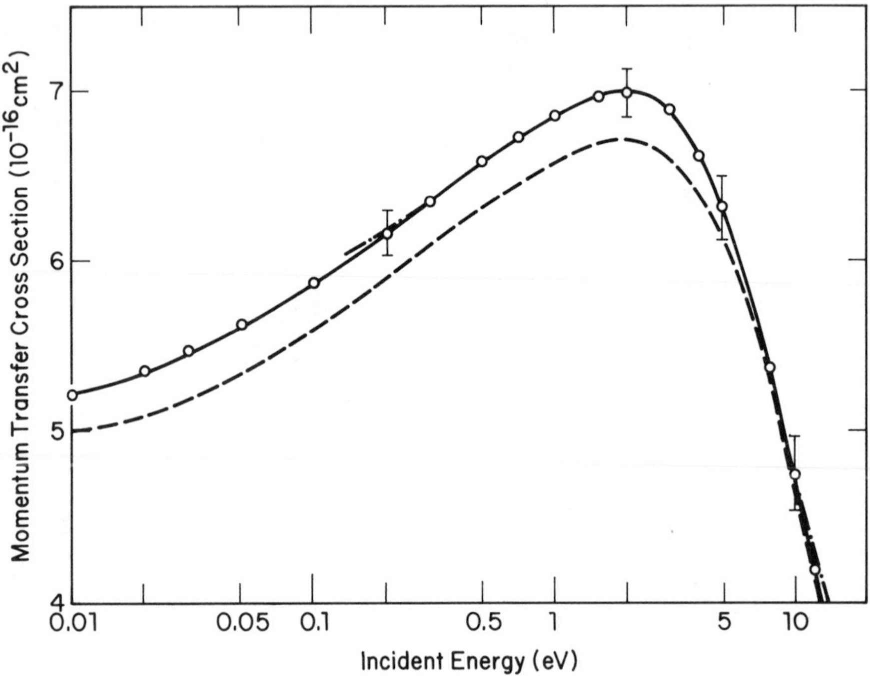

Figure 5-5 The momentum transfer cross section for electron-helium scattering.

– – – – – – Polarised orbital model (Callaway et al 1968)

———— Variational method of Nesbet (1979)

• • • • • • Experimental data of Milloy and Crompton (1977) and Crompton et al (1970)

The inert gases

The total cross sections for elastic scattering of electrons by the heavier inert gases, argon, krypton and xenon, exhibit very deep minima nearly vanishing at an energy close to 0.5 ev. This effect, known as the Ramsauer-Townsend effect is due to the s-wave ($\ell = 0$) phase shift passing through a multiple of π at an energy for which the phase shift for $\ell \geq 1$ are very small (see Chapter 3,p.128).

Using the Hartree-Fock wave functions for the target, polarized orbital calculations have been carried out for argon and neon (Thompson, 1966). The results for both the total and differential cross sections are remarkably good, the Ramsauer-Townsend minimum in the cross section being well reproduced in argon. Earlier calculations by Holtsmark (1930), using a semi-empirical polarization potential, include the case of electron-krypton scattering for which good agreement is also obtained. The parameters of the long range part of the potential are shown in Table 5-4.

Oxygen

The ground state of the oxygen atom is in a $2p^4$ configuration, the ^3P term lying lowest. The total spin of an electron-oxygen atom system is either S = 1/2 or S = 3/2. Bates and Massey (1943, 1947) calculated the s-wave phase shifts for each spin state using an empirical polarization term and, polarized orbital calculations have been made by Temkin (1957) and Henry (1967). In the work of Henry the dipole polarization terms were calculated assuming that no contribution arose from the closed $1s^2$ shell, that the 2s shell wave functions were perturbed only by p-states, and the 2p shell wave functions by s and d states. The calculated polarizability of 5.15 agrees well with that found experimentally (5.19). Using these results the cross section for photo-detachment from the oxygen negative ion O^- can be calculated and compares rather favourably with experiment.

Several other calculations have been made of elastic scattering in the low energy region up to ~12 ev. Perhaps the most accurate are those based on the Bethe-Goldstone method (Thomas and Nesbet, 1975) and those using a pseudo-state expansion (Tambe and Henry, 1976). The experimental data are not sufficiently precise to distinguish between the various models. Detailed reviews of these and related calculations and of similar work on electron scattering by carbon and nitrogen have been given by Nesbet (1977, 1980).

The alkali atoms

In the ground state of the alkali atoms there is a single valence electron in an s-state outside closed inner shells. The polarizability is large (see Table 5-4) and the coupling between the ground state and first excited p state contributes at least 98% of the sum (5-55) that determines $U_p(r)$. It follows that a good approximation is the inclusion of just these states, the $n_0 s$ and $n_0 p$ states in the close coupling expansion. Such two state calculations have been carried out by Karule (1965, 1972) for Li, Na, K and Cs at energies below the first inelastic threshold. The Bethe-Goldstone variational method (Sin Fai Lam and Nesbet, 1973) provides cross sections for Li, Na and for K in substantial agreement with the close coupling results and with the experimental data. In general, the polarized orbital method could not be expected to be very successful for targets having very large polarizabilities, but Vo Ky Lan (1971) has shown for e^--Li elastic scattering results agreeing with the close coupling model can be obtained if the exchange polarization potential is included in the model.

NOTES

1. The Pauli exclusion principle is discussed in the books by Merzbacher (1970) and by Bransden and Joachain (1982).

2. We follow the treatment of Castillejo et al (1960).

3. The polarized orbital method was introduced by Temkin (1957, 1960). Later developments have been reviewed by Drachman and Temkin (1972) and by Callaway (1973).

4. New methods are being developed with the aim of removing the requirement that the target wave function is known exactly (Blau et al, 1975).

5. Methods providing upper bounds can be formulated (Hahn, 1965; Sugar and Blankenbecler, 1964), but usually the matrix elements of H^2 are required for this purpose which are difficult to calculate.

6. The results to be described here and in Chapter 6 are mainly due to Spruch and his collaborators (Hahn et al. 1962, 1963, 1964a,b). Equivalent results have been obtained by Sugar and Blankenbecler (1964) in the determinantal method. See also the work of Gailitis (1965a,b) and Rosenberg (1965).

7. Surveys of the theory of positron scattering by atoms have been given by Bransden (1969) and by Humberston (1979)

8. Methods for obtaining approximate atomic wave functions are described in detail in the text by Bransden and Joachain (1982).

9. See Callaway et al (1968), Duxler et al (1971) and Yau et al (1978).

10. The earliest measurements of the differential cross sections were by Ramsauer and Kollath (1932). Recent results have been published by Andrick and Bitsch (1975). A least squares fit to the data to obtain experimental values of the phase shifts has been given by Williams (1979) who gives references to earlier work.

11. See Stein et al (1978) and Kennerley and Bonham (1978).

PROBLEMS

5.1 Using the amplitudes f_o and g_o defined by the boundary conditions (5-34) and (5-35), show that in the elastic scattering region, the optical theorem holds in the form

$$\sigma^s = \frac{4\pi}{k_o} \text{Im} \left(f_o(o) + (-1)^s g_o(o) \right)$$

where σ^s is the total cross section for scattering in the spin state s.

5.2 Starting from the definition (5-47) of the matrix potentials U_{nm} show that if n is an s-state (ℓ=0) and m is a state of angular momentum ℓ, then if $\ell \neq 0$

$$U_{nm}(r) \underset{r\to\infty}{\longrightarrow} A/r^{2\ell+1}$$

where A is a constant.
How does U_{nm} behave for large r if n is a p-state (ℓ=1)?

5.3 Starting from the perturbation expansions (5-58) obtain the results (5-59) and (5-61).

5.4 (a) Show that the explicit form of the direct potential W_{ij} appearing in (5-80) is

$$W_{ij}(r) = -2\delta_{ij}\left(\frac{1}{r}\right) + \sum_{\lambda} f_\lambda(\ell_i, L_i; \ell_j L_j; L) Y_\lambda(n_i \ell_i; n_j \ell_j | r)$$

where

$$Y_\lambda(n_i\ell_i; n_j\ell_j | r) = r^{-1-\lambda}\int_0^r dr' R_{n_i\ell_i}(r') R_{n_j\ell_j}(r') r'^{\lambda+2} + $$

$$+ r^\lambda \int_r^\infty dr' R_{n_i\ell_i}(r') R_{n_j\ell_j}(r') r'^{-\lambda+1}$$

and

$$f(\ell_i L_i; \ell_j L_j; L) = \sum_{m_i m_j} \left(\frac{(2\ell_j+1)(2L_j+1)}{(2\ell_i+1)(2L_i+1)}\right)^{\frac{1}{2}} \times$$

$$\times (\ell_j \lambda 00 | \ell_i 0)\ (L_j \lambda 00 | L_i 0) \times$$

$$\times (\ell_j \lambda m_j q | \ell_i m_i)\ (L_j \lambda M_j q | L_i M_i) \times$$

$$\times (\ell_i L_i m_i M_i | LM)\ (\ell_j L_j m_j M_j | LM)$$

where use has been made of the results of Appendix B.

(b) For $\ell_i, \ell_j < 2$, and $\pi = \pm 1$, find the range of values that can be taken by $L_i L_j$ and λ.

(c) Calculate $Y_\lambda(n_i\ell_i; n_j\ell_j | r)$ for $n_i=1$, $\ell_i=0$ and $n_i = 2$, $\ell_i = 0$; $n_i = 2$, $\ell_i = 1$.

(d) Show that the exchange kernel $K_{ij}(r,r')$ contains the angular momentum factor

$$g_\lambda(\ell_i L_i; \ell_j L_j; L) \equiv (-1)^{\ell_i+\ell_j-L} f_\lambda(\ell_i L_i; L_j \ell_j; L)$$

5.5 Show for elastic scattering of electrons by atomic hydrogen, if the projection operator $\mathcal{P}$ is defined by (5-96) and (5-97), then $\mathcal{Q}$ is an integral operator such that

$$\mathcal{Q}f(\vec{r}_1,\vec{r}_2) = \sum_{n\neq 0} \sum_{m\neq 0} \phi_n(\vec{r}_1)\phi_m(\vec{r}_2) \int d^3r_1' \int d^3r_2' \phi_n^*(\vec{r}_1') \times$$

$$\times \phi_m^*(\vec{r}_2')f(\vec{r}_1',\vec{r}_2')$$

where f is an arbitrary wave function.

5.6 Starting from the expression (5-132) obtain the static exchange equation satisfied by $F_0(\vec{r}_1)$ for electron scattering by helium, in a form resembling the corresponding equation for hydrogen (5-16).

Chapter 6

SCATTERING OF ELECTRONS BY ATOMS ABOVE THE INELASTIC THRESHOLD

In the last chapter, the scattering of electrons below the first excitation threshold was discussed. In this energy interval the scattering is purely elastic, although, because of the identity of the scattered and target electrons, exchange scattering, which can be considered as a particular case of a rearrangement collision is always possible. Above the inelastic threshold the elastic scattering can still be treated as a potential problem, but the effective (optical) potential V_p becomes complex, to allow for the loss of probability flux from the initial state. Using the optical theorem, such a treatment allows a calculation of the total cross section, but not of the cross sections for individual inelastic processes. To calculate individual cross sections most of the methods discussed for elastic scattering can be applied, provided the trial function contains components referring to both the incident and final channels and, in addition, methods based on perturbation theory are of considerable importance.

6-1 COUPLED CHANNEL AND RELATED APPROXIMATIONS

The exact wave function can be expanded in a complete set of target eigenfunctions under all circumstances, and above an inelastic threshold it is reasonable to use a truncated expansion as a trial function in the variational expression as we did for purely elastic scattering in Chapter 5. If the integral I is defined as

$$I = \int \psi^* (H - E) \psi d\tau \qquad (6\text{-}1)$$

then $\delta I = 0$, under arbitrary variations in ψ, provided that the trial functions satisfy boundary conditions of the same form as the exact functions. If $\delta I = 0$, the error in the scattering amplitude, or the reaction matrix, depending on the normalization adopted, will be of the second order. It follows that the coupled equations for the functions $F_n(r)$ are the same as those obtained for elastic scattering (5-78), but the boundary conditions satisfied by such of the F_n that represent open channels are now those specified in Chapter 4, equation (4-100). In the basis in which the angular momentum is diagonal, the equations are of the form (4-104) and the boundary conditions are those of equations (4-105). If the trial function ψ is properly symmetrized, thus allowing for exchange, the potentials U_{mn} are integral operators rather than simple local interactions.

The close coupling approximation, in which the truncated expansion in terms of the target eigenfunctions is employed without modification, can be satisfactory under some circumstances, but to obtain accurate cross sections improved methods are often necessary. These methods are extensions of those discussed in Chapter 5 and include the augmentation of the target eigenfunction expansion by the addition of pseudostates, and the application of the Bethe-Goldstone scheme of Nesbet in which a systematic variational method, based on a complete set of single particle orbitals, is used to construct the closed channel part of the wave function. The coupled equations can be solved by direct numerical methods or, indirectly by variational methods, by the R-matrix method, or by the Fredholm approach.

Provided all the open channels are represented in the trial wave function (which of course is not a practical possibility at higher energies for which the number of open channels becomes very large, or indeed, above the ionization threshold, infinite), the reaction matrix K calculated in a given approximation satisfies certain bounds which we shall now describe.

Bounds on the reaction matrix

In a single channel problem, it was shown that the phase shift was a monotonic function of the potential. The proof depended upon the potential being real and was only applicable to scattering that was purely elastic. When the potential is not local, but is an integral operator, the proof still holds, provided the potential operator is both self-adjoint and real. The extension of this result to many channel scattering has been discussed by several authors (Hahn et al., 1964a,b; Sugar and Blankenbecler, 1964) and we shall follows an argument due to Gailitis (1964).

Suppose there are N open channels, then the channel wave functions $f_{mi}(r)$ satisfy coupled equations of the form[1]

$$L_m f_{mi}(r) = \sum_{n=1}^{N} V_{mn} f_{ni}(r) \qquad m = 1,2,\ldots,N \tag{6-2a}$$

where

$$L_m = \frac{\hbar^2}{2\mu_m}\left(\frac{d^2}{dr^2} - \frac{\ell_m(\ell_m+1)}{r^2} + k_m^{\ 2}\right) \tag{6-2b}$$

As usual the subscript i on f_{mi} labels one of the N independent sets of solutions of the coupled equations defined by N sets of boundary conditions. The potential matrix V will be taken to be real and symmetrical and will be, in general, non-local so that

$$V_{mn} f_{ni} \equiv \int_0^\infty V_{mn}(r,r') f_{ni}(r') dr'$$

The effects of the closed channels can be described through the effective potential V, just as we discussed in Chapter 5 for the case of scattering in which only a single channel was open, but now V is an N x N matrix potential rather than a single potential. An expression for V is found below in equation (6-10).

The channel wave functions can be taken to be real, with the boundary conditions (cf.4-105)

$$f_{mi}(o) = o,$$

$$f_{mi}(r) \sim k_m^{-1}\left(s_{\ell_m}(k_m r)\delta_{mi} + \frac{\omega_i}{\omega_m} c_{\ell_m}(k_m r) K_{mi}\right) \tag{6-3}$$

where ω_i is defined by (4-50b)

$$\omega_i^{\ 2} = \hbar^2 / \left(\mu_i k_i\right)$$

and similarly for ω_m. The N x N quantities K_{mi} are the elements of the K or reaction matrix. Let us also consider a second set of equations similar to equations (6-2), but in which the potential matrix V is replaced by a different potential matrix $\overline{V}$, so that

$$\mathcal{L}_m \bar{f}_{mi}(r) = \sum_{n=1}^{N} \bar{V}_{mn} \bar{f}_{ni}(r) \qquad m = 1,2,\ldots.N \tag{6-4}$$

By multiplying equations (6-2) by $\bar{f}_{mj}$ and equations (6-4) by f_{mj}, subtracting the two sets of equations and summing over m, we find that

$$\sum_{m=1}^{N} \{\bar{f}_{mj}(r)\mathcal{L}_m f_{mi}(r) - f_{mj}(r)\mathcal{L}_m \bar{f}_{mi}(r)$$

$$= \sum_{m,n=1}^{N} \{\bar{f}_{mj}(r) V_{mn} f_{ni}(r) - f_{mj}(r)\bar{V}_{mn}\bar{f}_{ni}(r)\}$$

We now add these equations to the equations formed by interchanging i and j. On integrating over r, we obtain

$$\sum_{m=1}^{N} \frac{\hbar^2}{2\mu_m} \int_0^R dr \left(\bar{f}_{mj}(r)\frac{d^2}{dr^2} f_{mi}(r) - f_{mi}(r)\frac{d^2}{dr^2}\bar{f}_{mj}(r) + \right.$$

$$\left. + \bar{f}_{mi}(r)\frac{d^2}{dr^2} f_{mj}(r) - f_{mj}(r)\frac{d^2}{dr^2}\bar{f}_{mi}(r) \right)$$

$$= \sum_{m,n=1}^{N} \int_0^R dr \left(\bar{f}_{mj}(r)(V_{mn} - \bar{V}_{mn}) f_{ni}(r) + \right.$$

$$\left. + f_{mj}(r)(V_{mn} - \bar{V}_{mn})\bar{f}_{ni}(r) \right) \tag{6-5}$$

where on the right hand side we have used the fact that V and $\bar{V}$ are symmetrical. On integrating by parts the left hand side of the equation reduces to

$$\sum_{m=1}^{N} \frac{\hbar^2}{2\mu_m} \left| \bar{f}_{mj}(r)\frac{d}{dr} f_{mi}(r) - f_{mi}(r)\frac{d}{dr}\bar{f}_{mj}(r) + \right.$$

$$\left. + \bar{f}_{mi}(r)\frac{d}{dr} f_{mj}(r) - f_{mj}(r)\frac{d}{dr}\bar{f}_{mi}(r) \right|_0^R$$

On taking the limit $R \to \infty$ and using the asymptotic form of the functions f_{mi} and $\bar{f}_{mj}$, given by equation (6-3), this expression reduces to (using the fact that K is symmetrical)

$$\omega_i \omega_j \left(\bar{K}_{ji} - K_{ji} \right) \qquad (6\text{-}6)$$

and we can write finally, using a matrix notation, that

$$(\bar{K} - K) = d \int_0^\infty \left(\bar{\mathfrak{f}}^T (V - \bar{V}) \mathfrak{f} + \mathfrak{f}^T (V - \bar{V}) \bar{\mathfrak{f}} \right) dr \; d \qquad (6\text{-}7)$$

where $\mathfrak{f}^T$ denotes the transpose of the matrix $\mathfrak{f}$ and d is a diagonal matrix with elements:

$$d_{ij} = \delta_{ij} \left(\frac{1}{\omega_i} \right) \qquad (6\text{-}8)$$

It follows that if $\bar{V} < V$, then $\bar{K} > K$ provided the reaction matrix K varies continuously from K to $\bar{K}$ as V varies from V to $\bar{V}$. By the inequality $\bar{K} > K$, we mean that $(\bar{K} - K)$ is a positive matrix, which requires that

$$A^T (\bar{K} - K) A > 0 \qquad (6\text{-}9)$$

for all real column vectors A. If a matrix is positive, it follows that the eigenvalues and the trace of the matrix are all positive, but individual elements of the matrix may not be. In particular (6-9) implies that the sum of the eigenphase shifts for the potential $\bar{V}$ will be greater than the sum for V.

The continuity of K with the potential is essential to the argument, for if one of the eigenphases passes through $\pi/2$ as we pass from V to $\bar{V}$, K will become infinite at that point. However, at such a point the inverse reaction matrix K^{-1} will be continuous and this implies that the S matrix is always continuous in V. Writing $\bar{S} = S \exp(iW)$ we have, if $\bar{V} < V$, that W is always a positive matrix.

To use these results all that is necessary is to extend the definition of the projection operator P (introduced in Section 5-6), so that it projects, from the complete space spanned by the target eigenfunctions any sub-space that includes all the open channels. The coupled equations for $P\psi$ and $Q\psi$ can again be written in the form

$$P(H - E)P\psi = - PHQ\psi$$

$$Q(H - E)Q\psi = - QHP\psi$$

where the equation for $\mathcal{P}\psi$ is now a matrix equation like (6-2). Provided all the open channels are included in $\mathcal{P}\psi$, the matrix optical potential

$$\mathcal{V}_p = -\mathcal{P}H\mathcal{Q}\,\frac{1}{\mathcal{Q}(H - E)\mathcal{Q}}\,\mathcal{Q}H\mathcal{P} \tag{6-10}$$

is a negative definite operator, below the eigenvalue spectrum of $\mathcal{Q}H\mathcal{Q}$, and it follows that as the space spanned by $\mathcal{Q}\psi$ is progressively enlarged $\mathcal{V}_p$ becomes more and more negative. At each stage the eigenphases calculated from the solution of the coupled equations provide a lower bound. In particular, if all the open channels are included in the truncated expansion, the close coupling equations provide a bound on the eigenphases[2] which is improved as the closed channels are added, either directly or through algebraic trial functions.

<u>Excitation of hydrogen and the close coupling method</u>

An extensive investigation of the excitation of the 2s and 2p state of hydrogen was carried out within the close coupling approximation in the energy range between n = 2 threshold (k^2 = 0.75) and the n = 3 threshold (k^2 = 0.88), by Burke and his collaborators[3]. The explicit form of the close coupling wave function in the LS representation is given by (5-79); the appropriate boundary conditions being imposed on the radial functions. Correlation effects were investigated by adding to the close coupled part of the wave function additional closed channel terms depending explicitly on the inter-electron distance r_{12}. The additional terms were of the form

$$\Phi_{LM}^{S\Pi}(\vec{r}_1,\vec{r}_2) = \left(1+(-1)^S P_{12}\right)\sum_i\left(a_i e^{-\lambda_1 r_1-\lambda_2 r_2}+b_i e^{-\lambda_1 r_2-\lambda_2 r_1}\right)\times$$

$$\times\, r_1^{p_i}\, r_2^{q_i}\, r_{12}^{s_i}\, \mathcal{Y}_{\ell_i L_i}^{LM}(\theta_1,\phi_2;\theta_2,\phi_2) \tag{6-11}$$

where the parameters a_i, b_i... could be obtained by the variational method.

Provided the sum over the target eigenfunctions includes the 1s, 2s and 2p states, the trial function satisfies the correct boundary conditions below the n = 3 threshold and the calculated sum of the eigenphases represents a lower bound. Just below an excitation threshold resonances may exist, of the virtual bound state type. The resonance energies will be determined by the discrete spectrum of the closed channel Hamiltonian $\mathcal{Q}H\mathcal{Q}$ and it will be shown in the next chapter that the existence of a discrete spectrum is often connected with the long range forces associated with degenerate thresholds. In the present case, to allow for possible resonances just below the n = 3 threshold, the closed 3s, 3p and 3d states should be included in the close coupling expansion. Below the discrete spectrum of ($\mathcal{Q}H\mathcal{Q}$) there is no particular virtue in including the closed states explicitly, as algebraic terms of the Hylleraas type represent correlations between the electrons well, and it is comparatively easy to retain sufficient terms to obtain convergence. With these ideas in mind, Burke et al. presented results in the six state (1s - 2s - 2p - 3s - 3p - 3d) approximation (Burke et al., 1967a) at energies above the n = 2 threshold, supplemented (Taylor and Burke, 1967) by calculations in the very narrow energy range $k^2 = 0.75$ to $k^2 = 0.85$ in which up to 20 correlation terms were used together with the 1s - 2s - 2p open channel terms, securing apparent convergence. The results in the six state and in the (3 state + correlation) approximations agree satisfactorily. The correlation effects are not large and if only the three terms (1s - 2s - 2p) are retained, the cross section is within 15% of the most accurate values.

Below the n = 3 threshold the expected series of resonances are found. This is seen clearly in Fig. 6-1 which shows the cross section σ(1s - 2s), the cross section for excitation of the ground state to the (2s) state. Detailed analysis (Macek and Burke, 1967) shows that interference between resonant and non-resonant scattering controls the shape of the cross section in this region and is responsible for the peak observed in the 1s - 2s excitation cross section at 11.5 ev ($k^2 = 0.84$). Below the resonance region $k^2 < 0.84$, neither the explicit representation of the closed channels nor correlation is important and the 2s - 2s - 2p approximation is quite accurate. An interesting feature occurring in each approximation is a narrow resonance (width 1.5×10^{-3} ev) just above the n = 2 threshold in the ^1P state of the system[4]. Since this occurs in the (1s - 2s - 2p) approximation it has nothing to do with the closed channels, but is a 'shape' resonance of the kind observed in potential scattering and discussed in Chapter 1. Further work by Callaway and co-workers[5], has been based on a pseudostate expansion including the exact 1s, 2s and 2p hydrogenic wave functions. The coupled equations are

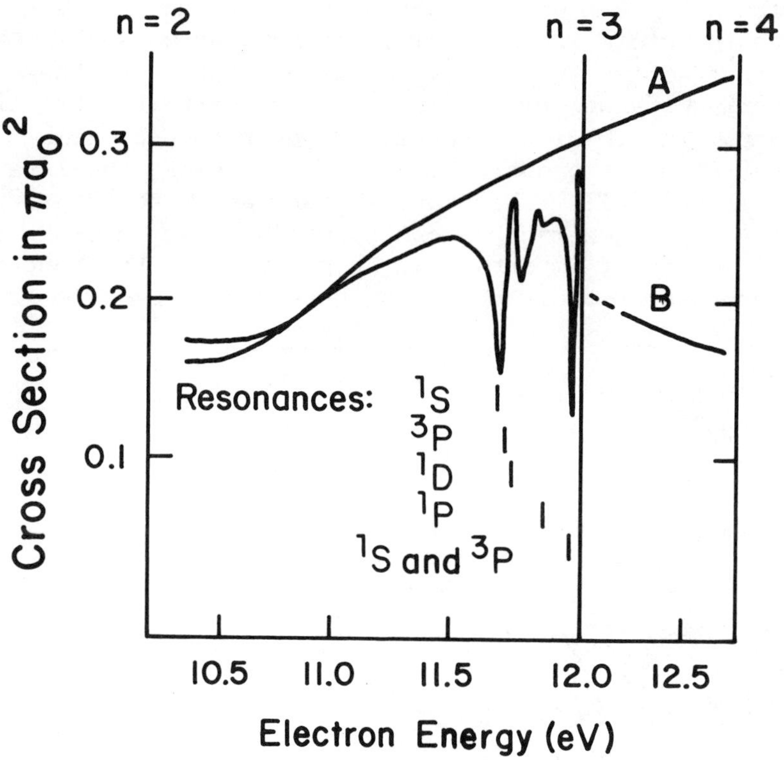

Figure 6-1 The total cross section σ(1s-2s) for the excitation of hydrogen by electron impact in the three-state (curve A) and the six state (curve B) approximation (Burke et al., 1967a).

solved using an algebraic variational method and the results in the region between n = 2 and n = 3 thresholds are considered to be very accurate. The coupled elastic and inelastic cross sections agree with the experimental data of Williams (1975, 1976) within the experimental error.

Scattering by atomic hydrogen at higher energies

Cross sections can be calculated at higher energies by the close coupling method and its extensions, however it becomes impossible to represent the open channel part of the wave function so completely, particularly at energies above the ionization threshold. Three state

(1s + 2s + 2p) close coupling cross sections have been calculated up to 300 ev by Kingston et al (1976). Such a calculation cannot be expected to reproduce the elastic scattering cross section well, because, as we saw in Chapter 5, the effective long range potentials acting in the elastic scattering channel receive substantial contributions from the continuum intermediate states. However the potentials of longest range (proportional to $1/r^2$) coupling the 1s and 2p channels are fully taken into account and also the coupling between the degenerate 2s and 2p channels which might be thought to be of importance. In practise up to about 50 ev, this approximation is very poor (see Fig. 6-2), the total

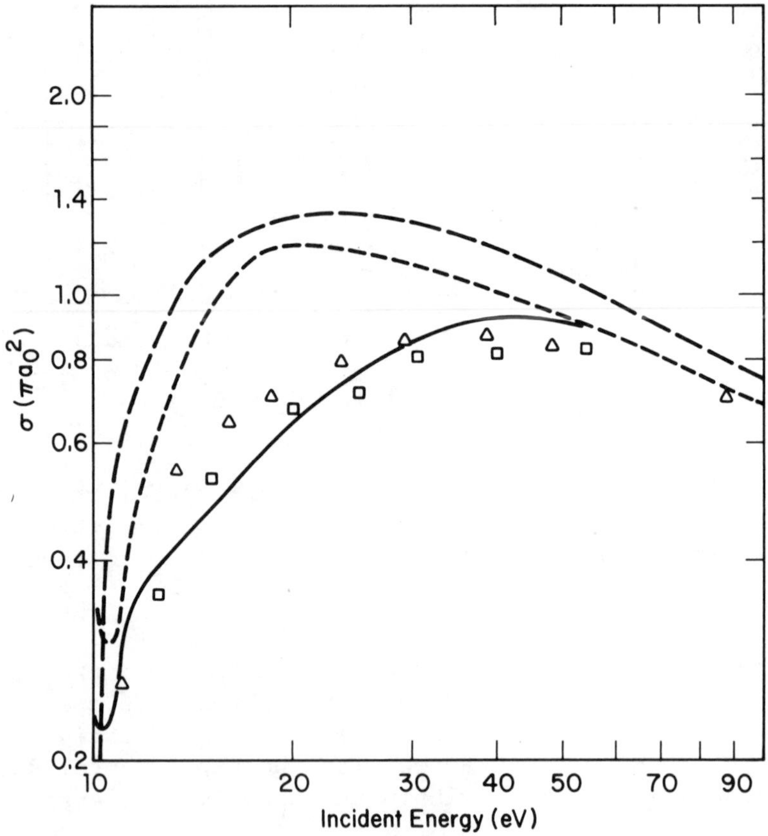

Figure 6-2 The cross section for excitation of atomic hydrogen to the 2p level by electron impact.

— — Born approximation.
- - - 3-state close coupling approximation.
——— Variational method (Callaway, 1978).
Δ, □ Experimental data (Long et al 1968; McGowan et al 1969

cross section for 2p excitation exceeding the measured values by a factor of nearly two at 20 ev. Above 50 ev, both the total and differential n = 2 excitation cross sections are in reasonable agreement with experiment (see Figs. 6-2 and 6-3), but the model does not represent well the angular correlation between the electron scattered after exciting the 2p level and the subsequently emitted photon (Williams 1981).

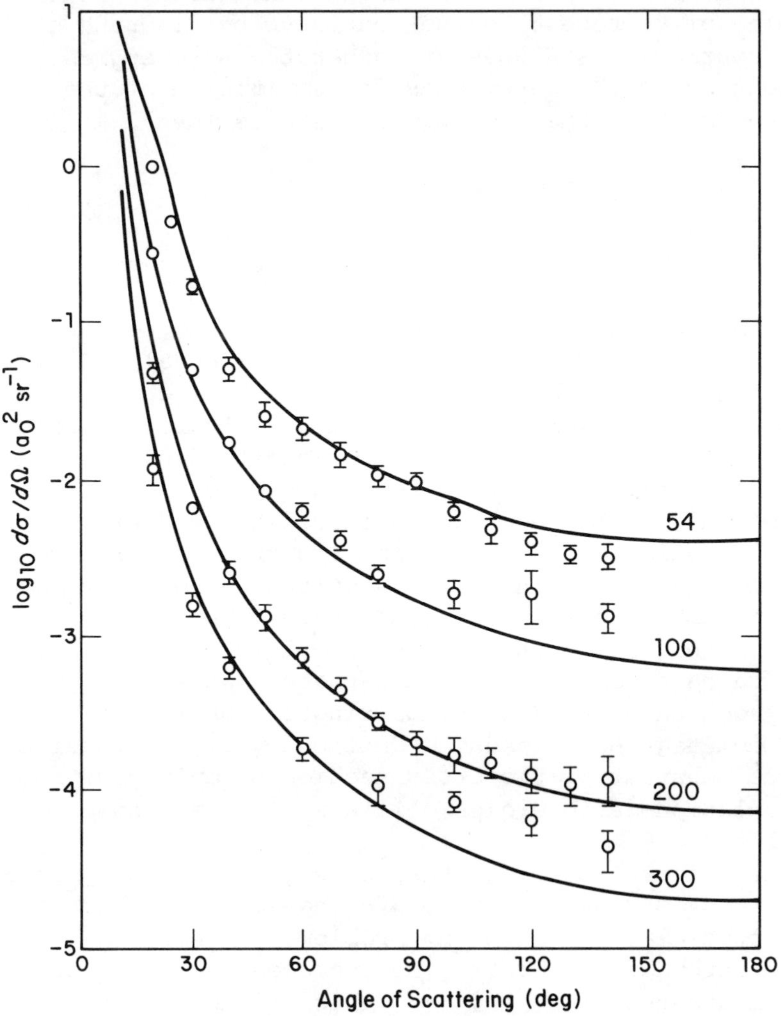

Figure 6-3 The cross section for excitation of the (2s + 2p) levels of hydrogen at 54, 100, 200 and 300 ev. The solid line is the result of a 3-state close coupling approximation. The data is due to Williams and Willis (1974).

In order to improve the model, some allowance must be made for coupling to higher discrete states and to the continuum states. This can be done by adding suitable pseudostates. No completely systematic method of generating such pseudostates has been devised, but if pseudofunctions are chosen by diagonalizing the target Hamiltonian on a finite basis, as in (5-85) in such a way that the energies $\bar{\varepsilon}_{n',\ell}$ are positive and lie in the hydrogenic continuum, it is possible to represent the continuum in an approximate way. The difficulty of representing the continuum by discrete states is that spurious resonances are generated at energies corresponding to the thresholds for excitation of the fictitious states, that is at the energies when

$$E = \frac{1}{2}k_i^{\,2} + \varepsilon_{1s} = \bar{\varepsilon}_{n',\ell}$$

Nevertheless, Burke and Webb (1970) showed that by adding two pseudofunctions designated $\overline{3s}$ and $\overline{3p}$ with $\bar{\varepsilon}_{3\ell} = 0$, much improved n = 2 excitation cross sections could be obtained. Subsequent work by Callaway et al (1976) (see also Callaway, 1978) using up to eight pseudostates in the energy region up to 54 ev agrees well with experiment. It is interesting to note that by calculating the probability flux entering the pseudostates, and knowing the overlap between the pseudofunctions and the hydrogenic continuum wave functions, reasonable estimates of the ionization cross section can be made. Elastic scattering cross sections up to 54 ev have also been calculated from a pseudostate expansion using the R-matrix method of solution, (Fon et al 1981a - see also similar calculations for helium targets, Fon et al 1981b and for neon targets, Fon and Berrington 1981). Callaway and his colleagues avoided the difficulty of the spurious resonance behavior of the cross section by only performing the calculations at energies well away from the pseudo thresholds.

Some information about the convergence of the pseudostate method is known. Poet (1978) has solved (numerically) a restricted $e^- - H$ scattering problem, in which the interelectron interaction $1/|\vec{r}_1-\vec{r}_2|$ is replaced by $1/r_>$ where $r_>$ is the greater of r_1 and r_2. This is the same as taking the total orbital angular momentum as L = 0 and including all hydrogenic s-states (both discrete and continuous) in the expansion of the wave function. These results can be compared with those of Burke and Mitchell (1973) who also took L = 0 and used an expansion including the exact 1s and 2s hydrogenic orbitals together with 3s, 4s and 5s pseudofunctions. The pseudostate calculations of the 2s excitation and elastic cross sections do exhibit the irregularities associated with the pseudo thresholds, but if a suitable average is taken, the computed cross sections are much closer to the exact results than those given by the ordinary close coupling method.

At energies above 50 - 100 ev, the idea that only a relatively few strongly coupled channels are important cannot be expected to be valid; rather a very large number of channels, including the continuum, are weakly coupled to the initial state. This suggests that methods, other than the expansion method, and based on perturbation expressions, should become attractive. This view point will be pursued in later sections.

Further applications

The close coupling method[6] has also been applied to the excitation of the n = 2 state in helium and to transitions among the n = 2 states. Apart from the ground state of the helium atom all four states with n = 2^3(2^3S,2^1S,2^3P,2^1P) were included in the expansion. The $2^{3,1}S$ states have very large polarizabilities because the $2^{2,1}P$ states are so close in energy. The energies of the five states concerned are shown in Table 6-1.

Table 6-1

Binding energies of levels in helium with n = 2

State		E(a.u.)
2^1S	$1s^2$	2.9037
2^3S	1s2s	2.1754
2^1S	1s2s	2.1461
2^3P	1s2p	2.1333
2^1P	1s2p	2.1238

The close coupling method gives a reasonable account (when the results are compared with experiment) of the energy interval between the 2^3S and 2^1S thresholds at 19.818 ev and 20.614 ev respectively and up to the 2^1P

threshold at 21.218 ev, however it fails to reveal the resonance structure below the n = 3 thresholds, which is predicted by more elaborate calculations based on the matrix-variational-Bethe-Goldstone technique (Oberoi and Nesbet 1973; Nesbet 1978) or the R-matrix-pseudostate technique (Berrington et al 1975; Sin Fai Lam 1976; Fon et al 1978).

The transitions between the ground state terms of carbon, nitrogen and oxygen due to electron impact are of considerable astronomical interest. As the ground state terms are strongly coupled this is also a favorable situation for the close coupling method and Smith et al (1967) calculated both the elastic cross sections and the inelastic transitions among the ground state terms of these atoms[7].

More recently cross sections have been computed by the matrix variational method (Thomas and Nesbet 1975a,b), by the pseudostate method (Tambe and Henry 1976a,b) and by the pseudostate R-matrix method (Le Dourneuf et al 1977). A detailed review of these calculations at lower energies with a full bibliography has been given by Nesbet (1977), and related work at higher energies has been reviewed by Bransden and McDowell (1977, 1978).

Calculations on the excitation of Li, Na, K and Cs (Karule and Peterkop, 1964, 1965) have been carried out on the basis, discussed earlier, that only the ground and first excited state are important because the first excited states contribute 98% of the polarizability. For calculational purposes the problem was simplified by only treating the incident and valence electrons explicitly. The effect of the remaining electrons and the nucleus was represented by an average (static) potential. More recent work has been reported by Moores and Norcross (1972) and in the Bethe-Goldstone approximation by Bardsley and Nesbet (1973) and Sin Fai Lam and Nesbet (1973).

Ions

No particular difficulty occurs in extending the close coupling method to the scattering of electrons by ions. All that is necessary is to modify the form of the radial functions in the open channels so that they are asymptotic to linear combinations of the regular and irregular Coulomb functions (Chapter 3); for example

$$f_\ell(r) \sim \delta_{ij} F_\ell(k_i r) + K_{ij} G_\ell(k_j r). \qquad (6\text{-}12)$$

Because a knowledge of excitation cross sections of ions by electron impact is very important in many branches of plasma research, both in terrestrial and astrophysical contexts, extensive close coupling (and other) calculations have been performed for a variety of systems including ions isoelectronic with hydrogen, helium, lithium and beryllium. These calculations have been reviewed by Henry (1981), who has given a full bibliography together with much tabulated and graphical information. As compared with excitation of neutral atoms, because of the overall Coulomb attraction, the resonances associated with thresholds play a much more dominant role in determining the average size of the excitation cross sections for positive ions.

6-2 OPTICAL POTENTIALS AND DISTORTED WAVE APPROXIMATIONS

At energies well above the ionization threshold, approximations based on retaining a limited number of terms in the trial wave functions may not be accurate since, in general, many channels are coupled with comparable strength to the incident channel. An alternative is to base an approximation on the optical potential introduced in Chapter 5. This is equivalent to retaining the infinite set of eigenfunction expansion equations, and approximating the solution to each of them.

Elastic scattering

For elastic scattering the optical potential can be approximated along the lines indicates in Chapter 5. At the energies in which we are interested many channels are open, and in these channels the Green's function G_o^C employed in (5-114) must be replaced by the outgoing wave free particle Green's function

$$G_o^+(\vec{r},\vec{r}\,') = -(4\pi)^{-1} \exp ik_n^2|\vec{r}-\vec{r}\,'|/|r-r'| \tag{6-14}$$

The second order approximation to the direct optical potential is then (see 5-117)

$$\begin{aligned} W_{oo}(\vec{r}_1,\vec{r}_2) &= \sum_{n\neq 0} G_o^+(k_n^2;\vec{r}_1,\vec{r}_2)U_{on}(\vec{r}_1)U_{no}(\vec{r}_2) \\ &+ \sum_n{}' G_o^C(\lambda_n^2;\vec{r}_1,\vec{r}_2)U_{on}(\vec{r}_1)U_{no}(\vec{r}_2) \end{aligned} \tag{6-15}$$

where the first sum runs over all the open channels ($k_n^2>0$) and the second over the closed channels. The optical potential, apart from being non-local and energy dependent is now also complex, since as we saw in Chapter 1 a potential which allows for inelasticity must develop an imaginary part. It is not difficult to write down the corresponding expressions including the exchange kernels. Expressions to any order in the potentials U_{nm} can also easily be written down; but the second order expression (6-15) is already difficult to evaluate numerically. For the particular case of electron scattering by atomic hydrogen an essentially exact evaluation of (6-15) has been made by McCarthy et al (1982) who work in momentum space and sum over all the important intermediate states, including the continuum states, numerically. Their computed elastic scattering cross sections agree well with the experimental data at energies above 54 ev (see Table 6-2), and also with the results of a similar calculation by Scott and Bransden (1981), who replaced the integration over continuum intermediate states, by a sum over suitably chosen discrete pseudostates.

An alternative to direct evaluation of W_{oo} is to replace k_n^2 in the Green's function by an average value $\bar{k}^2$ and to drop the second sum in (6-15) over the closed states. We can then write (Bransden and Coleman 1972)

$$W_{oo}(\vec{r}_1,\vec{r}_2) = \sum_{\text{all } n} G_o^+(\bar{k}^2;\vec{r}_1,\vec{r}_2)U_{on}(\vec{r}_1)U_{no}(\vec{r}_2)$$

$$- G_o^+(\bar{k}^2;\vec{r}_1,\vec{r}_2)U_{oo}(\vec{r}_1)U_{oo}(\vec{r}_2) \qquad (6\text{-}16)$$

The sum can now be evaluated by using the closure property of the target eigenfunctions

$$\sum_{\text{all } n} \phi_n(\vec{r})\phi_n^*(\vec{r}\,') = \delta(\vec{r}-\vec{r}\,')$$

Referring to (5-47) we see for the case of a hydrogen target

$$\sum_{\text{all } n} U_{on}(\vec{r}_1)U_{no}(\vec{r}_2) = 4\int d^3r\phi_o^*(\vec{r})\phi_o(\vec{r}) \frac{1}{|\vec{r}-\vec{r}_1|}\frac{1}{|\vec{r}-\vec{r}_2|} \qquad (6\text{-}17)$$

and this function can be calculated without difficulty. The average energy can be chosen so in the same closure approximation the correct polarizability of the atom is obtained. This ensures that the $1/r^4$ long range dipole

Table 6-2
The differential and total cross sections for elastic scattering of electrons by atomic hydrogen at intermediate energies in atomic units

	E = 50 ev		100 ev		200 ev	
θ(deg)	Expt.	OP	Expt.	OP	Expt.	OP
10	5.04	4.19	-	-	-	-
15	3.18	2.76	-	-	1.22	1.16
20	2.17	1.98	1.10	0.890	0.419	0.435
30	1.12	1.06	0.509	0.438	0.1720	0.174
50	0.308	0.338	0.132	0.104	0.0314	0.0335
70	0.146	0.129	0.0491	0.0391	0.0125	0.0111
90	0.0716	0.0661	0.0209	0.0181	0.00584	0.00485
110	0.0421	0.0383	0.0115	0.0102	0.00323	0.00271
140	0.0273	0.0237	0.0065	0.0059	0.00178	0.00157
σ_ℓ	3.83	4.30	1.75	1.50	0.669	0.672
σ	6.57	6.11	5.53	5.28	3.77	3.27

Experimental differential cross sections are from Williams (1975) and total cross sections are from de Heer et al (1977)

OP Optical potential calculations of McCarthy et al (1982).

polarization potential is given correct by the approximate second order potential. The closure approximation can be justified by comparison with the exact results, and has been shown to be accurate (for the e^--H system) down to 30 ev by Ermolaev and Walters (1979) in the context of the second Born approximation.

The second order potential method has been applied successfully to the elastic scattering of electrons by helium at 100 ev and above (Winters et al 1974), but the numerical calculations remain rather complex for application to scattering by heavier targets. For this reason it is interesting to try and replace the non-local potential $W_{oo}(\vec{r}_1,\vec{r}_2)$ by a local equivalent potential $\bar{W}(r_1)\delta(\vec{r}_1-\vec{r}_2)$. This can be done in various ways and applications have been made to scattering by the heavier rare gases[8] (ne, Ar....). Byron and Joachain (1981), working within a local potential approximation, have obtained a third order correction to the second order potential and have shown it makes a small contribution (<10%) at energies above 50 ev for scattering by hydrogen.

Excitation and the distorted wave method

The ideas of the optical potential model are easily extended to excitation. Suppose we are interested in excitation of a level labeled 1 from the ground state labeled 0. The channel functions $F_o(\vec{r})$, $F_1(\vec{r})$ satisfy coupled equations of the form

$$\left(\nabla^2 + k_o^2 - U_{oo} - W_{oo}\right)F_o(\vec{r}) = \left(U_{10} + W_{01}\right)F_1(\vec{r}) \qquad \text{(6-18a)}$$

$$\left(\nabla^2 + k_1^2 - U_{11} - W_{11}\right)F_1(\vec{r}) = \left(U_{10} + W_{10}\right)F_o(\vec{r}) \qquad \text{(6-18b)}$$

Here we have displayed only the direct part of the potential and have omitted the exchange potentials. The first order interactions are given by (5-47) for the case of hydrogen targets and the potentials W_{ij} are the exact matrix optical potentials. In second order, it is not difficult to show that

$$W_{ij}(\vec{r}_1,\vec{r}_2) = \sum_{n\neq 0,1} G_o(k_n^2;\vec{r}_1,\vec{r}_2)U_{in}(\vec{r}_1)U_{nj}(\vec{r}_2) \qquad \text{(6-19)}$$

where G_o is a free particle Green's function obeying outgoing wave boundary conditions if $k_n^2>0$, or closed channel boundary conditions if $k_n^2<0$, and as usual $k_n^2 = k_o + 2\ (\varepsilon_o - \varepsilon_n)$.

Equations (6-18) can be solved approximately by a distorted wave method akin to that discussed in Chapter 4, Section 4-4. The appropriate boundary conditions satisfied by the channel wave functions $F_i(r)$ are (cf. 4-100)

$$F_i^+(\vec{r}) = \delta_{io} \exp(i\vec{k}_o \cdot \vec{r}) - (2\pi)^{-1} T_{io} r^{-1} \exp(ik_i r) \quad (6\text{-}20)$$

The differential cross section for excitation is then

$$\frac{d\sigma_{10}}{d\Omega} = \frac{1}{4\pi^2} \frac{k_1}{k_o} |T_{10}|^2$$

In the absence of coupling between the two channels we can define elastic scattering solutions ("distorted waves") of the equations

$$\left(\nabla^2 + k^2 - U_{oo} - W_{oo}\right) \mathcal{F}_o(\vec{k},\vec{r}) = 0 \quad (6\text{-}21a)$$

and

$$\left(\nabla^2 + k^2 - U_{11} - W_{11}\right) \mathcal{F}_1(\vec{k},\vec{r}) = 0 \quad (6\text{-}21b)$$

Equation (6-18b) can be converted to integral form by introducing the Green's function $\mathcal{G}_{11}^+(\vec{r},\vec{r}\,')$ of the operator $(\nabla^2+k^2-U_{11}-W_{11})$. Proceeding as in Section 1-6 this is found to be

$$\mathcal{G}_{11}^+(\vec{r},\vec{r}\,') = (2\pi)^{-3} \int d^3k' \frac{\mathcal{F}_1^-(\vec{k}',\vec{r})\,\mathcal{F}_1^{-*}(\vec{k}',\vec{r}\,')}{(k^2 + i\varepsilon - k'^2)} \quad (6\text{-}22)$$

where ε is a small positive quantity. The functions $\mathcal{F}_1$ are required to satisfy incident plane wave plus converging spherical wave boundary conditions as indicated by the - label, for reasons that parallel the discussion in Section 5-2. Equation (6-18b) is then equivalent to the integral equation

$$F_1^+(\vec{r}) = \int d^3r' \mathcal{G}^+(\vec{r},\vec{r}\,')(U_{10} + W_{10}) F_o^+(\vec{r}\,') \quad (6\text{-}23)$$

and on taking the limit of large r and comparing with the asymptotic form (6-20) we find

$$T_{10} = \frac{1}{2}\int d^3r' \mathcal{F}^{-*}(\vec{k}_1,\vec{r}\,')(U_{10} + W_{10}) F_o^+(\vec{r}\,') \quad (6\text{-}24)$$

The integral form of equation (6-18a) is

$$F_o^+(\vec{r}) = F_o^+(\vec{k}_o,\vec{r}) + \int d^3r' G_{oo}^+(\vec{r},\vec{r}')U_{01}+W_{01})F_1^+(\vec{r}) \tag{6-25}$$

where G_{oo}^+ is the Green's function for the operator $(\nabla^2+k_o^2-U_{oo}-W_{oo})$ and the superscript + denotes outgoing wave boundary conditions.

By iterating equations (6-23) and (6-25) a series is obtained for $F_o(\vec{r})$ and, from (6-24), for T_{10} which is known as the distorted wave series. By stopping at the first term, we obtain the first order distorted wave approximation (often called the distorted wave Born approximation)

$$T_{10}^{DW} = \frac{1}{2}\int d^3r' F^{-*}(\vec{k}_1,\vec{r}')(U_{10} + W_{10})F^+(\vec{k}_o,\vec{r}') \tag{6-26}$$

Although the formulae have been written with only the direct parts of the matrix potentials, in practical calculations, the exchange kernels should be included so that U_{ij} is to be replaced by $U_{ij} \pm K_{ij}$ where K_{ij} is the appropriate exchange kernel and similarly W_{ij} is to include the higher order exchange terms.

To define a distorted wave calculation completely some approximations must be introduced for the matrix optical potentials W_{ij}. In the simplest approximation, we set W_{ij} = 0, in which case the distorted wave amplitude (6-26) is an approximation to that which would be obtained from a 2-state close coupling approximation. For excitation of the n = 2 levels of hydrogen from 100 to 300 ev, the distorted wave cross sections agree fairly well with experiment and with the 3-state close coupling results (Baluja et al 1978). A large number of calculations have been reported for excitation of the n = 2 levels of helium, both singlet and triplet. In the work of Madison and Shelton (1973), the distortion in the final state was taken to be due to the initial state potential U_{oo} (excluding the exchange kernel) which is an approximation that does not naturally follow from the theory we have outlined. Some typical results are shown in Fig.6-4 for the total excitation of the 2^1P level, compared with a similar calculation including the exchange kernel[9] by Thomas et al (1974).

To go beyond the approximation W_{ij} = 0, McDowell and his co-workers have approximated W_{oo} and W_{11} by adiabatic polarized orbital potentials, thus allowing for the effective potentials of longest range in the initial and final states,

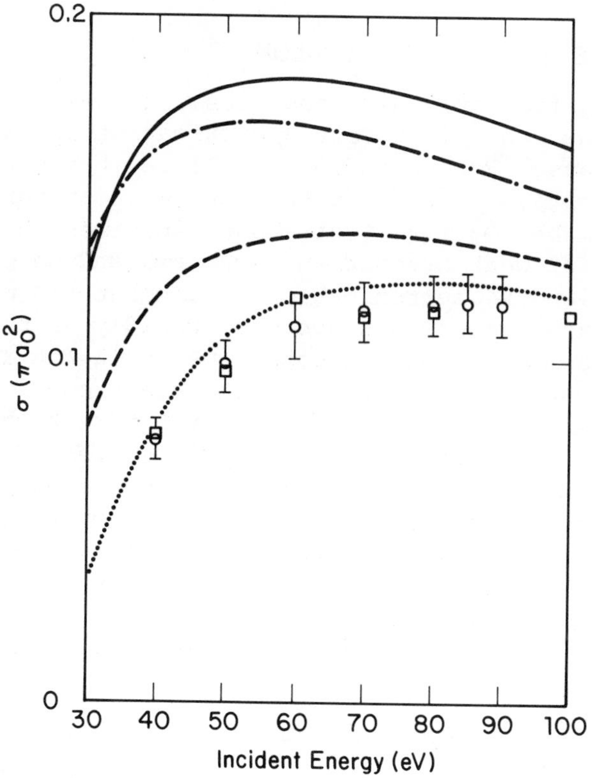

Figure 6-4 The total cross section for the excitation of the 2^1P level of helium

— · — · — First Born approximation

———— 5-state close coupling approximation (Bhadra et al 1979)

---------- Distorted wave approximation (Madison and Shelton 1973).

.... Many body theory distorted wave approximation (Thomas et al 1974).

Experimental data from Donaldson et al (1972).

while Bransden and Winters (1976) have considered the case in which W_{oo} is taken to be the second order optical potential in the closure approximation and W_{11} is set equal to zero. Details of these and other methods are given by Bransden and McDowell (1977, 1978) and Callaway (1980) and the importance of including both initial and final state distortion has been discussed in those articles and also by Winters (1978). For applications to the excitation of positive ions, which should be a particularly favorable situation because both $(U_{oo} + W_{oo})$ and $(U_{11} + W_{11})$ are dominated by the overall Coulomb attraction, the review of Henry (1981) should be consulted.

6-3 THE BORN APPROXIMATION

At sufficiently high energies, at least for total cross sections, the first Born approximation is expected to become accurate. For an optically allowed transition from the ground state, it is found that the Born approximation is accurate (at the 10% level) at about ten times the threshold energy, but for weak transitions s→s, s→d and so on, the energy at which the approximation is accurate is much higher.

As exchange effects decrease rapidly as the energy of the incident electron increases, we shall not at first take into account the identity of the electrons. This implie that collisions in which the spin of the target changes (for example, excitation of the triplet states of helium from the ground states) which, in the absence of spin dependent potentials, take place purely through electron exchange, will be excluded from our discussion. The Born approximation for the total cross section is given by (4-28) together with (4-41). The unperturbed wave functions are of the form (4-7) (with $N_m = 1$) and (in atomic units)

$$\sigma_{nm}(E) = \frac{1}{4\pi^2}\frac{k_n}{k_m}\int d\Omega \, |T^B_{nm}|^2 \tag{6-27}$$

with

$$T^B_{nm} = \int d^3r \int d^3x X_n^*(\vec{x}) e^{-i\vec{k}_n\cdot\vec{r}} V(\vec{r},\vec{x}) X_m(\vec{x}) e^{i\vec{k}_m\cdot\vec{r}} \tag{6-28}$$

and the transition is between initial and final states of the targets m and n corresponding to eigenfunctions X_m and X_n.

Conservation of energy requires that

$$\frac{1}{2}k_n^2 + \varepsilon_n = \frac{1}{2}k_m^2 + \varepsilon_m, \tag{6-29}$$

where ε_i is the energy of the ith state of the target. The interaction, $V(\vec{r},\vec{x})$, between the incident electron and the target is of the form

$$V(\vec{r},\vec{x}) = \frac{Z}{r} - \sum_{i=1}^{Z} \frac{1}{|\vec{r} - \vec{x}_i|}. \tag{6-30}$$

The first term represents the interaction of the incident electron with the nucleus of the target and which is taken to be a neutral atom and the second the interaction with each of the electrons in the target (coordinates

$\vec{x}_1, \vec{x}_2 \ldots \vec{x}_Z$). The orthogonality of the wave functions X_m and X_n for $m \neq n$, insures that the contribution of the first term vanishes except for elastic scattering.

Elastic scattering

In the case of elastic scattering with $\vec{k}_n = \vec{k}_o'$, $\vec{k}_m = \vec{k}_o$ and $|\vec{k}_o'| = |\vec{k}_o|$ from a level labeled with $n = m = 0$, the amplitude T_{oo} can be reduced by using the integral (known as Bethe's integral)

$$\int e^{i\vec{K}\cdot\vec{r}} \frac{1}{|\vec{r} - \vec{x}|} d^3r = \frac{4\pi e^{i\vec{K}\cdot\vec{x}}}{K^2} \tag{6-31}$$

From (6-28) and (6-30) and using (6-31) we find

$$T_{oo}{}^{B} = \frac{4\pi}{K^2}\Big(Z - S(K)\Big) \tag{6-32}$$

where $K = |\vec{k}_o' - \vec{k}_o| = 2k_o\sin(\theta/2)$ and θ is the angle of scattering. The function $S(K)$ is defined as

$$S(K) = \sum_{i=1}^{Z} \int d^3x_1 d^3x_2 \ldots d^3x_Z |X_o(\vec{x}_1, \vec{x}_2 \ldots \vec{x}_Z)|^2 \exp(i\vec{K}\cdot\vec{x}_i)$$

The form factor $S(K)$ is called the X-ray scattering factor and can be written as

$$S(K) = \int d^3x\rho(\vec{x})\exp(i\vec{K}\cdot\vec{x}) \tag{6-33}$$

where $\rho(\vec{x})$ is the electron density (see Bransden and Joachain 1982). The differential cross section in Born's approximation (in atomic units) is

$$\frac{d\sigma}{d\Omega} = \frac{4}{K^4}|Z - S(K)|^2 \tag{6-34}$$

The form factor $S(K)$ is, in general, a monotonically decreasing function of K as $K \to \infty$, and $S(0) = Z$. For example in the case of atomic hydrogen

$$S_H(K) = \Big(1 + K^2/4\Big)^{-2}$$

and for helium, using a simple variational ground state wave function

$$\psi(r_1,r_2) = \frac{\lambda^3}{\pi}\exp-\lambda(r_1+r_2)$$

with $\lambda = 27/16$, we find

$$S_{He}(K) = 2\left[1 + K^2/(4\lambda^2)\right]^{-2}$$

At energies for which the Born approximation is accurate measurements of the differential cross section determine S(K) and, by inverting the Fourier transform (6-33), the electron density $\rho(x)$ can be found[10]. For a given finite momentum transfer the Born approximation becomes accurate at sufficiently high energies. However at a given energy, the first order Born approximation must fail as $K \to 0$, because the long range polarization potential, which is a second order effect, dominates scattering near the forward direction. For example at 500 ev, the first Born approximation for electron-helium scattering is accurate for $K > 2$ a.u. corresponding to scattering angles $\theta > 19^o$. For heavier atoms, the energy for which the Born approximation is accurate increases, since the depth of the static potential well (corresponding to U_{oo}) is proportional to Z. Thus the Born approximation is useful to a similar accuracy for 500 ev electrons incident on helium, electrons of 12 kev incident on neon or 40 kev electrons incident on krypton. It should be noted that when the first Born approximation is accurate the elastic scattering differential cross section depends only on the momentum transfer K, in contrast to the general situation in which it depends both on K and k_o.

<u>Inelastic scattering</u>

It is convenient to use the momentum transfer K

$$\vec{K} = \vec{k}_m - \vec{k}_n, \tag{6-35}$$

as a variable in place of the angle of scattering θ. Since

$$K^2 = k_n^{\ 2} + k_m^{\ 2} = 2k_n k_m \cos\theta,$$

the total cross section can be written from (6-27) as

$$\sigma_{nm}(E) = \frac{1}{4\pi^2 k_m^{\ 2}} \int_0^{2\pi} d\phi \int_{K_{min}}^{K_{max}} KdK \left| T_{nm}^{\ B}(\vec{K}) \right|^2 \tag{6-36}$$

where $K_{max} = k_m + k_n$ and $K_{min} = k_m - k_n$, and

$$T_{nm}(\vec{K}) = -\sum_{i=1}^{Z}\int d^3r \int d^3x X^*_n(\vec{x}) X_m(\vec{x}) \frac{e^{i\vec{K}\cdot\vec{r}}}{|\vec{r} - \vec{x}_i|} \tag{6-37}$$

In (6-37), $\vec{x}_i$ is the position vector of the ith electron, and as usual $\vec{x}$ denotes the coordinates of all the target electrons collectively.

We obtain, using the Bethe integral (6-31),

$$\frac{K^2}{4\pi} T_{nm}(\vec{K}) = -\sum_{i=1}^{Z} \int d^3x X^*_n(\vec{x}) X_m(\vec{x}) e^{i\vec{K}\cdot\vec{x}_i}. \tag{6-38}$$

It is usual to write the cross section in terms of a generalized oscillator strength defined as

$$f_{nm}(\vec{K}) = \frac{2(\varepsilon_n - \varepsilon_m)}{K^2} \left| \sum_{i=1}^{Z} \int d^3x X_n^*(\vec{x}) X_m(\vec{x}) \exp(i\vec{K}\cdot\vec{x}_i) \right|^2 \tag{6-39}$$

In general f_{nm} depends both on K and on the direction of $\vec{K}$ with respect to the direction of quantisation. However if f_{nm} is summed over the magnetic quantum numbers of the final state, the result depends on $|\vec{K}|$ only. Thus if this sum is denoted by $\bar{f}_{nm}(K)$, the total cross section for the transition $m \to n$, summed over the magnetic quantum numbers of the final state is

$$\sigma_{nm}(E) = \frac{4\pi}{k_m^{\ 2}} \frac{1}{(\varepsilon_n - \varepsilon_m)} \int_{K_{min}}^{K_{max}} \frac{\bar{f}_{nm}(K)}{K} dK \tag{6-40}$$

When the change of energy of the atom $(\varepsilon_n - \varepsilon_m)$ is small compared with the incident energy, we can write

$$K_{max} \approx 2k_m \qquad K_{min} \approx (\varepsilon_n - \varepsilon_m)/k_m \tag{6-41}$$

The generalized oscillator strength becomes equal, in the limit $K \to 0$, to the optical oscillator strength $f_{nm}(0)$ which is proportional to the probability of an optical transition between the m and nth level of the target. The case of most interest is when the target is initially in the ground state (m = 0). It can then be shown (Mott and Massey, 1965, p.479) that the oscillator strengths obey the sum rule,

$$\sum_n f_{no}(K) = 1, \tag{6-42}$$

where the sum is over all states (discrete and continuous) of the target atom.

A multipole expansion of $f_{no}(K)$ can be performed by expanding the exponential in (6-39) in a Taylor's series. Taking $\vec{K}$ to be in the direction of the X axis,

$$f_{no}(K) = 2(\varepsilon_n - \varepsilon_o)\left| i(X_n|\sum_{i=1}^{Z} x_i|X_o) + \right.$$

$$\left. + (i)^2\frac{K}{2}(X_n|\sum_{i=1}^{Z} x_i^2|X_o) + \ldots\right|^2, \; n \neq 0, \tag{6-43}$$

where

$$(X_n|O|X_m) \equiv \int dx X^*_n(x) O X_m(x),$$

showing that, as $K \to 0$, $f_{no}(K)$ is proportional to the square of the matrix element of the atomic dipole moment. The differential cross section $(d\sigma_{no}/dK)$ is a slowly decreasing function of K, because at high energies the scattering is entirely concentrated in a forward direction (see Chapter 1). It follows that for optically allowed transitions ($\Delta\ell = 1$), the most important term in the expansion will be the dipole term and approximately (using (6-41)

$$\sigma_{no} = \frac{8\pi}{k_o^2}\left|(X_n|\sum_{i=1}^{Z} x_i|X_o)\right|^2 \log\left(\frac{4k_o^2}{k_o^2 - k_n^2}\right) \tag{6-44}$$

This is the Bethe approximation which becomes exact in the high energy limit. If the dipole matrix element vanishes, the quadrupole ($\Delta\ell = 2$) term in the expansion provides a corresponding approximation. It is important to notice that while the cross sections for the optically allowed transitions fall off as $k_o^{-2} \log (k_o^2)$ as k_o increases, those for quadrupole and higher transitions decrease like k_o^{-2}. The Bethe approximation is important in developing the theory of the stopping power of materials to fast charged particles.

Validity of Born approximation

An experimental check on the validity of the Born approximation is possible. The quantity

$$\bar{f}(K) = 2\pi k_o^{\,2}(k_o^{\,2} - k_n^{\,2})K\left(\frac{d\sigma_{no}}{dK}\right) \qquad (6\text{-}45)$$

is constructed from the measured cross section, $(d\sigma_{no}/dK)$. If the Born approximation holds, $\bar{f}(K)$ should depend on K but not on the incident energy $(k_o^{\,2}/2)$ and should equal the theoretical oscillator strength $f_{no}(K)$. Measurements of $(d\sigma_{no}/dK)$ have been carried out by Lassetre and his collaborators[11] for excitation of the 2^1S, n^1P states in helium with $n \leq 5$. They find that the Born approximation is well satisfied for energies greater than 400 ev. The shape of the function $\bar{f}(K)$ for the $1^1S \rightarrow 2^1P$ transition also agrees well with theoretical calculations although of course this is a test of the accuracy of the helium wave functions used as well as of the validity of the Born approximation.

Differential and total cross sections for the excitation of the 2^1P and 2^1S states have also been measured by Vriens et al (1968) for electron energies between 100 and 400 ev. The measured $\bar{f}(K)$ is shown in Fig. 6-5 for the transition $1^1S \rightarrow 2^1P$. It is seen that for this transition the Born approximation holds down to 100 ev, but for the $1^1S \rightarrow 2^1S$ transition departures from the Born approximation are evident below 300 ev.

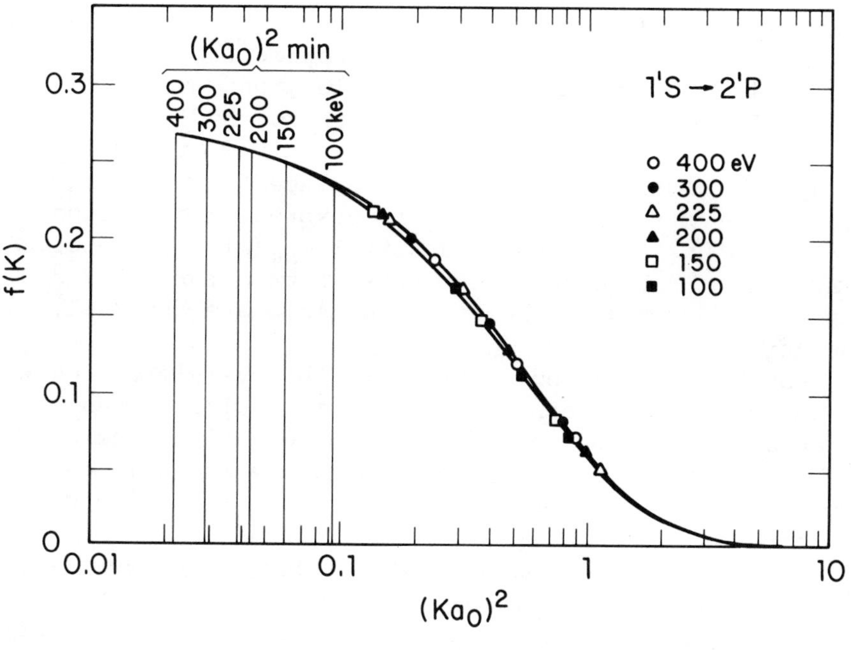

Figure 6-5 Apparent generalized oscillator strengths for the excitation of helium to the 2^1P state from the ground state, by electron impact.

It is interesting to notice that if measurements are made at high energies, for which the minimum value of K^2 is small, it is possible to obtain accurate values of the optical oscillator strengths $f_{no}(0)$, by extrapolating the measurements to $K = 0$.

Scattering or excitation of charged ions can be treated in the Coulomb-Born approximation by replacing the plane waves in the transition matrix (6-28) by Coulomb functions appropriate to the charge on the ion. We have in place of (6-28)

$$T_{nm}^{CB} = \int d^3r \int d^3x \left[X_n(\vec{x})\psi_c^-(\vec{k}_n,\vec{r})\right]^* V(\vec{r},\vec{x})X_m(\vec{x})\psi_c^+(\vec{k}_m,\vec{r}) \quad (6\text{-}46)$$

and it is important to notice that $(\psi^-)^*$ must be used to describe the final state in order to conform to the correct boundary conditions. The threshold law for excitation of ions differs from that of neutral atoms. In the latter case, the cross section is controlled by the behavior of the lowest ($\ell = 0$) partial wave and variables at threshold. This is not the case for the excitation of positive ions and from the behavior of $\psi_{k_m}^{-*}$ for small (kr) it can be shown that $\sigma_{nm}(E)$ approaches a non-zero value at threshold. Tully (1960) has obtained cross sections in this approximation for the 1s - 2s transition in the hydrogen iso-electronic sequence and Burgess (1961) has extended this work to the 1s - 2p transitions. For sufficiently large values of the incident energy, the Coulomb waves may be replaced by plane waves, then if the cross sections σ_{nm} are expressed as a function of $w = k_m^2/(k_m^2-k_n^2)$, the quantity $Z^4\sigma_{nm}(w)$ is independent of Z. Calculations show that this is true for $w > 3$ and that at high energies the cross sections are inversely proportional to Z^4.

For highly charged ions, where the overall charge Z′ exceeds 20 to 30, the non-relativistic Coulomb waves should be replaced by solutions of the Dirac equation (see Walker 1971, Callaway et al 1979), and for heavy atoms in general, whether ionized or neutral relativistic corrections may be significant.

Further information on applications of the Born and Coulomb-Born approximations can be found in the reviews by Inokuti (1971), Bell and Kingston (1974) and Henry (1981).

Unitarized Born approximation

At high energies the partial waves for all values of

the orbital angular momentum are small and can be determined from the first Born approximation. At lower energies, the partial waves for large angular momentum may still be given accurately by the Born approximation, but those for small values of angular momentum must be calculated by some more accurate method, such as the close coupling approximation. When using the Born approximation for large angular momentum in this way, a better approximation is generally obtained if the Born approximations to the K-matrix elements are computed, rather than those to the T-matrix elements. In particular this procedure produces a unitary S-matrix and allows to some extent for coupling between channels.

The second Born approximation

At lower energies when the first Born approximation is less accurate, better results should be obtained if the next term in the perturbation series is evaluated. The sum of the first two terms in the series is known as the second Born approximation. In this approximation the distortion of the atom by the field of the incident particle is taken into account. The transition matrix element is now given by

$$T_{nm}^{B_2} = T_{nm}^{1} + T_{nm}^{2}, \qquad (6\text{-}47)$$

where T_{nm}^1 is the first Born approximation to T_{nm} given by (6-28) and T_{nm}^2 is defined by

$$T_{nm}^{2} = 2\sum_q \int d^3r \int d^3r' e^{-i\vec{k}_n\cdot\vec{r}} V_{nq}(\vec{r}) G_o^{+}(k_q;\vec{r},\vec{r}') V_{qm}(\vec{r}') e^{i\vec{k}_m\cdot\vec{r}'} \qquad (6\text{-}48)$$

where we have used the Green's function of equation (4-46) and

$$V_{ij}(\vec{r}) = (X_i|V(\vec{r},\vec{x})|X_j). \qquad (6\text{-}49)$$

Whereas the amplitude in the first Born approximation is real, T_{nm}^2 is complex. In fact the amplitude for elastic scattering from a level labeled o,

$$f_{oo}^{B_2} = (2\pi)T_{oo}^{B_2}$$

obeys the optical theorem (4-33) to lowest order:

$$\text{Im} f_{oo}^{B_2}(\theta=0) = \left(\frac{k_o}{4\pi}\right) \sigma_{tot}^{B} \qquad (6\text{-}50)$$

where $\sigma_{tot}{}^{B}$ is the total cross section (elastic + inelastic) evaluated in the first Born approximation.

The sum over q in (6-48) is over all the discrete and continuum states of the target and in general an exact evaluation of $T_{nm}{}^{2}$ is not possible. However in the particular cases[12] of elastic scattering of electrons by atomic hydrogen, and for the 1s - 2s excitation of hydrogen by electron impact at 30 ev and certain larger energies, an accurate numerical evaluation has been performed by Ermolaev and Walters (1979, 1980). In addition, it has been shown that the sum over q can be performed in the limit of small momentum transfers (Byron and Joachain, 1973; Byron and Latour 1976; Bonham and Konaka 1978). The results indicate that for elastic scattering the real part of the second Born amplitude depends on the polarizability of the target, and exhibits the forward peak due to the long range α/r^4 interaction. Although at 50 ev and above, the second Born approximation describes the forward peak in the elastic scattering of electrons by hydrogen very well (and also in the case of helium for $E \geq$ 100 ev), it fails to describe large angle scattering properly (see Fig. 6-6). This is because the scattering at large angles is determined by the static potential V_{oo}, and this potential is too strong to be treated by the second Born approximation until much higher energies are reached. For this reason the optical potential method, in which V_{oo} is treated exactly is more successful in describing large angle scattering, or a distorted wave second Born approximation can be introduced in which

$$T_{oo}{}^{DW_2} = T_{oo}{}^{S} + T_{oo}{}^{S}$$

In this expression $T_{oo}{}^{S}$ is the exact amplitude for scattering by the potential V_{oo} alone, while $T_{oo}{}^{S2}$ is an expression similar in structure to (6-48) except that (i) the term q = 0, which has already been included in $T_{oo}{}^{S}$ is omitted from the sum and (ii) the plane waves are replaced by the distorted waves $F_o^{\pm}$ for scattering by the potential V_{oo}. An alternative to this procedure is to attempt to calculate the higher order Born terms approximately. This is the idea behind the eikonal-Born series method developed by Byron and Joachain (see Byron and Joachain 1977), which we will discuss a little later.

When an exact evaluation of the sum in (6-48) is not possible, the leading terms can be summed exactly and the remainder approximated by the closure method which has already been described in connection with the optical

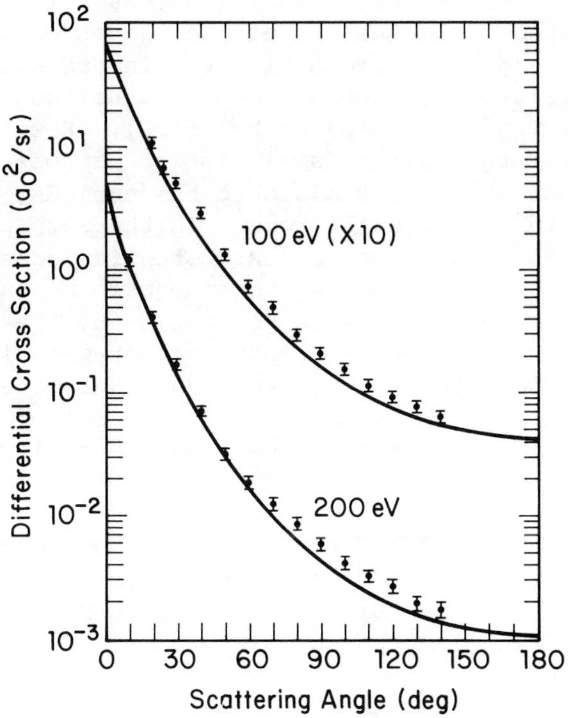

Figure 6-6 The differential cross section for the elastic scattering of electrons by hydrogen atoms at 100 and 200 eV.
———— Distorted wave second Born approximation
• • • • • Data of Williams 1975

potential (Holt and Moiseiwitsch 1968). Comparison with the exact results of Ermolaev and Walters shows that this procedure can be very accurate down to energies as low as (for hydrogen) 30 ev.

As we have already seen, at sufficiently high energies the total cross section for excitation is given accurately by the first Born approximation. The position is rather different for the differential cross section. The angular distribution at high energies is always strongly peaked about the forward direction. In the small angle region which contributes nearly all the total cross section, the first Born approximation is accurate, but at larger angles where the momentum transfer is large, the differential cross section in the first Born approximation decreases much too rapidly with increasing angle and is often orders of magnitude smaller than the experimental data. The reason for this is that because of the orthogonality of the target eigenfunctions the first term in (6-30) representing the interaction between the scattered electron and the nucleus does not contribute to the amplitude T_{nm}^{B}, $n \neq m$ given by (6-28). However it is clear that at large angles (small impact parameters) for which the electron penetrates close to the nucleus, this interaction should play a major role. In the second term in the Born series, T_{nm}^{2}, the nuclear potential does contribut among the second order terms are those describing an excitation followed by an elastic scattering by the nuclear potential and those in which an elastic scattering is followed by excitation. These terms dominate large angle inelastic scattering and in fact large angle amplitude converges to the second Born approximation in the high energy limit. It is clear that the distorted wave method will also contain these terms, provided the distortion is taken into account in both the initial and final states. It is not sufficient to use a plane wave for the final state and a distorted wave for the initial state since such a procedure excludes half the important nuclear potential terms (Potapov 1973).

6-4 EXCHANGE AND REARRANGEMENT COLLISIONS

By using wave functions having the correct symmetry there is no difficulty in including exchange effects in the close coupling and variational methods. There are however certain difficulties which arise when attempting to calculate the amplitude for a rearrangement or exchange collision with a perturbation scheme, such as the Born series. For excitation processes not involving changes in the spin of the target, at higher energies, where the Born approximation may be expected to be valid, it is not absolutely necessary to make allowances for exchange scattering since the exchange amplitude decreases rapidly with increasing energy, but for reactions where the spin of the target changes, for instance in the reaction

$$e + \mathrm{He}(1^1S) \rightarrow e + \mathrm{He}(2^3S), \qquad (6\text{-}51)$$

which can only take place through electron exchange, it is necessary to develop an approximation equivalent to the Born approximation for direct scattering. As the difficulties encountered are common to all rearrangement collisions we shall consider the following model problem. Three distinct particles 1, 2 and 3, with masses M_1, M_2 and M_3 interact together with potentials V_1, V_2 and V_3, where V_1 acts between particles 2 and 3, V_2 between 1 and 3, and V_3 between 1 and 2. We start by considering the rearrangement collision in which particle 1 is incident on a bound state of (2 + 3), and in the final state particles 1 and 2 are bound and 3 is free.

$$1 + (2 + 3) \rightarrow 3 + (1 + 2). \qquad (6\text{-}52)$$

We shall assume the total energy is below the threshold for the break-up of the system with three unbound particles. Coordinates will be introduced such that $\vec{R}_1$ is the relative position vector of 2 with respect to 3 and $\vec{r}_1$ is the position of 1 with respect to the center of mass of (2 + 3). $(\vec{R}_2,\vec{r}_2)$ and $(\vec{R}_3,\vec{r}_3)$ can be defined similarly. The transition matrix element for reaction (6-52) is, following the general expressions obtained in Chapter 4

$$T_{ji} = \int d^3R_1 \int d^3r_1 X_o^{3*}(\vec{R}_3) e^{-i\vec{k}_j \cdot \vec{r}_3} (V_2+V_3)\psi_i^+(\vec{R}_1,\vec{r}_1). \qquad (6\text{-}53)$$

The functions $X_m^3(\vec{R}_3)$ form a complete set of orthonormal wave functions for the sub-system (1 + 2) and in (6-53) it has been assumed that capture is into the ground state. In the incident channel the complete wave function ψ^+ has the asymptotic form

$$\psi_i^+ \xrightarrow[r_1\to\infty]{} X_o^1(\vec{R}_1)\left(e^{i\vec{k}_i \cdot \vec{r}} + f(\theta)\frac{e^{ik_i r_1}}{r_1}\right) \qquad (6\text{-}54)$$

where the functions $X_m^1(\vec{R}_1)$ are the complete set of eigenfunctions for the sub-system (2 + 3). We shall continue to use atomic units in which the conservation of energy relation is

$$\frac{1}{2\mu_1} k_i^2 + \varepsilon_o^1 = \frac{1}{2\mu_3} k_j^2 + \varepsilon_o^3. \qquad (6\text{-}55)$$

where μ_i is the reduced mass of particle i with respect to the other two particles and ε_n^1, ε_n^3 are the binding energies of the m and nth state of sub-systems (2 + 3) and (1 + 2) respectively.

In the rearranged channel, the asymptotic form of ψ is

$$\psi_i^+ \xrightarrow[r_3\to\infty]{} g(\theta)\frac{e^{ik_j r_3}}{r_3} X_o^3(\vec{R}_3), \tag{6-56}$$

where the rearranged amplitude is given by

$$g(\theta) = -\frac{\mu_3}{2\pi} T_{ji}(\theta), \tag{6-57}$$

and T_{ji} is given by equation (6-53). The Born-Oppenheimer approximation for T_{ji} is obtained by substituting the incident unperturbed wave function for ψ_i^+ in (6-53):

$$T_{ji}^B = \int d^3R_i \int d^3r_i X_o^{3*}(\vec{R}_3) e^{-i\vec{k}_j\cdot\vec{r}_3} (V_2+V_3) e^{i\vec{k}_i\cdot\vec{r}_1} X_o^1(\vec{R}_1) \tag{6-58}$$

This expression is defective for various reasons. Because the initial and final states of the system are not orthogonal, a constant added to the perturbation contributes a finite amount to T_{ji}^B. This trouble does not occur in the Born approximation for excitation, because in that case the initial and final states are orthogonal. When particle 2 is infintely heavy (as in electron scattering by hydrogen where 2 represents the proton), the cross section should vanish if the interaction between particles 1 and 3 is removed ($V_2 \to 0$). The matrix element T_{ji}^B does not have this property, but remains finite, again because of the non-orthogonality of the initial and final states.

In practice these theoretical difficulties cannot be ignored, since the Born-Oppenheimer cross sections are often grossly in error, giving results greatly exceeding the measured values. For example, the Born-Oppenheimer approximation provides cross sections about 20 times those observed at low energies for the $1^1S \to 2^3S$ excitation of helium.

To understand the origin of the difficulty let us examine the problem in the two-state approximation. For a trial wave function in the variational method we shall use the expression

$$\psi_i^+ = X_o^1(\vec{R}_1)F_o(\vec{r}_1) + X_o^3(\vec{R}_3)G_o(\vec{r}_3). \tag{6-59}$$

With this choice the Euler equations obtained by varying the functional I, with respect to independent variations of F_o and G_o, where

$$I = \int d\tau (\psi^* | H-E | \psi) \tag{6-60}$$

are

$$\int d^3R_1 X_o^{1*}(\vec{R}_1)(H - E)\left[X_o^1(\vec{R}_1)F_o(\vec{r}_1) + X_o^3(\vec{R}_3)G_o(\vec{r}_3)\right] = 0 \quad (6\text{-}61a)$$

$$\int d^3R_3 X_o^{3*}(\vec{R}_3)(H - E)\left[X_o^1(\vec{R}_1)F_o)(\vec{r}_1) + X_o^3(\vec{R}_3)G_o(\vec{r}_3)\right] = 0 \quad (6\text{-}61b)$$

Using the Schrödinger equations for X_o^1 and X_o^3, these equations reduce to

$$\left(\nabla^2_{r_1} + k_i^2 - U_{11}(\vec{r}_1)\right)F_o(\vec{r}_1) = \frac{\mu_1}{\mu_3}\int d^3R_1\{X_o^{1*}(\vec{R}_1)X_o^3(\vec{R}_3) \times$$

$$\times \left(-\nabla^2_{r_3} - k_j^2 + 2\mu_3(V_1+V_2)\right)G_o(\vec{r}_3)\}, \quad (6\text{-}62a)$$

$$\left(\nabla^2_{r_3} + k_j^2 - U_{33}(\vec{r}_3)\right)G_o(\vec{r}_3) = \frac{\mu_3}{\mu_1}\int d^3R_3\{X_o^{3*}(\vec{R}_3)X_o^1(\vec{R}_1) \times$$

$$\times \left(-\nabla^2_{r_1} - k_i^2 + 2\mu_1(V_3+V_2)\right)F_o(\vec{r}_1)\} \quad (6\text{-}62b)$$

where U_{11}, U_{33} are the static interactions in the initial and final states.

$$U_{11}(\vec{r}_1) = 2\mu_1\int d^3R_1\{X_o^{1*}(\vec{R}_1)X_o^1(\vec{R}_1)(V_2 + V_3)\} \quad (6\text{-}63a)$$

$$U_{33}(\vec{r}_3) = 2\mu_3\int d^3R_3\{X_o^{3*}(\vec{R}_3)X_o^3(\vec{R}_3)(V_1 + V_2)\} \quad (6\text{-}63b)$$

The boundary conditions to be satisfied by F_o and G_o are

$$F_o(\vec{r}_1) \sim e^{i\vec{k}_i\cdot\vec{r}_1} + r_1^{-1}\exp(ik_i r_1)f(\theta_1), \quad (6\text{-}64)$$

$$G_o(\vec{r}_3) \sim r_3^{-1}\exp(ik_j r_3)g(\theta_3).$$

The plane wave, or 'Born-Oppenheimer' approximation, then consists in replacing $F_o(\vec{r}_1)$ by $\exp(i\vec{k}_i\cdot\vec{r}_1)$ in (6-62b) and omitting U_{33}. In this approximation the terms

$-(\nabla^2_{r_1} + k_i^{\,2})F_o(\vec{r}_1)$ occurring on the right hand side of (6-62b) vanish, but as pointed out by Feenberg (1933) these terms are of first order in the potential since from equation (6-62a), to first order

$$\left(\nabla^2_{r_1} + k_i^{\,2}\right)F_o(\vec{r}_1) \cong U_{11}(r_1)F_o(\vec{r}_1). \tag{6-65}$$

This shows that the Born-Oppenheimer approximation cannot provide a consistent approximation to the solution of the 2-state coupled equations (6-62), or indeed to the full Schrödinger equation. In fact in many cases it is known that the correct high energy form of an amplitude for a rearrangement collision is given by the second, and not the first, Born approximation (Shakeshaft 1978). It is interesting to note that this inconsistency does not happen in the distorted wave Born approximation (or in the Coulomb-Born approximation) provided the distorting potentials include the static potentials $U_{11}$and U_{33}, as we shall see.

The distorted wave method

The distorted wave approximation to the equations (6-62), using U_{11} and U_{33} as the distorting potentials, is

$$T_{ji}^{\,DW} = \int d^3R_i \int d^3r_i X_o^{\,3*}(\vec{R}_3)\mathcal{G}^{-*}(\vec{r}_3)\left[-\frac{1}{2\mu_1}\left(\nabla^2_{r_1} + k_i^{\,2}\right) + \right.$$
$$\left. + (V_2 + V_3)\right]X_o^{\,1}(\vec{R}_1)\mathcal{F}(\vec{r}_1) \tag{6-66}$$

where $\mathcal{G}$ and $\mathcal{F}$ satisfy the uncoupled equations

$$\left(\nabla^2_{r_1} + k_i^{\,2} - U_{11}\right)\mathcal{F}^+(\vec{r}_1) = 0, \tag{6-67a}$$

$$\left(\nabla^2_{r_3} + k_j^{\,2} - U_{33}\right)\mathcal{G}^-(\vec{r}_3) = 0, \tag{6-67b}$$

with the boundary conditions

$$\mathcal{F}^+(\vec{r}_1) \sim \exp(i\vec{k}_i\cdot\vec{r}_1) + r_1^{-1}\exp(ik_ir_1)\bar{f}(\theta_1,\phi_1), \tag{6-68a}$$

$$\mathcal{G}^-(\vec{r}_3) \sim \exp(i\vec{k}_j\cdot\vec{r}_3) + r_3^{-1}\exp(-ik_jr_3)\bar{g}(\theta_3,\phi_3). \tag{6-68b}$$

From the equation satisfied by $\mathcal{F}^+$ we have, that

$\left(\nabla^2_{r_1} + k_i^{\,2}\right)F^+$ is equal to $U_{11}F^+_{,}$, so that since

$$\frac{1}{2\mu_1} U_{11} = V_{11} = \int d^3R_1 \left|X_o^{\,1}(\vec{R}_1)\right|^2 (V_2 + V_3) \qquad (6\text{-}69)$$

the effective perturbation is

$$\left(- V_{11} + V_2 + V_3\right)$$

This has none of the previous objectionable features. A constant potential added to V_2 or V_3 does not contribute to the perturbation, and in the limit in which the particle 2 is infinitely heavy and represents a proton, 1 and 3 representing electrons, the electron-proton interaction V_3 cancels from the perturbation, leaving as the effective perturbing potential

$$\left(V_2 - \int d^3R_1 \left|X_o^{\,1}(\vec{R}_1)\right|^2 V_2\right) \qquad (6\text{-}70)$$

so that the amplitude vanishes if $V_2 \to 0$.

Although the distorted wave approximation cannot be expected to be accurate at low energies near a rearrangement threshold, the calculations of Massey and Moiseiwitsch (1954) for the $1^1S \to 2^3S$ excitation of helium are shown in Fig. 6-7, for historical interest. Unlike the Born-Oppenheimer cross section, the distorted wave cross section is of the order of magnitude of the experimental data, although the energy is too low for accurate results to be obtained.

The Ochkur approximation

A different approach to obtaining an adequate high energy approximation for exchange scattering is due to Ochkur (1964).

If it is assumed that at sufficiently high energies the Born-Oppenheimer amplitude accurately represents the exact rearrangement amplitude (which is certainly not always the case), then it follows that the leading term in an expansion of the Born-Oppenheimer amplitude in inverse powers of $k_i^{\,2}$ must coincide with the leading term in the expansion of the exact amplitude. On the other hand other terms in the expansion of the approximate amplitude may be in serious error, being modified by contributions from higher terms of the Born series. These ideas led Ochkur (and independently Bonham) to suggest that the leading term

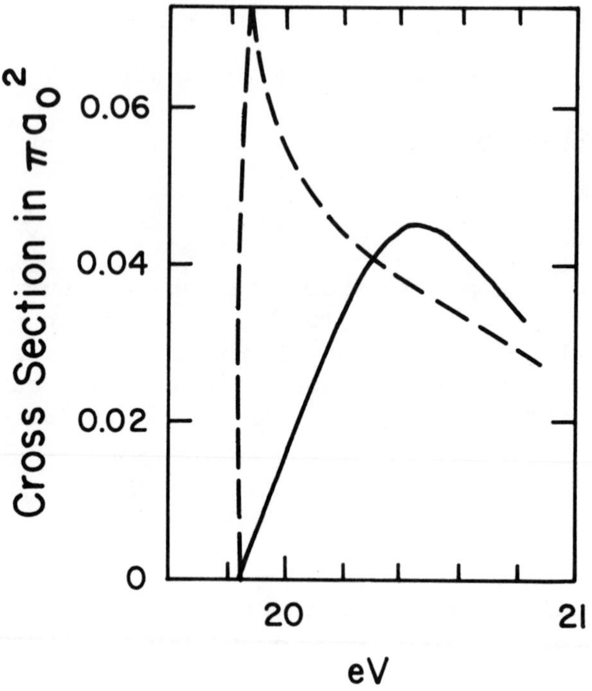

Figure 6-7 Low energy cross section for excitation of the $2\,^3S$ state of helium from the ground state by electron impact.
——————— Experimental curve (Schultz and Fox 1957)
— — — — Exchange distorted wave method (Massey and Moiseiwitsch 1954)

of the Born-Oppenheimer amplitude should be isolated and used as an approximation.

Let us consider the particular case of excitation of atomic hydrogen by electron impact. The exchange amplitude for excitation to the nth level of hydrogen is

$$g_{no}(\theta,\phi) = -\frac{1}{2\pi}\int \phi_n{}^*(\vec{r}_2)e^{-i\vec{k}_n\cdot\vec{r}}\left(\frac{1}{|\vec{r}_1 - \vec{r}_2|} - \frac{1}{r_2}\right)\phi_o(\vec{r}_1)e^{i\vec{k}_o\cdot\vec{r}_2}\,d^3r_1d^3r_2, \qquad (6\text{-}71)$$

where $\vec{r}_1$ and $\vec{r}_2$ are the position vectors of the two electrons. The term $(1/r_2)$, which represents the interaction between electron 2 and the proton, does not contribute to the terms of leading order in $(1/k_o^2)$ and may be dropped. The integral over $\vec{r}_2$ is then of the form

$$I(\vec{r}_1) = \int d^3r_2 \phi_n^*(\vec{r}_2) \frac{1}{|\vec{r}_1 - \vec{r}_2|} e^{i\vec{k}_o \cdot \vec{r}_2} \tag{6-72}$$

Introducing the Fourier transform of $\phi_n(\vec{r}_2)$ by

$$\tilde{\phi}_n(p) = \left(\frac{1}{2\pi}\right)^{3/2} \int e^{-i\vec{p}\cdot\vec{r}_2} \phi_n(\vec{r}_2) d^3r_2,$$

we find that

$$I(\vec{r}_1) = \int d^3p \int d^3r_2 \left(\frac{1}{2\pi}\right)^{3/2} \tilde{\phi}_n^*(\vec{p}) \frac{e^{i(\vec{p}+\vec{k}_o)\cdot r_2}}{|\vec{r}_1 - \vec{r}_2|}$$

$$= \left(\frac{2}{\pi}\right)^{\frac{1}{2}} \int d^3p \tilde{\phi}_n^*(\vec{p}) \frac{e^{+i(\vec{p}+\vec{k}_o)\cdot r_1}}{|\vec{p} + \vec{k}_o|^2} \tag{6-73}$$

where we have used the result (6-31)

For large k_o^2, $|\vec{p}_2 + \vec{k}_o|^2$ in the denominator of (6-73) can be replaced by k_o^2 and the integral then reduces to the Fourier transform of $\tilde{\phi}_n(\vec{p})$, which is of course just $\phi_n(\vec{r}_1)$. Thus we have the result:

$$I(\vec{r}_1) \underset{\text{large } k_o}{\rightarrow} \frac{(4\pi)}{k_o^2} e^{i\vec{k}_o\cdot\vec{r}_1} \phi_n^*(\vec{r}_1). \tag{6-74}$$

The exchange amplitude using this approximation for $I(\vec{r}_1)$ is

$$g_{no}(\theta) = \frac{-2}{k_o^2} \int \phi_n^*(\vec{r}_1) e^{i\vec{k}_o\cdot\vec{r}_1} \phi_o(\vec{r}_1) e^{-i\vec{k}_n\cdot\vec{r}_1} d^3r_1 \tag{6-75}$$

Referring to equation (6-38), the integral is seen to be proportional to the direct Born approximation amplitude $f_{no}(\theta)$, (for electron scattering $f_{no}(\theta) = -T_{no}/(2\pi)$) and:

$$g_{no}(\theta) = \frac{K^2}{k_o^{\,2}} f_{no}(\theta), \tag{6-76}$$

where $\vec{K} = \vec{k}_o - \vec{k}_n$. The differential cross section for e - H excitation for a beam of unpolarized electrons is then

$$\frac{d\sigma}{d\Omega} = \frac{k_n}{4k_o} \left(|f_{no}(\theta)|^2 \left[\left(1 + \frac{K^2}{k_o^{\,2}}\right)^2 + 3\left(1 - \frac{k^2}{k_o^{\,2}}\right)^2 \right] \right) \tag{6-77}$$

Since exchange scattering is small compared with direct scattering at high energies, the Ochkur approximation for the exchange amplitude has often been used in conjunction with more accurate approximations (such as optical potential models, second Born approximations and so on) for the direct amplitude. Many of these applications have been reviewed by Bransden and McDowell (1977, 1978).

6-5 SEMI-CLASSICAL MODELS

In Chapter 2, it was shown that semi-classical approximations become accurate for scattering by short range potentials of range a when the wave number k is sufficiently large for the condition ka >> 1 to hold. Semi-classical methods can also be applied in various ways to scattering of particles by a complex system and there have been several applications to the scattering of electrons by atoms at moderate and high energies, where by moderate energies, it is meant that the incident energy must be greater than the average potential strength in each scattering channel. For hydrogen and helium targets, this energy region might start at ~50 ev, and for heavier atoms at suitably higher energies.

At the high energies exchange effects are small and can be neglected to some reasonable degree of approximation. In that case, the wave function for the system of scattered electrons plus target can be represented by the expansion (4-93)

$$\psi_i^{+}(\vec{x},\vec{r}) = \sum_m X_m(\vec{x}) F_{mi}(\vec{r}) \tag{6-78}$$

where the sum is over a complete set of orthonormal target eigenfunctions X_m (including the continuum functions). The position vectors of the Z target electrons are $\vec{x}_1, \vec{x}_2 \ldots \vec{x}_Z$, denoted collectively by $\vec{x}$ and $\vec{r}$ is the position vector of the scattered electron with respect to the target nucleus.

The functions X_n satisfy the Schrödinger equation (4-95), corresponding to a target Hamiltonian H_0 and the total wave function satisfies the Schrödinger equation (in atomic units)

$$\left(-\frac{1}{2}\nabla_r^2 + V(\vec{x},\vec{r}) + H_o - E\right)\psi_i^+(\vec{x},\vec{r}) = 0 \tag{6-79}$$

where the interaction $V(\vec{x},\vec{r}) \equiv V_\alpha$ has the form

$$V(\vec{x},\vec{r}) = -\frac{Z}{r} + \sum_{i=1}^{Z} \frac{1}{|\vec{r}-\vec{x}_i|} \tag{6-80}$$

By projecting equation (6-79) with the function X_m, we find the coupled equations (4-98), which for the particular case of electron scattering become

$$\left(\nabla_r^2 + k_m^{\ 2}\right)F_{mi}(\vec{r}) = \sum_n U_{mn}(\vec{r})F_{mi}(\vec{r}) \qquad m = 0,1,2.... \tag{6-81}$$

where

$$k_m^{\ 2} = 2E - \varepsilon_m \tag{6-82}$$

and

$$U_{mn}(\vec{r}) = 2\ V_{mn}(\vec{r}) = 2\int d\vec{x}X_m^{\ *}(\vec{x})V(\vec{x},\vec{r})X_n(\vec{x}) \tag{6-83}$$

As we have seen truncation of the set of equations (6-81) leads to the close coupling approximation, and by replacing the functions X_n by pseudofunctions, we obtain the pseudo-state expansion approximation.

One possibility for a semi-classical treatment is to make an angular momentum decomposition and solve the radial equations (such as 4-104) using the Jeffreys (WKB approximation). Another is to follow the ideas of Flannery and McCann[13] and use the eikonal approximation (see Chapter 2, Section 2-4) in each of the coupled equations (6-81). To do this, we suppose that in each channel m the scattered electron follows a classical trajectory

$$\vec{r} = \vec{r}_m(\vec{b},t) \tag{6-84}$$

specified by a two dimensional parameter vector $\vec{b}$ lying in the X,Y plane and the time t, and determined from an effective potential V_m. An obvious choice is to take V_m as the diagonal term in the potential matrix V_{mn}, $V_m = V_{mm} = U_{mm}/2$; alternatively V_m can be considered to be an approximation to the full optical potential describing elastic scattering in the channel m. The wave function $\mathcal{F}_m(\vec{r})$ for elastic scattering by the potential V_m is given in the semi-classical approximation by (see 2-118 and 2-122)

$$\mathcal{F}_m(\vec{r}) = \exp iS_m(\vec{r}_m) \tag{6-85}$$

where

$$S_m(\vec{r}_m) = \int ds \left(k_m{}^2 - 2V_m(r')\right)^{\frac{1}{2}} \tag{6-86}$$

and the integration is along a trajectory. In terms of the time t we can also write

$$S_m(\vec{r}_m) = \int dt\ v_m{}^2(\vec{b},t) \tag{6-87}$$

where $\vec{v}_m$ is the velocity of the electron at a point on the trajectory and $|\vec{v}_m| = [k_m - 2V_m]^{\frac{1}{2}}$. If $t = 0$ is the time of closest approach, then $v_m \to k_m$ as $t \to -\infty$.

The channel functions F_{mi} are now expressed in terms of the distorted waves $\mathcal{F}_m$ and amplitudes a_m by

$$F_{mi}(\vec{r}) = \mathcal{F}_m(\vec{r})\ a_{mi}(\vec{r}) \tag{6-88}$$

Inserting (6-88) into the coupled equations (6-81) and making the semi-classical approximation

$$\nabla^2 S_m << |\vec{\nabla} S_m|^2;\ \nabla^2 a_{mi} << |\vec{\nabla} a_{mi}|^2$$

we obtain a set of coupled equations for the amplitudes a_{mi}:

$$2i\vec{\nabla}S_m\cdot\vec{\nabla}a_{mi} = \sum_n e^{-iS_m}\left(U_{mn}-2V_m\delta_{mn}\right)e^{iS_n}a_{ni}$$

$$\equiv \sum_n 2H_{mn}\ a_{ni} \qquad m = 0,1,2,\ldots \tag{6-89}$$

Since the direction of $\vec{\nabla}S_m$ is parallel to a trajectory and

$$\vec{\nabla}S_m \cdot \vec{\nabla} = \sqrt{k_m{}^2 - 2V_m}\ \frac{\partial}{\partial s}$$

$$= \frac{\partial}{\partial t}$$

the coupled equations can be written in impact parameter form as

$$i \frac{\partial}{\partial t} a_{mi}(\vec{b},t) = \sum_n H_{mn}(\vec{r})\, a_{ni}(\vec{b},t)$$

$$m = 0,1,2,\ldots \qquad (6\text{-}90)$$

where in the mth channel $\vec{r}$ is to be considered as a function of $\vec{b}$ and t through the trajectory equations (6-84).

Boundary conditions and cross sections

Referring to (6-87) and (6-88), it is seen that, since the functions F_m are of unit modulus, the amplitude of a particular target eigenfunction X_m in the expression of ψ_i^+ is given by $|a_m(\vec{b},t)|$. It is easy to show that if N terms are retained in the expansion (6-78) then

$$\frac{d}{dt} \sum_{m=1}^{N} |a_{mi}(\vec{b},t)|^2 = 0 \qquad (6\text{-}91)$$

and this is the condition which ensures conservation of probability and unitarity of the S-matrix. It follows that if the amplitudes are normalized so that

$$\sum_{i=1}^{N} |a_{mi}(\vec{b},t)|^2 = 1 \qquad (6\text{-}92)$$

then

$$|a_{mi}(\vec{b},t)|^2$$

is the probability of finding the target in the level m at time t. Since in the initial state the target is in the level i, the boundary conditions are imposed that

$$\underset{t\to-\infty}{\ell t} |a_{mi}(\vec{b},t)|^2 = \delta_{mi} \qquad (6\text{-}93)$$

in which case the probability of finding (for a given impact parameter) the system in the level m after the collision is

$$P_{mi}(\vec{b}) = \underset{t\to+\infty}{\ell t} |a_{mi}(\vec{b},t)|^2 \qquad (6\text{-}94)$$

and the excitation total cross section is

$$\sigma_{mi} = \frac{k_m}{k_i} \int d^2b\; P_{mi}(\vec{b}) \qquad (6\text{-}95)$$

Although the functions F_{mi} do not have the correct asymptotic form, as we saw in Chapter 2, the differential cross section can be determined from an integral equation for the scattering amplitude which only requires a knowledge of F_{mi} in the region in which the interaction is significant. The transition matri T_{mi} can be computed by using the integral equations (4-101) an the differential cross section for excitation, in atomic units is then

$$\frac{d\sigma_{mi}}{d\Omega} = \frac{k_m}{4\pi^2 k_i} \left|T_{mi}(E,\theta)\right|^2 \tag{6-96}$$

The total cross section computed from this differential cross section is not identical with that given by (6-95), except at high energies and the total cross section obtained from (6-96) should be more accurate. In the high energy limit, in which the integral equation (4-101) can be approximated using the method of stationary phase, the differential cross section reduces to

$$\frac{d\sigma_{mi}(\theta,\phi)}{d\Omega} = \left(\frac{d\sigma_m{}^c(\theta,\phi)}{d\Omega}\right) P_m(\vec{b}) \tag{6-97}$$

where $d\sigma_m{}^c/d\Omega$ is the classical cross section for scattering by the potential V_m and $\vec{b}$ is the impact parameter of the trajectory leading to the angle of scattering θ. The discussion in Chapter 2 about the interference which arises when two trajectories lead to the same angle of scattering can be developed in this case along the same lines.

The common trajectory approximation

The procedure outlined above can be simplified in many ways. At sufficiently high energies the functions S_m can be approximated as in equation (2-126):

$$S_m(\vec{r}) = k_m z - \frac{1}{k_m}\int_{-\infty}^{z} dz' \, V_m(\vec{b},z') \tag{6-98}$$

A further simplification is to take a common effective potential W and a common trajectory in each channel, so that $V_m = W$, all m and to take the initial velocity along the common trajectory to be $v_i = k_i$. If, in addition, the high energy approximation is made that

$$k_m z \approx k_i z + (\varepsilon_i - \varepsilon_m) z / v_i \tag{6-99}$$

with $z = v_i t$, the potential H_{mn} in equations (6-90) reduces to

$$H_{mn}(t) = \left[V_{mn}(\vec{r},t) - W(\vec{r},t)\right]e^{i(\varepsilon_m-\varepsilon_n)t} \qquad (6\text{-}100)$$

In this approximation equations (6-90) can be obtained from the time dependent Schrödinger equation

$$\left[H_o + V(\vec{x},\vec{r}(t)) - W(\vec{r},t) - i\frac{\partial}{\partial t}\right]\Phi(\vec{x},t) = 0 \qquad (6\text{-}101)$$

which represents the time dependence of the wave function for the target electrons in the field of a charge moving along the predetermined trajectory $\vec{r} = \vec{r}(t)$, for a given impact parameter. Equations (6-90) are obtained directly from the impact parameter expansion

$$\Phi(\vec{x},t) = \sum_m X_m(\vec{x})e^{-i\varepsilon_m t}a_m(\vec{b},t) \qquad (6\text{-}102)$$

Martir et al (1982) have calculated cross sections using the common trajectory approximation for electron scattering by atomic hydrogen[14], using a very large basis set containing both hydrogen functions and pseudofunctions. Their results for excitation of the n = 2 and n = 3 levels and also for ionization have been obtained in three approximations (a) W = 0 (b) W = V_{OO}, the static potential appropriate to the 1s ground state of hydrogen (c) W = $-r^{-1}$, the unscreened potential of the nucleus. The agreement with the data from approximation (a) is close, above 40 ev, for the excitation of the 2s and 3s levels, while below this energy allowing for the non-linear nature of the trajectory as in approximations (b) and (c) greatly improves the agreement with experiment. Agreement is less good for excitation of the np levels and also for ionization. The straight line approximation (W = 0) is known to give poor results for the differential cross sections, except near the forward direction $\theta \leq 20^o$, for electron scattering even at energies up to 200 ev (see Bransden and McDowell 1977, 1978), but it is not known at the time of writing how accurate the differential cross sections are in the non-linear trajectory approximations.

The Glauber approximation

A less accurate semi-classical approximation, which however can be obtained in closed form, is similar in structure to the eikonal approximation for potential scattering (2-130) and can be developed from equation (6-101) in the approximation W = 0 with a straight line trajectory

$$\vec{r}(r) = \underset{\sim}{b} + \underset{\sim}{v}_i t$$

or alternatively from the original Schrödinger equation (6-79). To start from (6-79), ψ_i^+ is written as

$$\psi_i^+(\vec{x},\vec{r}) = g(\vec{x},\vec{r})X_i(\vec{x}) \tag{6-103}$$

On substitution in (6-79) and neglecting derivatives of $g(\vec{r},\vec{x})$ with respect to the internal coordinates $\vec{x}$, we find

$$\left(-\frac{1}{2}\nabla_r^2 + V(\vec{x},\vec{r}) - \frac{1}{2}k_i^2\right)g(\vec{x},\vec{r}) = 0 \tag{6-104}$$

It is seen that this equation depends parametrically on $\vec{x}$ and represents the elastic scattering from a target with Z electrons fixed at the positions $\vec{x}_i$. This approximation can only be accurate when the velocity of the scattered electron is large compared with the orbital velocities of the target, so that the incident electron scatters before the target can respond. The eikonal approximation to (6-104) is now

$$g(\vec{x},\vec{r}) = \exp i\left(k_i z - \frac{1}{2k_i}\int_{-\infty}^{z} dz' V(\vec{x},\vec{r}')\right) \tag{6-105}$$

where $\vec{r}'$ is the vector with components x,y and z'. In terms of an impact parameter $\vec{b}$, $x = b_x$ and $y = b_y$.
The transition matrix T_{mi} can be obtained from the integral

$$\begin{aligned} T_{mi} &= \int d^3x \int d^3r\, X_m^*(\vec{x}) e^{-i\vec{k}_m\cdot\vec{r}} V(\vec{x},\vec{r})\psi_i^+(\vec{x},\vec{r}) \\ &= \int d^3x \int d^3r\, X_m^*(\vec{x}) e^{i\vec{K}\cdot\vec{r}} V(\vec{x},\vec{r}) e^{-\frac{i}{2k_i}\int_{-\infty}^{z} dz' V(\vec{x},\vec{r}')} X_i(\vec{x}) \end{aligned} \tag{6-106}$$

where $\vec{K}$ is the momentum transfer, $\vec{K} = \vec{k}_i - \vec{k}_m$. If the longitudinal component of the momentim transfer is neglected[15] so that $\vec{K}\cdot\vec{r} \approx \vec{K}\cdot\vec{b}$, the integration over z can be performed (cf.2-129) and T_{mi} becomes

$$T_{mi} = \frac{k_i}{2\pi_i}\int d^2b\, \exp(i\vec{K}\cdot\vec{b}) \int d^3x X_m^*(\vec{x}) \left(\exp i\chi(\vec{x},\vec{b}) - 1\right) X_o(\vec{x}) \tag{6-107}$$

where

$$\chi(\vec{x},\vec{b}) = -\frac{1}{2k_i}\int_{-\infty}^{\infty} V(\vec{x},\vec{r}')dz' \tag{6-108}$$

This is the Glauber approximation which has excited considerable attention because for Coulomb potentials $\chi(\vec{x},\vec{b})$

can be obtained analytically and the subsequent integrations to compute T_{mi} can be carried out. The exchange amplitude can also be computed by using the same approximation for ψ_i in the appropriate integral expression. The Glauber approximation for ψ_i^+ can also be found from the impact parameter coupled equations (6-90) in the straight line W = 0, provided the energy differences $(\varepsilon_m - \varepsilon_n)$ are ignored in the potential matrix H_{mn} given by (6-100). The effect of this additional approximation is severe. For example, the elastic scattering differential cross section in the Glauber approximation is singular in the forward direction. Also it is seen, by expanding the term $\exp i\chi$ in a power series, that the terms are alternately real and imaginary, with the result that the real part of the second order term in the Born expression is not represented in the corresponding Glauber series. As this term is known to be important, it is difficult to justify the Glauber approximation in general, although it has been widely employed.

The eikonal-Born series

Although the Glauber approximation itself is open to question, Byron and Joachain[16] have shown that the third term in the Glauber series for T_{mi}, formed by expanding $\exp i\chi$, provides the leading correction to the second-Born approximation. Their eikonal-Born series approximation consists of evaluating the amplitude in the second Born approximation by the closure method and correcting this amplitude by using the Glauber series for the third order term (and in some cases for all higher order terms). The amplitude in this approximation is free from singularities and provides accurate results at both small and large angles. This important method has been successfully applied to the elastic scattering of electrons by hydrogen, helium (see Figure 6-8) and other rare gases and also to a number of inelastic processes. Byron and Joachain (1981) have also shown that the third order term in the Glauber series for elastic scattering can be used to provide a third order correction to the second optical potential discussed in Section 6-2.

6-6 IONIZATION

When the total energy of the system is great enough the target atom may be ionized in an electron-atom collision; that is, one or several electrons may be ejected. As an example, the ionization of hydrogen by electron impact

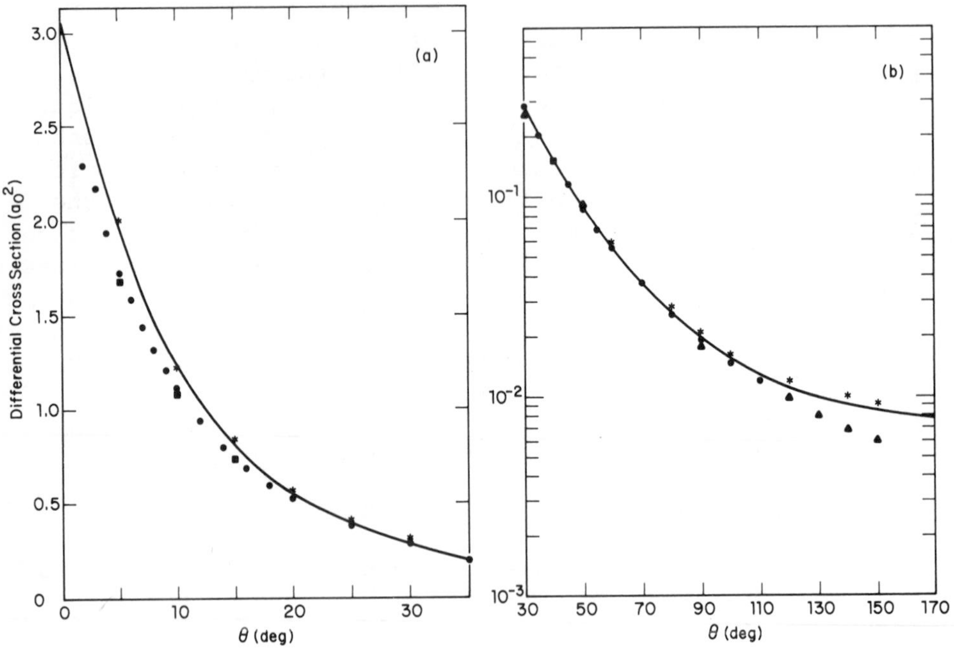

Figure 6-8 The differential cross section for the elastic scattering of electrons by helium at 200 ev.

• • • • • • Experimental data

______ Theoretical cross section in the Eikonal-Born-Series method.

will be discussed, but the approximations employed may be extended to more complicated systems. The notation established in Chapter 5 will be followed, using atomic units.

The total wave function $\psi(\vec{r}_1,\vec{r}_2)$ can always be expanded in terms of the complete set of hydrogenic wave functions $\phi_n(\vec{r})$, as in equation (5-43). Assuming that in the incident state electron 1 is free and 2 is bound, and displaying the continuum terms explicitly, the expansion is (in the unsymmetrized form)

$$\psi(\vec{r}_1,\vec{r}_2) = \sum_n \left(\phi_n(\vec{r}_2)F_n(\vec{r}_1) + \phi_n(\vec{r}_1)G_n(\vec{r}_2)\right) +$$
$$+ \int d^3K\left(\phi^-(\vec{K},\vec{r}_2)F(\vec{K},\vec{r}_1) + \phi^-(\vec{K},\vec{r}_1)G(\vec{K},\vec{r}_2)\right) \tag{6-109}$$

Here the sum over n runs over the bound hydrogenic states and the integral over $\vec{K}$ is over the continuum states $\phi^-(\vec{K},\vec{r})$, where $\vec{K}$ is the momentum of the state, with energy $K^2/2$. The normalization assumed for the continuum states is

$$\int d^3r\left(\phi^-(\vec{K},\vec{r})\right)^* \phi^-(\vec{K}',\vec{r}) = \delta(\vec{K}-\vec{K}') \tag{6-110}$$

The functions ϕ^- must be used rather than the functions ϕ^+, so that $\psi(\vec{r}_1,\vec{r}_2)$ contains only outgoing waves, as discussed in Chapter 5.

As also explained in Chapter 5, the functions $F(\vec{K},\vec{r})$ and $G(\vec{K},\vec{r})$ can be chosen to be non-singular in K and this ensures that only the functions F_n contribute in the asymptotic region to direct scattering and only the functions G_n contribute in the asymptotic region for rearrangement scattering. In ionization where both electrons appear in the final state, there can be no distinction between the direct and rearranged situations, but it is useful to speak of direct scattering if electron 2 is ejected with a smaller energy than the final energy of electron 1 and of exchange scattering if the reverse situation applies.

The boundary conditions satisfied by F_n and G_n are those discussed earlier:

$$F_o(\vec{r}_1) \sim e^{i\vec{k}_o\cdot\vec{r}_1} + r_1^{-1}e^{ik_o r_1} f_o(\theta_1),$$
$$F_n(\vec{r}_1) \sim r_1^{-1}e^{ik_n r_1} f_n(\theta_1), \quad n \neq 0, \tag{6-111}$$
$$G_n(\vec{r}_2) \sim r_2^{-1}e^{ik_n r_2} g_n(\theta_2) \quad \text{all } n,$$

while for $F(\vec{K},\vec{r}_1)$ and $G(\vec{K},\vec{r}_2)$ we must have that[17]

$$F(\vec{K},\vec{r}_1) \sim r_1^{-1} e^{i(kr_1+\eta(r_1))} f(\vec{K},\vec{k}), \quad K^2 < k^2, \tag{6-112}$$

$$G(\vec{K},\vec{r}_2) \sim r_2^{-1} e^{i(kr_2+\eta(r_2))} g(\vec{K},\vec{k}), \quad K^2 < k^2,$$

$$r_1 F(\vec{K},\vec{r}_1) \xrightarrow[r_1 \to \infty]{} 0, \quad K^2 < k^2 \tag{6-112}$$

$$r_2 G(\vec{K},\vec{r}_2) \xrightarrow[r_2 \to \infty]{} 0, \quad K^2 < k^2$$

The restriction that $F(\vec{K},\vec{r}_1)$ and $G(\vec{K},\vec{r}_2)$ must vanish at large distances when $K^2 < k^2$, is to ensure that each direct and exchange amplitude is counted only once. By conservation of energy, K^2 and k^2 are related by

$$E = \frac{1}{2}k_o^{\ 2} + \varepsilon_o = \frac{1}{2}k_n^{\ 2} + \varepsilon_n = \frac{1}{2}(k^2 + K^2). \tag{6-113}$$

The appearance of phase factors $\eta(r)$ in the asymptotic forms of $F(\vec{K},\vec{r})$ and $G(\vec{K},\vec{r})$ is a consequence of the long range nature of the interactions. For discrete transitions the target electron completely shields the scattered electron from the nuclear charge if the target is a neutral atom, and the scattered electron can be described by ordinary plane or spherical waves at large distances. In ionization, the screening is not complete and the phase factors η are of the logarithmic type that were encountered in the treatment of Coulomb scattering in Chapter 3. We have that

$$\eta = (-\alpha/2k)\log\ (2kr),$$

where $\alpha = -2$ in the present case[18].

The total ionization cross section for distinguishable electrons would be

$$\sigma(\text{ion}) = \int_{K^2<k^2} d^3K \ \frac{k}{k_o} \int d\Omega(\vec{n})\,[\,|f(\vec{K},\vec{k})|^2 + |g(\vec{K},\vec{k})|^2] \tag{6-114}$$

where $\vec{n}$ is a unit vector in the direction of $\vec{k}$. The integrat[illegible] over $\vec{K}$ is carried out only for $K^2 < k^2$, to avoid double counti[illegible] The sum over final states is consistent with the normalizatio[illegible] and closure relations assumed for the hydrogenic wave functio[illegible] For indistinguishable electrons, amplitudes of a definite spin S are formed as in equation (5-44a) and the cross sectio[illegible] for an unpolarized beam is (compare equation 5-44b)

$$\sigma(\text{ion}) = \int\limits_{K^2<k^2} d^3K \frac{k}{k_o} \int d\Omega(\vec{n}) \{ |f(\vec{K},\vec{k})|^2 + |g(\vec{K},\vec{k})|^2 -$$

$$-\text{Re}[f(\vec{K},\vec{k}) g^*(\vec{K},\vec{k})] \} \quad (6\text{-}115)$$

Instead of restricting the domain in which $f(\vec{K},\vec{k})$ is defined to the region $K^2 < k^2$, that is to $K^2 < E$, and remembering that there is no real distinction between direct and exchange ionization, we can <u>define</u> $f(\vec{K},\vec{k})$ for $K^2 > k^2$ by

$$f(\vec{K},\vec{k}) \equiv g(\vec{k},\vec{K}) \quad K^2 > k^2. \quad (6\text{-}116)$$

An alternative form for (6-115) is, where the integration is now over all allowed values of K^2, $K^2 < 2E$:

$$\sigma(\text{ion}) = \int d^3K \frac{k}{k_o} \int d\Omega(\vec{n}) \left(|f(K,k)|^2 - \right.$$

$$\left. - \frac{1}{2}\text{Re}\{ f(\vec{K},\vec{k}) f^*(\vec{k},\vec{K}) \} \right) \quad (6\text{-}117)$$

<u>Calculation of $f(\vec{K},\vec{k}), g(\vec{K},\vec{k})$</u>

In calculating $f(\vec{K},\vec{k})$ let us first treat the case in which the interaction is of short range. It is then possible to proceed as in Chapter 4 and it is found that

$$-2\pi f(\vec{K},\vec{k}) = \int d^3r_1 \int d^3r_2 \Phi^*(\vec{r}_1,\vec{r}_2) [V(r_1) + v(|\vec{r}_1 - \vec{r}_2|)] \psi(\vec{r}_1,\vec{r}_2)$$

$$0 \leq K \leq k \quad (6\text{-}118)$$

where Φ is the final state wave function

$$\Phi(\vec{r}_1,\vec{r}_2) = \phi^-(\vec{K},\vec{r}_2) \exp(i\vec{k}\cdot\vec{r}_1) \quad (6\text{-}119)$$

Similarly the exchange amplitude is given by

$$-2\pi g(\vec{K},\vec{k}) = \int d^3r_1 \int d^3r_2 \Phi^*(\vec{r}_2,\vec{r}_1) [V(r_2) + v(|\vec{r}_1 - \vec{r}_2|)] \psi(\vec{r}_1,\vec{r}_2)$$

$$0 \leq K \leq k \quad (6\text{-}120)$$

An unperturbed solution of the wave equation for the e-H system, for energies E above the ionization threshold,

$$\left(-\frac{1}{2}\nabla_1^2 - \frac{1}{2}\nabla_2^2 + V(r_1) + V(r_2) + v(|r_1 - r_2|) - E \right) \psi = 0$$

$$(6\text{-}121)$$

cannot be defined because the potentials are Coulomb potentials which cannot be neglected for any value of r_1 or r_2 however large. If logarithmic terms could be neglected, the function (6-119) would be an asymptotic solution of (6-121) in the region r_1 large and $r_1 << r_2$. A more accurate representation of the wave function in the asymptotic region is obtained by assuming that electron 1 moves in Coulomb field $-Z_1/r_1$ and electron 2 in a field $-Z_2/r_2$, where Z_1 and Z_2 are effective changes representing the partial screening from the nuclear charge of one electron by the other. This distorted wave function is

$$\chi(\vec{r}_1,\vec{r}_2) = \phi^-(Z_2;\vec{K},\vec{r}_2)\phi^-(Z_1;\vec{k},\vec{r}_1) \tag{6-122}$$

where the Coulomb functions ϕ^- are labeled by the appropriate charge.

The amplitude $f(\vec{K},\vec{k})$ is then found to be given by (Rudge and Seaton 1965)

$$-2\pi f(\vec{K},\vec{k}) = e^{i\beta}(2\pi)^{3/2}\int d^3r_1\int d^3r_2\ \chi^*(\vec{r}_1,\vec{r}_2)\ \times$$
$$\times\left(V(r_1)+V(r_2)+v(|r_1-r_2|)+\frac{Z_1}{r_1}+\frac{Z_2}{r_2}\right)\psi(\vec{r}_1,\vec{r}_2) \tag{6-123}$$

where β is the phase factor:

$$\beta(\vec{K},\vec{k}) = \frac{Z_1}{2k}\log\left(\frac{K^2}{2E}\right) + \frac{Z_2}{2K}\log\left(\frac{k^2}{2E}\right) \tag{6-124}$$

To determine Z_1 and Z_2 the following argument can be invoked. In an ionization experiment, each electron is detected simultaneously in two counters situated at position vectors $\vec{r}_1$ and $\vec{r}_2$ with respect to the scattering center. If the time of flight from the scattering center to the detectors is t, we must have

$$t = \frac{r_1}{v_1} = \frac{r_2}{v_2} \tag{6-125}$$

where v_1 and v_2 are the velocities of the two electrons. In atomic units $v_1 = k$ and $v_2 = K$, so the asymptotic region of interest is that with r_1 and r_2 large and also $r_1/r_2 = k/K$. The wave function (6-122) satisfies a Schrodinger equation containing the interaction $-(Z_1/r_1) - (Z_2/r_2)$. The effective charges can be chosen so that this potential equals the true potential (V_1+V_2+v) in the desired asymptotic region, that is

$$-\frac{Z_1}{r_1} - \frac{Z_2}{r_2} = \frac{1}{r_1} - \frac{1}{r_2} + \frac{1}{|\vec{r}_1 - \vec{r}_2|}$$

for $r_1/r_2 = k/K$. Since $\vec{r}_1$ is in the direction of $\vec{k}$ and $\vec{r}_2$ is in the direction of $\vec{K}$ at the position of the detectors, the condition becomes

$$\frac{Z_1}{k} + \frac{Z_2}{K} = \frac{1}{K} + \frac{1}{k} - \frac{1}{|\vec{K} - \vec{k}|} \qquad (6\text{-}126)$$

This condition does not define the charges Z_1 and Z_2 completely, but for any choice of Z_1, Z_2 can be determined from (6-126).

Low energy approximations

In applications of (6-123), or the appropriate generalizations of (6-123) for ionization of targets containing more than one electron, some approximation must be used for the exact wave function ψ appearing in the integrand. At low energies for which the ionization channels may be strongly coupled to the elastic scattering and excitation channels, a good approximation would be to take an expansion wave function for ψ in which the basis included a large number of pseudofunctions overlapping the hydrogenic continuum. The total ionization cross section has been calculated directly from such calculations by first finding the total (all channel) cross section from the computed forward elastic scattering amplitude via the optical theorem and then subtracting the calculated total elastic and total excitation cross sections. This procedure, and similar procedures used in connection with optical potential models, appears to provide total ionization cross sections of reasonable accuracy for hydrogen and helium targets. In the case of helium, for many electron atoms in general, the excitation of autoionizing levels provides a contribution to the ionization cross section at the lower energies and a satisfactory approximate wave function must include the doubly excited levels, which occur as intermediate states.

Total cross sections at high energies

At high energies, the Born approximation is expected to be accurate for the total cross section. A variety of first order calculations have been carried out on the basis of the amplitude (6-123) but in none of them has the correct relationship between Z_1 and Z_2 been retained. In the most simple approximation, the Born approximation, the complete wave function ψ which appears in (6-123) is replaced by the unperturbed wave function for the initial state

$$\psi^{+}(\vec{r}_1,\vec{r}_2) \cong \phi_o(\vec{r}_2)e^{i\vec{k}_o\cdot\vec{r}_1} \tag{6-127}$$

and at the same time it is usual to set $\beta=0$ and take $Z_1 = 0$, $Z_2 = 1$, so that the ejected electron screens the scattered electron completely. In this approximation interference between the direct and exchange amplitudes is neglected and the second term in (6-117) is ignored.

Exchange effects are included in the Born-Oppenheimer approximation. Here β is again taken to be zero, but when $k>K$, the scattered electron is screened ($Z_1 = 0$, $Z_2 = 1$), but for $k<K$, the ejected electron is screened ($Z_1 = 1$, $Z_2 = 0$) and the complete expression (6-117) is employed.

These plane wave approximations agree well with experiment at energies above 200 ev in the case of $e^- - H$, and 400 ev for e^- - He collisions; but at low energies the calculated cross sections are much too large. Some improvement can be obtained with other choices of Z_1 and Z_2.

At lower energies, a more promising approximation is that introduced by Ochkur and discussed above for excitation. In this approximation, the cross section becomes (Ochkur, 1964)

$$\sigma(\text{ion}) = \int_{K^2<k^2} d^3K \int d\Omega(\vec{n})\, \frac{k}{2k_o}\, |f(\vec{K},\vec{k})|^2 \left(1 - \frac{|\vec{K}-\vec{k}_o|^2}{k_o^2} + \right.$$
$$\left. + \frac{|\vec{K}-\vec{k}_o|^4}{k_o^4}\right) \tag{6-128}$$

The calculations of Peach (1966) for ionization of hydrogen and helium are shown in figure 6-9 for the Ochkur approximation and for modifications of the Born approximations. The Ochkur approximation is seen to be quite successful.

Calculations for the ionization of several different atoms have been carried out in the Born approximation and also in the approximation of Ochkur. We may single out the work of Peach (1965, 1966a,b) on H, He, Li, Be, Na, Mg (see Fig. 6-9) and that of Bates et al (1965) on Na. Subsequent work is described in the review of Bell and Kingston (1974). Few attempts have been made to improve on the use of the unperturbed function of the initial state, but a step in this direction was taken by Burke and Taylor (1965), who

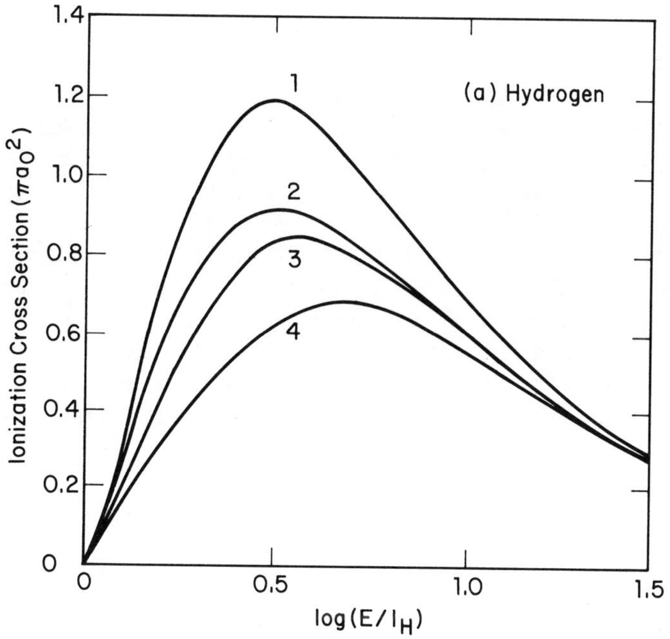

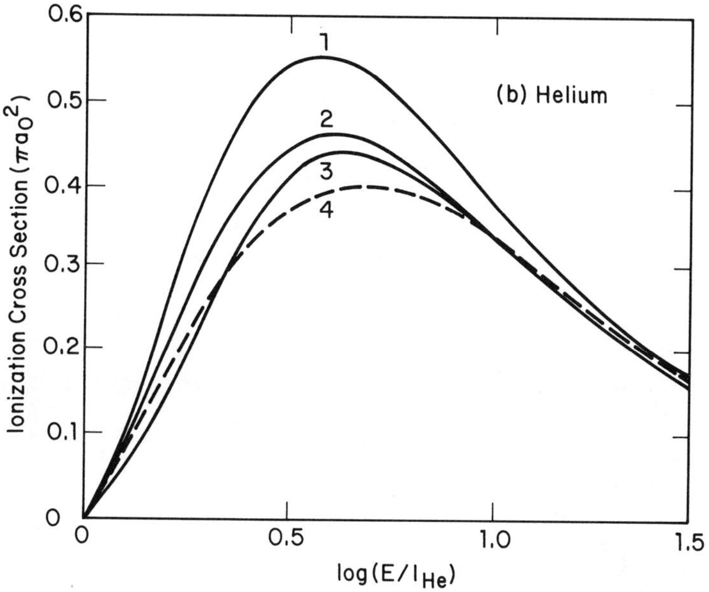

Figure 6-9a,b Cross sections for the ionization of hydrogen and helium by electron impact (after Peach, 1966).

1. Calculated cross sections, Born approximation.
2. Calculated cross sections, Born-exchange approximation.
3. Calculated cross sections, Ochkur's approximation.
4. Experimental cross section. (H: Fite and Brackman, 1958, He: Schram et al., 1965).

used a close coupling wave function in the 1s - 2s - 2p approximation for ψ and found that the effects of departure from a plane wave were considerable. Several studies have employed distorted waves in place of the plane waves $\exp(i\vec{k}_0 \cdot \vec{r})$ in the initial state, but this does not lead to a great improvement in the total cross section (Bransden et al 1978, 1979; Smith et al 1979).

Since ionization could not takeplace in the absence of the electron-electron interaction $v(|\vec{r}_1-\vec{r}_2|)$, it is important to take this potential into account as fully as possible. If the amplitude given by (6-123) is expanded in a perturbation series, all those terms which involve v alone can be summed to produce the scattering operator t_{12} where

$$t_{12} = v_{12} + v_{12}\,(T - E - i\varepsilon + v_{12})^{-1} v_{12}$$

and T is the kinetic energy operator $T = -\tfrac{1}{2}(\nabla_1^2+\nabla_2^2)$ The amplitude $f(\vec{K},\vec{k})$ is then represented as

$$-2\pi f(\vec{K},\vec{k}) = \int d^3r_1 \int d^3r_2\; \chi^*(\vec{r}_1,\vec{r}_2)\, t_{12}(\vec{r}_1-\vec{r}_2)\, \chi_i(\vec{r}_1,\vec{r}_2)$$

where χ_i represents a distorted wave in the incident (elastic scattering) channel. This distorted wave impulse approximation has been developed to a high degree by McCarthy and his co-workers[19], making full allowance for the identity of the electrons, and has been successfully applied to the study of the ionization of a wide range of atoms and molecules.

Differential cross sections

In both hydrogen and helium, the differential cross section

$$\frac{d^3\sigma}{d\Omega_1 d\Omega_2 dE_2}$$

has been measured at certain energies up to 500 ev, for selected ranges of the variables θ_1, θ_2, E_2 and ϕ_2 (taking $\phi_1=0$). As would be expected the first Born approximation, while giving a reasonable description of the angular distributions in regions in which the cross section is large, does not describe the experimental data in detail. An overall improvement can be obtained using the distorted wave method (Bransden et al 1979) and by the distorted wave impulse approximation. The second Born approximation has been evaluated by Byron et al (1980, 1982) for hydrogen and helium targets using the closure approximation. Under suitable kinematical conditions for which closure is justified (k>>K), the second Born approximation exhibits a marked improvement over the first Born approximation, the corrections being of the order of 20% in the region in which the cross section is large and much greater in regions in which the cross section is small.

NOTES

1. Equations (6-2) are a slight extension of (4-104) in that the orbital angular momentum of the scattered electron is allowed to have a different value in each channel. The potential matrices U_{mn} and V_{mn} are connected by

$$U_{mn} = \frac{2\mu_m}{\hbar^2} V_{mn}$$

in conformity with our usual notation.

2. It should be remembered that true bounds can only be obtained when the potential elements connecting the open channels are known exactly, which is only the case for hydrogenic targets.

3. Burke et al (1967a,b); Taylor and Burke (1967); Macek and Burke (1967).

4. Experimental support for resonance structure just above the n = 2 threshold is given by McGowan et al (1969) and Williams and Willis (1974).

5. See Callaway and Wooten (1974); Callaway et al (1975, 1976); Morgan et al (1977). For a critical review of the work see Callaway (1978).

6. See Burke et al (1969).

7. These calculations were corrected by Henry et al (1969).

8. This work has been reviewed by Bransden and McDowell (1977, 1978).

9. In the work of Thomas et al (1964), the distorted wave matrix element was deduced from many body theory in which the continuum functions are expressed in terms of the set of Hartree-Fock orbitals appropriate to the ground state of helium. This procedure forces the distorting potential in both initial and final states to be the initial state potential U_{oo}.

10. The extensions and applications of this idea are the subject of a monograph by Bonham and Fink (1974).

11. Lassetre and Silverman (1964); Lassetre et al (1964); Lassetre and Jones (1964).

12. Within the semi-classical approximation, the second Born approximation has been evaluated numerically by Bransden and Dewangan (1979) for the excitation of the 2s and 2p levels of hydrogen by proton impact at energies between 100 and 200 kev.

13. See Flannery and McCann (1974). For applications and further references see the review of Bransden and McDowell (1977, 1978).

14. Results have also been presented by Martir et al (1982) for scattering of muons, protons and anti-protons by atomic hydrogen.

15. It is important to notice that while for elastic scattering at high energies $\vec{K}$ is nearly at right angles to $\vec{k}_i$ (the Z direction), for inelastic scattering $\vec{K}$ is nearly parallel to $\vec{k}_i$. The neglect of K_z has to be justified in some other way. For example the Z axis and hence the classical trajectory can be taken to be at right angles to $\vec{K}$; but in some ways this appears to be a rather strange notion.

16. The best source of detailed information about the eikonal Born series method with a full bibliography is the review by Byron and Joachain (1977), see also the review by Bransden and McDowell (1977, 1978).

17. The following conditions apply when $|\vec{r}_1-\vec{r}_2|$, r_1 and r_2 are all large.

18. A detailed discussion of the asymptotic forms (6-112) and the general theory of ionization is given in the monograph of Peterkop (1977).

19. This work is described in a review by McCarthy and Weigold (1976, 1978).

PROBLEMS

6.1 The second order contribution to the direct optical potential is given by (6-15). (a) Write down the corresponding third order term, (b) find a second order expression for the exchange potential.

6.2 Find the average energy $\frac{1}{2}\bar{k}^2$ to be used in (6-16) by requiring the polarizability of the hydrogen atom to be given exactly in the closure approximation.

6.3 If in calculating the polarizability of hydrogen, the 2p level is treated exactly and the remaining levels by closure, what is the new value of $\frac{1}{2}\bar{k}^2$?

6.4 Prove that (6-24) follows from (6-23).

6.5 Write down the second order distorted wave amplitude using (6-23), (6-24) and (6-25).

6.6 Find a pair of coupled equations (the 2-state approximation) to describe excitation of ground state helium (a) to a singlet level and (b) to a triplet level.

6.7 Examine the perturbation and distorted wave solutions to the equations of problem 6(a,b) in the light of the discussion in Section 6-4.

6.8 Prove the conservation of probability condition (6-91).

6.9 Show that if the S-matrix is calculated from the T-matrix in the Glauber approximation (6-107), then S is unitary.

6.10 Show that in the high energy limit the Glauber amplitude (6-107) becomes equal to the amplitude in the first Born approximation.

6.11 Prove equations (6-118) and (6-120) for the case in which the potentials $V(r_1)$, $V(r_2)$ and $v(|\vec{r}_1-\vec{r}_2|)$ are short range.

Chapter 7

AUTO-IONIZATION AND RESONANCES IN ELECTRON-ATOM COLLISIONS

7-1 THE FORMATION AND PRODUCTION OF RESONANT STATES

In earlier chapters, we have seen that metastable states, with life times long compared with natural collision times, may be formed in a scattering process, and that the existence of such states leads to resonant behavior in cross sections as a function of energy. In general there are two kinds of experiments which demonstrate the existence of a resonant state[1]. There are "formation" experiments in which the scattered particles combine with the target to form a metastable complex:

$$A + B \rightarrow C^{*}. \tag{7-1}$$

Subsequently the metastable state C^{*} may decay into the incident channel

$$C^{*} \rightarrow A + B, \tag{7-2}$$

or, if sufficient energy is available, other decays may be possible. For example C^{*} may decay into excited states of A and B,

$$C^{*} \rightarrow A^{*} + B^{*}. \tag{7-3}$$

Some examples of this kind of experiment have been noted in connection with electron scattering by atoms in earlier chapters. We saw that below the first (n = 2) excitation threshold several resonances occur in electron-hydrogen atom scattering:

$$e^- + H(1s) \rightarrow H^{-*} \rightarrow e^- + H(1s). \tag{7-4}$$

It is also possible to form a metastable state in a "production" experiment. In this case, the metastable system is produced in a collision along with other particles. One simple case is where the target is itself excited to a metastable state

$$A + B \rightarrow A + B^*. \tag{7-5}$$

The unstable complex formed, B^*, will subsequently decay,

$$B^* \rightarrow C + D. \tag{7-6}$$

In this example, the resonance can be detected by measuring the loss in energy of the scattered particle A, which is equal to the difference in energy of B and B^*. If the resonant state, B^*, is long lived the uncertainty in its energy will be small and the energy loss is correspondingly well defined.

The unstable states may be formed, or may decay, by a radiative process. A particular case occurs when states of helium are formed in which both electrons are excited, such as in the $^1P(2s,2p)$ state. The double excited helium atom may decay either into the ground state of He^+ ejecting an electron or else, through radiation, to the ground state of helium:

$$He^*(2s,2p) \nearrow He^+(1s) + e^- \tag{7-7a}$$

$$He^*(2s,2p) \searrow He(1s,2s) + h\nu. \tag{7-7b}$$

These two processes are in competition, but the probability of the radiationless decay or "auto-ionization" of helium is much greater than that for the radiative decay. This means that the width of the spectral line observed, which is the sum of the partial widths for transitions into each of the channels, is much greater than would be expected for an emission line[2]. It was by observing the broadened emission lines in the vacuum ultra-violet spectrum of helium that the existence of double excited auto-ionizing states was first established[3] (Compton and Boyce, 1928; Kruger, 1930).

These doubly excited helium states were observed again a few years later in electron scattering experiments by Whiddington and Priestly (1934). This early work has been repeated more recently by Silverman and Lassetre (1964) and Simpson (1964), again using electrons as the incident particles, while Rudd (1964, 1965) and others have excited the same states using heavy particles as projectiles. In Fig. 7-1, two peaks are shown in the energy loss spectrum of 500 ev electrons scattered by helium, occurring at energies of 60.0 ± 0.1 and 63.5 ± 0.1 ev above the ground state of helium.

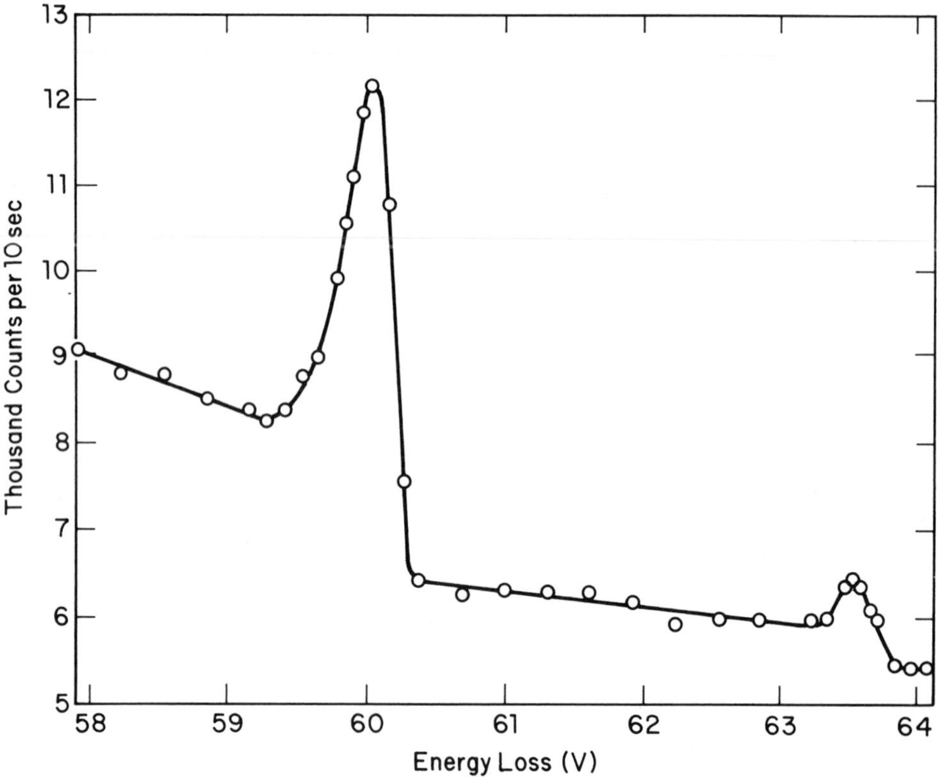

Figure 7-1 The energy loss spectrum of 500 ev electrons scattered by helium (Silverman and Lassetre, 1964)

By treating the doubly excited states as if they were stable, it is possible to use the Rayleigh-Ritz variational method to estimate the corresponding energies. Early work showed that series of states with different configurations might be expected to exist. States of the type (2s, ns) or (2s, np), (2p, ns) and (2p, np) would be among the lowest lying. In a series such as (2s, ns) as n increases, the energy of the system must increase until eventually the situation is reached in which one electron occupies the 2s state of the helium ion He^+ (2s) and the other is free. In other words, the doubly excited states (2s, ns) converge on the threshold for electron scattering by the (2s) state of He^+. It would then be expected that a corresponding series of resonances would occur in the elastic scattering of electrons by helium ions below the $n = 2$ threshold. In the same way, similar series of states such as (3s, ns), (3p, ns) exist below the $n = 3$ threshold for elastic scattering by He^+ and, in general, below higher thresholds. That series of auto-ionizing states do exist was clearly shown in the photon absorption experiments of Madden and Codling (1963, 1965) who radiated helium with ultraviolet light, in the region 100-600 Å, arising from a 180 Mev electron synchrotron. Superimposed on the uniform absorption spectrum due to the ionization of helium was a series of 21 discrete lines lying at energies which could be grouped into series converging on the $n = 2$, 3 and 4 states of He^+. In optical absorption, as the ground state of helium is ^1S, the final state must be ^1P. Two of the series converge on the $n = 2$ state of He^+ and must be associated with configurations (2s,np), (2p, ns). As the lowest state of both series is the same (2s, 2p), and as in the absence of the electron-electron interaction the states (ns, mp) and (ms, np) are degenerate, the two series mix and because of this a better set of hydrogenic basis functions is

$$\psi_{\pm}(mn) = \frac{1}{\sqrt{2}} [\phi(ns)\phi(mp) \pm \phi(ms)\phi(np)]. \tag{7-8}$$

For each value of n there will be two series, which may be denoted by $^1P(ps,nm+)$ and $^1P(ps,nm-)$. Note that the ± designation here has nothing to do with the symmetry of the wave function. For singlet states an overall spatially symmetric and for triplet states an overall spatially anti-symmetric combination must be formed. The energies and classification of the states observed by Madden and Codling for $n = 2$, 3 and 4 are shown in Table 7-1, together with the widths where these could be measured.

Table 7-1

The ^1P auto-ionizing levels in helium, observed by Madden and Codling (1965).

Series converging on the n = 2 level of He^+ (65.4 ev)*

Level (n,m)	Position (ev)	Width (ev)
(2,2)+	60.13	0.172
(2,3)+	63.66	0.83
(2,4)+	64.47	-
(2,5)+	65.01	-
(2,3)-	62.70	-
(2,4)-	64.15	-
(2,5)-	64.67	-

Series converging on the n = 3 and n = 4 levels of He^+

(n,m)	Position* (ev)	(n.m)	Position* (ev)
(3,3)+	69.75	(4,4)+	73.77
(3,4)+	71.67	(4,5)+	74.65
(3,5)+	72.21	(4,6)+	75.01
(3,6)+	72.48		
(3,7)+	72.62		
(3,8)+	72.71		

(*Level positions are given in terms of the incident energy).

Scattering experiments, in which the energy loss of the projectile is measured, can detect not only the optically allowed states but also the forbidden states, such as the $^1S(2s)^2$ state, and measurements have demonstrated several series of levels belonging to ^1S and ^3P states. Rudd (1964), and Rudd and Lang (1965) have observed $^1S(2s)^2$ at 57.82 ev, $^1S(2p)^2$ at 62.15 ev, $^1S(1s,3s)$ at 62.95 ev, $^3P(2s,2p)$ at 58.24 ev and so on (see also Simpson et al., 1964).

The resonances predicted by the theory in electron-hydrogen atom scattering are due to the formation of double excited states of H^-. Some of these resonances have been confirmed in "formation" experiments carried out in the elastic scattering region (Schultz, 1964; Kleinpoppen and

Raible, 1965). Similar experiments on both the elastic and inelastic scattering of electrons by He have shown that several unstable states of the negative helium ion He^- exist. In elastic scattering a resonance at 19.3 ev just below the n = 2 threshold (Schultz, 1963) is assigned to a ^2S state with the mixed configuration $(1s,2s^2) + (1s,2p^2)$ and inelastic scattering experiments have shown resonance effects in the $2^1S \to 2^3S$ excitation cross section and also that levels of He^- exist below the n = 3 and n = 4 levels of He^4.

Atoms other than hydrogen and helium

Auto-ionizing levels are known from spectroscopic and scattering experiments in many atomic and molecular systems. As an example, the rare gases Ne, Ar, Kr and Xe all exhibit series of levels like those in He while resonances have been shown to be of importance in electron scattering by H_2 and N_2. The spectroscopic evidence has been reviewed by Garton (1966) and the scattering experiments are discussed in the review of Golden (1978).

7-2 CALCULATION OF POSITIONS AND WIDTHS OF RESONANT STATES

There are many ways in which the theory of resonant states may be developed. We shall not attempt to survey the very extensive literature that has grown up, but one or two methods that allow calculations to be made of the positions and widths of the states will be outlined.

Let us return to the problem, discussed in Chapter 5, of electron scattering by atoms at energies below the first excitation threshold. The wave function is divided into a part $P\psi$ containing the open channel and $Q\psi$ containing the closed channels. It was shown that $P\psi$ and $Q\psi$ satisfy the coupled equations,

$$P(H - E)P\psi = - PHQ\psi \tag{7-9a}$$

$$Q(H - E)Q\psi = - QHP\psi \tag{7-9b}$$

In these equations P is an operator projecting out the (single) open channel, $P^2 = P$ and

$$Q = 1 - P, \quad QP = PQ = 0. \tag{7-10}$$

Roughly speaking, two types of resonance may arise in discussing these equations. The potential in the single channel wave equation

$$\mathcal{P}(H - E)\mathcal{P}\psi = 0$$

may have the strength and shape necessary to support a resonant state of the kind discussed in Chapter 1. We shall call this a shape resonance. Alternatively, as discussed in Chapter 5, resonances occur at energies associated with the discrete eigenvalue spectrum of the operator $\mathcal{Q}H\mathcal{Q}$, that describes the closed channel system. Clearly situations intermediate in character may also occur. Because the resonances discussed in the previous paragraph are usually of the second type, and may be identified with the virtual bound state resonances[5], often called Feshbach resonances, introduced in Chapter 4, we shall discuss how to calculate the parameters of a resonance in this case, using a formalism developed by Feshbach and applied to the atomic situation by O'Malley and Geltman (1965).

Our starting point will be the expansion of the optical potential in terms of the eigenfunctions of the operator $\mathcal{Q}H\mathcal{Q}$, given by equations (5-109) to (5-111). Suppose that the total energy E is close to one particular eigenvalue of $(\mathcal{Q}H\mathcal{Q})$, then the corresponding term in V_p, which is a rapidly varying function of energy, can be separated from the remainder of V_p by writing the equation for $\mathcal{P}\psi$ as

$$(H' - E)\mathcal{P}\psi = -\frac{\mathcal{P}H|\phi_s)(\phi_s|H\mathcal{P}}{E - \varepsilon_s}\mathcal{P}\psi \tag{7-11}$$

where

$$H' = \mathcal{P}H\mathcal{P} + \sum_{n\neq s}\frac{\mathcal{P}H|\phi_n)(\phi_n|H\mathcal{P}}{E - \varepsilon_n} \tag{7-12}$$

In Chapter 3, section 3-2, the problem of scattering by the sum of two potentials was discussed. This theory can be applied here, taking

$$\bar{V}_p = \frac{\mathcal{P}H|\phi_s)(\phi_s|H\mathcal{P}}{E - \varepsilon_s} \tag{7-13}$$

as one of the potentials, and the remainder of the interaction as the other. Then as in equation (3-60), the solution of (7-11) can be written as

$$|\mathcal{P}\psi = |\chi) + G_1\bar{V}_p|\mathcal{P}\psi) \tag{7-14a}$$

$$= |\chi) + (E - \varepsilon_s)^{-1} G_1 PH|\phi_s)(\phi_s|H|P\psi), \tag{7-14b}$$

where $|\chi)$ is the solution of

$$(H' - E)|\chi) = 0, \tag{7-15}$$

and the Green's function G_1 satisfies

$$(H' - E)G_1 = -1. \tag{7-16}$$

The boundary conditions imposed will be different from those assumed in Section 3-2. We shall use an angular momentum representation and standing wave boundary conditions so that

$$\chi(\vec{x},\vec{r}) \sim r^{-1} X(\vec{x}) \left(\frac{2\pi}{k}\right)^{\frac{1}{2}} \sin\left(kr - \frac{\ell\pi}{2} + \delta_\ell\right) Y_{\ell,m}(\theta,\phi), \tag{7-17}$$

where $\vec{x}$ denotes collectively the internal coordinates of the target, (r,θ,ϕ) are cooordinates of the scattered particle and the internal wave function of the target has been denoted by $X(\vec{x})$.

The Green's function G_1 is also chosen to satisfy the standing wave boundary conditions, so that for large r,

$$G_1(\vec{x},\vec{r};\vec{x}',\vec{r}') \sim -\left(\frac{2\pi}{k}\right)^{\frac{1}{2}} X(\vec{x}) Y_{\ell,m}(\theta,\phi) \frac{\cos(kr - \ell\pi/2 + \delta_\ell)}{r} \cdot \chi)\vec{x}',\vec{r}') \tag{7-18}$$

The potential $\bar{V}_p$ is separable so that an exact solution of (7-14) can now be found. Multiplying (7-14b) on the left by $(\phi_s|H$, we see that

$$(\phi_s|H|P\psi) = (\phi_s|H|\chi) + \frac{(\phi_s|HPG_1PH|\phi_s)(\phi_s|H|P\psi)}{E - \varepsilon_s} \tag{7-19}$$

Solving this equation for $(\phi_s|H|P\psi)$

$$(\phi_s|H|P\psi) = \frac{(\phi_s|H|\chi)}{1 - (E - \varepsilon_s)^{-1}(\phi_s|HPG_1PH|\phi_s)} \tag{7-20}$$

enables equation (7-14b) to be written as

$$|P\psi) = |\chi) + \frac{G_1 PH|\phi_s)(\phi_s|H|\chi)}{E - \varepsilon_s - \Delta_s} \tag{7-21}$$

where Δ_s is defined as

$$\Delta_s \equiv (\phi_s | H\mathcal{P}G_1\mathcal{P}H | \phi_s). \tag{7-22}$$

The asymptotic form of $\mathcal{P}\psi$ can now be determined with the help of (7-17) and (7-18):

$$\mathcal{P}\psi \underset{r\to\infty}{\sim} X(x) \left(\frac{2\pi}{k}\right)^{\frac{1}{2}} r^{-1} \left\{ \sin\left(kr - \frac{\ell\pi}{2} + \delta_\ell\right) + \cos\left(kr - \frac{\ell\pi}{2} + \delta_\ell\right) \tan \eta_\ell \right\} Y_{\ell,m}(\theta,\phi), \tag{7-23}$$

where

$$\tan \eta_\ell = - \frac{\Gamma_s/2}{E - \varepsilon_s - \Delta_s}, \tag{7-24}$$

and

$$\frac{\Gamma_s}{2} = |(\chi|H|\phi_s)|^2 \tag{7-25}$$

The phase shift η_ℓ resonates as E passes through the energy E_r, where $E_r = (\varepsilon_s + \Delta_s)$, and Δ_s has the significance of a level shift, while the level width is Γ_s. Combining the terms in (7-23), we see that

$$\mathcal{P}\psi \sim X(\vec{x}) \left(\frac{2\pi}{k}\right)^{\frac{1}{2}} \frac{1}{\cos \eta_\ell} r^{-1} \sin\left(kr - \frac{\ell\pi}{2} + \delta_\ell + \eta_\ell\right) Y_{\ell,m}(\theta,\phi). \tag{7-26}$$

The total phase shift is $(\delta_\ell + \eta_\ell)$, from which we see that the partial cross section of order ℓ is

$$\sigma_\ell = \frac{4\pi(2\ell + 1)}{k^2} \sin^2 (\delta_\ell + \eta_\ell). \tag{7-27}$$

A complete calculation of the parameters of a resonance requires the eigenvalue ε_s of $(\mathcal{Q}H\mathcal{Q})$, the level shift Δ_s from (7-22) and the width Γ_s from (7-25).

If it is assumed that the level shifts are small, then a calculation of the eigenvalues of $(\mathcal{Q}H\mathcal{Q})$ will determine the resonance energies. This eigenvalue problem can be solved by the Rayleigh-Ritz method provided that the trial function ϕ_s is orthogonal to the ground state of the target and does not contain part of the open channel. O'Malley and Geltman have determined in this way the energies[6] of a large number of the $^{1,3}S$ and $^{1,3}P$ states of H^- and of He.

The results for the ^1P series of doubly excited He states are shown in Table 7-2. It is seen that the agreement with the experimental results shown in Table 7-1 is good. Also included in Table 7-2 are the results of the close coupling calculations[7] (1s - 2s - 2p) of Burke and McVicar (1965). In these calculations the total phase shift is obtained as a function of energy so that both the resonance energy E_r and the width Γ can be found directly. The agreement with experiment is extremely good.

Table 7-2

Calculated positions and widths of ^1P states in helium

O'Malley and Geltman (1965) ^1P	ε_s (ev)	Burke and McVicar (1965) E_r (ev)	Γ (ev)
(2s,2p)	60.19	60.27	0.044
(2s,3p-2p,3s)	62.82	62.77	0.00014
(2s,3p+2p,3s)	63.88	63.69	0.0087
(2s,4p-2p,4s)	64.20	64.11	5.0×10^{-5}
(2p,3d)	64.43	64.12	1.5×10^{-6}

In the close coupling calculations of Burke and McVicar, the predicted states of doubly excited helium include the ^3P, ^1P and ^3S. This work was extended in order to determine the D states that lie below the n = 2 level (Cooper et al., 1967). In this case as well, good agreement is obtained with the experimental results, which have been analyzed by Altick and Moore (1967).

The auto-ionizing states of He^-, that give rise to resonances near the n = 2 threshold in electron scattering by helium, have been discussed in the close coupling approximation (Burke et al., 1966, 1967). In this work, in order to describe the polarization of the 2^1S and 2^3S states of helium in the field of the incident electron, it is important to include the 2^1P and 2^3P states in the close coupling wave function. The $2^{1,3}P$ states lie close in energy to the $2^{1,3}S$ states (see Table 7-3), and the effect of polarization is large. These four states, together with the ground state, were included in the expansion, using Hartree-Fock wave functions. The results of the calculations showed that in addition to the ^2S state of He^- at 19.3 ev, ^2P and ^2D states also occur at 20.2 ev (width 0.52 ev) and 21.0 ev (width 0.4 ev) respectively.

Table 7-3

The first four excited states of helium

State	Energy (atomic units
$^1S(1s,2s)$	2.1753
$^3S(1s,2s)$	2.1461
$^1P(1s,2p)$	2.1332
$^3P(1s,2p)$	2.2217

These resonances have been observed by Chamberlain and Heideman (1965) in experiments on the inelastic scattering of electrons by helium in the forward direction. Further calculations were carried out in which just the four excited states of He were included in the expansion and further resonances attributed to the ^2F, ^2G and ^2H levels of He^- were discovered. The cross sections for transitions between the excited states of helium are shown in Fig. 7-2. Analysis shows that these cross sections are dominated by the level structure of He^-. The three peaks in the 2^3S - 2^1S cross section are caused by the ^2S, ^2P and ^2D resonances, and the steep rise and peaking of all the other cross sections are also due to the effect of the various resonances in varying proportions.

Since the pioneering calculations referred to in the previous paragraphs there have been many coupled channel calculations, based on the algebraic variational method, the R-matrix method and the Bethe-Goldstone method in which the resonant structure of electron scattering cross sections has been examined. Some of this work has been discussed in Chapters 5 and 6, where the particularly important influence of resonances on the excitation of positive ions was emphasized[8].

Line profiles

As we have seen, a resonant state may be formed by photon absorption. In this case, the shape of the absorption line can be studied (Fano, 1961, O'Malley and Geltman, 1965). The radiative part of the interaction is always given accurately by perturbation theory, so that the transition probability for the reaction

$$h\nu + A \rightarrow A^{**} \rightarrow A^{*} + e,$$

is proportional to a matrix element of the form

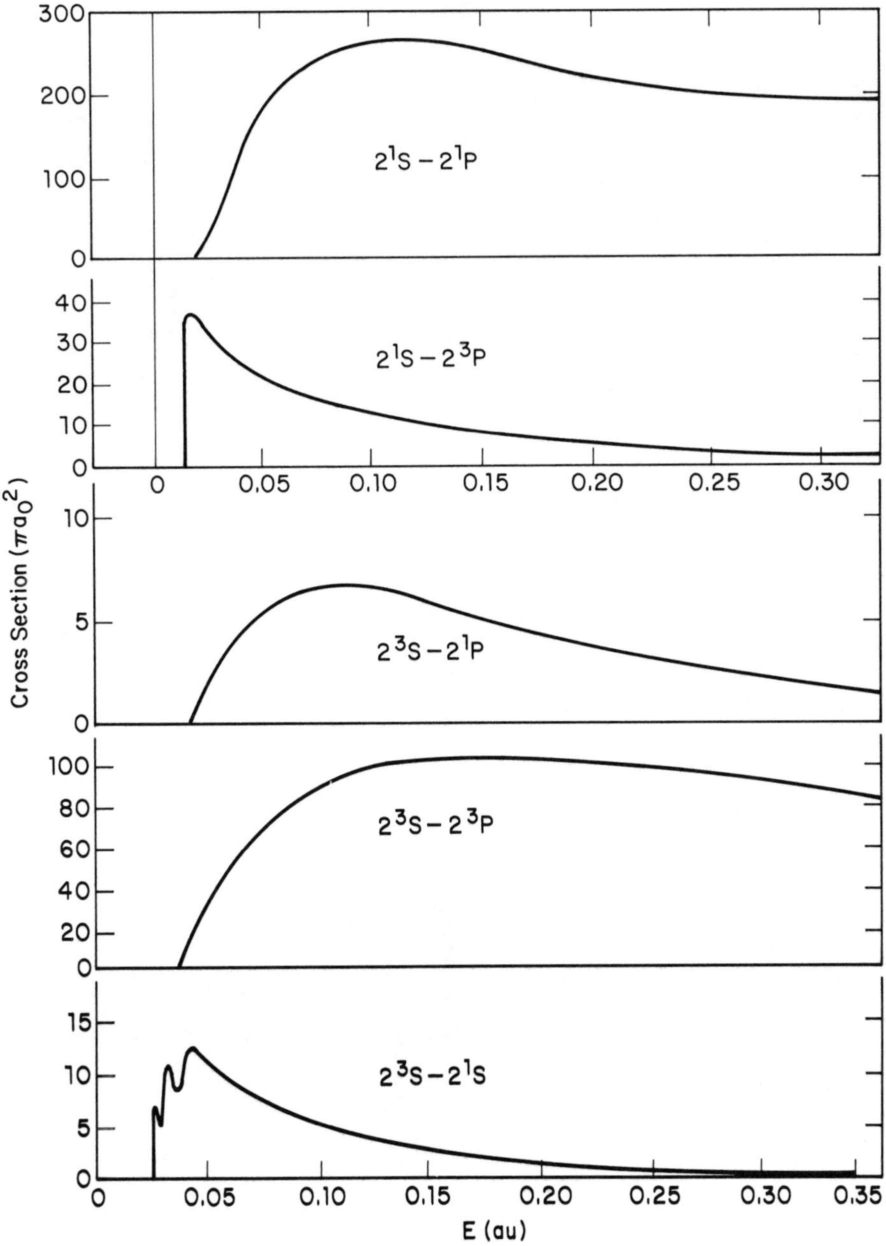

Figure 7-2 Cross sections for transitions among the n = 2 levels of helium induced by electron impact, calculated in a close coupling approximation (Burke et al., 1967).

$$(i|T|\psi_f), \tag{7-28}$$

where ψ_f is the wave function for the final state of the system and $(i|$ is the initial state, T being the transition operator. The final state wave function is just the one we have considered except that the normalization of $P\psi$ required in (7-28) differs from that assumed in (7-26) by the factor $1/\cos \eta_\ell$. We need then

$$P|\psi_f) = \cos \eta_\ell |P\psi) = \cos \eta_\ell |\chi) - \sin \eta_\ell |\psi_1), \tag{7-29}$$

where, using (7-21), (7-24) and (7-25), $|\psi_1)$ is defined as

$$|\psi_1) = \frac{G_1 PH|\phi_s)}{(\chi|H|\phi_s)}. \tag{7-30}$$

Neither $|\chi)$ nor $|\psi_1)$ are rapidly varying functions of energy and, if the resonance is narrow, these functions may be treated as energy independent, the energy variation being concentrated in the factors $\sin \eta_\ell$ and $\cos \eta_\ell$. To obtain ψ_f we also need $Q\psi_f$. This can also be split into parts containing $\sin \eta_\ell$ and $\cos \eta_\ell$ as factors, and O'Malley and Geltman show that $\psi_f = P\psi_f + Q\psi_f$ can be written as

$$\psi_f = \psi_o \cos \eta_\ell - \bar{\psi}_1 \sin \eta_\ell, \tag{7-31}$$

where

$$|\psi_o) = |\chi) + \sum_{n\neq s} \frac{|\phi_n)(\phi_n|QH|\chi)}{(E - \varepsilon_n)} \tag{7-32}$$

$$|\bar{\psi}_1) = \frac{|\phi_s) + G_1 PH|\phi_s)}{(\chi|H|\phi_s)} +$$

$$+ \sum_{n\neq s} \frac{1}{(\chi|H|\phi_s)} (E - \varepsilon_n)^{-1} |\phi_n)(\phi_n|QHPG_1PHQ|\phi_s).$$

In terms of the resonance parameters, $\sin \eta_\ell$ and $\cos \eta_\ell$ are

$$\sin \eta_\ell = \frac{(\Gamma_s/2)}{\left[(E - \varepsilon_s - \Delta_s)^2 + 1/4\Gamma_s^2\right]^{1/2}} \tag{7-33}$$

$$\cos \eta_\ell = \frac{(\varepsilon_s + \Delta_s - E)}{[(E - \varepsilon_s - \Delta_s)^2 + 1/4\,\Gamma_s^{\,2}]^{1/2}}$$

from which

$$(i|T|\psi_f) = \frac{(\varepsilon_s + \Delta_s - E)(i|T|\psi_o) - 1/2\,\Gamma_s(i|T|\psi_1)}{[(E - \varepsilon_s - \Delta_s)^2 + 1/4\Gamma_s^{\,2}]^{1/2}} \tag{7-34}$$

Well away from the resonance the transition probability is given by the amplitude $(i|T|\psi_o)$, so that the ratio of the transition probability over the resonance region to the non-resonant background is

$$\left|\frac{(i|T|\psi_f)}{(i|T|\psi_o)}\right|^2 = \frac{(\varepsilon + q)^2}{1 + \varepsilon^2}, \tag{7-35}$$

where

$$\varepsilon = -\cot \eta_\ell = \frac{E - \varepsilon_s - \Delta_s}{1/2\Gamma_s}; \quad q = \frac{(i|T|\psi_1)}{(i|T|\psi_o)}. \tag{7-36}$$

Burke and McVicar (1965) have calculated q and ε for the photo-ionization of helium using the close-coupling wave functions in the (1s - 2s - 2p) approximation; an elaborate variational wave function was used for the initial helium ground state. The shape of the absorption line for the $(2s2p)\,^1P$ resonance is shown in Fig. 7-3; it is in close agreement with the observed line given by Madden and Codling (1965). The quantity plotted in Fig. 7-3 is the oscillator strength for the transition (df/dE), which is related to the cross section by

$$\frac{df}{dE} = \frac{1}{4\pi^2\alpha}\sigma$$

where α is the fine structure constant. The limit of (df/dE) for large ε is denoted by $(df/dE)_o$, so that

$$\frac{df}{dE} = \left(\frac{df}{dE}\right)_o \frac{(\varepsilon + q)}{(1 + \varepsilon^2)}.$$

The calculated value of $(df/dE)_o$ was 0.1710. A zero in the cross section occurs when $\varepsilon + q = 0$, and whether this zero occurs above or below the resonance position (ε=0) depends

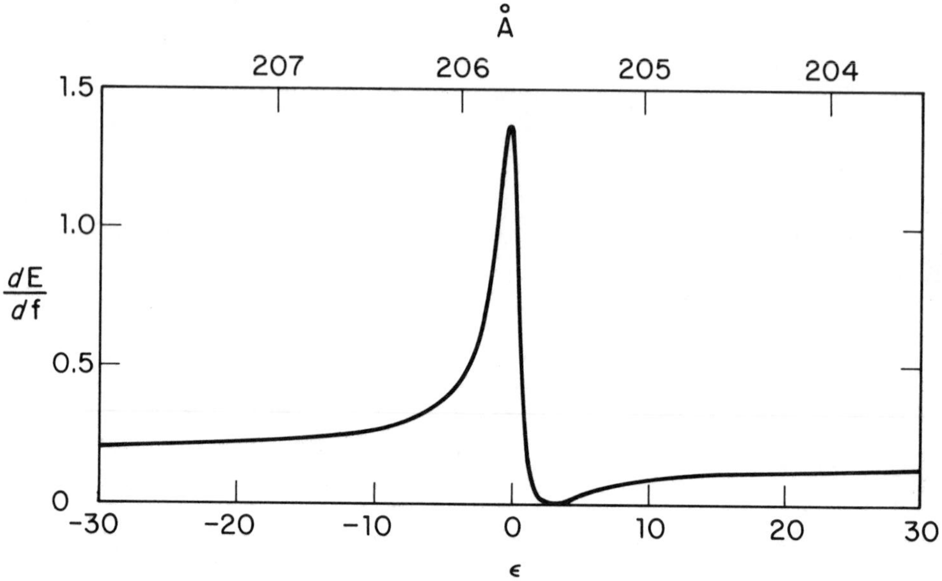

Figure 7-3 The shape of the absorption line associated with the (2s2p) ^{1}P double excited state of helium (Burke and McVicar, 1965).

on the sign of q. In the case shown in Fig. 7-3, q = -2.5 so that the zero is above the point of maximum absorption. The maximum absorption does not occur at the resonance position (ε=0), but, as can be seen from (7-35), at the position $\varepsilon = 1/q$. If the energy for which this occurs is E_m, then

$$E_m = \varepsilon_s + \Delta_s + \frac{\Gamma_s}{2q} . \tag{7-37}$$

Many channel scattering

The theory presented above may be generalized to cover the case where several channels are open at the resonance energy. That this is a case of importance is seen from the fact that series of resonances occur below the higher thresholds in hydrogen, helium and other systems. In Chapter 4, the general form of the transition matrix was obtained near energies at which one eigenphase shift passes through $\pi/2$.

From these formulae the effect of a resonance on not only the elastic scattering but also on the excitation threshold can be discussed. A case of importance concerns the influence of the resonances below the n = 3 threshold in e^- - H scattering on the n = 1 to n = 2 excitation cross section. This has been studied in detail by Burke et al. (1966) and by Macek and Burke (1967), but the analysis is too lengthy to be given here.

If the forces are of short range, the behavior of the cross section near a threshold can be obtained from the general expressions (4-130) and (4-131). If the eigenphase shift Δ_0 is resonant just above a certain threshold m, then the excitation cross section σ_{mi} is

$$\sigma_{mi} \propto \frac{\gamma_i \gamma_m}{(E'_r - E) - i\gamma/2}$$

where the width γ_m is proportional to $k_m^{2\ell+1}$. (Notice that the energy variation of the eigenphases and the parameters R_{mi} near a threshold, follows from (4-140). The excitation cross section is then proportional to the partial width in channel α. If the resonance is just below the open threshold, the excitation cross section is still proportional to the partial width of the resonance in the incident channel. If there are only two channels, then σ_{mi} is just proportional to the total width. This can be shown by using the M matrix extrapolation through the threshold. In general, the existence of one or more resonances below a threshold leads to a rapidly rising or peaked excitation cross section and the rate of rise is proportional to the width of the resonance.

The Herzenberg-Mandl resonance theory

The projection operator technique outlined earlier in this chapter is not the only method that can be employed in the description of resonant states. An alternative approach, originally used in the theory of nuclear reactions, is to locate the position of the resonances by looking for the eigenvalues of the complete Hamiltonian when certain modified boundary conditions are imposed (Kapur and Peierls, 1937). This approach has been adapted by Herzenberg and Mandl (Herzenberg and Mandl, 1963; Herzenberg, Kwok and Mandl, 1964a,b; Mandl, 1967) to a form more suitable for atomic calculations, where long range potentials are encountered. This formulation has the advantage that no distinction is made between the Feshbach, or virtual bound state resonances, discussed earlier and the shape resonances, that are not associated with bound states of the closed channel Hamiltonian ($\mathcal{Q}H\mathcal{Q}$).

In Chapter 1, it was explained that resonant states are associated with points, $E_n = W_n - i\Gamma_n/2$, in the complex energy plane, at which the scattering amplitude has a pole. At these complex energies the wave function satisfies a purely outgoing wave boundary condition. Such complex energy states with purely outgoing waves are called Siegert states (Siegert, 1939). In the Kapur-Peierls method, outgoing wave boundary conditions (that is no plane wave or incoming spherical wave in the asymptotic wave function) are imposed on the Hamiltonian of the complete system of scattered particle plus target. This constitutes an eigenvalue problem which has solutions only at the complex energies E_n. The actual scattering wave function can be expanded in the set of eigenfunctions ψ_n corresponding to the energies E_n and the scattering amplitude obtained. The method has something in common with the R-matrix method, but the boundary condition used in defining the expansion functions ψ_n are different. When one of the poles at $E=E_n$ is close to the real axis, the scattering amplitude shows a resonant behavior and W_n can be identified with the resonance energy. In the Herzenberg-Mandl method, these basic ideas are modified first so that a new eigenvalue problem is obtained, with real eigenvalues which is more convenient, and secondly, so that the long range potentials occurring in electron-atom interactions can be properly treated.

Using a variational method to obtain the required eigenvalues, Herzenberg and Mandl have calculated the position of the auto-ionizing levels in a number of atomic and molecular problems. Herzenberg and Mandl (1963) discussed the s-wave singlet resonance in $e^- - H$ scattering. They were able to find the resonance at 9.6 ev using a very simple trial function: the sum of products of modified hydrogenic functions. In a similar way Kwok and Mandl (1965) were able to obtain the resonance below the excitation threshold in electron helium scattering. Both the calculated position E = 19.5 ev and the width $\Gamma = 0.8 \times 10^{-2}$ to 3×10^{-2} ev agree well with the observations. This formalism has also been used to discuss resonances in the vibrational excitation and dissociative attachment of hydrogen molecules by electron impact. The resonant states are in this case states of the molecular ion H_2^-.

7-3 LONG RANGE FORCES AND RESONANCES NEAR THRESHOLDS

In Chapter 4, it was seen that if the elements of the $\mathcal{K}$ or $\mathcal{M}$ matrices are known above a threshold, and using the effective range formula satisfied by $\mathcal{M}$, the $\mathcal{K}$ matrix could be obtained below threshold. If the extrapolated $\mathcal{K}$ matrix satisfied condition (4-146) at a particular energy, a virtual bound state resonance occurred in the open channels below the particular threshold of interest. The extrapolation of the $\mathcal{M}$ matrix, discussed in Chapter 4, is valid when the forces are at short range. In many important cases, in electron-atom scattering, the forces are long range and the extrapolation must be modified, but before discussing the modification, it is interesting to examine the case of short range forces in a little more detail. An example has been given by Damburg and Peterkop (1962), who discussed the excitation of the 2s state of hydrogen by electron impact on the ground state. Above the threshold, they calculated the matrix elements of the $\mathcal{M}$ matrix for the $\ell=0$ partial wave function of energy, in the two state approximation, retaining only the 1s and 2s states of hydrogen in the close-coupling wave function. These matrix elements were fitted to the effective range formula

$$\mathcal{M}(E) = \mathcal{M}(E_O) + (E - E_O)\mathcal{R}_O(E_O), \qquad (7\text{-}38)$$

where E_O is the threshold energy ($k_O{}^2 = 0.75$). The results for triplet and singlet scattering and also in the no-exchange approximation are shown in Table 7-4.

Table 7-4

Elements of the matrices $\mathcal{M}(E_O)$ and $\mathcal{R}_O(E_O)$ for (1s - 2s) excitation of hydrogen

Matrix element	Triplet (s = 1)	Singlet (s = 0)	No exchange
M_{11}	1.13	0.0301	0.9373
M_{12}	-0.0629	-0.0017	-0.3097
M_{22}	-0.356	-0.1206	-0.2043
R_{O11}	4.82	1.20	7.64
R_{O12}	-4.32	-0.06	-10.68
R_{O22}	11.54	5.14	19.2

The transition matrix is given in terms of M by

$$T = \frac{K}{1 - iK} \quad k^{\ell+1/2} \frac{1}{M - k^{2\ell+1}} k^{\ell+1/2}, \tag{7-39}$$

where k is a diagonal matrix with elements k_1 and k_2, the channel momenta. Extrapolating below threshold we find poles in T at the point where

$$\det\left|M - ik^{2\ell+1}\right| = 0, \tag{7-40}$$

that is, where

$$D = (M_{11} - ik_1)(M_{22} - ik_2) - M_{12}M_{21} = 0 \tag{7-41}$$

Below threshold we have $k_2 \to iK_2$, where K_2 is real, and

$$\varepsilon_0 + \frac{1}{2}k_1{}^2 = \varepsilon_1 - \frac{1}{2}K_2{}^2, \tag{7-42}$$

where ε_0 and ε_1 are the energies of the ground and first excited states of hydrogen.

When the coupling between the channels is ignored, the bound state poles in channel 2, that give rise to resonances in channel 1 when the coupling is switched on, must be on the imaginary k_2 axis. The pole positions in the absence of coupling are given by the zero of the equation (in atomic units)

$$M_{22} + (R_0)_{22} \frac{1}{2}k_2{}^2 - ik_2 = 0 \tag{7-43}$$

Using the figures given in Table 7-4, the zeros for the triplet case do not lie on the imaginary k_2 axis and so do not give rise to resonances. In the singlet case, both zeros are on the imaginary axis and the zero near the origin ($k_2 = 0$) leads to a narrow resonance in the elastic scattering in channel 1. In the no-exchange case, the zeros are also on the imaginary axis, but the lower zero which is near the threshold ($k_2 = 0$) lies on the negative real axis. This is an anti-bound state (see Chapter 1) and it gives rise to an increase in scattering near threshold, but not to a resonance below threshold, as the pole produced is on the wrong sheet in the k_1 plane.

The transition matrix below threshold in the first channel is given by

$$T_{11} = k_1 M_{22} D(E) \tag{7-44}$$

and the cross section by

$$\sigma = \frac{4\pi}{k_1^2 + \gamma^2}, \tag{7-45}$$

where

$$\gamma = M_{11} - \frac{|M_{12}|^2}{M_{22} + K_2} .$$

The resonance energy can be defined as the energy for which γ vanishes and σ takes on its maximum value.

Long range forces at degenerate thresholds

The potential terms coupling s and p states are proportional to $1/r^2$ for large r (Chapter 5). In the case of electron scattering by hydrogen atoms, close-coupling equations for the radial wave functions connecting the 2s and 2p levels become asymptotically, for zero total angular momentum,

$$\left(\frac{d^2}{dr^2} + k_2^2\right) F_{2s}(r) = -\frac{6}{r^2} F_{2p}(r) \tag{7-46a}$$

$$\left(\frac{d^2}{dr^2} - \frac{2}{r^2} + k_2\right) F_{2p}(r) = -\frac{6}{r^2} F_{2s}(r) \tag{7-46b}$$

Because the (2s) and (2p) states are degenerate, the same value of the energy, k_2^2, appears in both equations. In this case, by taking linear combinations of F_{2p} and F_{2s} the equations can be uncoupled. If the equations are written in matrix form with a potential matrix

$$\mathcal{V}(r) = \frac{1}{r^2}\begin{pmatrix} 0 & -6 \\ -6 & 2 \end{pmatrix}, \tag{7-47}$$

uncoupling the equations is equivalent to diagonalizing V. This can be achieved through the introduction of an orthogonal matrix $\mathcal{A}$, such that (Seaton, 1961)

$$(\mathcal{A}^{-1}\mathcal{V}(r)\mathcal{A})_{ij} = \delta_{ij}\lambda_i(\lambda_i + 1)/r^2. \tag{7-48}$$

Such a diagonalization can be carried out at any degenerate threshold. In the case of the 2s - 2p threshold, we find that $\lambda(\lambda+1) = 1 \pm (37)^{\frac{1}{2}}$ or

$$\lambda_1 = -\frac{1}{2} \pm \left[(37)^{\frac{1}{2}} + \frac{5}{4}\right]^{\frac{1}{2}}$$
$$\lambda_2 = -\frac{1}{2} \pm i\left[(37)^{\frac{1}{2}} - \frac{5}{4}\right]^{\frac{1}{2}} \qquad (7\text{-}49)$$

The form of solution of the Schrödinger equation when the potential is asymptotic to an inverse square power of r was discussed in Chapter 3 and it was shown that an attractive potential (corresponding to λ_2) supports an infinite number of bound states. From (3-79) we see that in the present case ($\gamma^2 < 0$) the wave function is proportional to

$$\cos\,[\mathrm{Im}\,\lambda \log r + B]. \qquad (7\text{-}50)$$

Successive nodes occur at positions r_1, r_2 where

$$\mathrm{Im}\,\lambda \log\left(\frac{r_1}{r_2}\right) = \pi \qquad (7\text{-}51)$$

For large r, the bound state wave functions become equal to $\exp(-K_2 r)$, where $K_2{}^2 = (ik_2)^2$, and this implies that the ratio in energy of successive levels is

$$R = \frac{r_1{}^2}{r_2{}^2} = \exp\left(\frac{2\pi}{\mathrm{Im}\lambda}\right) \qquad (7\text{-}52)$$

For the 2s - 2p threshold, R = 17.4 and the bound states form an infinite sequence just below the threshold. In practice because of the relativistic splitting between the 2s and 2p levels this sequence will not be infinite. For non-zero total angular momentum L, it can be shown that at the n = 2 threshold, only the L = 0, L = 1 and L = 2 states possess sequences of levels in this way, but as n increases, more and more values of L possess resonant series. For the higher thresholds there can be more than one series of levels, with different level spacings.

Because of the coupling to the open channel, the levels below the n = 2 threshold become unbound and are metastable rather than stable. These metastable states of the complete system at the degenerate levels give rise to the resonances observed beneath the threshold, and in general it is the existence of long range forces that explains the close association of thresholds and sequences of resonances. To make the connection quantitative, the M matrix extrapolation procedure has been modified for use in the presence of an inverse square law potential by Gailitis and Damburg (1963). (The case of the Coulomb interaction has also been discussed: Gailitis, 1963; Seaton, 1966).

NOTES

1. A review of experiments on resonances has been given by Golden (1978) and further information about the theory can be found in an article by Burke (1968).

2. The general formulae for resonant and non-resonant scattering developed in Chapter 4 in terms of the reaction matrix may be extended to the situation in which one of the open channels contains a photon as in (7-7b).

3. Another phenomenon of the same nature as auto-ionization is the Auger effect (Auger, 1925, Burhop, 1952), which occurs following the ionization of an inner shell electron in a heavy atom. The resulting ion is unstable and can undergo a radiationless decay through the ejection of an electron.

4. Schultz and Philbruck (1964), Chamberlain (1965), Chamberlain and Heideman (1965).

5. Shape resonances also play an important role in atomic phenomena, for example there is a shape resonance in the cross section for electron scattering by atomic hydrogen just above the n = 2 threshold, and such resonances occur in the cross section for the vibrational excitation of diatomic molecules.

6. The positions of a large number of resonances in two-electron systems have been calculated by Lipsky et al (1977).

7. Note that when considering the scattering of electrons by positive ions as in this case: $e^- + He^+ \rightarrow He^{**} \rightarrow e^- + He^+$, the asymptotic wave functions must be expressed in terms of Coulomb wave functions rather than plane waves.

8. Good examples are the resonances below the n = 3 threshold in the excitation of the one-electron ions C^{5+}, Ne^{9+} (Hayes and Seaton 1978), or the excitation of the lithium like ion C^{3+} (Callaway et al 1979). See particularly the review of Henry (1981).

PROBLEMS

7.1 Use first order perturbation theory to locate the positions of the doubly excited helium levels (2s2p) ^1P and (2s3p + 3s2p) ^1P, taking the unperturbed functions to be hydrogenic orbitals appropriate to nuclear charge Z = 2.

7.2 Use the Rayleigh-Ritz method to locate the positions of the $^{3,1}P$(2s2p) doubly excited states of helium, by taking as a trial function the product of hydrogeni orbitals appropriate to a nuclear charge Z and treatin Z as a variational parameter.

7.3 Extend the analysis which starts with the coupled equations (7-9) and leads to (7-23) to a case in which two channels are open, so that $P\psi$ is a two dimensional column vector. Starting from (7-9) and assuming the closed channel space contains one discrete state, show that the two dimension $\mathcal{T}$-matrix has a resonant form.

7.4 Use the numbers given in Table 7-4 to verify the discussion of the pole positions in the Damburg-Peterkop two channel problem (Section 7-3).

7.5 Check that the parameters λ_i of (7-48) are given by (7-49).

Chapter 8

COLLISIONS BETWEEN ATOMS

The theory of the scattering of atoms by atoms, or of atoms by ions, is formally similar to that for electron-atom scattering, but there are important differences of scale and complexity. Because the projectile is heavy, except at very low impact velocities, many channels are open and excitation or ionization of the projectile or target atom is possible as well as charge transfer. For example, an electron with an energy of 1 a.u. (27.2 ev), has a velocity of 3.09×10^8 cm/sec. An atom of atomic weight, A, with the same velocity, possesses an energy of (1836A) a.u. (50 A kev). For a given velocity not only the energy, but the momentum $\hbar k$, is much larger for an atomic than for an electronic collision, and taking the distance of closest approach, r_0, in a collision to be of the order of 1 a.u., this implies that the inequality $(kr_0) > 1$ holds down to very low energies. In the case of proton-hydrogen scattering $kr_0 = 1$ at an energy of $E = 5.4 \times 10^{-4}$ a.u. $(1.48 \times 10^{-2}$ ev), in the center of mass sytem, and for heavier ions the corresponding energy is even lower. When the condition $(kr_0) \gg 1$ holds, classical or semi-classical methods can provide an accurate description of the heavy particle motion, except for very small angles of scattering $\theta < (1/kr_0)$ and this will be true for all systems of interest. An exception is the theory of the viscosity and diffusion of monatomic gases at low temperatures, for which $(kr_0) \leq 1$ and which falls outside the scope of this book. Of course, while for $(kr_0) \gg 1$ the large number of partial waves which are of importance make it convenient to use semi-classical methods, a full quantum treatment is always possible in principle and, at the lower energies is often a practical alternative. Classical conditions do not, in general, apply to the electronic motion which must be treated by the methods of quantum theory.

In this Chapter and the next, some general methods will be developed and some applications described, for the scattering of atoms by atoms, or atoms by ions, which are useful at low or at intermediate impact velocities ($v \leq 2$ a.u. Specifically high velocity methods will be discussed in Chapter 10.

8-1 SLOW ELASTIC COLLISIONS

While the differential cross section for elastic or charge exchange scattering may exhibit an oscillatory behavior the total elastic cross section at low, but not too low, energies is accurately given by applying the classical theory to the average effective potential between the atoms or ions. At thermal energies, the collisions are so slow that only the long range part of the potential will influence the cross section, while at higher energies, the potential may be represented as the sum of the long range terms and parameterised short range terms. Much effort has gone into the determination of effective inter-atomic forces by analysing the total elastic cross sections, which for many processes have been measured as a function of energy from a few electron volts to a few kev.

The long range part of the potential can be discussed by perturbation theory or by using variational methods, in the same general way that the long range $1/r^4$ potential was determined in Chapter 5. The long range interaction between a charged ion and a neutral atom is found to be

$$V(r) \sim -\frac{Z^2\alpha}{2r^4} \quad \text{(in atomic units)} \tag{8-1}$$

where Z is the charge on the ion and α is the dipole polarizability of the neutral atom. The leading term in the potential between two neutral systems behaves like $1/R^6$ and arises because both systems may be polarized, and to the lowest order the interaction is of dipole-dipole form. The elementary theory of the Van der Waal's interaction is reviewed in the text by Bransden and Joachain (1982), and we will not repeat the discussion here. A comprehensive review of the methods of calculating the coefficients in the expansion of the long range interaction in powers of 1/R,

$$V(R) = -\sum_{\ell=1}^{\infty}\sum_{L=1}^{\infty} \frac{C(\ell,L)}{R^{2(\ell+L+1)}} \tag{8-2}$$

has been given by Dalgarno (1966). The higher terms in this expansion arise from dipole-quadrupole, quadrupole-quadrupole interactions and so on. The coefficients $C(\ell,L)$ have been calculated for a wide variety of systems, including hydrogen with intert gases, alkali metal with inert gases, and inert gases with inert gases.

Departures from the $1/R^6$ variation of the potential can occur in cases of degeneracy, for example in collisions between atoms of the same species, one of which is in an excited state and one in an unexcited state. As in the case of electron scattering near a degenerate threshold, the degeneracy has the effect of increasing the range of the potential. If the excited state and the ground state are connected by an optically allowed transition, then the potential behaves like the $1/R^3$ and in general if the transition connecting the two states is governed by a multipole of order ℓ then the potential varies like $1/R^{2\ell+1}$, unless both the excited and unexcited states are S-states, in which case as usual, the interaction decays exponentially.

We shall consider two examples of transitions that at low velocities take place through the long range part of the interaction; both are of astrophysical importance.

Transitions in the total angular momentum of an atom

During a slow collision, transitions can occur between states of an atom that differ only in the total angular momentum j, for example the reaction

$$H + O(^3P_{j=2}) \rightarrow H + O(^3P_{j=1,0}) \qquad (8\text{-}3)$$

which is an important source of cooling in interstellar space, and has been investigated by Callaway and Dugan (1967). The four oxygen electrons in s-states can be ignored and the interaction arises between the hydrogen atom and the four p-state electrons. The long range van der Waal interaction is

$$V_{eff} = \sum_i v_i(\vec{r}_i), \qquad (8\text{-}4)$$

where the sum is over the coordinates of the four p-electrons and (in atomic units)

$$v(\vec{x}_i) = -\frac{1}{2}\frac{\alpha r_i}{R^6}(3\cos^2\theta_i + 1). \qquad (8\text{-}5)$$

In this expression α is the polarizability of atomic hydrogen. The time-dependent equations coupling the $j = 2$ and the $j = 0$ and 1 states can be written down and they were solved approximately using a method, due to Callaway and Bauer (1965), which insures unitarity (see also Callaway and Bartling, 1966). Similar calculations were carried out for hydrogen-carbon interactions.

Spin transitions

A similar process, that occurs mainly through the long range interactions at low velocities, is spin exchange. The total spin F of a hydrogen atom can be either F = 1 (triplet) or F = 0 (singlet), and transitions between these states can occur during collisions with other atoms. Spin exchange in collisions between hydrogen atoms provide a cooling mechanism of importance in astrophysical contexts (Purcell and Field, 1956). At low velocities, the singlet and triplet interaction energies, ${}^{1,3}V(R)$, have been calculated accurately by Dalgarno and Lynn (1956) using second order perturbation theory; ${}^{1,3}V(R) \cong 13/R^6$ (atomic units) for large R. Although asymptotically ${}^{1}V(R)$ approaches ${}^{3}V(R)$, at small R the two functions are different, in fact

$$ {}^{3}V(R) - {}^{1}V(R) = 3.435\, R^2 e^{-1.974R}. $$

The wave functions ${}^{1,3}F(\vec{R})$ describing the relative motion of the two atoms satisfy

$$ \{\nabla^2 + [k^2 - {}^{1,3}V(R)]\}\,{}^{1,3}F(\vec{R}) = 0, \tag{8-6} $$

where

$$ {}^{1,3}F(\vec{R}) \sim \exp(i\vec{k}\cdot\vec{R}) + R^{-1}\,{}^{1,3}f(\theta)\exp(ikR). $$

The amplitudes ${}^{1,3}f(\theta)$ for elastic scattering by the potentials ${}^{1,3}V(R)$ can be expanded in partial waves which are determined by the phase shifts ${}^{1,3}\delta_\ell$ in the usual way. Labeling the two protons A and B, and ignoring their identity, we can consider states in which proton A has a spin wave function $\alpha(A)$ and proton B has spin function $\chi(B)$, where χ can be either α or β. The complete wave function for the singlet and triplet electron states is, including spin functions, asymptotically

$$ {}'\psi \sim [\exp(i\vec{k}\cdot\vec{R}) + R^{-1}\,{}^{1}f(\theta)\exp(ikR)]\alpha(A)\chi(B) \times $$

$$ \times \frac{1}{\sqrt{2}}[\alpha(1)\beta(2) - \beta(1)\alpha(2)], \tag{8-7} $$

where $\alpha(i)$, $\beta(i)$, i = 1,2 are the spin functions of the electrons, and

$$^3\psi \sim [\exp(i\vec{k}\cdot\vec{R}) + R^{-1}\,{}^3f(\theta)\exp(ikR)]\alpha(A)\chi(B) \times$$

$$\times \quad \frac{1}{\sqrt{2}}[\alpha(1)\beta(2) + \beta(1)\alpha(2)]. \tag{8-8}$$

where in the second line the Z component of the total electron spin S_Z has been taken to be zero. As S_Z is a constant of the motion, we do not have to consider the other members of the triplet multiplet with spin functions $\alpha(1)\alpha(2)$ and $\beta(1)\beta(2)$, which cannot couple to cause spin exchange in the approximation in which nuclear exchange is ignored.

Consider an initial state in which the hydrogen atom A has spin F = 1, with Z component M = 1. The spin wave function of the atom A is then $\alpha(A)\alpha(1)$ and corresponds to the wave function $({}^1\psi + {}^3\psi)$; in fact

$$\begin{aligned} {}^1\psi + {}^3\psi \sim 2^{1/2}\, e^{i\vec{k}\cdot\vec{R}}\alpha(A)\alpha(1)\chi(B)\beta(2) + \\ + R^{-1}e^{ikR}\, 2^{-1/2}S \end{aligned} \tag{8-9}$$

where

$$\begin{aligned} S = \{{}^1f(\theta) + {}^3f(\theta)\}\alpha(A)\alpha(1)\chi(B)\beta(2) + \\ + \{{}^3f(\theta) - {}^1f(\theta)\}\frac{1}{2}\Big(\alpha(A)\beta(1) + \beta(A)\alpha(1)\Big)\chi(B)\alpha(2) + \\ + \frac{1}{2}\Big(\alpha(A)\beta(1) - \beta(A)\alpha(1)\Big)\chi(B)\alpha(2)\} \end{aligned} \tag{8-10}$$

The scattered wave contains three terms, the first two of which correspond to the state with F = 1 and the last to F = 0. The cross section for the transitions from F = 1 to F = 0 is then determined by the scattering amplitude (normalizing to an incident wave of unit amplitude)

$$g(F = 1 \rightarrow F = 0) = 2^{-3/2}\{{}^3f(\theta) - {}^1f(\theta)\} \tag{8-11}$$

Expanding in phase shifts ${}^{1,3}\delta_\ell$

$$g\,(\theta) = \frac{1}{4ik\sqrt{2}}\sum_{\ell=0}^{\infty}\Big(e^{2i\,{}^3\delta_\ell} - e^{2i\,{}^1\delta_\ell}\Big)(2\ell + 1)P_\ell(\cos\theta), \tag{8-12}$$

and the total cross section is

$$\sigma(F = 1 \rightarrow F = 0) = \sum_{\ell=0}^{\infty} \frac{\pi}{2k^2} (2\ell + 1) \sin^2 ({}^3\delta_\ell - {}^1\delta_\ell). \tag{8-13}$$

The phase shifts ${}^3\delta_\ell$, ${}^1\delta_\ell$ were calculated by Dalgarno and Henry (1964) from the radial equations (atomic units),

$$\frac{d^2}{dR^2}[{}^{1,3}f_\ell(R)] + \left(k^2 - {}^{1,3}V(R) - \frac{\ell(\ell + 1)}{R^2} \right) {}^{1,3}f_\ell(R) = 0 \tag{8-14}$$

and their results are shown in Fig. 8-1 for energies between threshold and 20 x 10^{-3} ev. The maximum at 0.005 ev is due to (${}^3\delta_\ell$ - ${}^1\delta_\ell$) passing through $\pi/2$ at this energy for certain ℓ values.

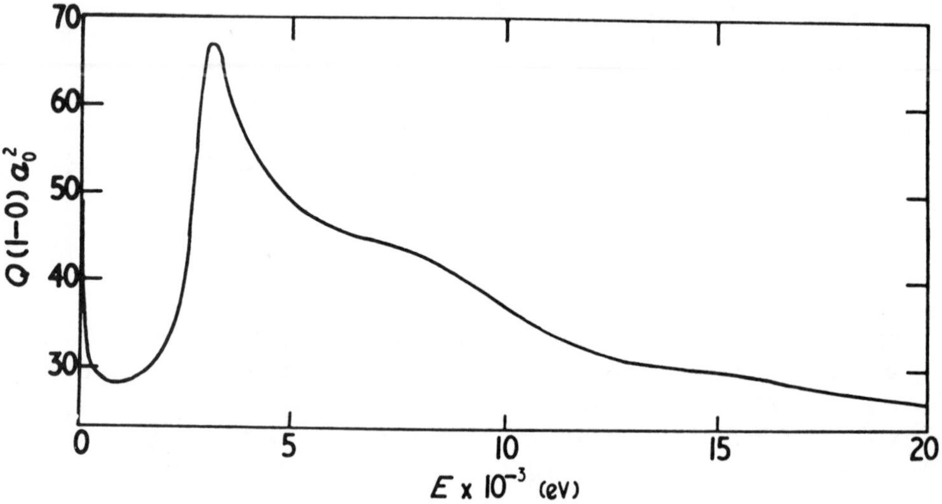

Figure 8-1 The spin exchange cross section for scattering of hydrogen atoms by hydrogen atoms (Dalgarno and Henry, 1964).

Smith (1966) has considered the effects of nuclear exchange, using the JWKB method to determine the phase shifts. The amplitude for spin exchange in this case is obtained by replacing ${}^{1}f(\theta)$ and ${}^{3}f(\theta)$ by $[{}^{1,3}f(\theta) - {}^{1,3}f(\pi - \theta)]$. The exchange effects are considerable for H - H scattering, but in proton-hydrogen scattering the exchange effects cancel.

Elastic scattering at higher velocities

Except at the very lowest velocities, elastic scattering is determined by both the inner and outer part of the interatomic potentials. At small distances these potentials are repulsive and can be represented empirically by simple parametric forms. One such form used to describe the interaction between two neutral atoms is the Lennard-Jones potential

$$V(R) = C\left(\frac{1}{2}\left(\frac{R_o}{R}\right)^{12} - \left(\frac{R_o}{R}\right)^{6}\right) \tag{8-15}$$

where C and R_o are parameters, which can be determined by fitting the elastic scattering cross sections to the experimental data. The classical deflection function Θ corresponding to this general form of potential is shown in Fig. 8-2.

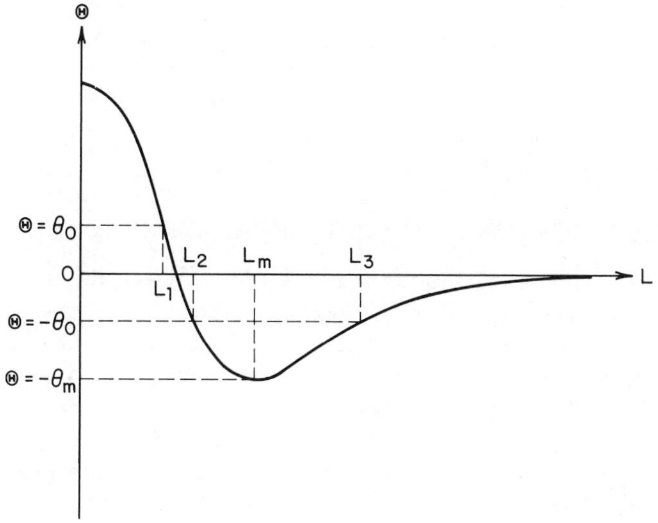

Figure 8-2 Schematic diagram of the deflection function Θ as a function of the classical angular momentum L for a Lennard-Jones potential.

At small values of the classical angular momentum (small values of the impact parameter), the deflection will be mainly influenced by the repulsive inner part of the potential and Θ is positive ($\Theta \to \pi$ as $L \to 0$), while for large L (peripheral collisions) the deflection is due to the outer (attractive) part of the potential and Θ is negative. As we saw in Chapter 2, at an angle of scattering such as θ_0 (see Fig. 8-2) the cross section is made up of three contributions, one from the repulsive part of the deflection function and two from the attractive part and we have (see 2-176)

$$\frac{d\sigma}{d\Omega} = \left| \sum_i \left(\frac{d_{\sigma i}}{d\Omega}\right)^{\frac{1}{2}} e^{i\beta_i} \right|^2 \tag{8-16}$$

where

$$\left(\frac{d\sigma_i}{d\Omega}\right)$$

is the classical cross section corresponding to the angular momentum Li and βi is the semi-classical phase, which can be calculated by the method of stationary phase as in Chapter 2. The angular distribution for $\theta \to \theta_r$, where θ_r is the rainbow angle is controlled by interference between the three contributions to the amplitude[1]. The cross section oscillates about a mean, determined by the purely classical cross section. As the energy increases, the scattering becomes very strongly peaked in the forward direction and for energies above a few hundred electron volts per atomic mass unit the corresponding classical trajectory can be approximated by a straight line.

8-2 INELASTIC SCATTERING - GENERAL THEORY

To discuss inelastic scattering the interaction of a beam of protons with a neutral atomic target will be taken as an example. To avoid unnecessary complication, the target atom, A, will be represented by a model in which one active electron is bound by an effective potential to an inert core composed of the remaining electrons and the nucleus. The extension of the theory to a many electron system is not difficult in principle, although there may be considerable complexities in practise. During the collision between a proton and the atom A the following reactions can occur

$$
\begin{aligned}
H^+ + A &\to H^+ + A^* && \text{(a)} \\
&\to H^* + A^+ && \text{(b)} \qquad (8\text{-}17)\\
&\to H^+ + A^+ + e^- && \text{(c)}
\end{aligned}
$$

representing excitation (and elastic scattering), charge exchange and ionization. We shall denote the Bohr velocity of the electron in the initial state by v_o. It is found that when the relative velocity v of the proton and the atom A is smaller than, or comparable to, v_o, both the excitation and charge exchange cross sections are large and the ionization cross section is smaller, while for $v > v_o$, the probability of charge exchange decreases rapidly compared with the probability of excitation. In contrast the ionization cross section rises to a maximum at some velocity greater than v_o, and at high energies ionization is the most important process. The laboratory energy of an ion of mass M (in atomic units) incident on a stationary target is $E_L = 25Mv^2$keV, where v is the relative velocity in atomic units and the conditions $E_L < 25Mv_o{}^2$keV and $E_L >> 25Mv_o{}^2$keV will be taken to define low and high energy regions.

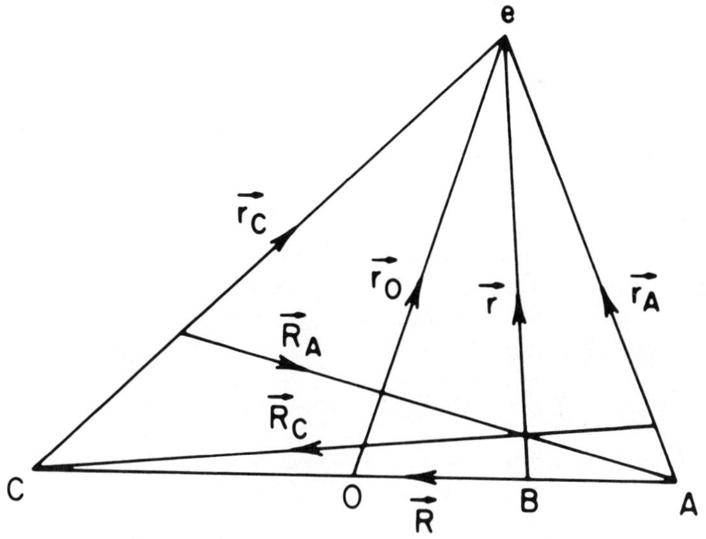

Figure 8-3 A coordinate system for heavy particle reactions

Let us introduce the system of coordinates shown in Fig. 8-3, for the active electron. The masses of the inert core electrons and nucleus of the atom A will be lumped together, so that the system is treated as a three-body system. For the sake of brevity, the system of (core electrons + nucleus) of A will be referred to as the 'nucleus of A'. The proton is situated at C and the nucleus of the target atom at A. The position vector of C with respect to A is $\vec{R}$, while the position vectors with respect to A, C and the center of mass B of the two nuclei, are $\vec{r}_A$, $\vec{r}_C$ and $\vec{r}$ respectively. The vectors $\vec{R}_A$ and $\vec{R}_C$ represent the positions of A relative to the center of mass of the electron and proton and of C relative to the center of mass of the target atom respectively. Each of the pairs $(\vec{R}, \vec{r})$, $(\vec{R}_A, \vec{r}_A)$ and $(\vec{R}_C, \vec{r}_C)$ are a set of center of mass coordinates for the three body system, but because of the mass of the electron compared with those of the nuclei, it is most convenient to take $\vec{R}$ and $\vec{r}$ as the independent variables, so that the kinetic energy operator in atomic units[2] can be expressed as

$$T = -\frac{1}{2}\nabla_r^2 - \frac{1}{2\mu}\nabla_R^2 \tag{8-18}$$

where the reduced mass of the electron has been approximated as $\mu_e = 1$ a.u. and the reduced mass of the two nuclei with masses M_A, M_C is $\mu = M_A M_C/(M_A+M_C)$. The three body Schrödinger equation in the center of mass system is

$$(T + V_{AC} + V_{Ae} + V_{Ce} - E)\psi(\vec{R},\vec{r}) = 0 \tag{8-19}$$

where E is the total energy and the potential between the pairs of particles are $V_{AC}(R)$, $V_{Ae}(r_A)$ and $V_{Ce}(r_C)$, where V_{AC} is the interaction between the proton and the (core electrons + nucleus) at the atom A, V_{Ae} is the effective interaction between the electron and the (core electrons + nucleus) of A, while V_{Ce} is the Coulomb potential between the proton and the electron. We have that

$$V_{AC} \underset{\text{large } R}{\sim} \frac{1}{R}, \quad V_{Ae} \underset{\text{large } r_A}{\sim} -\frac{1}{r_A}, \quad V_{Ce} = -\frac{1}{r_C} \tag{8-20}$$

The potentials must be considered as functions of the chosen independent variables $\vec{R}$ and $\vec{r}$, through the relations:

$$\begin{aligned} \vec{r}_A &= \vec{r} - q\vec{R} \\ \vec{r}_C &= \vec{r} + p\vec{R} \end{aligned} \tag{8-21}$$

where

$$q = M_C/(M_A + M_C); \quad p = M_A/(M_A + M_C) \tag{8-22}$$

The boundary conditions satisfied by $\psi(\vec{R},\vec{r})$ are defined in terms of the eigenfunctions χ_j of the atom A and the corresponding eigenenergies η_j, which satisfy

$$\left(-\frac{1}{2}\nabla^2_{r_A} + V_{Ae} - \eta_j\right)\chi_j(\vec{r}_A) = 0 \qquad (8\text{-}23)$$

and the eigenfunctions ϕ_m and eigenenergies ε_m of the hydrogen atom formed from the electron and the proton at C, which satisfy

$$\left(-\frac{1}{2}\nabla^2_{r_C} + V_{Ce} - \varepsilon_m\right)\phi_m(\vec{r}_C) = 0 \qquad (8\text{-}24)$$

The channels and quantities belonging to the initial arrangement will be labeled by the index j (and if necessary by i and k), while the rearranged charge exchange channels will be labeled by the index m (and if required by n and p). From the general theory of Chapter 4, the asymptotic form of $\psi(\vec{R},\vec{r})$ for large R can be written down. It is:

$$\psi(\vec{R},\vec{r}) \underset{R\to\infty}{\sim} \sum_j \left(\delta_{ji}e^{i\vec{k}_i\cdot\vec{R}_C} + f_{ji}(\theta_C)R_C^{-1}e^{ik_jR_C}\right)\chi_j(\vec{r}_A)$$

$$+ \sum_m \left(g_{mi}(\theta_A)R_A^{-1}e^{iK_mR_A}\right)\phi_m(\vec{r}_C) \qquad (8\text{-}25)$$

The first sum in (8-25) runs over the open channels of the initial arrangement and the second over the open charge exchange channels and i denotes the incident channel. The wave numbers k_j, k_m satisfy the conservation of energy relation:

$$E = \frac{1}{2\mu}k_j^{\,2} + \eta_j = \frac{1}{2\mu}K_m^{\,2} + \varepsilon_m \qquad (8\text{-}26)$$

where the mass of the electron has been ignored in the reduced masses.

It is now possible to proceed along the lines very similar to those used in Chapters 5 and 6 for electron scattering. Given a set of expansion functions $A_j(\vec{R},\vec{r})$ asymptotic (at large R) to the atomic functions $\chi_j(\vec{r}_A)$ and set of functions $C_j(\vec{R},\vec{r})$ asymptotic to the atomic functions $\phi_m(\vec{r}_C)$ a trial function can be formed by writing:

$$\psi(\vec{R},\vec{r}) = \sum_j F_j(\vec{R})\exp(-i\ell_1\vec{k}_j\cdot\vec{r}_A)A_j(\vec{R},\vec{r})+\sum_m G_m(\vec{R})\exp(i\ell_2\vec{K}_m\cdot\vec{r}_c)C_m(\vec{R},\vec{r}) \tag{8-27a}$$

where $\ell_1 = 1/(M_A + 1)$ and $\ell_2 = 1/(M_C + 1)$, and

$$F_j(\vec{R}) \underset{R\to\infty}{\sim} \delta_{ji}\exp(i\vec{k}_i\cdot\vec{R}) + R^{-1}f_{ji}(\Theta)\exp(ik_jR)$$

$$G_m(\vec{R}) \underset{R\to\infty}{\sim} R^{-1}g_{mi}(\pi - \Theta)\exp(iK_mR) \tag{8-27b}$$

The exponential factors included in (8-27a) are required so that $\psi(\vec{R},\vec{r})$ satisfies the boundary condition (8-25) and represent the translational motion of the active electron with respect to the origin B, when attached to the moving centers A and C.

The variational method can be used to find coupled equations for the channel wave functions F_j and G_m and these equations can be reduced to radial form by a partial wave decomposition. Because of the large number of partial waves involved except at the lowest energies, the radial equations are often solved with the help of the JWKB approximation (see Chapter 2). Alternatively the coupled equations for F_j and G_m can be treated exactly as in Section 6-5, by expressing these functions in terms of an eikonal approximation to scattering by the effective potential in each channel[3].

The impact parameter method

A simple treatment will now be developed in which it is assumed the nuclear motion can be determined by an average potential W(R), which is the same for all channels. This approximation is accurate when the initial kinetic energy $mv^2/2$ of the projectile is much greater than the average change in electronic energy during the collision. The lower limit of this energy interval is in the region of $E \cong 100\mu eV$ where μ is expressed in atomic mass units. The Schrödinger equation (8-19) can be written as

$$\left(-\frac{1}{2}\nabla^2_R + W(R) + H_e - E\right)\psi(\vec{R},\vec{r}) = 0 \tag{8-28}$$

where H_e is an electronic Hamiltonian defined by

$$H_e = -\frac{1}{2}\nabla^2_r + V_{Ae} + V_{Be} + (V_{AB} - W) \tag{8-29}$$

The relative motion of the two nuclei is described by a wave function $F(\vec{R})$ which satisfies the potential scattering equation

$$\left(-\frac{1}{2\mu}\nabla_R^2 + W(R) - E\right) F(\vec{R}) = 0 \qquad (8\text{-}30)$$

Various choices of W(R) are possible, for example, W(R) can be taken to be the average (static) interaction in the incident channel

$$W(R) = \int d^3 r_A |\chi_i(\vec{r}_A)|^2 \{V_{AB} + V_{Ae}\} \qquad (8\text{-}31)$$

In general it is a good approximation to ignore the binding energy of the atom in the initial state when calculating E, so that

$$E \cong k_i{}^2/2\mu = \mu v^2/2 \qquad (8\text{-}32)$$

Making the substitution

$$\psi(\vec{R},\vec{r}) = F(\vec{R})\Psi(\vec{R},\vec{r}) \qquad (8\text{-}33)$$

where Ψ is a function to be determined, in (8-28) we find

$$-\frac{1}{2\mu}F(\vec{R})\nabla_R^2\Psi(\vec{R},\vec{r}) - \frac{1}{\mu}\vec{\nabla}_R F(\vec{R})\vec{\nabla}_R\Psi(\vec{R},\vec{r}) +$$

$$+F(\vec{R})H_e\Psi(\vec{R},\vec{r}) = 0 \qquad (8\text{-}34)$$

As already discussed at the beginning of this Chapter, semi-classical approximations are accurate for the heavy particle motion and the solution of (8-30) can be approximated by (see 2-118 and 2-122).

$$F(\vec{R}) = \exp iS(\vec{R}) \qquad (8\text{-}35a)$$

where

$$S(\vec{R}) \cong \int ds\ [2\mu\{E - W(R)\}]^{\frac{1}{2}} \qquad (8\text{-}35b)$$

and the integration is along a trajectory which we can write in terms of an impact parameter vector $\vec{b}$ and the time t

$$\vec{R} = \vec{R}(\vec{b},t) \qquad (8\text{-}36)$$

At sufficiently high energies (in fact as low as a few hundred eV for proton-hydrogen atom collisions), the deflection of the heavy particles can be neglected and

$$\vec{R} = \vec{b} + \vec{v}t \ ; \quad \vec{b}\,\vec{v} = 0 \qquad (8\text{-}37)$$

where $\vec{v}$ is the constant relative velocity taken parallel to the Z axis. In this case $F(\vec{R})$ reduces to the plane wave

$$F(R) \cong \exp\, ik_i Z_R = \exp\, i\mu v Z_R \qquad (8\text{-}38)$$

where (X_R, Y_R, Z_R) are the Cartesian components of $\vec{R}$.

The first two terms in (8-34) couple the nuclear and electronic motion. On substituting (8-38) into (8-34) and remembering that μ is a large parameter[4], the first term is seen to be much smaller than the second, and it can be neglected, so that (8-34) reduces to

$$H_e \Psi(\vec{R},\vec{r}) = iv\frac{\partial}{\partial Z_R} \Psi(\vec{R},\vec{r}) \qquad (8\text{-}39)$$

Since from (8-37), $Z_R = vt$, this in turn can be written as a time dependent Schrödinger equation

$$H_e \Psi(\vec{r},t) = i\frac{\partial}{\partial t} \Psi(\vec{r},t) \qquad (8\text{-}40)$$

The Hamiltonian H_e depends on time through equations (8-20) and (8-21) together with (8-37) and both H_e and Ψ depend on b as a parameter. If the non-linear nature of the inter-nuclear motion is allowed for, and dropping the first term in (8-34), the time dependent equation (8-40) is again obtained, but this time $\vec{R}$ is determined by the non-linear trajectory (8-36) rather than by (8-37).

The solutions of the impact parameter equation (8-40) will now be discussed. The electronic wave function $\Psi(\vec{r},t)$ can be expanded in some basis functions A_j and C_m (which differ from the $\mathcal{A}_j$ and $\mathcal{C}_m$ of (8-27) by phase factors), such that A_j and C_m are asymptotic as $|t|\to\infty$ to atomic orbitals centered about A and C respectively:

$$\Psi(\vec{r},t) = \sum_j a_j(b,t)A_j(\vec{r},t) + \sum_m c_m(b,t)C_m(\vec{r},t) \qquad (8\text{-}41)$$

where a_j and c_m are expansion coefficients. In the limit $|t|$ large and $r_C >> r_A$ we must require that

$$A_j(\vec{r},t) \xrightarrow[|t|\to\infty]{} X_j(\vec{r},t) \qquad (8\text{-}42)$$

where X_j satisfies (from 8-40 and 8-20) the equation

$$\left(-\frac{1}{2}\nabla_r^2 + V_{Ae}(r_A) - i\frac{\partial}{\partial t}\right)X_j(\vec{r},t) = 0 \qquad (8\text{-}43)$$

The solutions of this equation are:

$$X_j(\vec{r},t) = \chi_j(\vec{r}_B)\exp i\alpha_j \qquad (8\text{-}44)$$

where

$$\alpha_j = -\eta_j t - q\,\vec{v}\cdot\vec{r} - \frac{1}{2}q^2v^2t \qquad (8\text{-}45)$$

and q is defined by (8-22). The exponential terms in v are required because the electron when bound to the nucleus at A is moving with a velocity $-q\vec{v}$ and with a kinetic energy $1/2q^2v^2$ with respect to the origin B (see Fig.8-3). To check that X_j satisfies (8-43), we remember that the operator $\partial/\partial t$ is to be taken with $\vec{r}$ fixed and using (8-21), we have

$$\frac{\partial}{\partial t}X_j = -i\left(\eta_j + \frac{1}{2}q^2v^2\right)X_j + q\left(\frac{\partial}{\partial t}\vec{R}\right)\cdot\vec{\nabla}_{r_B}\chi_j(\vec{r}_B)\exp i\alpha_j \qquad (8\text{-}46)$$

We also note that

$$-\frac{1}{2}\nabla_r^2X_j = \left(-\frac{1}{2}\nabla_{r_B}^2\chi(\vec{r}_B) - iq\,\vec{v}\cdot\vec{\nabla}_{r_B}\chi_j(\vec{r}_B) + (-iqv)^2\chi_j(\vec{r}_B)\right)\exp i\alpha_j \qquad (8\text{-}47)$$

and since $\partial\vec{R}/\partial t = \vec{v}$ and using (8-23), we see that X_j satisfies (8-43). It should be noted that if the trajectory $\vec{R} = \vec{R}(t)$ is non-linear, then the direction of $\vec{v}$ after the collision as $t\to+\infty$ is different from the initial direction of $\vec{v}$ which is parallel to the Z axis.

In just the same way, we require that in the limit $|t|\to\infty$ and $r_C \ll r_A$

$$C_m(\vec{r},t)\xrightarrow[|t|\to\infty]{}\Phi_m(\vec{r},t) \qquad (8\text{-}48)$$

where

$$\Phi_m(\vec{r},t) = \Phi_m(\vec{r}_C)\exp i\gamma_m \qquad (8\text{-}49)$$

and

$$\gamma_m = -\varepsilon_m t + p\,\vec{v}\cdot\vec{r} - \frac{1}{2}p^2v^2t \qquad (8\text{-}50)$$

When the colliding partners are both charged α_j and γ_m must be modified[5]. In this case $p\,\vec{v}$ is velocity of the electron attached to C relative to B and p is defined by (8-22).

Without loss of generality the functions A_j can be taken to form an orthonormal set for all t, and so can the functions C_m

$$\int d^3r\, A_j^* A_k = \delta_{jk} \; ; \quad \int d^3r\, C_m^* C_n = \delta_{mn} \tag{8-51}$$

The overlap between the functions C_m and A_j is defined by the matrix $S_{jm}(t)$ where

$$S_{jm}(t) = \int d^3r\, A_j^* C_m \tag{8-52}$$

and this is non zero except in the limit $|t| \to 0$.

The amplitudes a_j and c_m can be found from a variational method. Defining I by

$$I = \int_{\infty}^{\infty} dt \int d^3r\, \Psi^* \left(H_e - i\frac{\partial}{\partial t}\right)\Psi \tag{8-53}$$

and imposing the condition $\delta I=0$ under the independent first order variations $a_j \to a_j + \delta a_j$; $c_m \to c_m + \delta c_m$, we find the coupled equations

$$\begin{aligned} \int d^3r\, A_j^* \left(H_e - i\frac{\partial}{\partial t}\right)\Psi &= 0 \\ \int d^3r\, C_m^* \left(H_e - i\frac{\partial}{\partial t}\right)\Psi &= 0 \end{aligned} \tag{8-54}$$

These equations are easily reduced to the form:

$$\begin{aligned} i\left(\dot{a}_j + \sum_m S_{jm}\dot{c}_m\right) &= \sum_k H_{jk}a_k + \sum_m K_{jm}c_m \\ i\left(\sum_k S_{kn}^*\dot{a}_k + \dot{c}_n\right) &= \sum_k \bar{K}_{nk}a_k + \sum_m \bar{H}_{nm}c_m \end{aligned} \tag{8-55}$$

where

$$H_{jk} = \int d^3r A_j^* \left(H_e - i\frac{\partial}{\partial t}\right) A_k \tag{8-56a}$$

$$\bar{H}_{nm} = \int d^3r C_n^* \left(H_e - i\frac{\partial}{\partial t}\right) C_m \tag{8-56b}$$

$$K_{jm} = \int d^3 r A_j^* \left(H_e - i\frac{\partial}{\partial t}\right) C_m \tag{8-56c}$$

$$\bar{K}_{nk} = \int d^3 r C_n^* \left(H_e - i\frac{\partial}{\partial t}\right) A_k \tag{8-56d}$$

Because H_{jk} and $\bar{H}_{nm}$ connect states belonging to the same arrangement, these are known as direct matrix elements, while K_{jm} and $\bar{K}_{nk}$ are known as exchange matrix elements.

Boundary conditions and cross sections

Although equations (8-59) and (8-60) have a somewhat complicated appearance, these equations are first order coupled differential equations and easier to solve than the second order integro-differential equations of the close coupling method for electron scattering. The boundary conditions follow by requiring that initially as $t\to-\infty$, the nucleus C is free and the electron is bound to nucleus A in the level i. We then must have

$$\ell t_{t\to-\infty}\, a_j(b,t) = \delta_{ji}\ ; \quad \ell t_{t\to-\infty}\, c_j(b,t) = 0 \tag{8-57}$$

The cross section for excitation of the atom $(A+e^-)$ is determined by the value of

$$\ell t_{t\to+\infty}\, a_j(b,t) \equiv a_j(b,\infty)$$

and is

$$\sigma_{ji} = 2\pi \int_0^\infty b\,db\,|a_j(b,\infty)|^2 \tag{8-58}$$

and similarly the cross section for charge exchange into the mth level of the atom $(C+e^-)$ is

$$\sigma_{mi}^E = 2\pi \int_0^\infty b\,db\,|c_m(b,\infty)|^2 \tag{8-59a}$$

It can be seen intuitively that the corresponding differential cross sections should be given by

$$\frac{d\sigma_{ji}}{d\Omega} = \frac{d\sigma^c(\theta)}{d\Omega}\,|a_j(b,\infty)|^2 \tag{8-59b}$$

where $d\sigma^c/d\Omega$ is the classical (or semi-classical) cross section for scattering by the potential W and b is the impact parameter appropriate to the angle θ, with a similar expression for the charge exchange cross section. Even if $W = 0$ and the integration of (8-40) is along a straight line trajectory, the differential cross section can still be computed. We proceed from the integral expression for the scattering amplitude, which on making the semi-classical approximations reduces to

$$f_{ji}(\theta) = -\frac{\mu}{2\pi}\int d^3R\int d^3r\, e^{-i\mu\vec{v}_f\cdot\vec{R}}\, X_j^*\left(V_{Ce}+V_{AC}\right)e^{i\mu\vec{v}\cdot\vec{R}}\Psi(\vec{R},\vec{r})$$

where $\vec{v}_f$ is the relative velocity of the nuclei after the collision, and consistently with our approximations $|\vec{v}_f| = |\vec{v}|$.

Making the small angle approximation (see Chapter 2, page 93) that $(\vec{v}-\vec{v}_f)\cdot\vec{R}\sim(\vec{v}-\vec{v}_f)\cdot\vec{b}$ and noting from (8-43) that

$$\left(V_{Ce} + V_{AC}\right) X_j^* = \left(H_e + i\frac{\partial}{\partial t}\right) X_j^*$$

$$= \left(H_e + iv\frac{\partial}{\partial Z_R}\right) X_j^*$$

an integration by parts with respect to Z_R gives the result

$$f_{ji}(\theta) = -\frac{i\mu v}{2\pi}\int d^2b\int d^3r\, e^{i\vec{q}\cdot\vec{b}}\, \left|X_j^*\Psi\right|_{t=-\infty}^{\infty} \tag{8-60}$$

where $\vec{q} = \mu(\vec{v}_f-\vec{v})$; $|q| = 2v\mu\sin\theta/2$. Using (8-41), (8-51) and the fact that $S_{jm}\to 0$ as $|t|\to\infty$, we find[6]

$$f_{ji}(\theta) = -\frac{i\mu v}{2\pi}\int d^2b\, e^{i\vec{q}\cdot\vec{b}}\left(a_j(b,\infty) - \delta_{ij}\right)$$

$$= -i\mu v\int_0^\infty bdb\, J_0(qb)\left(a_j(b,\infty) - \delta_{ij}\right) \tag{8-61a}$$

and finally

$$\frac{d\sigma_{ji}}{d\Omega} = |f_{ji}(\theta)|^2 \tag{8-61b}$$

The cross sections for charge exchange can be found in exactly the same way. We have

$$g_{mi}(\theta) = -i\mu v\int_0^\infty bdb\, J_0(qb)c_m(b,\infty) \tag{8-62a}$$

and

$$\frac{d\sigma^E_{mi}}{d\Omega} = |g_{mi}(\theta)|^2 \tag{8-62b}$$

Since q is large, except at very small angles, (8-61a) or (8-62a) can be further reduced by using the asymptotic form

$$J_0(qb) \sim \left(\frac{2}{\pi bq}\right)^{\frac{1}{2}} \sin\,(bq + \pi/4)$$

and using the method of stationary phase to evaluate the integral over b. Provided $|a_j|^2$ is slowly varying with b, the result normally reduces to the expression (8-59b), for excitation and to a similar expression for charge exchange.

Unitarity and time reversal

It is not difficult to show that the set of equations (8-55) using any linearly independent set of functions A_j, C_m satisfying the boundary conditions meets the requirements of unitarity (probability flux conservation) expressed in this case by the requirement

$$\sum_j |a_j(b,\infty)|^2 + \sum_m |c_m(b,\infty)|^2 = 1 \tag{8-63}$$

where the sums run over the finite basis used. By placing the incident wave in each channel in turn, all the elements of the S-matrix can be calculated, and it can be shown that time reversal invariance is satisfied in the form that the S-matrix is symmetrical.

Choice of basis functions

The functions A_j and C_m have been specified in terms of the asymptotic forms (8-44) and (8-48) together with the orthonormality conditions (8-51). The construction of suitable sets of functions must be guided by physical considerations with the aim of providing an accurate representation of the wave function when the expansion set is truncated to a fairly small number of terms so that the coupled equations are of manageable size. At low velocities $v \ll 1$ a.u., the expansion set can be based on a molecular orbital approximation. For each fixed internuclear distance R, the two center Schrödinger equation can be solved

$$H_e(\vec{r},\vec{R})\psi_n(\vec{R},\vec{r}) = E_n(R)\psi_n(\vec{R},\vec{r}) \tag{8-64}$$

to provide a set of orthonormal functions ψ_n and corresponding molecular potentials $E_n(R)$. The expansion functions can then be taken as[7]

$$A_j = \psi_j \exp i\alpha_j; \; C_m = \psi_m \exp i\gamma_m \tag{8-65}$$

where the phase factors α_j and γ_m are given by (8-45) and (8-50) and where in the limit $R\to\infty$ $\psi_j\to\chi_j$ and $\psi_m\to\phi_m$. In many cases, the molecular orbitals are asymptotic to linear combinations of atomic orbitals and if this is the case combinations of the molecular orbitals ψ_n must be taken which satisfy the boundary conditions. If the phase factors α_j and γ_m are set equal to zero in (8-65) the original perturbed stationary state (PSS) method of Massey and Smith (1933) is obtained which is similar in spirit to the polarized orbital method described earlier. Although it would seem reasonable to omit the phase factors when v satisfies $v \ll 1$, if this is done, because the basis functions do not individuall satisfy the wave equation (8-40) in the limit $|t|\to\infty$, the equations (8-56) remain coupled at large t which causes considerable difficulty and results in the need for larger basis sets than would otherwise be required.

When v becomes comparable with v_0, the electronic Bohr velocity, the wave function cannot be expected to adjust adiabatically so that for each value of t it resembles a molecular orbital. The electron will be associated for most of the time with one or other of the centers A and C and this situation can be represented by identifying the expansion functions with the asymptotic forms Φ_m and X_j.

$$A_j = X_j; \qquad C_m = \Phi_m \tag{8-66}$$

This will be called the atomic expansion. This kind of expansion can be augmented by pseudofunctions which take account of the continuum, as in the pseudostate approach to electron scattering by atoms described earlier.

Rotating coordinates

One further important general point remains to be discussed before considering some particular applications of the theory. The scattering equations have been developed with respect to a coordinate axes fixed in space, the Z axis being taken as the direction of incidence. This implies that the axis of quantization of the atomic and molecular expansion functions should also be fixed in space. However, since the internuclear line is an axis of symmetry, when generating molecular orbitals this line is usually taken as the axis of quantization, and since the internuclear line rotates through 180° during a collision, the quantization is with respect to a rotating coordinate system. Let us take the plane of scattering of the nuclei to be the XZ plane and consider the case of the rectilinear trajectory (8-37), then the angle $\Theta(t)$ which $\vec{R}$ makes with the Z axis is given

by (see Fig. 8-4)

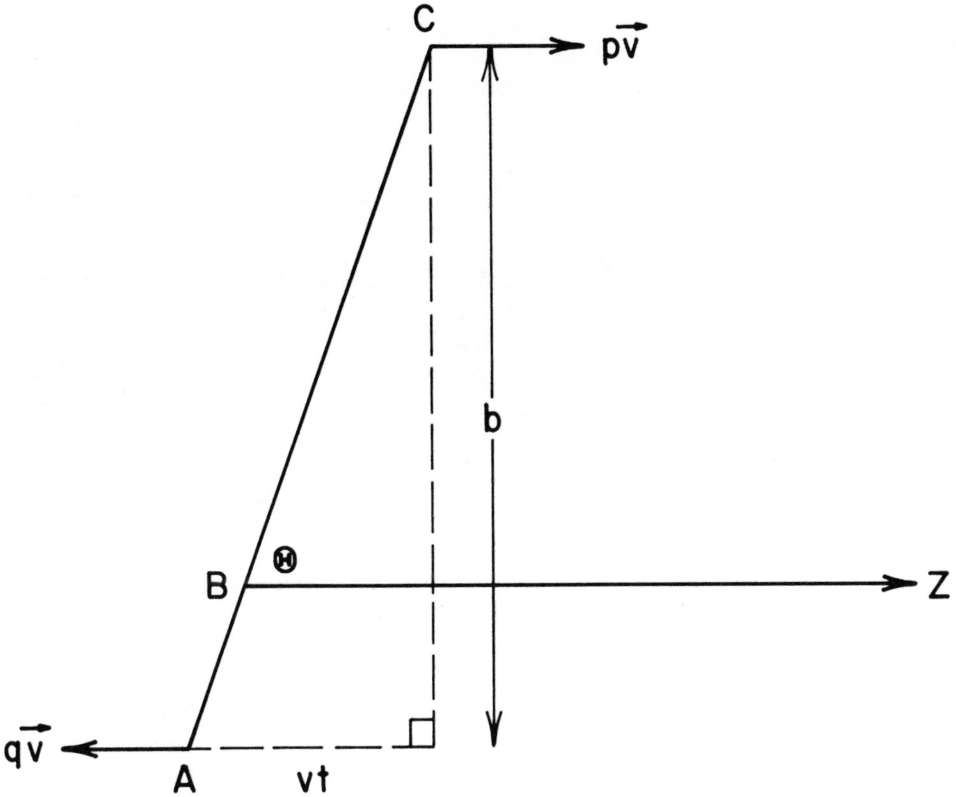

Figure 8-4 Rotation of the internuclear line during a heavy particle collision

$$\sin \Theta = \frac{b}{R}; \ \cos \Theta = \frac{vt}{R} \tag{8-67}$$

The position vector of the electron with respect to the center of mass B is $\vec{r}$ in the space fixed frame with components (x,y,z). In the rotating frame, with the Z axis along $\vec{R}$, let the corresponding vector be $\vec{r}'$ with components (x', y', z'). We then have

$$\begin{aligned} x' &= x \cos \Theta + z \sin \Theta \\ y' &= y \\ z' &= -x \sin \Theta + z \cos \Theta \end{aligned} \tag{8-68}$$

The molecular orbital functions ψ_j are available as functions of $\vec{r}'$ and R, $\psi_j = \psi_j\ (R, \vec{r}')$. Referring to (8-65) and (8-56), we see that we require $\partial/\partial t \psi_j$ where the time derivative is to be taken with $\vec{r}$ fixed. Using (8-68) we have

$$\frac{\partial}{\partial t}\psi_j(R,\vec{r}') = \dot{R}\frac{\partial}{\partial R}\psi_j + \dot{\Theta}\{z'\frac{\partial}{\partial x'} - x'\frac{\partial}{\partial z'}\}\psi_j \qquad (8\text{-}69)$$

which can be written as

$$\frac{\partial}{\partial t}\psi_j = (R,\vec{r}') = \{\dot{R}\frac{\partial}{\partial R} - i\dot{\Theta}L_{Y'}\}\psi_j(R,\vec{r}') \qquad (8\text{-}70)$$

where $L_{Y'}$ is the Y component of the orbital angular momentum operator in the rotating frame. The radial velocity $\dot{R}$ is equal to v^2t/R and the angular velocity $\dot{\Theta}$ is equal to bv/R^2. The rotational coupling proportional to $\dot{\Theta}$, connects states with different (non-zero) magnetic quantum numbers, while the radial coupling connects states belonging to the same angular momentum quantum numbers. Further discussion of the molecular orbital expansion will be deferred until the next Chapter.

8-3 EXPANSIONS BASED ON ATOMIC EIGENFUNCTIONS

A few particular examples of the one electron theory developed in Section 8-2 will now be discussed starting with the atomic expansion in which the functions A_j and C_m are identified with X_j and Φ_m as in (8-66). This one electron theory can be extended in obvious ways to many electron systems, the only new feature being that the wave functions should be anti-symmetrized in the electron spin and space coordinates. This is important at low velocities (E_L < 10M kev), but the identity of the electrons attached to different centers can be ignored at higher energies. The direction of quantization for the atomic wave functions can either be taken to be along the direction of incidence or along the rotating internuclear line. Here only the former possibility will be pursued.

The two state approximation - excitation

To obtain some insight into the structure of the equations (8-55), the simple two state approximation will be examined, starting with excitation. We then set all the functions C_m equal to zero and retain two of the functions A_j, with (see 8-44 and 8-66)

$$A_0 = \chi_0(\vec{r}_A)\exp i\alpha_0; \; A_1 = \chi_1(\vec{r}_A)\exp i\alpha_1 \qquad (8\text{-}71)$$

with the quantization axis being fixed in space parallel to the Z axis. The potential matrix elements (8-56) are all zero with the exception of the elements H_{jk} which become

$$H_{jk} = e^{i(\eta_j-\eta_k)t} V_{jk} \tag{8-72}$$

where

$$V_{jk} = \int d^3r_A \chi^*_j(\vec{r}_A)\left(V_{CA} + V_{Ce}\right)\chi_k(\vec{r}_A) \tag{8-73}$$

The coupled equations for the amplitudes a_0 and a_1, take the simple form

$$i\,\dot{a}_j = \sum_k^v e^{i(\eta_j-\eta_k)t} V_{jk}(t)a_k \tag{8-74}$$

These equations are effectively the same as those we wrote down for excitation by electron impact in (6- 90), the potentials V_{jk} being equal in magnitude, but of opposite sign. It is important to notice that since the matrix elements H_{jk} refer to the same arrangement, the velocity dependent parts of the translational factors α_j have cancelled from the final result, and also the equations are independent of position of the origin B on the inter-nuclear line.

The diagonal (secular) terms in equations (8-74) can be removed by the phase transformation

$$a'_k = a_k \exp i\int_{-\infty}^t dt' V_{kk}(t) \tag{8-75}$$

the new amplitudes satisfying the equations

$$i\,\dot{a}'_j = \sum_{k\neq j} e^{i(\delta_j-\delta_k)} V_{jk}a'_k\,; \qquad j = 0,\,1 \tag{8-76}$$

where

$$\delta_k(t) = \eta_k + \int_{\infty}^t V_{kk}(t')dt' \tag{8-77}$$

The boundary conditions to be imposed on the solutions of (8-76) are

$$a'_0(b,t= -\infty) = 1; \quad a'_1(b,t= -\infty) = 0 \tag{8-78}$$

and the cross section for the excitation of the level 1 from the level 0 is

$$\sigma_{10} = 2\pi \int_0^{\infty} b \; |a'_1(b,\infty)|^2 \; db \tag{8-79}$$

The coupling terms in the equations (8-74) and (8-76) oscillate with a frequency that depends on the factor ΔE, where ΔE is the energy difference between the states. Thus when ΔE is large the effective coupling oscillates rapidly and the transition probability is small. When ΔE is small the two states concerned will be strongly coupled. The two state approximation is particularly useful when ΔE for the pair of states concerned is smaller than the corresponding energy differences between either of the states and any other state. As $v \to 0$, the transition probability is also expected to decrease rapidly except in the case of resonance for which $\Delta E = 0$. The terms involving V_{00} and V_{11} in the exponents of (8-76) represent the first order perturbation of the energies η_0, η_1 by the interaction. The lowest order approximation to $a'_1(b,\infty)$ is obtained by setting $a'_0(b,t)=1$ on the right hand side of (8-76) and ignoring V_{00} and V_{11}. On integrating we have

$$a'_1(b,\infty) = \int_{\infty}^{\infty} dt \exp i(\eta_1-\eta_0)t \; V_{10}(t) \tag{8-80}$$

The approximations leading to (8-80) are the same as those of the Born approximation and it can be shown that the cross section obtained is in fact identical with that obtained in the Born approximation (Arthurs, 1961). Setting $a'_0(b,t)=1$ but retaining V_{00} and V_{11} leads to the semi-classical version of the distorted wave Born approximation

$$a'_1(b,\infty) = \int_{\infty}^{\infty} dt \exp i(\delta_1-\delta_0)V_{10}(t) \tag{8-81}$$

where $\delta_k(t)$ is defined by (8-77). Unless $V_{00} \approx V_{11}$, the effect of distortion may be considerable, reducing the cross section from that given by the Born approximation. Neither of these approximations guarantees the unitarity of the theory and the failure of these approximations is often signalled by $|a_1(b,\infty)|^2$ exceeding unity for some range of the impact parameter b. Some applications of the Born and distorted wave approximations will be discussed in Chapter 10.

The two state approximation - charge exchange

In the case of charge exchange some interesting new features appear in the coupled equations. In the two state approximation we retain one of the functions A_j centered about A and one of the functions C_m centered about C, taking

$$A_0 = X_0(\vec{r}_A)\ \exp\ i\alpha_0 \text{ and } C_1 = \phi_1(\vec{r}_c)\exp\ i\gamma_1 \qquad (8\text{-}82)$$

A little algebra shows that the matrix elements (8-56) and the overlap integral (8-52) reduce to the following:

$$S_{01} = e^{i(\eta_0-\varepsilon_1)t}\int d^3r' e^{i\vec{v}\cdot\vec{r}_o}\ \chi_o^*(\vec{r}_A)\phi_1(\vec{r}_c)$$

$$H_{00} = \int d^3r_A|\chi_o(\vec{r}_A)|^2\left(V_{CA} + V_{Ce-}\right)$$

$$\bar{H}_{11} = \int d^3r_c|\phi_1(\vec{r}_c)|^2\left(V_{CA} + V_{Ae-}\right)$$

$$K_{01} = e^{i(\eta_0-\varepsilon_1)t}\int d^3r' e^{+i\vec{v}\cdot\vec{r}_o}\chi_o^*(\vec{r}_A)\phi_1(\vec{r}_c)\left(V_{CA} + V_{AC}\right)$$

$$\bar{K}_{10} = e^{i(\varepsilon_1-\eta_0)t}\int d^3r' e^{-i\vec{v}\cdot\vec{r}_o}\phi_1^*(\vec{r}_c)\chi_o(\vec{r}_A)\left(V_{CA} + V_{CC}\right)$$

(8-83)

where $\vec{r}_o$ is the position vector of the electron with respect to the mid point of the line CA. In this form it is clear that the values of the matrix elements are independent of p and q and therefore independent of the position of the origin B and the theory is translationally invariant. The matrix elements connecting the two channels, K_{01}, $\bar{K}_{10}$ and S_{01} contain the factors $\exp\pm i\vec{v}\cdot\vec{r}_o$ which represent the change in the momentum of the electron when transferred from the A to C. As v increases this factor oscillates and is responsible for the rapid decrease in the magnitude of the exchange matrix elements compared with the direct matrix elements.

In the two state approximation equations (8-55) are easily solved for the time derivatives $\dot{a}_0$, $\dot{c}_1$, (for more than two equations this is a matrix operation to be carried out for each value of t), we find

$$i\ \dot{a}_0 = L\ a_0 + MC_1$$
$$i\ \dot{c}_1 = \bar{M}\ a_0 + \bar{L}\ _1 \qquad (8\text{-}84)$$

where

$$L = (1 - |S|^2)^{-1}(H - S\bar{K}) \qquad (a)$$

$$\bar{L} = (1 - |S|^2)^{-1}(\bar{H} - S^*K) \qquad (b)$$

$$M = (1 - |S|^2)^{-1}(K - S\bar{H}) \qquad (c) \qquad (8\text{-}85)$$

$$\bar{M} = (1 - |S|^2)^{-1}(\bar{K} - S^*H) \qquad (d)$$

A further simplification of the equations can be made by making the phase transformations

$$a' = a_0 \exp i\int_{\infty}^{t} dt'\, L(t')$$
$$c' = c_1 \exp i\int_{\infty}^{t} dt'\bar{L}(t') \qquad (8\text{-}86)$$

the new amplitudes then satisfy

$$\dot{a}' = M\, e^{i\delta} c'$$
$$\dot{c}' = \bar{M}\, e^{-i\delta} a' \qquad (8\text{-}87)$$

where

$$\delta = \int_{\infty}^{t}\left(L(t') - \bar{L}(t')\right)dt' \qquad (8\text{-}88)$$

Since $|a'| = |a_0|$ and $|c'| = |c_1|$, equations (8-87) can be solved subject to the boundary conditions

$$a' \to 1, \quad c' \to 0 \quad \text{as } t \to -\infty$$

in which case the cross section for charge exchange is

$$\sigma_{10} = 2\pi\int_{0}^{\infty} bdb\, |c'(b,\infty)|^2 \qquad (8\text{-}89)$$

By inspection of (8-85) and (8-88), it can be seen that M, $\bar{M}$ and do not depend on the internuclear potential V_{CA}, and in fact in the linear trajectory approximation this potential has no influence on the probability for charge exchange. This, of course, follows because V_{CA} can be removed by a phase transformation from the original time dependent Schrödinger equation (8-40). The differential cross section does depend on the phase of the wave function, and while V_{CA} can be omitted when calculating total cross sections, this is not the case when calculating angular distributions. The independence of the total cross section from V_{CA} can be used as check on the consistency of an approximate method

The first order approximation to (8-87) is found by setting $a'=1$ in the second equation, so that

$$c'(b,\infty) \approx \int_{\infty}^{\infty} \bar{M}(t)\exp-i\delta(t)dt \tag{8-90}$$

This is usually called the distorted wave approximation (Bates, 1958). It does not guarantee unitarity, but a unitarized version of this approximation has been developed by Ryufuku and Watanabe (1978, 1979a,b) and applied to charge exchange between fully stripped ions and atomic hydrogen, the cross sections for which are of practical importance in research into thermonuclear fusion.

If the distortion term $\delta(t)$ is set equal to zero, a first order approximation analogous to the ordinary Born approximation is obtained

$$c'(b,\infty) \approx \int_{\infty}^{\infty} \bar{M}(t)dt = \int_{\infty}^{\infty} dt \left(\frac{\bar{K} - S^{*}H}{1 - |S|^{2}}\right) \tag{8-91}$$

The overlap integral S occurs because of the non-orthogonality of the basis used. Both the distorted wave expression (8-90) and the first order Born expression (8-91) provide amplitudes which are close to those obtained by solving the coupled equations (8-87) at energies above ~25kev/amu, for the particular example of an incident proton. If the incident particle is highly charged, the first order approximations will not represent the two state problem accurately until higher energies are reached.

Symmetrical Resonance

Of particular interest is the case in which the target atom is a hydrogen atom in the ground state. If capture occurs into the ground state the initial and final systems are identical and form an example of what is called 'symmetrical resonance':

$$H^{+} + H(1s) \rightarrow H(1s) + H^{+} \tag{8-92}$$

The electronic Hamiltonian H_e for an electron moving in the field of two nuclei having the same charge Z (but not necessarily the same mass) is

$$H_e(\vec{R},\vec{r}_o) = -\frac{1}{2}\nabla^2_{r_o} - \frac{Z}{r_A} - \frac{Z}{r_C} + \frac{Z^2}{R} \tag{8-93}$$

where $\vec{r}_o$, the position vector of the electron with respect to the mid-point, 0, of the internuclear line has been taken to be an independent variable. The Hamiltonian is unaltered by a reflection at 0, $\vec{r}_o \to -\vec{r}_o$, so that the solutions of the equation (8-40) can be divided into two parity classes such that

$$\Psi^{\pm}(-\vec{r}_o,t) = \pm\,\Psi^{\pm}(\vec{r}_o,t) \tag{8-94}$$

This division corresponds to the division into gerade and ungerade states of the static molecular problem. It is easy to show that this parity is a constant of the motion and that the states Ψ^+ and Ψ^- propagate independently. Now let us see what happens to the two state equations (8-87) when applied to the reaction (8-92). Since the initial and final channels are identical, $L = \bar{L}$ so that $\delta = 0$. In addition $M = \bar{M}$, so that equation (8-87) can be uncoupled by introducing the new amplitudes $A_{\pm} = a' \pm c'$ which satisfy

$$i\dot{A}_{\pm} = \pm\, MA_{\pm} \tag{8-95}$$

The uncoupled amplitudes A_+ and A_- are the amplitudes for the two parity states with wave functions Ψ^+ and Ψ^-. Since $a' \to 1$ and $c' \to 0$ as $t\to -\infty$, it follows that $A_+ \to 1$ and $A_- \to 1$ as $t\to -\infty$, so that

$$A_{\pm} = \exp\mp i \int_{\infty}^{t} M(t)\,at \tag{8-96}$$

The probability for charge exchange $|c'(b,\infty)|^2$ is determined by

$$|c'(b,\infty)|^2 = \frac{1}{4}|A_+(b,\infty) - A_-(b,\infty)|^2 = \sin^2 \int_{\infty}^{\infty} M(t)\,dt$$

Now the exchange matrix element M is a function of v and b in addition to t, and as b, or v, varies the charge exchange probability in the two state approximation oscillates between 0 and 1.

Experiments have measured the probability of charge exchange $P_{CE}(\theta)$ at a given angle of scattering θ, which is equal to the ratio of the charge exchange differential cross section, to the sum of the charge exchange and elastic scattering differential cross sections. If the same potential

W(R) determines the classical trajectory in each channel, relating the impact parameter b to the angle of scattering by b = b(θ), then

$$\frac{d\sigma^E}{d\Omega} = \frac{d\sigma^C}{d\Omega}\,|c'(b(\theta),\infty)|^2$$

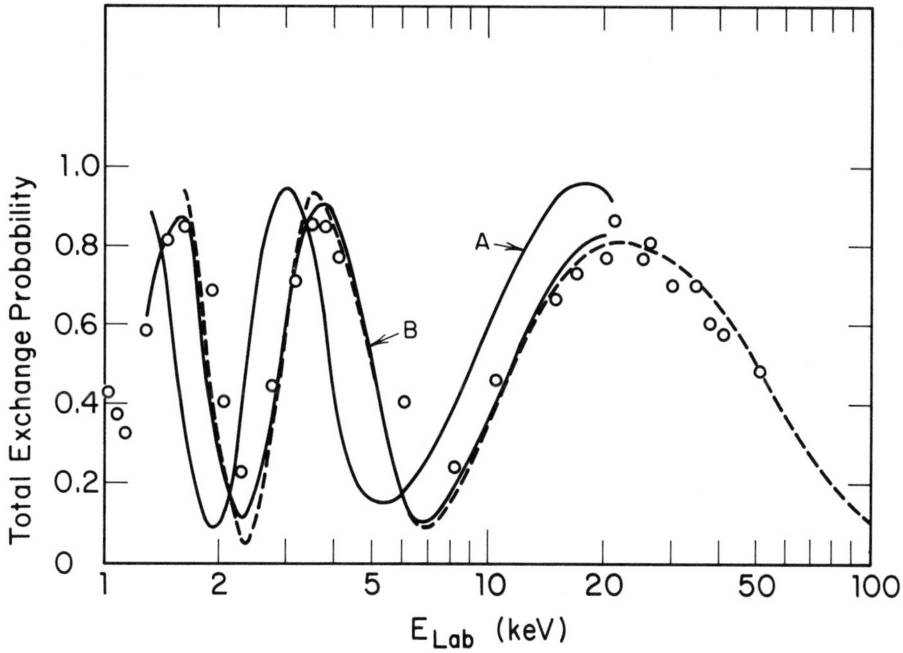

Figure 8-5 Differential cross section at fixed angle (3°) for the reaction p + H(1s) → H(1s) + p

Experimental data (Everhart and Helbig, 1965).
Calculated cross section
A 4-state hydrogenic expansion
B 4-state Sturmian expansion
- - - - - 3-state Sturmian expansion

$$\frac{d\sigma_{e\ell}}{d\Omega} = \frac{d\sigma^C}{d\Omega}\,|a'(b(\theta),\infty)|^2 \qquad (8\text{-}97)$$

where $d\sigma^C/d\Omega$ is the classical or semi-classical differential cross section for scattering by W(R) (see (8-59). Then

$$P_{CE}(\theta) = \frac{|c'(b(\theta),\infty)|^2}{|a'(b(\theta),\infty)|^2 + |c'(b(\theta),\infty)|^2} \qquad (8\text{-}98)$$

and since the denominator is unity, $P_{CE}(\theta)$ oscillates between 0 and 1 for a fixed angle as the velocity varies in the two state approximation. In Fig.8- 5, the experimental data of Everhart and Helbig is shown for $\theta = 3^{o}$ for laboratory proton energies between 1 and 50 kev. Almost all the contributions to the charge exchange cross section comes from angles $\theta < 3^{o}$ and in this sense 3° is a large angle, which corresponds to small impact parameters and, at this angle the cross section $d\sigma^{c}/d\Omega$ arising from the effective interaction W, is practically that for Coulomb scattering between the two nuclei. The expected oscillations in $P_{CC}(\theta)$ are exhibited, but $P_{CE}(\theta)$ varies over a range of approximately from 0.2 to 0.8 rather than from 0 to 1. There are two contributions to this damping. The major reason is that other channels, in particular the p + H(2p) channel, are quite strongly coupled to the initial state and these must be represented in the expansion of the wave function to obtain an accurate approximation. The second cause of damping is due to the difference in effective potential in the + and - parity states, and we shall discuss this effect in the next Chapter.

Applications of the atomic expansion method

The atomic expansion method with a limited basis set can be expected to be useful over an energy range from perhaps 1kev/amu to 100kev/amu ($0.2 \leq v \leq 2$au). At lower energies the adiabatic molecular nature of the problem becomes well established, and at high energies the charge exchange cross section becomes very small and the interaction is dominated by ionization, with the result that continuum states in the expansion become relatively more important. When there is little or no change in electronic energy between the initial and final arrangements as in

$$H^{+} + H(1s) \rightarrow H(1s) + H^{+} \qquad (a)$$

$$He^{++} + H(1s) \rightarrow He^{+}(n = 2) + H^{+} \qquad (b)$$

$$H^{+} + He(1s^{2}) \rightarrow H(1s) + He^{+}(1s) \qquad (c) \qquad (8\text{-}99)$$

The atomic expansion method has been shown to give accurate cross sections, on the other hand for a reaction like

$$H^{+} + He^{+}(1s) \rightarrow H(1s) + He^{++} \qquad (8\text{-}100)$$

with a large change in electronic energy from -2au to -0.5au, direct coupling is small and the cross section is also small

(~ $10^{-17}cm^2$) compared with that for (8-99b) (~ $10^{-15}cm^2$) and again many terms, including continuum terms are required in the expansion.

For the proton-hydrogen atom system, calculations retaining 1s, 2s, $2p_0$ and $2p_{\pm 1}$ orbitals about each nucleus were carried out by Gallaher and Wilets (1968) and later by Rapp and Dinwiddie (1972) who also included the 3s and 2p levels in the expansion. The ground state capture cross section is not much altered from that given by the two state approximation when additional states are added, but much better agreement is found with the $\theta=3^o$ charge exchange probability measurements (see Fig.8-5). The cross sections for capture into the 2s and 2p levels have been measured and agree quite well with computed cross sections (Figs. 8-6 and 8-7)

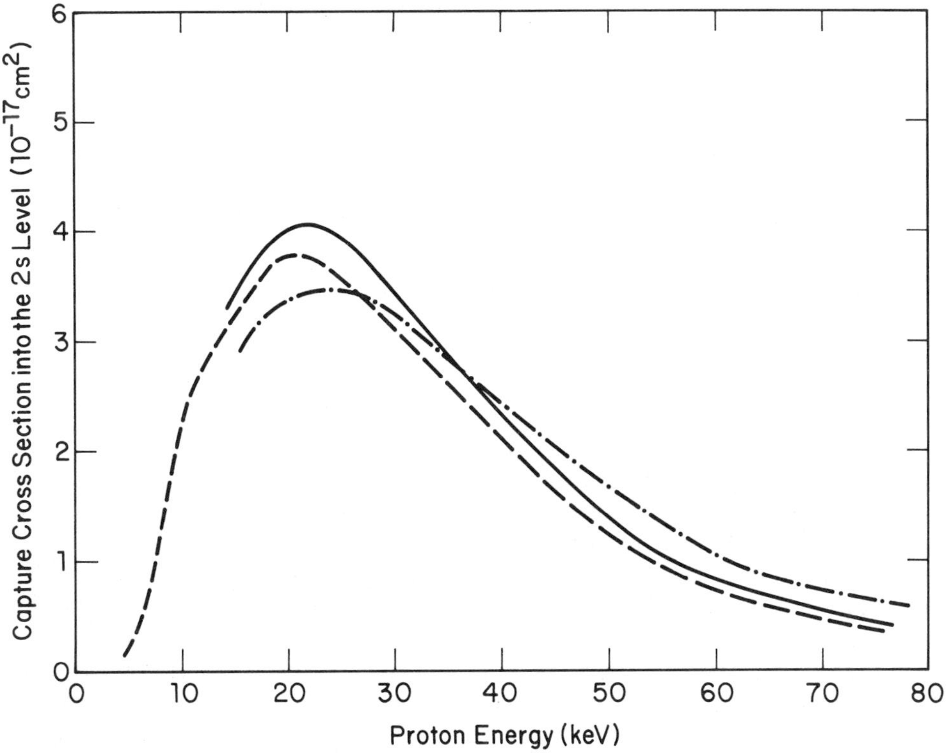

Figure 8-6 Cross sections for electron capture into the 2s level of hydrogen in $H^+ + H(1s)$ collisions

_ . _ . Atomic expansion cross section of Rapp and Dinwiddie (1972).

_ _ _ _ Pseudostate expansion of Shakeshaft (1978)

——— Experimental data Bayfield (1969)

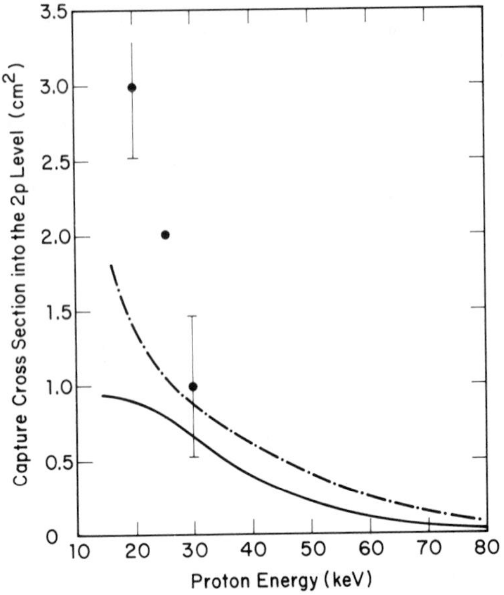

Figure 8-7 Cross sections for electron capture into the 2p level of hydrogen in $H^+ + H(2p)$ collisions

— · — · Atomic expansion cross section of Rapp and Dinwiddie (1972)

______ Pseudostate expansion of Shakeshaft (1978)

• • • • Experimental data Stebbings et al (1965)

Other one electron systems for which extensive atomic expansion calculations have been made include $He^{++} + H(1s)$ (Winter, 1982; Bransden and Noble, 1981) and $Li^{3+} + H(1s)$ (Bransden and Noble, 1982) and in both cases good agreement has been obtained with the experimental data for the total capture cross section. As an example, the cross sections for $Li^{3+} + H$ are shown in Fig. 8-8.

For the two electron system $H^+ + He(1s^2) \rightarrow H + He^+$, the 2-state approximation (Bransden and Sin Fai Lam 1966; Green et al 1965) provides ground state capture cross sections which agree well with experiment near the cross section maximum at 25kev/amu. Much more extensive calculations by Winter and Lin (1974) included in the expansion the ground state and all H and He^+ orbitals with $n \leq 3$. At the higher energies the results are not very different from those of the distorted wave approximation (8-81) to the 2-state equations. The total capture cross section agrees well with the experimental data over an energy region of from 15 to 100kev. Above 100kev, the computed cross sections appear to be too large, by a factor of about 1.7 by 400kev and thus may be a reflection of the increasing importance of continuum

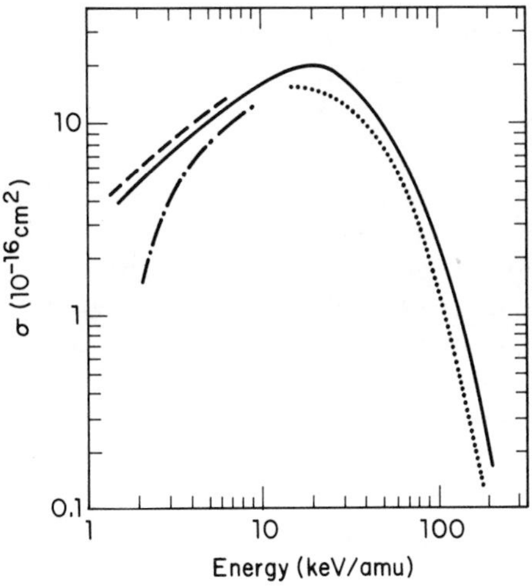

Figure 8-8 The total cross section for electron capture by Li^{3+} from H(1s)

_______ 20 state atomic expansion calculations with all orbitals with $n \leq 3$ about each nucleus (Bransden and Noble 1982).

—·—·—·— 6 state M.O. expansion (Kimura and Thorsen, 1981)

– – – – Experimental data Seim et al (1980)

······· Experimental data Shah et al (1978)

intermediate states. Below 10kev the approximation begins to fail badly and this is rather surprising since the corresponding calculation for H^+ + H(1s), He^{++} + H(1s), Li^{3+} +H(1s) appear to be accurate down to energies of at least 1 kev/amu.

In addition to the total capture cross section, data exists for the capture cross sections into the 2s, 2p, 3s, 3p and 3d levels, the experimental position is confused, at the time of writing, and for a critical comparison of the theory and experiment reference may be made to the review of Basu et al (1978), where other work using the atomic expansion model on the systems H^+ + H^-, He^{++} + He and He^+ + He is discussed (see also Bransden 1972, 1979).

8-4 SPECIAL EXPANSIONS AND METHODS

The idea of augmenting the atomic expansion with terms containing pseudofunctions to represent the atomic continuum has already been discussed in connection with electron scattering. In their study of the $H^+ + H$ system Cheshire et al (1970) introduced pseudofunctions with the idea of representing the wave function better when the two nuclei are close. In the limit $R \to 0$, the system becomes the united atom He^+, and terms were added to the expansion about each proton which were orthogonal to the 1s, 2s and 2p hydrogen orbitals, but which had a maximum overlap with the low lying He^+ levels. This work was very successful in reproducing the wide angle charge exchange probability and other data. A different approach was introduced by Gallaher and Wilets (1968) which will now be discussed briefly.

Expansion in Sturmian functions

In so far as the impact parameter approximation is valid, the scattering problem reduces to solving the time dependent Schrödinger equation (8-40), with the specified boundary conditions. The wave function $\psi(\vec{r},t)$ can be expanded in any complete set of functions of $\vec{r}$, and we are not limited to its usual atomic or molecular functions that have the disadvantage of possessing a continuum, which is difficult to deal with. A complete basis is provided by the Sturmian functions, which form a discrete set and which are defined as:

$$f_{\ell,m,n}(\vec{r}) = r^{-1} S_{n,\ell}(r) Y_{\ell,m}(\theta,\phi), \qquad (8\text{-}101)$$

where $S_{\ell,n}(r)$ satisfies (atomic units)

$$\left(-\frac{1}{2}\frac{d^2}{dr^2} + \frac{\ell(\ell+1)}{2r^2} - \frac{\alpha_{n\ell}}{r}\right) S_{n,\ell}(r) + E_\ell S_{n,\ell}(r), \qquad (8\text{-}102)$$

and

$$E_\ell = -\frac{1}{2(\ell+1)^2}.$$

If the boundary condition is imposed that $S_{n,\ell}(r)$ vanishes as $r \to \infty$, then for a given fixed value of E_ℓ, $\alpha_{n\ell}$ is determined as an eigenvalue of equation (8-102). The functions $S_{n,\ell}(r)$ are discrete hydrogenic functions, apart from a factor, and E_ℓ can be chosen so that the first Sturmian function for each ℓ coincides with the corresponding hydrogenic function. The wave function $\psi(\vec{r},t)$ is expanded in terms of Sturmian functions centered about each nucleon A and B, just as in the hydrogenic expansion. The expansion coefficients are obtained by solving similar coupled equations, and the physical amplitudes are found by expanding the Sturmian function in terms of hydrogenic functions.

Each Sturmian function includes a contribution from the continuum of hydrogenic functions, so that the effect of the continuum is included to some extent. The convergence of the expansion has been tested by including up to ten states and appears to be satisfactory. The 3° charge exchange probabilities calculated by this method agree very well with the data (see Fig. 8-4). The Sturmian basis was also used by Shakeshaft (1976), who showed that ionization cross sections for the $H^+ + H(1s)$ collision could be calculated from a knowledge of the overlap between the Sturmian functions and hydrogenic continuum. In further work, Shakeshaft (1978) employed a different basis formed from scaled hydrogenic orbitals and he used a very much larger number of functions, retaining 35 terms centered about each proton. His calculations extend from 15 to 200kev. To illustrate the relative importance of excitation, capture and ionization a selection of his results are shown in Table 8-1. The total excitation cross sections for the n = 2 and n = 3 levels have been measured by Park et al (1976) and this data is in good agreement with the calculated results (the n = 2 cross section is shown in Fig. 8-9). The calculated cross sections are also in good agreement with the 2s,2p capture cross sections (see Figs. 8-6 and 8-7).

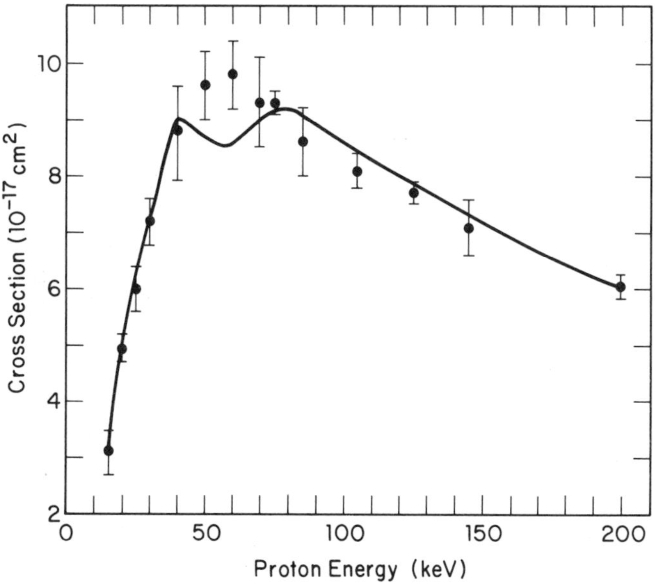

Figure 8-9 The cross section for excitation of atomic hydrogen to the n = 2 level by proton impact
——— Calculated cross section of Shakeshaft (1978)
• • • • Data of Park et al (1976)

Table 8-1
Cross sections for the collisions of protons with hydrogen atoms calculated using a large pseudostate basis (from Shakeshaft 1978)

Cross sections in units of $10^{-17} cm^2$

E(keV)	1s	2s	2p	3s	3p	3d	Ionization
15 EX	-	0.88	2.46	0.18	0.47	0.21	3.1
CE	58.4	3.41	3.10	0.53	0.74	0.20	
25 EX	-	1.56	4.85	0.44	0.86	0.34	8.5
CE	30.35	3.98	1.74	0.93	0.52	0.060	
60 EX	-	1.32	7.29	0.38	1.32	0.39	16.0
CE	4.10	0.82	0.21	0.29	0.88	0.02	
145 EX	-	0.80	6.53	0.40	1.20	0.15	9.4
CE	0.19	0.040	0.008	0.002	0.003	0.001	

E is the laboratory energy of the incident proton

EX - excitation cross sections

CE - charge exchange cross sections

The computed cross section for ionization is in general agreement with the data of Park et al (1977), but near the cross section maximum (40-70keV), the calculated values lie a little below the data. Similar two center pseudo-function expansions have been carried out for the He^{++} + H(1s) and H^{+} + He(1s) reactions by Winter (1982).

Although single center expansions are formally complete, no finite number of expansion functions can represent the rearranged channel as the internuclear distance R becomes very large. For this reason single center expansions centered about the target nucleus even with a very large basis set fail when the charge exchange becomes important. Reading et al (1981) have shown that the speed and convenience of a single center expansion can be obtained by using a trial function of the form:

$$\psi(\vec{r},t) = \sum_j a_j(b,t)X_j(\vec{r},t) + \sum_m c_m(b,\infty)f(t)\phi_m(\vec{r},t) \quad (8\text{-}103)$$

The first sum is over a large basis set of functions X_j centered on the target and containing both real and pseudostates, while the second sum runs over the charge exchange channels of importance represented by the atomic functions ϕ_m centered on the projectile. The trial function satisfies the boundary conditions provided f(t) which is a predetermined function satisfies

$$f(t) \to 0 \quad t \to -\infty \qquad f(t) \to 1 \quad t \to +\infty$$

Varying the time dependent amplitudes $a_j(b,t)$ and the time independent asymptotic amplitudes $c_m(b,\infty)$ in the standard variational procedure, provides a set of coupled first order differential equations for the amplitudes $a_j(t)$ coupled with algebraic equations for the small number of coefficients C_m. This technique, which was designed in particular for the case in which the nucleus of the target is highly charged compared with the projectile, has been shown by Reading et al to provide accurate cross sections in the energy range above 15keV for the apparently unfavourable symmetrical case of H^+ + H(1s).

Expansion in spherical harmonics

It is always possible to expand the wave function in a series of spherical harmonics which have as their argument the polar angles of $\vec{r}$,

$$\psi(\vec{r},t) = \sum_{\ell,m} f_{\ell,m}(r,t)Y_{\ell,m}(\theta,\phi) \qquad (8\text{-}104)$$

Coupled equations for the radial functions $f_{\ell,m}$ are then found that are similar to those derived by Temkin for electron scattering by hydrogen (see Chapter 5). In this form, it is not easy to see how to apply the boundary conditions of the problem, so Cheshire and Sullivan have considered ψ as a function of $\vec{r}_A$, the coordinate joining the electron to the nucleus A, rather than of $\vec{r}$ the center of mass coordinate. They then expand

$$\psi(\vec{r}_A,t) = \sum_{\ell,m} \phi_{\ell,m}(r_A,t)Y_{\ell,m}(\theta_A,\phi_A) \qquad (8\text{-}105)$$

and solve the coupled equation for $\phi_{o,o}$ and $\phi_{\ell,m}$ ignoring higher order terms. The boundary conditions are that as $t \to -\infty$ the wave function must represent a proton incident on a hydrogen atom in the ground state,

$$\phi_{\ell,m}(\vec{r},t) \underset{t \to -\infty}{\sim} \phi_o(r)e^{-i\varepsilon_o t}\delta_{\ell,0}\delta_{m,0} \qquad (8\text{-}106)$$

This procedure is equivalent to including all s and p states of hydrogen in the expansion terms based on the target, but does not explicitly include any of the rearranged terms, represented by the expansion based on the projectile. Because of this only excitation cross sections could be computed. The 2p excitation cross section exceeded that computed by Wilets and Gallaher, using the two centered hydrogenic expansion, by about a factor of three at 25 kev and this illustrates that the terms in the wave function that allow for charge exchange are effective in lowering excitation cross sections at these energies.

NOTES

1. A detailed account of the analysis of the elastic scattering of atoms by atoms has been given by Child (1974).
2. Atomic units will be used throughout this Chapter except where stated.
3. See, for example, Bates and Holt (1966).
4. The minimum value of μ occurs when both nuclei are protons, in which case μ = 938.

5. If the collision partners are both charged so that an overall Coulomb interaction Z/R is effective in the asymptotic region the factors α_j and γ_m must be replaced by α'_j and γ'_m where

$$\alpha'_j = \alpha_j + (Z/v)\log\,(vR - v^2t)$$

$$\gamma'_m = \gamma_m + (Z/v)\log\,(vR - v^2t)$$

The asymptotic functions then satisfy

$$\left(-\frac{1}{2}\nabla_r^2 + V_{Ae} + Z/R - i\frac{\partial}{\partial t}\right) X_j = 0$$

$$\left(-\frac{1}{2}\nabla_r^2 + V_{Ce} + Z/R - i\frac{\partial}{\partial t}\right) \Phi_j = 0$$

which can be verified straightforwardly.

6. If the magnetic quantum number changes by Δm in the transition a_j contains a factor $\exp i\Delta m\phi$ and in (8-61) J_0 should be replaced by $J_{\Delta m}$.

7. The phase factors α_j and γ_m need not be identified with (8-45) and (8-50). Other forms can be taken, which are asymptotic as $|t| \to \infty$ to (8-45) and (8-50) and which satisfy certain conditions such that the model is translationally invariant. The optimal choice of such 'translational factors' has been discussed by, among others, Schneiderman and Russek (1969), Riley and Green (1971) and Ponce (1979).

PROBLEMS

8.1 Coupled equations for the functions F_j and G_m appearing in (8-27) can be obtained from the projections

$$\int d^3r \left(A_j \exp(-i\ell_1 \vec{k}_j \cdot \vec{r}_A)\right)^* (H-E)\psi(\vec{R},\vec{r}) = 0$$

$$\int d^3r \left(C_m \exp(i\ell_2 \vec{K}_m \cdot \vec{r}_B)\right)^* (H-E)\psi(\vec{R},\vec{r}) = 0$$

Form these equations and reduce them by a semi-classical approximation in which a different trajectory is associated with each channel as in Section (6-5).

8.2 The amplitude a_{mi} for charge exchange, which satisfies (8-55) depends on the internuclear potential through the phase factor (using a straight line trajectory)

$$a_{mi}(b,t) = a'_{mi}(b,t)\exp -i\int_{\infty}^{t} V_{AC}(t')dt' \equiv a'_{mi}(b,t)\exp\delta(t)$$

Consider the case in which A is a proton and $V_{AC} = 1/R$, the integral is then infinite but remains finite if a cut-off is imposed on the Coulomb potential so that $V_{AC} = 0$ if $R>a$. Show that

$$\ell t_{t\to\infty} \quad \delta(t) = 2v^{-1}\left(\log\{a-\sqrt{a^2-b^2}\} - \log b\right) i$$

Provided $b << a$, we may set $\delta(\infty) = -\frac{i}{v}\log b$ and this is accurate except for very small angles $\theta < 1/(\mu va)$.

8.3 Assume that in (2), the amplitude $a'_{mi}(b,\infty)$ varies slowly with b. Then evaluate the expression for the scattering amplitude (8-61a) by using the asymptotic form of J_o and show that

$$f_{ji}(\theta) = -i\mu v\,\frac{1}{2}a'_{mi}(b(\theta),\infty)\left(\frac{2vb(\theta)}{q}\right)^2 (b(\theta))^{1+2i/v}\exp(-ib(\theta$$

where $b(\theta) = \{\mu v^2 \sin\theta/2\}^{-1}$

and hence show that

$$\frac{d\sigma}{d\Omega} = \left(\frac{d\sigma}{d\Omega}\right)_{Coul} |a'(b(\theta),\infty)|^2$$

where $\left(\frac{d\sigma}{d\Omega}\right)_{Coul}$ is the differential cross section for Coulomb scattering.

8.4 Prove the unitarity relationship (8-63), and show that as a consequence of unitarity the relationship

$$i\frac{d}{dt}\left(S_{jm}\right) = \vec{K}^*_{mj} - K_{jm}$$

is satisfied at all values of t.

8.5 Use the trial function (8-103) in the variational integral

$$I = \int_{\infty}^{\infty} dt \int d^3r \; \psi^* (H_e - i\frac{\partial}{\partial t}) \psi^*$$

and by varying $a_j(b,t)$ and the time independent coefficients C_m (B,∞) find a set of equations from these quantities that can be determined.

Chapter 9

SLOW COLLISIONS BETWEEN ATOMS AND THE MOLECULAR ORBITAL EXPANSION

9-1 THE MOLECULAR ORBITAL BASIS

In Chapter 8, it was explained that at low velocities ($v \lesssim 1$ a.u.), a suitable basis for the expansion of the wave function describing an ion-atom collision is a set of molecular orbitals. If these orbitals are the eigenfunctions of the electronic Hamiltonian $H_e(\vec{r},R)$, for fixed values of the internuclear separation R, the orbitals form an adiabatic basis. If a new set of orbitals is formed by a linear transformation of the adiabatic set, so that the new orbitals satisfy some other condition such as minimising the radial coupling terms, the basis is said to be diabatic, and in a diabatic basis H_e is not diagonal. In this Chapter, some of the properties of the molecular orbital expansion will be examined, with reference to the same one-electron model which was employed in Chapter 8. Many electron molecular orbital wave functions can be built from one-electron orbitals and the theory can be generalized straightforwardly[1]. The discussion will again be based on the impact parameter approximation, but at very low energies, for which kinetic energy of the heavy particles is not much larger than the average change in electronic energy, the molecular orbital basis should be used in conjunction with the expansion (8-27a), and coupled equations should be obtained for the functions F_j and G_m. The corresponding radial equations, following a partial decomposition, can then either be solved directly or through the JWKB approximation.

The two centers problem

As in Chapter 8, we shall examine the problem of one active electron moving in the field of two heavy particles A and C. The same coordinate system (shown in Fig.8-3) will be used as before, but in this Chapter we shall not confine the discussion to the case in which the incident particle C is a proton, and C will represent either a bare nucleus of charge Z_C, or a composite system interaction with the electron and with A through effective potentials V_{Ce}, V_{CA}. The adiabatic molecular orbitals $\psi_n(\vec{R},\vec{r})$ are defined as the bounded solutions of the eigenvalue problem

$$H_e\psi_n(R,\vec{r}\,') = E_n(R)\psi_n(R,\vec{r}\,') \quad (9\text{-}1a)$$

where

$$H_e = -\frac{1}{2}\nabla^2_{r'} + V(R,\vec{r}\,') \quad (9\text{-}1b)$$

and

$$V(R,\vec{r}\,') = V_{Ae}(r_A) + V_{Ce}(r_C) + V_{AC}(R) \quad (9\text{-}1c)$$

The internuclear distance R enters equations (9-1) as a fixed parameter. It is normal to take the direction of quantization of the functions ψ_n to be parallel to the internuclear line, and in this body-fixed system of coordinates the position vector of the electron with respect to the center of mass of A and C has been written as $\vec{r}\,'$. The functions ψ_n are orthogonal to each other and can be normalized to unity:

$$\int d^3r'\psi_n(R,\vec{r}\,')\psi_m(R,\vec{r}\,') = \delta_{nm} \quad (9\text{-}2)$$

The internuclear potential is a constant, for fixed R, so that the total energy $E_n(R)$ is just the sum of V_{AC} and an electronic energy $\varepsilon_n(R)$,

$$E_n(R) = V_{AC} + \varepsilon_n(R) \quad (9\text{-}3)$$

The system is symmetrical with respect to rotations about the internuclear axis, so that the component of the angular momentum along the internuclear axis, λ, is a good quantum number. The eigenvalues of the Hamiltonian will depend on $|\lambda|$ rather than λ because the Hamiltonian is invariant under the reflections ($\vec{r}\rightarrow -\vec{r}$; $\vec{R}\rightarrow -\vec{R}$). Two further quantum numbers are required to specify a state completely. One way of choosing these numbers is to consider the united atom limit, in which the nuclei A and C coincide, ($R \to 0$), forming a united atom. In that case, the wave function is specified by the principal quantum number n, the orbital angular momentum ℓ and a magnetic number m. In this limit λ coincides with m, so that λ ranges in integer steps between $-\ell$ and $+\ell$. The states then can be designated as $1s\sigma$, $2p\sigma$, $2p\pi$, and so on, where σ, π, δ .... stand for $|\lambda| = 0,1,2,\ldots$ If there is more than one electron the component of the angular momentum along the axis is still a constant of the motion. In this case the total component of the angular momentum is designated by Σ, Π, Δ, ... for $|\Sigma\lambda_i| = 0,1,2,\ldots$ The quantum numbers n and ℓ do not represent constants of the motion at any finite separation of the nuclei. In the limit of large R, the molecular wave function must tend to an atomic function representing the situation in which the electron is attached to one or other of the centers A and C, or to a linear combination of such functions. On the other hand in the limit $R \to 0$ A and C coincide and the molecular wave function must become equal to an atomic wave function representing the united atom. A correlation diagram can be constructed which relates the level in the united atom limit, designated as $n\ell m$, with those in the separated limit designated as $n'\ell'm'$. As we saw above $m = m' = |\lambda|$ and a given molecular orbital can be designated either by its united atom limit $n\ell|\lambda|$ or by the separated atom limit written as $|\lambda|n'\ell'$. A diagram for a homonuclear system in which A and C are bare nuclei of equal charge (but not necessarily equal mass) is shown in Fig. 9-1. A corresponding diagram for a heteronuclear system is given in Fig. 9-2. In this case A and C are bare nuclei with charges Z_A, Z_C such that $Z_A > Z_C$ and the difference $(Z_A - Z_C)$ is not large.

The adiabatic potential energy curves (in which $E_n(R)$ is considered as a function of R) have the property that if the levels n and m belong to the same symmetry class then the curves $E = E_n(R)$ and $E = E_m(R)$ cannot cross as R varies between $R = 0$ and $R = \infty$. In other words there is no value of R for which $E_n(R) - E_m(R) = 0$. For a heteronuclear system this theorem, due to von Neumann and Wigner (1929), requires that two potential curves belonging to the same value of $|\lambda|$ cannot cross. The homonuclear case is a little different and is discussed below. The proof of the no-crossing theorem is very simple (Teller, 1936). Suppose all the molecular wave functions are known except for two, ϕ_1 and ϕ_2, which may be taken as orthogonal to one another and to all the other functions. Then the energy

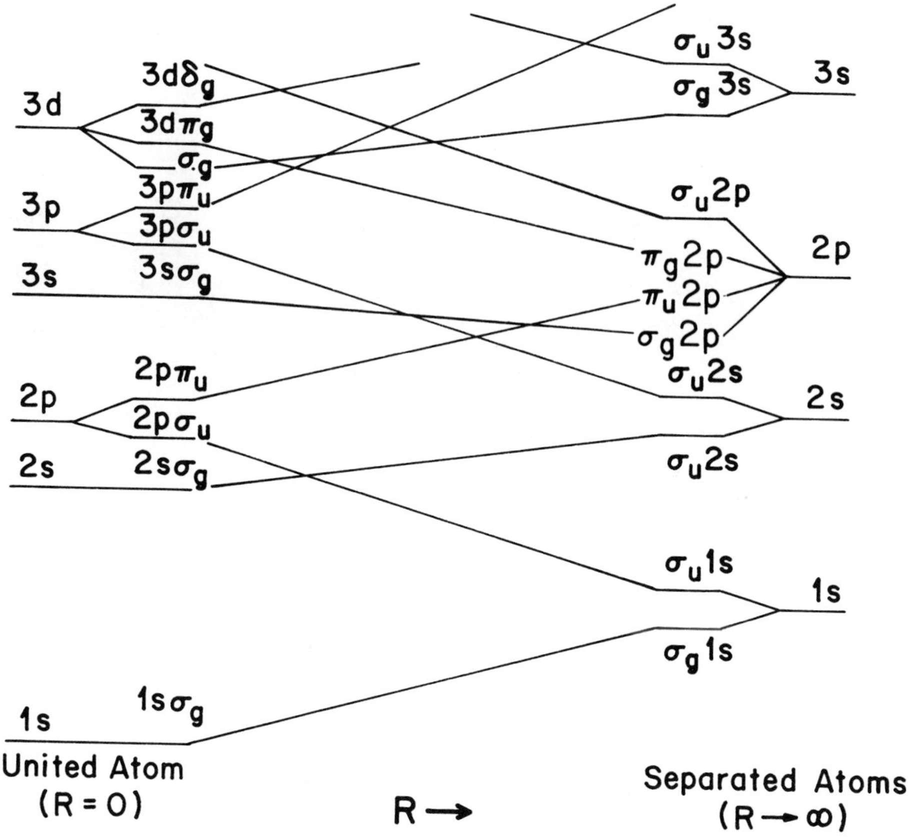

Figure 9-1 A diagram showing the correlation between united atom and separated atom states for homonuclear diatomic molecules. The diagram is not to scale and the actual energies of the united and separated atoms vary from molecule to molecule.

levels are given by the roots of the equation

$$\begin{vmatrix} H_{11} - E & H_{12} \\ H_{21} & H_{22} - E \end{vmatrix} = 0, \qquad (9\text{-}4)$$

where $H_{ij} = (\phi_i, H_e\phi_j)$. For the levels to cross the roots must be equal, that is $(H_{11} - H_{22})^2 + 4H_{12}^2 = 0$. When ϕ_1 and ϕ_2 belong to different symmetries, $H_{12} = 0$ and it is quite possible that the crossing will occur if, for a certain value of R, $H_{11} = H_{22}$. If ϕ_1 and ϕ_2 have the same symmetry then H_{12} will in general be non-zero and the levels cannot cross. Accidental crossing cannot be ruled out in

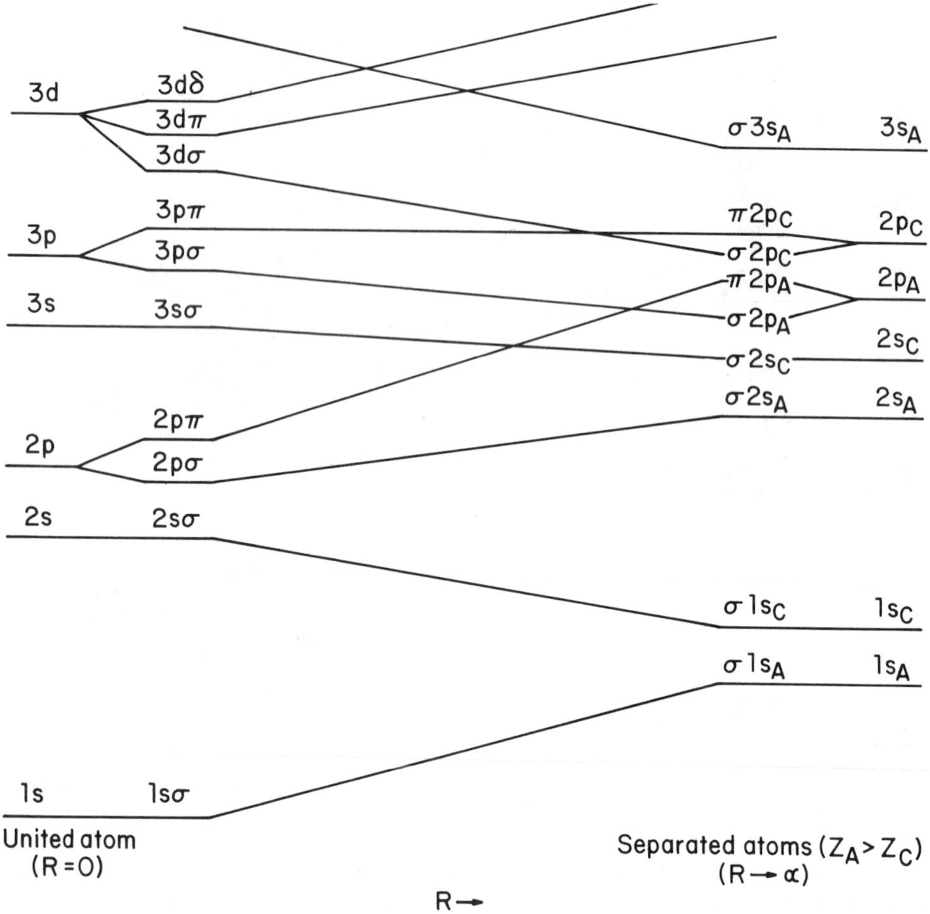

Figure 9-2 A correlation diagram for heteronuclear diatomic molecules. As in Fig. 9-1, the diagram is not to scale and the actual energies vary from molecule to molecule

which, by coincidence, $H_{12} = 0$ at the same value of R as $H_{11} = H_{22}$. This rule then forbids levels with the same value of $|\lambda|$ to cross, but allows crossing of σ states with π states and so on.

Homonuclear molecules

When the nuclei A and C are identical, the system is invariant under reflections about the mid-point of the internuclear line ($\vec{r} \to -\vec{r}$). The solutions then divide into even (or gerade) or odd parity (ungerade) classes. In the separated atom limit the even or symmetrical functions are of the form

$$\psi_g \sim \psi_A + \psi_C \qquad (9\text{-}5)$$

and the odd or anti-symmetrical functions are

$$\psi_u \sim \psi_A - \psi_C \qquad (9\text{-}6)$$

In the united atom limit, the wave function has the parity $(-1)^{\ell}$, so ψ_g is connected to functions with even ℓ, and ψ_u to functions with odd ℓ.

For the special case of the one electron system the wave equation can be separated and numerical solutions[2] have been obtained for several cases including the molecular ions H_2^+ and HHe^{++} (Bates et al., 1953; Bates and Carson, 1956). The fact that a separation of variables can be made corresponds to an extra hidden symmetry in the one electron problem, and because of this the "no crossing" rule does not always apply in the same form in the single electron case. The levels can be classified by the value of the separation constant S and the no-crossing rule then applies in the form that potential energy curves corresponding to the same values of both S and $|\lambda|$ cannot cross. The two lowest electronic states of H_2^+, the hydrogen molecular ion, are designated in the united atom limit as $(1s\sigma_g)$ and $(2p\sigma_u)$. The total interaction energy E(R) is shown in Fig. 9-3 for these two states. The ground state of H_2^+ is associated with the $(1s\sigma_g)$ potential which provides an attraction, while the $(2p\sigma_u)$ potential is everywhere repulsive. Both states tend asymptotically to H(1s) + p and both are important in the scattering problem.

9-2 THE SCATTERING EQUATIONS IN A MOLECULAR ORBITAL BASIS

The interaction matrix elements

When required for clarity, the superscripts A and C will be added to ψ_n to show which atomic function the molecular orbital becomes in the separated atom limit. The functions A_j and C_m (see 8-65) required for the scattering problem are then

$$A_j = \psi_j^A \exp i\alpha_j ; \qquad C_m = \psi_m^C \exp i\gamma_m \qquad (9\text{-}7)$$

where α_j and γ_m are defined by (8-45) and (8-50) respectively. In the homonuclear problem, the combination $(\psi_g + \psi_u)$ is asymptotic to the separated atom A and $(\psi_g - \psi_u)$ to the atom

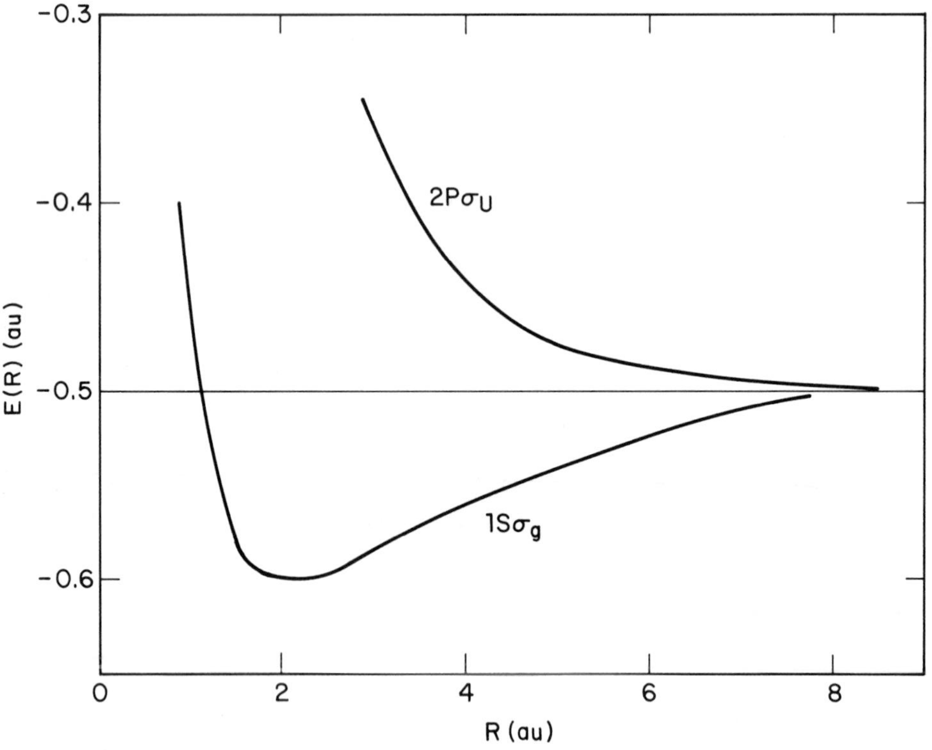

Figure 9-3 The total interaction energy in the lowest gerade and ungerade states of H_2^+.

C and (9-7) is accordingly replaced by

$$A_j = \frac{1}{\sqrt{2}} (\psi_{g,j} + \psi_{u,j}) \exp i\alpha_j$$

$$C_m = \frac{1}{\sqrt{2}} (\psi_{g,m} - \psi_{u,m}) \exp i\gamma_m \tag{9-8}$$

In a heteronuclear system, and using (9-7), the direct matrix elements H_{jk} and $\bar{H}_{nm}$ defined in (8-56) become (assuming the functions ψ_j^A, ψ_m^C are real)

$$H_{jk} = E_j^{\,A}(R)\delta_{jk} - i\int d^3r\left(\psi_j^{\,A}\frac{\partial}{\partial t}\psi_k^{\,A}\right)\exp i(\eta_j t - \eta_k t)$$

$$\bar{H}_{nm} = E_n^{\,C}(R)\delta_{nm} - i\int d^3r\left(\psi_n^{\,C}\frac{\partial}{\partial t}\psi_m^{\,C}\right)\exp i(\varepsilon_n t - \varepsilon_m t)$$

(9-9)

where $E_j^{\,A} = E_j - \eta_j$ and $E_n^{\,C} = E_n - \varepsilon_n$ and the exchange matrix elements are

$$K_{jm} = E_m^{\,C}(R)S_{jm} - i\int d^3r\left(\psi_j^{\,A}\frac{\partial}{\partial t}\psi_m^{\,C}\right)\exp i(\vec{v}\cdot\vec{r}_o + \eta_j t - \varepsilon_m t)$$

$$\bar{K}_{mj} = E_j^{\,A}(R)S^*_{mj} - i\int d^3r\left(\psi_m^{\,C}\frac{\partial}{\partial t}\psi_j^{\,A}\right)\exp i(-\vec{v}\cdot\vec{r}_o + \varepsilon_m t - n_j t)$$

(9-10)

where the overlap integral S_{jm} is

$$S_{jm} = \int d^3r\,\psi_j^{\,A}\psi_m^{\,C}\exp i(\vec{v}\cdot\vec{r}_o + \eta_j t - \varepsilon_m t) \qquad (9\text{-}11)$$

The matrix elements containing $\partial/\partial t$ are expressed in terms of the radial and rotational coupling through (8-70). If a diabatic, rather than an adiabatic base, is used the radial coupling terms are zero (or small), but H_e is no longer diagonal in the basis functions and interaction matrix elements must be expressed in the form (8-56).

If the translational motion of the electron is neglected, which is a reasonably accurate (~10%) approximation at impact energies less than ~1keV/amu, as in the original perturbed stationary state (PSS) method, $S_{jm} = 0$ and the equations simplify. Defining new amplitudes by the phase transformations:

$$a_j = a_j' \exp -i\int_{\infty}^{t} dt' E_j^{\,A}(R)$$

$$c_m = c_m' \exp -i\int_{\infty}^{t} dt' E_m^{\,C}(R)$$

(9-12)

and combining the amplitudes a_j', c_m' into one vector d so that

$$(d_1, d_2, d_3 \;.....) = (a'_1, a'_2 \;..., c'_1, c'_2 ...) \qquad (9\text{-}13)$$

it is found that the coupled equations become

$$i\dot{d}_i = \sum_{n \neq i} M_{in} d_n \tag{9-14}$$

where

$$M_{in} = -i \int d^3r \left(\psi_i \frac{\partial}{\partial t} \psi_n \right) \exp - i \int_{\infty}^{t} dt' \left(E_n(R') - E_i(R) \right) \tag{9-15}$$

where $R'^2 = b^2 + v^2 t'^2$

In a diabatic basis, the operator $-i\partial/\partial t$ is replaced by $H_e - i\partial/\partial t$ and E_n and E_i are replaced by the diagonal matrix elements of H_e.

If the difference $(E_n - E_i)$ is large for all internuclear separations the matrix element is small and the two molecular states i and n are weakly coupled. On the other hand, if $E_n - E_i$ vanishes for a particular value of the internuclear separation, the coupling is, in general, strong. The potential curve crossing can not occur between states of the same symmetry in an adiabatic representation. However two potential curves of the same symmetry can approach each other closely. This is called a pseudo-curve crossing and in the region of a pseudo crossing the radial coupling matrix element is very large and the two states are strongly coupled[3]. An example with two pseudo crossings is shown in Fig. 9-4 for the system $N^{7+} + H(1s)$, which shows pseudo crossings between the 6kσ and 5gσ levels at 11.6au and the 5gσ and 4fσ levels at 6.4au. The energy differences at the two pseudo crossings are 0.024 and 0.24au respectively. At a crossing or pseudo crossing it is possible to solve the coupled equations, connecting the pair of levels involved, in an analytic approximation and this will be discussed at a later point.

At a pseudo crossing the radial matrix elements are large because of the sharp curvature of the two potential energy curves, which implies that the nature of the orbitals to the left and right of the pseudo crossing point has changed. Since a diabatic representation is defined as one in which the radial matrix elements are small, it follows that the diabatic curves do not vary rapidly and must cross at the point at which the corresponding adiabatic curves have a pseudo crossing (see Fig. 9-9 below). The diabatic orbitals do not change their structure rapidly at a crossing and, if the crossing is at a large value of R for which the interaction matrix elements are small, the system will tend to follow a particular diabatic curve corresponding to one diabatic state through a crossing and the probability of a transition to the other diabatic state will be small.

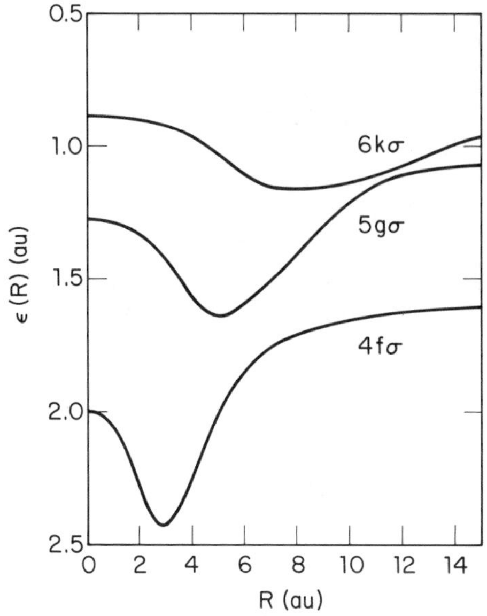

Figure 9-4 Some σ levels of the system $(N^+ + H)$ illustrating pseudo crossings at 11.6 and 6.4au.

Switching factors

In general, it is not possible to ignore the translational invariance of the theory and the phase factors α_j and γ_m must be included. As pointed out in Chapter 8, the particular forms (8-45) and (8-50) for α_j and γ_m need only apply in the limit of large nuclear separations. In fact at small velocities and for small values of R, the forms (8-45) and (8-50) are undesirable since the electron is associated by these forms with one or other of the nuclei, which seems unphysical. The freedom to choose α_j and γ_m in a different way for small R can be combined with the idea of a switching factor, introduced by Schneiderman and Russek (1969). They write

$$\begin{aligned} \alpha_j &= -\eta_j t - \frac{1}{2}q^2 v^2 t + f\,\vec{v}\cdot\vec{r} \\ \gamma_m &= -\varepsilon_m t - \frac{1}{2}p^2 v^2 t + f\,\vec{v}\cdot\vec{r} \end{aligned} \qquad (9\text{-}16)$$

where f is a function of both $\vec{r}$ and $\vec{R}$ with the property

$$f(\vec{r},\vec{R}) \to -q \text{ if } R \to \infty \text{ and } r_C >> r_A$$
$$\to +p \text{ if } R \to \infty \text{ and } r_A >> r_C \qquad (9\text{-}17)$$

so that the asymptotic conditions are satisfied. If in addition it is required that

$$f \to 0 \text{ as } R \to 0 \qquad (9\text{-}18)$$

the wave function does not associate the electron with a particular nucleus in the united atom limit. Several forms of switching factor have been suggested, a typical example is

$$f = \frac{pr_A^3 - qr_C^3}{(r_A{}^3 - r_C{}^3)} \times \frac{R^2}{(R^2+\lambda^2)} \qquad (9\text{-}19)$$

where λ is a "cut-off" parameter, but many other ways of choosing f have been suggested. Using the translational factors (9-16), it is seen that the overlap S_{jm} is zero because of the orthogonality of the orbitals ψ_j and ψ_m, which leads to a simplification of the equations. There is a penalty to be paid for this simplification, because f depends on both $\vec{r}$ and t, and hence the direct and exchange matrix elements contain extra terms[4] depending on $\dot{f}$ and $\nabla(f\vec{v}\cdot\vec{r})$.

Applications

The molecular orbital expansion method has been widely applied and just a few typical applications for heteronuclear systems will be mentioned here. The interaction of fully stripped ions with atomic hydrogen is interesting, because this process is important in the plasmas investigated in thermonuclear research. The full molecular orbital approach including translational factors has been implemented for the cases He^{2+} (Hatton et al 1979; Winter and Hatton, 1980; Kimura and Thorsen, 1981a) Li^{3+} (Kimura and Thorsen, 1981b) and C^{6+} (Fritsch, 1982; Green et al 1982a,b). For Li^{3+}, the results of Kimura and Thorsen, who used a basis consisting of the 3dσ, 2pσ, 2pπ, 2sσ, 3dσ and 3pσ levels have been illustrated in Fig. 8-8.

For the system $(A^{Z+} + H(1s))$ where A^{Z+} is a fully stripped ion and $Z \neq 1$, the number of pseudo crossings is limited and hence the number of states strongly coupled to the initial channel is small. This has the effect that (at low velocities v $\lesssim$ 1au) charge transfer takes place to very specific final states and that other cross sections (excitation and ionization) are small. For example if Z=2, the initial channel is represented by the 2pσ orbital which correlates to He^{2+} + H(1s) in the separated atom limit. The 2pσ and 3dσ orbitals have a pseudo crossing at R=4.5au (see Fig. 9-5) and (for b>4.5au) the corresponding radial coupling

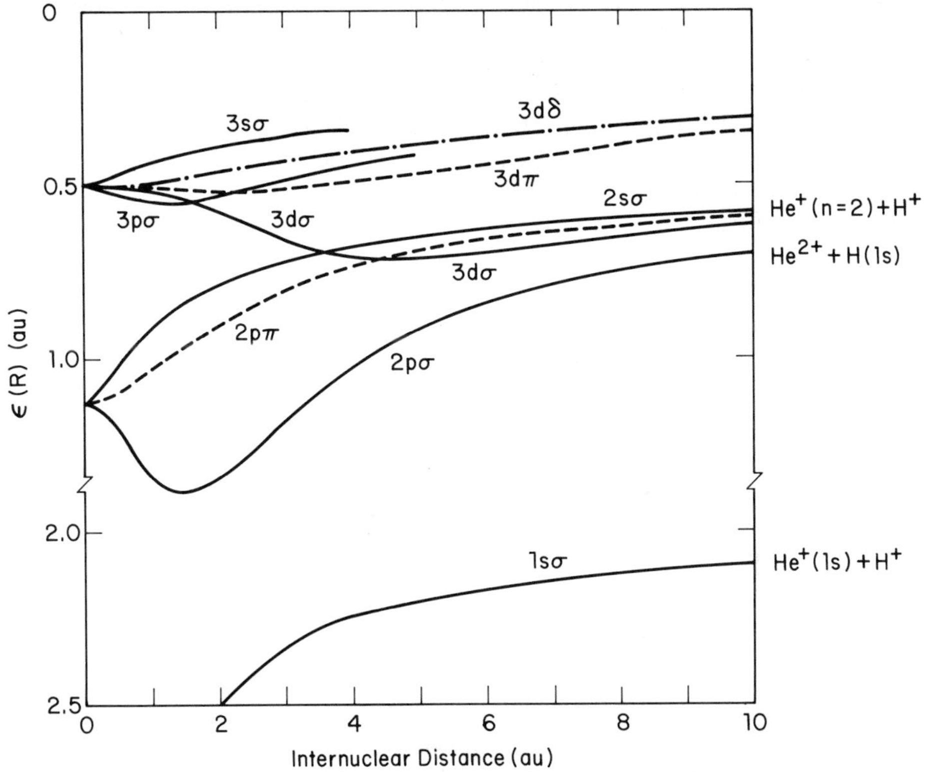

Figure 9-5 The adiabatic potential energies of $(HeH)^{2+}$

is strong. The other important coupling is the rotational coupling between the 2pπ and 2pσ levels which is effective at small values of R (small b), because the 2pπ and 2pσ levels are degenerate in the united atom limit. No other couplings are of such importance, and although a large basis set is required for accurate results, the qualitative features of the cross section are well represented by calculations using the (2pσ + 2pπ + 3dσ) basis. Since the 2pπ and 3dσ levels correlate to the n = 2 levels of He^+ in the separated atom limit. The dominant reaction at low energies is He^{++} + H(1s) → He^+(n=2) + H^+.

Similarly for Z=3, the most likely reaction is charge transfer to Li^{3+} in the n=2 or n=3 level, and for Z=6 charge transfer is mainly to the n=4 level. For large Z. the n distribution broadens with a most likely value of n being $n \approx Z/2$.

In general, when comparison is possible it would seem that using basis set of similar size both the atomic and molecular orbital expansions produce results of similar accuracy for energies above 100eV/amu. The interaction of protons with alkali atoms provides a simple example of a many electron system which has been studied successfully at energies up to ~4keV (Kubach and Sidis, 1981). Very many calculations have been made in the original PSS model in which the momentum transfer factors are ignored. A typical calculation is represented by the work of Shipsey et al (1981) on the systems C^{5+} + H, N^{5+} + H and O^{6+} + H, and the interested reader can find in this paper an interesting discussion of how the molecular orbital calculations are carried out for systems with more than one electron. At thermal energies, where many cross sections are required in the interpretation of the behavior of astrophysical plasmas several calculations have been made of the interaction of positive ions of C, N, O.... with neutral hydrogen and helium atoms (Heil et al, 1981; Butler et al, 1980), while in a different realm of physics, interesting applications to inner shell excitation and capture processes have been made which have been reviewed by Briggs (1976).

9-3 SYMMETRICAL RESONANCE COLLISIONS

The one electron homonuclear system has features of particular interest and has been studied intensively. To illustrate some of these features and to compare with the atomic orbital treatment given in Chapter 8, we shall start by considering the two state approximation for the system p + H(1s), in which only the $1s\sigma_g$ and $2p\sigma_u$ orbitals, which are both connected with the H(1s) atomic ground state in the separated atom limit, are retained.

Writing $\psi_g \equiv \psi(1s\sigma_g)$ and $\psi_u \equiv \psi(2p\sigma_u)$, we see that

$$\frac{1}{\sqrt{2}}(\psi_g + \psi_u) \xrightarrow[R\to\infty]{} \phi_{1s}(r_A)$$

and (9-20)

$$\frac{1}{\sqrt{2}}(\psi_g - \psi_u) \xrightarrow[R\to\infty]{} \phi_{1s}(r_C)$$

where ϕ_{1s} is the ground state orbital. The wave function (8-41) reduces, in the two state approximation, to:

$$\Psi(\vec{r},t) = a(b,t)2^{-\frac{1}{2}}(\psi_g + \psi_u)\exp i(-\varepsilon_{1s}t - \vec{v}\cdot\vec{r}/2 - v^2t/8)$$
$$+ c(b,t)2^{-\frac{1}{2}}(\psi_g - \psi_u)\exp i(-\varepsilon_{1s}t + \vec{v}\cdot\vec{r}/2 - v^2t/8) \qquad (9\text{-}21)$$

and the required boundary conditions are

$$a(b, -\infty) = 1 , \qquad c(b, -\infty) = 0 \qquad (9\text{-}22)$$

The wave function (9-21) can be expressed in terms of functions of definite parity (see (8-94) by writing

$$\Psi = \Psi^+ + \Psi^- \qquad (9\text{-}23)$$

where

$$\Psi^{\pm} = 2^{-\frac{1}{2}}A_{\pm}\left((\psi_g+\psi_u)e^{-i\vec{v}\cdot\vec{r}/2} \pm (\psi_g-\psi_u)e^{+i\vec{v}\cdot\vec{r}/2}\right) \times$$
$$\times \exp(-i\varepsilon_{1s}t - iv^2t/8) \qquad (9\text{-}24)$$

The new amplitudes $A_{\pm}$ are given by

$$A_{\pm} = \frac{1}{2}(a \pm c) \qquad (9\text{-}25)$$

The two functions ψ^+ and ψ^- propagate independently, and the two state approximation reduces to the solution of two separate elastic scattering equations, just as in the atomic orbital approximation given by equation (8-95). In the limit of small velocities, and with the neglect of the exponential factors in v, we find from (8-40) that the functions $A_{\pm}(b,t)$ satisfy:

$$i\dot{A}_{\pm} = E_{\pm}(R)A_{\pm} \qquad (9\text{-}26)$$

where $E_+(R) = E_g(R)-\varepsilon_{1s}$, $E_-(R) = E_u(R)-\varepsilon_{1s}$ and $E_{g,u}(R)$ are the potential energies of the lowest gerade and ungerade levels corresponding to the eigenfunctions $\psi_{g,u}$. On solving (9-26) with the boundary conditions $A_+(b,-\infty) = A_-(b,-\infty) = \frac{1}{2}$, and forming $c(b,\infty) = (A_+(b,\infty)-A_-(b,\infty))$ the probability for charge exchange is found to be

$$|c(b,\infty)|^2 = \sin^2\left(\int_{\infty}^{\infty}(E_g(R)-E_u(R))dt\right) \tag{9-27}$$

This expression may be compared with that obtained in the two state atomic expansion in Chapter 8. If E_g and E_u are evaluated using the LCAO wave functions

$$\psi_{u,g} = \phi_{1s}(r_A) \pm \phi_{1s}(r_C) \tag{9-28}$$

the two expressions coincide (neglecting the transitional exponential factors involving v).

If the translation factors are not neglected (see Bates and McCarroll, 1962; Bates and Holt, 1966), the solution is

$$|c(b,\infty)|^2 = \sin^2\{\beta_g^* - \beta_u + \int_{\infty}^{\infty}dt\left[E_g(R)-E_u(R)\right]dt\} \tag{9-29}$$

where β_g and β_u are complicated functions that have the effects of cancelling the integral term at high velocities and thus reducing the cross section.

In the two state approximations, the probability of charge transfer (or elastic scattering) oscillates with unit amplitude for fixed impact parameter as a function of energy. We have already seen that an important source of damping is the coupling to higher electronic states, and that a distinct source of damping arises from the interference between different classical trajectories. This can be seen within the two state approximation (Smith, 1964; Bates and Holt, 1966).

Using (8-61a) and (8-62a), the scattering amplitudes for elastic scattering and for charge exchange are found to be

$$\begin{aligned} f(\theta) &= -i\mu v\int_0^{\infty} bdb\ J_0(qb)\frac{1}{2}\left(e^{i\chi_g}+e^{i\chi_u}\right) \\ g(\theta) &= -i\mu v\int_0^{\infty} bdb\ J_0(qb)\frac{1}{2}\left(e^{i\chi_g}-e^{i\chi_u}\right) \end{aligned} \tag{9-30}$$

where $q \cong \mu v\theta$ and $\chi_{g,u}$ are the semi-classical phases[5] for scattering by the potentials $E_{g,u}(R)$, so that

$$\chi_{gu} = -\int_{\infty}^{\infty} dt\ E_{g,u}(R)$$

Using the stationary phase approximation to evaluate the

integrals, we obtain

$$f(\theta) = \frac{1}{2}\left|\frac{d\sigma_g}{d\Omega}\right|^{\frac{1}{2}} e^{i\chi_g} + \frac{1}{2}\left|\frac{d\sigma_u}{d\Omega}\right|^{\frac{1}{2}} e^{i\chi_u}$$

$$g(\theta) = \frac{1}{2}\left|\frac{d\sigma_g}{d\Omega}\right|^{\frac{1}{2}} e^{i\chi_g} - \frac{1}{2}\left|\frac{d\sigma_u}{d\Omega}\right|^{\frac{1}{2}} e^{i\chi_u} \qquad (9\text{-}31)$$

where $d\sigma_g/d\Omega$ and $d\sigma_u/d\Omega$ are the classical cross sections for elastic scattering by the potentials E_g and E_u. Defining the probability of charge exchange at the angle θ as in Chapter 8, by

$$P_{CE}(\theta) = \frac{|g(\theta)|^2}{|f(\theta)|^2+|g(\theta)|^2} \qquad (9\text{-}32)$$

we obtain

$$P_{CE}(\theta) = \frac{1}{2}\,[1 - g\cos(\chi_g-\chi_u)] \qquad (9\text{-}33)$$

where

$$g = 2\left(\frac{d\sigma_g}{d\Omega}\right)\left(\frac{d\sigma_u}{d\Omega}\right)\left(\frac{d\sigma_g}{d\Omega} + \frac{d\sigma_u}{d\Omega}\right)^{-1} \qquad (9\text{-}34)$$

If the phases χ_g and χ_u differ appreciably, the oscillations in P_{CE} as a function of v, for fixed θ, are damped, otherwise in the two state approximation P_{CE} oscillates with unit amplitude. This damping is quite distinct from that which arises in a many state approximation. If a many state approximation is used the terms $\exp i\chi_{g,u}$ must be replaced by a sum of terms $\exp i\chi_{g,u} \to \Sigma_j c_j^{g,u} \exp i\chi_{g,u}^{(j)}$ where the $\chi_{g,u}^{(j)}$ are appropriate phases arising from each state in the expansion and the $c_j^{g,u}$ are the asymptotic values of the expansion coefficients.

When the nuclei are identical as in the $H^+ + H(1s)$ system further interference effects will arise because of the identity of the nuclei and will disappear when one of the nuclei is replaced by a different isotope. Smith (1967) has investigated these effects and has shown they are not significant except at very low energies $E \lesssim 15$eV.

Proton scattering by hydrogen

The two state approximation was applied to the proton-hydrogen atom system by Dalgarno and Yadav (1953) and Peek (1966), neglecting the translational motion of the electron and by Ferguson (1961) who did not make this approximation. Ferguson used simple analytic forms for $\Psi_{g,u}$ given by Dalgarno and Poots (1954) in atomic units,

$$\Psi_g = N_g \left\{ e^{-r_A - r_C} + p\left(e^{-r_A} + e^{-r_C}\right) \right\}$$

$$\Psi_u = N_u \left\{ (r_A \cos \theta_A - r_C \cos \theta_C) e^{-(r_A + r_C)/2} - q\left(e^{-r_A} - e^{-r_C}\right) \right\}$$

where N_g, N_u are normalization factors and p,q variational parameters. These functions are exact in both the separated and united atom limits and reproduce the energies $E_{g,u}(R)$ to within 1%.

Ferguson found that when the momentum transfer of the electron was allowed for, the cross section decreased by 5% at 2keV, by 16% at 5keV and 45% at 20keV. Below 2keV it appears that the translational motion of the electron can be neglected. It does not follow that this is the case when the nuclei A and B are different. In the symmetrical case in the 2-state approximation, charge exchange takes place without an electronic transition, the equations for A_+ and A_- being uncoupled, but, in general, charge exchange takes place through the coupling terms which involve the matrix element of the operator $(\partial/\partial t)$ between the different electronic states, and these terms are sensitive to the exponential momentum transfer factors. Below 20keV and down to 1keV, the results of Ferguson agree quite closely with those of McCarroll based on the two state atomic expansion. In particular, the theory fails to predict the oscillations observed in the fixed angle experiments with the correct turning points of damping. This is in part due to the strong coupling between the $2p\sigma$ and $2p\pi$ states because of the rotation of the internuclear line. This coupling is included in a four state approximation in which the $2s\sigma$, $2p\sigma$, $2p\pi$ and $3d\pi$ terms are retained (Bates and Williams, 1964). In this work the turning points agree well with those observed (see Table 9-1), but the amplitude of the oscillations is greater than that shown in the experiments (see Fig. 8-4).

The strong rotational coupling between the $2p\sigma$ and the $2p\pi$ levels arises because these levels become degenerate in the united atom limit $R \to 0$. In the separated atom limit

Table 9-1

Turning points of the differential cross section as a function of energy for $H + H^+$ collisions at 3° scattering angle, in keV.

Theory (Bates and Williams, 1964)		Experiment (Lockwood and Everhart, 1962)	
Maximum	Minimum	Maximum	Minimum
0.79		0.78	
	1.09		1.11
1.55		1.57	
	2.33		2.39
3.70		3.92	

the $2p\pi$ level approaches the $2p_0$ level of atomic hydrogen, so that there is a strong probability of exciting this level in the collision $H^+ + H(1s)$. This type of excitation which is due to two molecular orbitals approaching each other in the united atom limit has been termed 'promotion' by Fano and Lichten, who showed this is a major factor in the production of K-shell vacancies in ion-atom collisions (see Briggs, 1976).

Since the work of Bates and Williams there have been a large number of multistate molecular orbital calculations which have been reviewed by Basu et al (1978). A large ten state basis ($1s\sigma_g$, $2p\sigma_u$, $3d\pi_g$, $2p\pi_u$, $4d\pi_g$, $3p\pi_u$, $2s\sigma_g$, $3p\sigma_u$, $3d\sigma_g$ and $4f\sigma_u$) has been used by Schinke and Krüger (1976) in the energy range 250eV to 2keV. The total cross sections for capture into the 2s and 2p±1 levels agree reasonably well with the experimental data of Morgan et al (1973). Knudson and Thorsen (1970), Bates and Sprevak (1970) and Gaussorgues et al (1975) have all avoided the impact parameter approximation and used the partial wave expansion coupled with the JWKB method and in general the agreement with the experimental data including the angular dependence of the probability for charge exchange is satisfactory. Further progress within the impact parameter method has been made by Crothers and Hughes (1978a,b) who have employed optimized translational factors using the variational method and who have found close agreement with the large angle scattering data and the data for production of H(2s) and H(2p) in the energy interval 1 to 7 keV using a 10 state molecular orbital expansion.

Scattering of helium ions by helium

The angular distribution of the elastic scattering of

He^+ by He has been measured in the angular range 0° to 36° by Lorents and Aberth (1965) at energies from 20 to 600 ev. Fixed angle cross sections have also been measured at higher energies up to 25 kev by Lockwood et al (1963). In the wide angle scattering data (an example of which is shown in Fig. 9-6), the oscillations observed can be interpreted as being due in the main to interference between the gerade and ungerade states of the He_2^+ molecular ion. In addition at large angles small oscillations are seen superimposed on the main oscillations. These are due to nuclear interference effects, and this is confirmed by the disappearance of the oscillations when the experiments are conducted with He^{4+} scattered by He^3 (Aberth et al., 1965). At the lower energies the sharp increase in cross section at small angles (see Fig.9-7) is attributed to rainbow scattering (see Chapter 2).

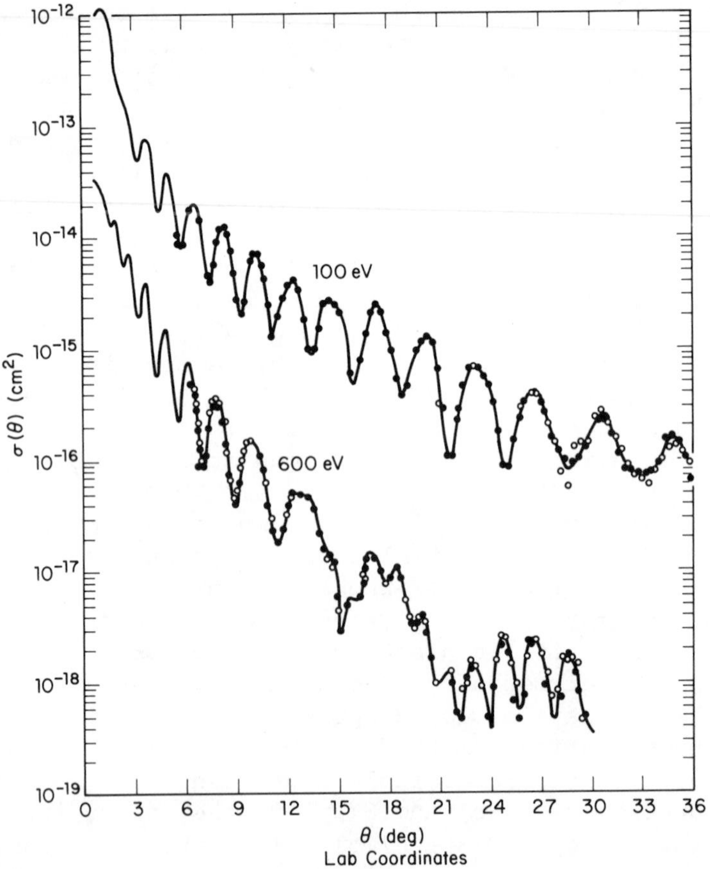

Figure 9-6 The angular distribution of the elastic scattering of He^+ by He (Lorents and Aberth, 1965).

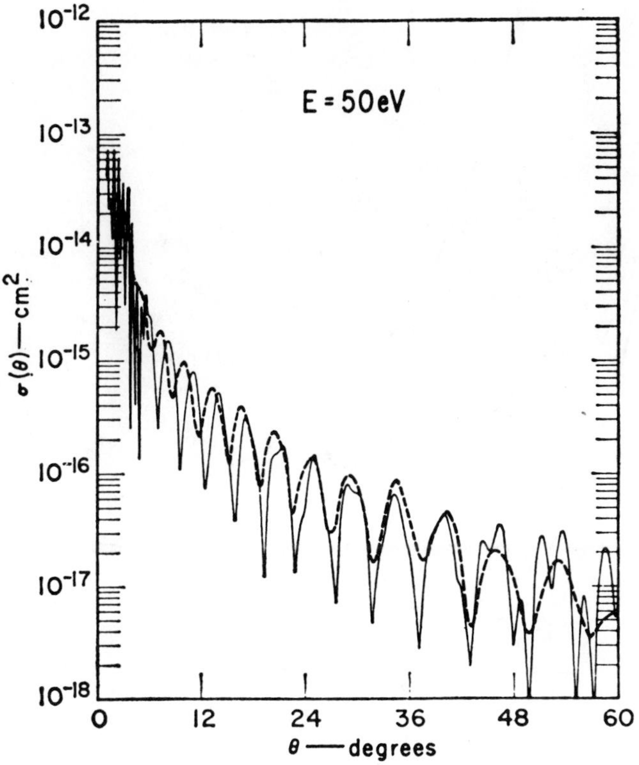

Figure 9-7 The angular distribution of the elastic scattering of He^+ by He.
- - - - Experimental data (Lorents and Aberth, 1965)
——— Theoretical calculation (Marchi and Smith, 1965)

A theoretical interpretation of these results has been given by Marchi and Smith (1965). They have determined the classical cross section and the semi-classical phases for scattering by the lowest gerade and ungerade potentials for the He + He^+ system. The potentials are shown in Fig. 9-8. The ungerade potential is related to the configuration $Be^+((2s)^2 2p)$ in the united atom limit and the gerade potential to $Be^+((1s)(2p)^2)$. It is seen that the ungerade potential has an attractive region and, as we noted in Chapter 2, potentials of this kind always give rise to rainbow scattering and the observed rainbow angle can be satisfactorily explained in this way. The calculated differential cross sections agree rather well with the

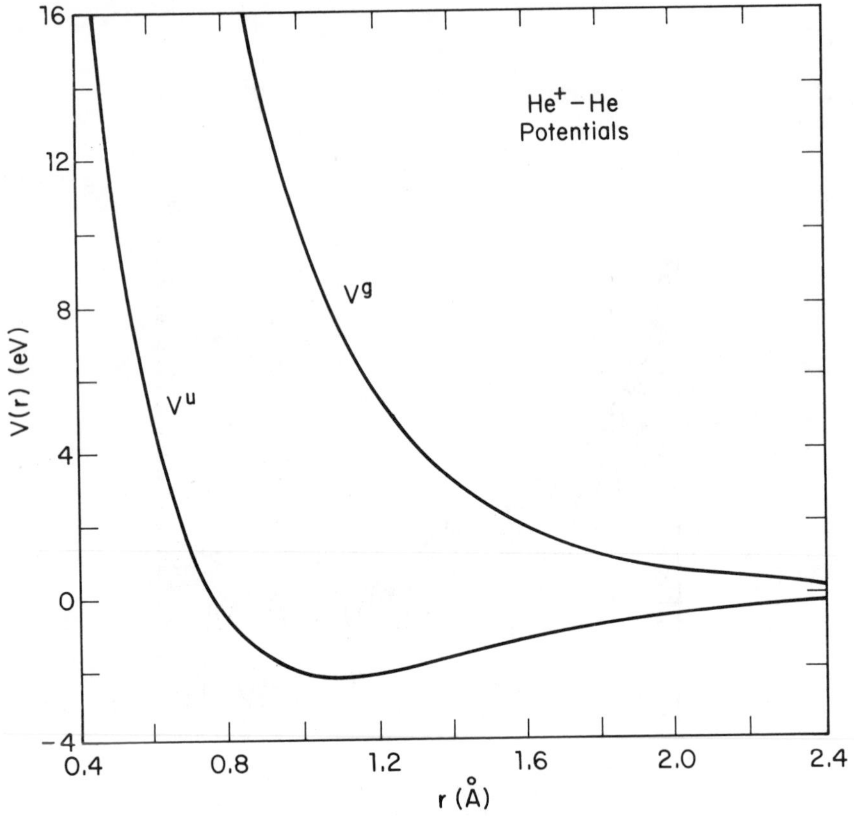

Figure 9-8 The interaction potential between He^+ and He in the lowest gerade and ungerade states.

observations as shown in Fig. 9-7. The differences where they occur are due to the effects of inelastic processes, to describe which requires further terms in the expansion of the wave function. The terms concerned have been discussed by Litchen (1963), who has shown that they are connected with curve crossing in the gerade potential. Smith et al. (1965) have given a qualitative discussion of these inelastic effects and have shown that they can account satisfactorily for most of the anomalies. A quantitative discussion based on a 3-state expansion has been given by Rai Dastidar and Bhattacharya (1976)

9-4 THE LANDAU-ZENER-STÜCKELBERG APPROXIMATION

If the interaction between a particular pair of molecular levels 1 and 2, of the same symmetry, is dominated by a pseudo crossing, an approximate analytical solution of the corresponding pair of coupled perturbed stationary state equations can be found (Landau 1932; Zener 1932; Stückelberg 1932). Consider the situation illustrated in Fig. 9-9a, in which the two adiabatic potential energy curves $E_1(R)$ and $E_2(R)$ make a pseudo

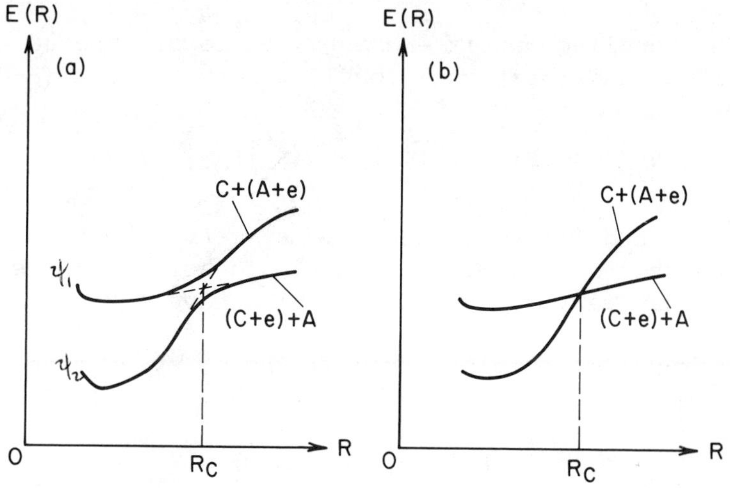

Figure 9-9 Potential curves illustrating
(a) pseudo crossing of adiabatic curves
(b) the corresponding crossing of diabatic curves

crossing at the point $R = R_C$. Let curve 1 correspond to the atomic state C+ $(A + e^-)$ in the limit $R\to\infty$ and curve 2 to the rearranged atomic state $(C + e^-) + A$. As we have already noted, the adiabatic orbitals, corresponding to the two potentials, ψ_1 and ψ_2 undergoes a rapid change near $R=R_C$ and in fact just to the left of the point R_C, ψ_2 will have a similar structure to ψ_1 at a point just to the right of R_C. Similarly ψ_1 to the left of R_C will be similar to ψ_2 to the right of R_C. The adiabatic orbitals satisfy

$$H_e\psi_i = E_i(R)\psi_i \qquad i = 1,2 \qquad (9\text{-}35)$$

and are orthonormal so that

$$(\psi_i|\psi_j) = \delta_{ij} \qquad (\text{all } R) \qquad (9\text{-}36)$$

In the PSS approximation,[6] the amplitudes d_1 and d_2 of the level 1 and 2 satisfy (from 9-14 and 9-15)

$$i\dot{d}_i = \sum_{n\neq j} M_{in} d_n \qquad i = 1,2 \tag{9-37}$$

where

$$M_{in} = -i(\psi_i|\frac{\partial}{\partial t}|\psi_n)\exp-i\int_{\infty}^{t} dt'\left(E_i(R')-E_n(R')\right) \tag{9-38}$$

The coupling matrix elements can be decomposed into a radial and rotational coupling term through (8-70):

$$M_{in} = -i\dot{R}(\psi_i|\frac{\partial}{\partial R}|\psi_j) - \dot{\Theta}(\psi_i|L_{y'}|\psi_n) \tag{9-39}$$

As ψ_1 and ψ_2 are of the same symmetry the rotational coupling vanishes in the present case. To work in terms of less rapidly varying functions, which have a real crossing point (see Fig. 9-9b) a diabatic pair of states ϕ_1 and ϕ_2 are introduced, obtained from ψ_1 and ψ_2 by an orthogonal transformation[7]

$$\begin{aligned} \phi_1 &= \cos\,\theta(R)\psi_1 + \sin\,\theta(R)\psi_2 \\ \phi_2 &= -\,\sin\,\theta(R)\psi_1 + \cos\,\theta(R)\psi_2 \end{aligned} \tag{9-40}$$

in which the parameter $\theta(R)$ depends on the internuclear distance. If the boundary condition $\theta(R)\to 0$ as $R\to\infty$ is imposed, the asymptotic amplitudes are unchanged by the transformation, and in view of (9-36) we note that the functions ϕ_i are orthonormal

$$(\phi_i|\phi_j) = \delta_{ij} \qquad \text{all } R \tag{9-41}$$

In terms of the new basis, the matrix elements of the interaction $(H_e - i\partial/\partial t)$ are

$$(\phi_i|H_e - i\partial/\partial t|\phi_n) = H_{in} - i\dot{R}(\phi_i|\frac{d}{dR}|\phi_n) \tag{9-42}$$

where

$$H_{in} = (\phi_i|H_e|\phi_n) \tag{9-43}$$

There is no rotational coupling as ϕ_1 and ϕ_2 have the same symmetry. Now we have that (from 9-40)

$$(\phi_1|\frac{d}{dR}|\phi_2) = (\psi_1|\frac{d}{dR}|\psi_2) - \frac{d\theta}{dR} \tag{9-44}$$

and θ (R) can be determined by requiring that the radial coupling vanishes in the dibatic basis:

$$(\phi_1|\frac{d}{dR}|\phi_2) = 0 \tag{9-45}$$

However it is usually impractical to determine θ and hence ϕ_1 and ϕ_2 from (9-45), instead approximate diabatic orbitals are constructed from the perturbed asymptotic atomic orbitals. If this is done a connection between the diabatic orbitals ϕ_i and the adiabatic orbitals ψ_i is made as follows. A variational approximation to the adiabatic orbitals is given by a linear combination of ϕ_1 and ϕ_2

$$\Psi = c_1\phi_1 + c_2\phi_2 \tag{9-46}$$

and from the Rayleigh-Ritz method using this trial function and varying the parameters c_i, we find the approximate eigenvalues E of the Hamiltonian H_e satisfy the equations

$$(H_{11} - E)c_1 + H_{12}c_2 = 0$$

$$H_{21}c_1 + (H_{22} - E)c_2 = 0 \tag{9-47}$$

which are compatible if

$$(H_{11} - E)(H_{22} - E) - H_{21}^2 = 0 \tag{9-48}$$

The two roots of this equation are approximations to the adiabatic energies E_1 and E_2.

$$2E_{1,2} = (H_{11} + H_{22}) \pm \{(H_{11} - H_{22})^2 + 4\, H_{21}{}^2\}^{\frac{1}{2}} \tag{9-49}$$

At the crossing point $H_{11}(R_c) = H_{22}(R_c)$ and we note that

$$E_1(R_c) - E_2(R_c) = 2H_{21}(R_c) \tag{9-50}$$

a result required later.

The PSS equations then take the form (with transformed amplitudes d'_1, d'_2)

$$i\dot{d}'_1 = H_{12}[\exp i\int_{\infty}^{t} dt'(H_{11}-H_{22})]d'_2 \tag{9-51a}$$

$$i\dot{d}'_2 = H_{21}[\exp -i\int_{\infty}^{t} dt'\,(H_{11}-H_{22})]d'_1 \tag{9-51b}$$

with a real crossing[8] at $R=R_c$ and boundary conditions

$d'_1 \to 1$ and $d'_2 \to 0$ as $t \to \infty$. By differentiating (9-51b) and substituting from (9-51a), a second order differential equation is found for d'_2,

$$\ddot{d}'_2 = \frac{1}{H_{21}}\left(\frac{dH_{21}}{dt}\right)\dot{d}'_2 - i(H_{11}-H_{22})\dot{d}'_2 - (H_{12})^2 d'_2 \quad (9\text{-}52)$$

So far no approximations to the 2-state PSS equation have been made. It is now possible to solve (9-52), if specific assumptions are made about the behavior of H_{in} near the crossing point. In the Landau-Zener model $(H_{11}-H_{22})$ is expanded about $R=R_c$, and since $R^2=b^2+v^2t^2$, we can write

$$H_{11}(R) - H_{22}(R) \approx v(t-t_c)\alpha \quad (9\text{-}53)$$

where α is a constant and $R_c{}^2=b^2+v^2t_c{}^2$. The second assumption is that H_{21} can be treated as a constant, $H_{21}=\beta$ for values of R near R_c. β can be calculated from the adiabatic potentials through (9-50). Equation (9-52) then reduces to

$$\ddot{d}'_2 = -iv\alpha(t-t_i)\dot{d}'_2 - \beta^2 d'_2 \quad (9\text{-}54)$$

Zener (1932) showed that this equation can be transformed to Weber's equation, which has a known solution from which it is found that

$$|d'_2(b,\infty)|^2 = |d_2(b,\infty)|^2 = 1-\exp(-\gamma) \quad (9\text{-}55)$$

where

$$\gamma = 2\pi\beta^2/(v|\alpha|) \quad (9\text{-}56)$$

In this approximation only one passage of the point $R=R_c$ has been allowed for, but in fact the system passes through this point twice, once for $t<0$ and once for $t>0$, where $t=0$ is the time of closest approach. The probability $P=\exp(-\gamma)$ is the probability that the system will be found on the diabatic curve 2 in the region $R<R_c$ after one passage of the crossing point, while $(1-P)$ is the probability for the system remaining on the curve 1. At the second transition of the crossing point, the probability of finding the system on curve 2 will be $P_{12} = 2P(1-P)$, so that the cross section for charge exchange is

$$\sigma_{21} = 2\pi\int_0^\infty bdb\, P_{12}(b) \quad (9\text{-}57)$$

The Landau-Zener approximation has the merit of simplicity, but it must be used with care. For example, because of the strong rotational coupling between states with different magnetic quantum number, it is usually only satisfactory for σ-σ transitions. The basic approximation is that transitions only occur in a region closely localized about $R=R_C$. However the size of the region from which transition occurs rapidly can be estimated (Bates, 1960). Assume this region is of width $\Delta Z=2v\tau$ and that transitions are important if the phase factors in 9-51a,b change through an angle $\sim\pi$ as t varies between $t_C - \tau$ and $t_C + \tau$. Thus τ is determined by

$$\left|\int_{t_c-\tau}^{t_c+\tau} (H_{11}-H_{22})dt\right| = \pi \tag{9-58}$$

from which

$$\Delta Z = 2v\tau = \left(\frac{2\pi v}{\alpha}\right)^{\frac{1}{2}} \tag{9-59}$$

The transition region is unbounded as v increases, and because of this the Landau formulae leads to an inverse variation of the cross section with velocity; however, the cross section found from the exact solution of the coupled equation is proportional to $1/v^2$ for large v. (In both cases the important effect of the translational motion of the electron has been ignored). A more serious objection is that even at low velocities ΔZ can be of the order Z_C which destroys the basis of the approximation, which assumes that the region over which transitions occur is narrow.

Despite these difficulties the Landau-Zener approximation has been used to discuss a variety of reactions. Particularly favorable cases arise for exothermic reactions such as

$$A + B^{++} \rightarrow A^{+} + B^{+} + \text{kinetic energy}$$

or endothermic reactions such as

$$A + B \rightarrow A^{+} + B^{-} - \text{kinetic energy}$$

In such cases, the crossing point is controlled by the long range forces and occurs at large atomic separations where the LCAO (linear combination of atomic orbitals) wave functions can be used. In the first case, the interaction in the initial state is attractive because of the $1/R^4$ polarization potential between a charge and a neutral system (see Chapter 5), while in the final state the interaction is proportional to 1/R and is repulsive. In the second example, the final state interaction is strongly attractive, like 1/R, and in the initial state the interaction is the Van der Waals polarization potential which behaves like $1/R^6$.

Some examples for which numerical calculations have been made are (Bates and Moiseiwitsch, 1954)

$$H + Be^{++} \rightarrow H^{+} + Be^{+}$$

$$H + Si^{++} \rightarrow H^{+} + Si^{+}$$

$$H + Mg^{++} \rightarrow H^{+} + Mg^{+}$$

and (Dalgarno, 1954)

$$H + A\ell^{+++} \rightarrow H^{+} + A\ell^{++}(^{2}S \text{ and } ^{2}P)$$

$$H + B^{++} \rightarrow H^{+} + B^{+}(^{1}P)$$

$$H + Li^{++} \rightarrow H^{+} + Li^{+}(^{3}S \text{ and } ^{1}P)$$

$$H + A\ell^{++} \rightarrow H^{+} + A\ell^{+}.$$

These processes involve the transfer of an electron from an orbital around one passive closed core to an orbital around another, and can be treated as one-electron problems. The crossing points are determined by the charges and polarizabilities of the ions and occur at large distances of separation; for example, in the second group of reactions, at 3.34, 6.58, 11.1, 8.80, 20.9 and 5.29 atomic units respectively.

A particular example of astrophysical interest (Butler and Dalgarno, 1980) is the set of exothermic reactions between a positive ion A^{q+} and atomic hydrogen

$$A^{q+} + H(1s) \rightarrow A^{(q-1)+} + H^{+} + \Delta\varepsilon$$

at collision energies up to ~10eV/amu, where A is C, N, O or Ne and q = 2 or 3. To the lowest order the diabatic curves (in atomic units) are

$$H_{11} = \varepsilon_1 - 0.5 - \frac{\alpha q^2}{2R^4} \tag{9-60a}$$

$$H_{22} = \varepsilon_2 + \frac{q-1}{R} \tag{9-60b}$$

where in the initial A^q + H(1s) state 1, α is the polarisability of atomic hydrogen and ε_1 is the energy of the ion A^{q+}, and in the final state 2, ε_2 is the energy of the ion $A^{(q-1)+}$. The crossing points can be estimated by neglecting the term in α, so that

$$R_c \approx \frac{q-1}{(\varepsilon_1-\varepsilon_2)-0.5} \tag{9-61}$$

Specific calculations of the matrix elements H_{12} are found to fit the formula (atomic units)

$$E_1(R_c)-E_2(R_c) = 2H_{12}(R_c) \simeq R_c^2 \exp(-R_c) \simeq 2\beta \tag{9-62}$$

where E_1 and E_2 are the adiabatic energy curves and this is consistent with analyses based on asymptotic expansions[9] of the wave functions at large R. The remaining parameter required in the Landau-Zener formulae is the value of $\alpha = d(H_{11}-H_{22})/dR$ at $R=R_C$. The short range repulsion in channel 1, can be represented as a potential such as $A\exp(-BR)$, where it is found that $A\cong q$ and $B\cong 1.8$, and from (9-60a)

$$H_{11}(R) = \varepsilon_1 - 0.5 - \frac{\alpha q^2}{2R^4} + A\exp(-BR) \tag{9-63}$$

where $H_{22}(R)$ is sufficiently well determined by (9-60b).

Proceeding in this general way, the calculation of charge exchange cross sections only requires a knowledge of the energy differences $(\varepsilon_2-\varepsilon_1)$ for each ion A. Some values obtained for the charge transfer rate coefficients at a temperature of 10^4K are shown in Table 9-2 compared with the results of coupled channel quantum calculations.

Table 9-2
Rate coefficients for charge exchange at 10^4K (Butler and Dalgarno, 1980)

Initial system	Landau-Zener	Quantum coupled channel
$C^{2+} + H$	0	1.0×10^{-12}
$C^{3+} + H$	1.8×10^{-9}	3.6×10^{-9}
$O^{2+} + H$	1.0×10^{-10}	7.7×10^{-10}
$O^{3+} + H$	2.8×10^{-9}	8.6×10^{-9}
$Ne^{3+} + H$	3.8×10^{-9}	5.7×10^{-9}

Although no great accuracy is expected from the Landau-Zener model, in suitable cases it provides a very useful estimate of the magnitude of the cross sections.

Generalizations of the Landau-Zener model have been devised for the case of multiple, but non-overlapping crossing regions and alternative methods for obtaining approximate solutions of the two-state equations have been developed. Some of these methods have been reviewed by Greenland (1982) and by Janev and Presynakov (1981), (see also Litchen, 1965).

NOTES

1. An introduction to the theory of the structure of diatomic molecules can be found in the text by Bransden and Joachain (1982).

2. A detailed discussion of the one electron problem has been given by Power (1973).

3. At an adiabatic pseudo crossing, the corresponding potential curves in the diabatic representation (i.e. the diagonal elements of H_e) actually cross.

4. For further details about switching factors, the reviews of Briggs (1976) and Delos (1981) can be consulted, see also Vaaben and Taulbjerg (1981).

5. More exactly change in velocity as each path is traversed can be taken into account by using

$$\chi_{g,u} = \int ds [\{2\mu(E - E_{g,u}(R))\}^{\frac{1}{2}} - (2\mu E)^{\frac{1}{2}}]$$

where the integration is along the appropriate classical path.

6. This is not an essential approximation.

7. Note that ψ_1, ψ_2 and ϕ_1, ϕ_2 can be chosen to be real functions.

8. As an alternative to transforming to a diabatic representation, an analytical continuation in the complex t (or z) plane to reach the point at which the adiabatic potentials cross, following which approximations based on the stationary phase evaluation of integrals can be developed, see in particular Crothers (1971).

9. See Janev (1976).

PROBLEMS

9.1 If ψ_m and ψ_n are adiabatic molecular orbitals satisfying equation (9-1a), show the radial coupling matrix elements are given by

$$(\psi_m|\frac{\partial}{\partial R}|\psi_n) = \frac{1}{E_n - E_m} (\psi_m|\frac{\partial V}{\partial R}|\psi_n) \qquad m \neq n$$

$$= 0 \qquad m = n$$

where E_m, E_n and V are defined in (9-1a) and (9-1c).

9.2 Evaluate the adiabatic potentials $E_g(R)$ and $E_u(R)$ for the lowest hydrogen molecular ion states $H_2{}^+$ by representing the orbitals ψ_g and ψ_u as

$$\psi_{g,u} = \frac{1}{\sqrt{2}}[\phi_{1s}(r_A) \pm \phi_{1s}(r_C]$$

where $\phi_{1s}(r)$ is the wave function of H(1s)

9.3 Show that the matrix elements $M_{nm} = (\Phi_n|H_e - i\frac{\partial}{\partial t}|\Phi_m)$ where $\Phi_n = \psi_n \exp(if\vec{v}\cdot\vec{r})$

and $\Phi_m = \psi_m \exp(if\vec{v}\cdot\vec{r})$ and ψ_n, ψ_m are adiabatic orbitals can be expressed as

$$M_{nm} = (\psi_n|H_e - i\frac{\partial}{\partial t} - if\vec{v}\cdot\vec{\nabla}|\psi_m)$$

$$-i(\psi_n|(\vec{v}\cdot\vec{r})(\vec{\nabla}f)\cdot\vec{\nabla} + (\vec{v}\cdot\vec{r})(\tfrac{1}{2}\nabla^2 f) + \vec{v}\cdot(\vec{\nabla}f)|\psi_m)$$

$$+ (\psi_n|\frac{\partial}{\partial t}(f\vec{v}\cdot\vec{r}) + \tfrac{1}{2}[\vec{\nabla}_r(f\vec{v}\cdot\vec{r})]^2|\psi_m)$$

where f is a switching factor defined by (9-17).

9.4 Show that if terms of order v are neglected in the matrix element M_{nm} of Problem 3, M_{nm} can be reduced to

$$M_{nm} = E_n \delta_{nm} - i(\psi_n|\frac{\partial}{\partial t}|\psi_m)$$

$$-i(\psi_n|f\vec{v}\cdot\vec{r}|\psi_m)(E_n - E_m)$$

9.5 Use the stationary phase method to evaluate the integrals (9-30) and obtain the results (9-31).

9.6 Use the following data in conjunction with the approximations of (9-60), (9-61), (9-62) and (9-63) to evaluate the Landau-Zener cross sections for the reactions

$$A^{q+} + H(1s) \rightarrow A^{(q-1)+} + H^+$$

at energies of 10eV/amu and 20eV/amu

A^{q+}	$A^{(q-1)+}$	$\Delta\varepsilon=\varepsilon_2-\varepsilon_1$ (eV)
$C^{2+}(^1S)$	$C^+(^2D)$	1.38
	$C^+(^2P^o)$	10.67
$N^{3+}(^1S)$	$N^{2+}(^2S)$	6.39
	$N^{2+}(^2D)$	21.30

9.7 Show that the Schrödinger equation describing a one-electron homonuclear system, with equal nuclear charges Z, that is

$$\left(-\frac{1}{2}\nabla^2 - Z/r_A - Z/r_C - i\partial/\partial t\right)\Psi(\vec{r},t) = 0$$

where $\vec{r}$ is the position vector of the electron with respect to the mid-point of the internuclear line AC, and the internuclear potential has been omitted, can be reduced to the equation for the system of one electron and two protons (Z=1), by the transformations $\vec{r}' = Z\vec{r}$, $t' = Z\,t$, $R'(t') = ZR(t)$. Hence show that if $\sigma(v)$ is the cross section for a particular reaction in the H_2^+ system with Z=1, the corresponding reaction in homonuclear system with charge Z is given by $\sigma(Z,v) = Z^{-2}\sigma(v/Z)$.

Chapter 10

FAST COLLISIONS BETWEEN ATOMS

When collisions between two atoms, or between an atom and an ion, take place at relative velocities substantially greater than 1 a.u., a simplified theoretical treatment is often possible, although the general expansion methods discussed in Chapter 8 remain valid. The chief simplification arises because charge exchange rapidly becomes unimportant compared with ionization and excitation, as the energy increases, and cross sections for the latter processes can be evaluated without taking into account the charge exchange channels.

10-1 EXCITATION AND IONIZATION

Expansion methods

Let us consider again a system containing one active electron bound to a center A, as in Section 8-2. To describe the excitation or ionization of the atom $(A + e^-)$ by the impact of a proton C

$$\begin{aligned} C + (A + e^-) &\rightarrow C + (A + e^-)^* \\ &\rightarrow C + A + e^- \end{aligned} \tag{10-1}$$

an expansion can be made in the atomic orbitals and pseudostates $\chi_j(\vec{r}_A)$, centered on A. If N terms are retained, to form a finite basis the pseudostates can be determined so that the target Hamiltonian is diagonalized.

$$\int d^3r_A \chi_j^*(r_A)\left(-\tfrac{1}{2}\nabla^2 + V_{Ae}(r_A)\right)\chi_k(r_A) = \eta_j \delta_{jk} \tag{10-2}$$

Since the charge exchange channels to not have to be represented explicitly, the origin of coordinates can be taken to be at A (see Fig.8-3) and the solution of the impact parameter equation (8-40) can be expanded as

$$\Psi(\vec{r}_A,t) = \sum_{j=1}^{N} a_j(b,t)\chi_j(\vec{r}_A)\exp(-i\eta_j t) \tag{10-3}$$

and in the high velocity region, the straight line trajectory

$$\vec{R}(t) = \vec{b} + \vec{v}t, \qquad \vec{v}\cdot\vec{b} = 0 \tag{10-4}$$

is sufficiently accurate. On substituting (10-3) into (8-40) and projecting with the functions $\chi_k^*(r_A)$, the coupled equations for the amplitudes a_j are found to be

$$i\dot{a}_j = \sum_{k=1}^{N} V_{jk}(R(t))e^{i(\eta_j-\eta_k)t} a_k(b,t)$$

$$j = 1,2,\ldots.N \tag{10-5}$$

where

$$V_{jk}(R) = \int d^3r_A \chi_j^*(r_A)\left[V_{Ce}(\vec{R} + \vec{r}_A) + V_{CA}(R)\right]\chi_k(r_A) \tag{10-6}$$

These equations can be obtained directly from (8-55) and (8-56) by omitting all terms c_m which describe the rearranged channel. The total cross section σ_{fi} for excitation of a level f, from a level i, can be obtained by solving equations (10-5) subject to the boundary condition

$$\ell t_{t\to-\infty}\; a_j(b,t) = \delta_{ij} \tag{10-7a}$$

in which case σ_{ji} is

$$\sigma_{fi} = 2\pi\int_0^\infty b\,|a_f(b,\infty)|^2 db \tag{10-7b}$$

In the two state approximation, equations (10-6) reduce to the pair of coupled equations (8-74), and the corresponding first Born and distorted wave approximations are given by (8-80) and (8-81) respectively. The differential cross section can be found, as before, using (8-61a). To generalize the theory to the case in which several electrons are centered on nucleus A and several on nucleus C is straightforward provided electron exchange between electrons on different centers is neglected. This effect is however negligible at high velocities[1]. For example, if one electron is attached to center C, described by atomic wave functions $\phi_n \exp -i\varepsilon_n t$, in addition to the electron attached to A, the expansion is in terms of the functions

$$\chi_j(r_A)\phi_n(r_B)\exp -i(\eta_j + \varepsilon_n)t$$

Although coupled channel calculations have been made for many systems[2], the proton-atomic hydrogen system provides a particularly illuminating example. The most elaborate study is by Fitchard et al (1977), who used the basis set

$$\chi_j(r_A) = Y_{\ell,m}(\theta_A,\phi_A) \sum_{n=1}^{N} C_n^j r^\ell \exp(-\lambda_j r/\eta_j) \qquad (10\text{-}8)$$

The complex constants λ_j are chosen so that the more important bound states of the atomic hydrogen target are represented accurately and the linear constants C_n^j are found by diagonalizing the target Hamiltonian. Taking a rather large basis set with 10s, 22p and 21d states, cross sections have been computed for the excitation of the n = 2 and n = 3 levels of hydrogen. Since the pseudostate set overlapped the hydrogenic continuum, the ionization cross section could also be found by computing the difference between the total cross section (into all states) and the sum of the cross sections for excitation of real hydrogenic levels and elastic scattering. The results of these calculations are shown in Figs. 10-1 and 10-2. Above 60 keV very good agreement is obtained with the experimental data. Below this energy the charge exchange channels are important and the approximation breaks down. As we saw in Chapter 8, by representing the boundary conditions in the rearranged channel, Reading and his co-workers using the same basis set, could extend the agreement with experiment down to low energies $E \approx 15$ keV. The cross sections computed in this model (OHCE) are also included in Figs. 10-1 and 10-2.

The Born approximation

Also shown in Figure 10-1 are the results of the first Born approximation calculations, which begin to agree with the data, and with the coupled channel calculations (to ~ 10%) by about 200 keV.

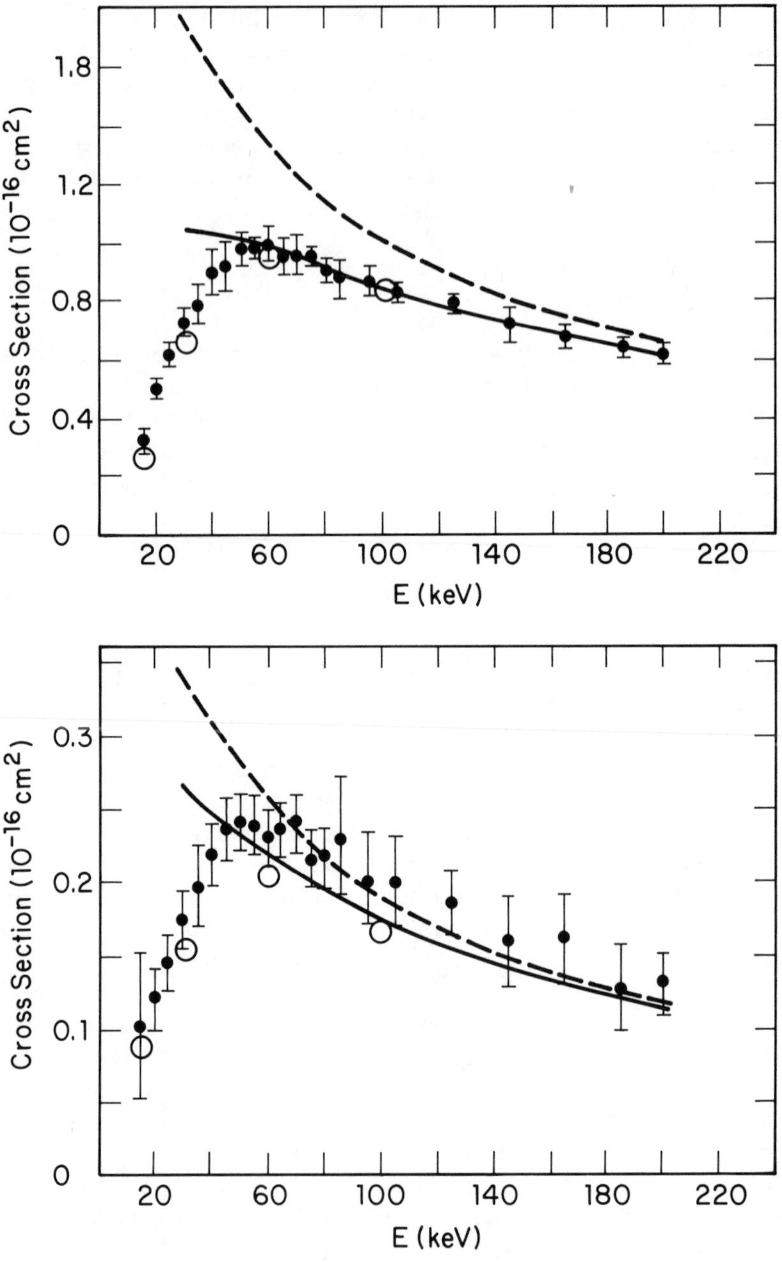

Figure 10-1 Total cross section for (a) n=2 (b) n=3 excitation of atomic hydrogen by proton impact.

- - - -Born approximation

——— Coupled channel calculations of Fitchard et al (1977)

O O O OHCE coupled channel expansion (Reading et al 1981)

• • • •Data from Park et al (1975, 1977).

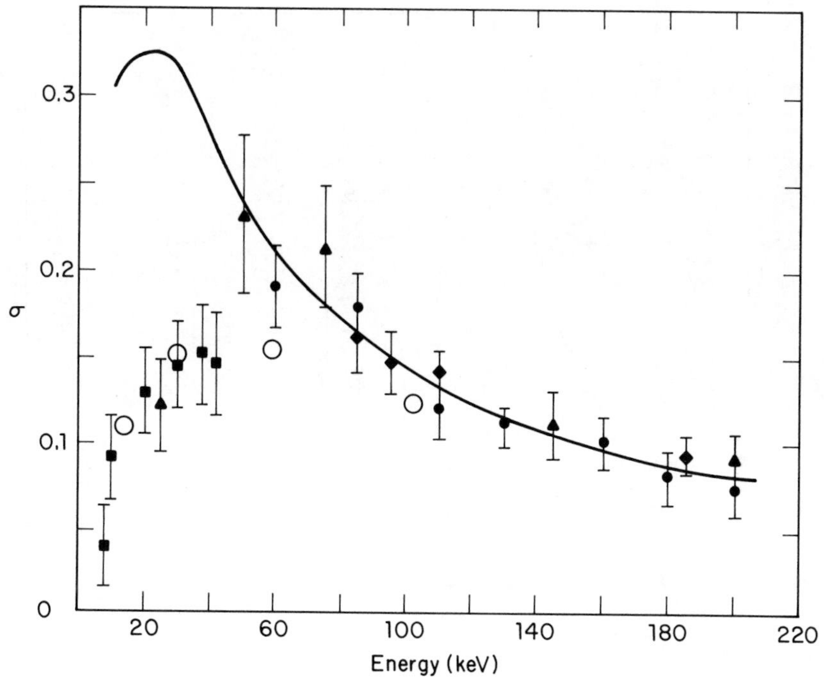

Figure 10-2 The cross section for ionization of atomic hydrogen by proton impact
——— Coupled channel calculations of Fitchard et al (1977)
O O O OHCE coupled channel expansion (Reading et al 1981)
■ • ▲ Data from Park et al (1977) and Gilbody and Ireland (1963)

For excitation of optically allowed transitions it would appear that the Born approximation for total cross sections is generally satisfactory for impact energies above 200-300 keV/amu and that, if the distorted wave approximation (8-81) is used, the lower energy limit can be reduced in some cases to ~100keV/amu (see Fig. 10-3). On the other hand, for weak $s \to s$ or $s \to d$ transitions, it is known[3] that the Born approximation does not become accurate until energies of from 600keV to 1MeV/amu are reached. If the active electron is bound to a nucleus of charge Z_A and is ionized or excited by a particle of charge Z_C with $Z_C \ll Z_A$, Born's approximation is accurate at lower velocities because the perturbation Z_C/r_C is small compared with the binding potential. A useful discussion of this situation which occurs in the ionization of the inner shells of heavy atoms by the impact

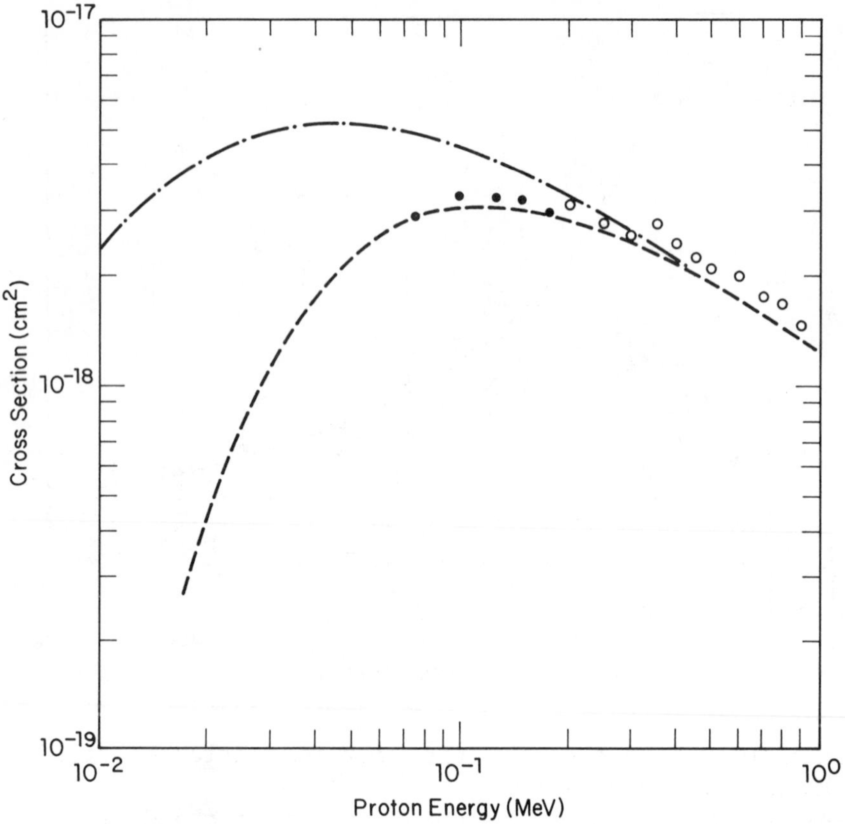

Figure 10-3 Proton excitation of helium to the 3^1P level
∘ ∘ ∘ Proton impact experimental
• • • Deuteron impact experimental (Thomas and Bent, 1967)
—·—·— Born approximation (Bell, 1961)
- - - Distorted wave approximation (Bell, 1961)

of light ions, has been given by Briggs and Taulbjerg (1978). In the impact parameter version of Born's approximation a straight line trajectory is usually employed, but if $Z_A Z_C$ is large the integration can be carried out along a Coulomb trajectory without difficulty (see Kochbach 1976; Pauli and Trautmann 1978).

Many calculations have been carried out in the Born approximation[4], both for excitation and ionization by proton impact and for collisions between two composite systems. Among the earlier comprehensive studies were those of Bates and Griffing (1953, 1954 and 1955) on the reactions

$$H(1s) + H(1s) \rightarrow H(n'\ell') + H(n\ell) \qquad (a)$$
$$H(1s) + H(1s) \rightarrow H(n\ell) + e^- \qquad (b)$$

The calculations can be made in a wave formulation, expressing the cross section in terms of generalized oscillator strengths (see Chapter 6) or in terms of the impact parameter expression (8-80) and as remarked in Chapter 8, these formulations are equivalent for heavy particle collisions. This can be seen as follows. In the wave formulation the excitation cross section for a transition from a level 0 to a level 1 not involving a change in magnetic quantum number is

$$\sigma_{10} = \frac{\mu^2}{2\pi k_0^2} \int_{K_{min}}^{K_{max}} K\, dK \int_0^{2\pi} d\phi\, |T^B_{10}\ (\vec{K})|^2 \tag{10-9}$$

where

$$T^B_{10}\ (\vec{K}) = \int d^3R\, e^{i\vec{K}\cdot\vec{R}}\, V_{10}(R) \tag{10-10}$$

This only differs from the expression (6-36) by the factor μ^2 where μ is the reduced mass of the heavy particles. The interaction matrix element V_{10} is defined in (10-6) and $\vec{K}$ is the momentum transfer $(\vec{k}_1 - \vec{k}_0)$. Since the nuclear kinetic energy is large compared with the change in electronic energies $|\eta_0 - \eta_1|$ the following approximations can be made

$$k_0^2 \cong \mu^2 v^2,\ K_{min} \cong \frac{|\eta_0 - \eta_1|}{v} \text{ and } K_{max} \cong \infty \tag{10-11}$$

Using these results it is seen that (1) the cross section is a function of the relative velocity v only, and not of μ (2) for large v, the cross sections for electron excitation and proton excitation become equal

$$\left(\sigma_p(v) - \sigma_e(v)\right) \to 0 \text{ as } v \to \infty \tag{10-12}$$

Introducing the two dimensional impact parameter vector $\vec{b}$ as the vector with components X and Y where (X,Y,Z) are the components of $\vec{R}$, we have

$$T^B_{10}\ (K) = \int e^{i\vec{b}\cdot\vec{K}} \int_{-\infty}^{\infty} dZ\, e^{iK_z Z}\, V_{10}(R)\, d^2b \tag{10-13}$$

and since the scattering is almost entirely in the forward direction

$$K_z \cong k_1 - k_0 \cong \frac{\eta_0 - \eta_1}{v} \tag{10-14}$$

Setting Z=vt and comparing with (8-80), T^B_{10} is seen to be given by

$$T^B_{10}(\vec{K}) = \int e^{i\vec{b}\cdot\vec{K}} \, v \, a_1'(b,\infty) \, d^2b \tag{10-15}$$

Finally using the result

$$\int d^2K \, e^{i(\vec{b}-\vec{b}^1)\vec{K}} = (2\pi)^2 \, \delta(\vec{b} - \vec{b}^1) \tag{10-16}$$

where the integration is over the 2-dimensional space defined by K and ϕ, we obtain

$$\sigma_{10} = 2\pi \int_0^\infty bdb \left| a_1'(b,\infty \right|^2 \tag{10-17}$$

the impact parameter result.

Higher order methods

Although the first Born (and distorted wave) approximations are usually not accurate until rather high energies are reached, it is interesting to investigate whether the second (or higher) Born approximations are useful. To do this Bransden et al (1979) represented the proton-hydrogen atom system by a wave function expanded on finite basis as in (10-3). The basis included the real 1s, 2s and 2p hydrogenic orbitals together with a number of s, p and d pseudostates. The solution of the corresponding set of coupled equations for the amplitudes a_j, provided cross sections in close agreement with those obtained by Fitchard et al with a much larger basis set. The integral form of the equations (10-5) is

$$a_j(b,t) = \delta_{ij} - i\int_\infty^t dt' \sum_{k=1}^N V_{jk}(R(t'))e^{i(\eta_j-\eta_k)t'} a_k(b,t')$$

$$j = 1,2,\ldots N \tag{10-18}$$

This set of equations can be solved iteratively. First, $a_k^0 = \delta_{ik}$ is substituted into the right hand side to obtain the first order Born approximation $a_j^1(b,t)$; this in turn is substituted into the right hand side to find the second Born approximation $a_j^2(b,t)$ and so on. In this way, the convergence of the Born series to the model represented by the finite set of coupled equations (10-5) could be investigated. Apart from the fact that the model provided realistic 2s and 2p excitation cross sections, it was also known[5] that the second Born approximation amplitudes given by the model accurately represented the 'exact' second Born amplitudes obtained by summing and integrating over all the important intermediate states. The results, some of which are shown in Table 10-1 are illuminating. The 2s and 2p cross sections are everywhere less well represented by the second Born approximation than by the first Born approximation.

Table 10-1

Cross sections for the 2s and 2p excitation of atomic hydrogen by proton impact

(Units of πa_o^2)

E(keV)	75		105		145		200	
	2s	2p	2s	2p	2s	2p	2s	2p
C	0.19	1.01	0.13	0.93	0.09	0.81	0.06	0.68
B1	0.13	1.26	0.08	1.06	0.07	0.88	0.05	0.73
B2	0.37	1.37	0.20	1.12	0.14	0.92	0.09	0.74

If the iteration is continued, the cross sections do converge to those obtained from the direct numerical solution of the coupled differential equations, but from 4 to 6 iterations are required. The distorted wave Born series was also investigated, but the convergence was nearly as slow. The conclusion must be, that if the first order distorted wave, or Born, cross sections are not sufficiently accurate, then it is best to go to a full solution of the coupled equations, rather than to calculate the second order approximations.

Ionization and charge exchange into the continuum

When a light atom is ionized by proton impact, or by the impact of some other light ion, the majority of the ejected electrons emerge with low velocities, as predicted by the Born approximation. However there is a significant enhancement of the cross section, above the Born approximation, for ejected electrons with velocities $\vec{v}_E$ close to the velocity $\vec{v}$ of the incident ion, and in this region the cross section exhibits a cusp, behaving like $1/|\vec{v}-\vec{v}_E|$ (Crooks and Rudd, 1970; Harrison and Lucas, 1970). This effect is seen very clearly in the experiments of Manson et al (1975) on the ionization of helium by proton impact at energies between 300keV and 5MeV and in Fig. 10-4, the ratio of their experimental cross section to the Born approximation is shown as a function of energy for a number of angles of ejection with $v_E = v$. One way of looking at this enhancement is as an electron capture process, in which the electron is captured into a continuum rather than a discrete state of the incident ion. This final state interaction has been

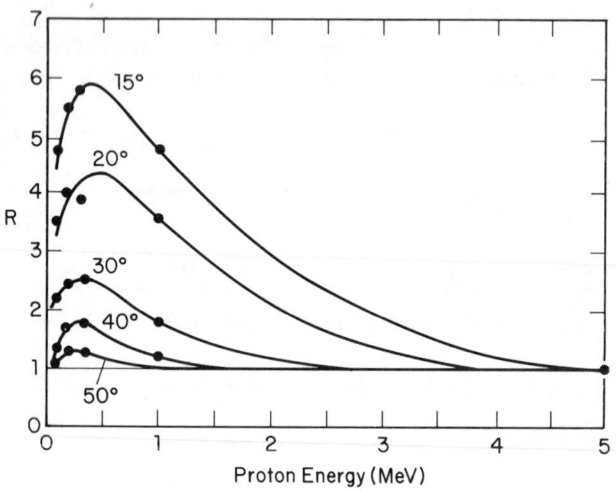

Figure 10-4 The ratio R of the measured differential cross section to the cross section in the Born approximation for the ionization of He by H^+, for the case in which the ejected electrons have the same speed as the incident proton.

discussed in theoretical models developed by Salin (1969) Macek (1970) and Dettmann et al (1974). The approach of Belkić (1978) similar in spirit to the continuum distorted wave model of charge exchange, which is discussed below, has been employed to successfully explain the data for the ionization of H(1s) by H^+

10-2 CHARGE EXCHANGE AT HIGH ENERGIES

The Born series

The Born series for charge exchange (or excitation) can be based on the full Schrödinger equation as in Chapter 4, but here the corresponding series will be obtained in the straight line impact parameter formalism, starting from equation (8-40), with the Hamiltonian (8-29):

$$H_e \Psi(\vec{r},t) = i \frac{\partial}{\partial t}\Psi(\vec{r},t) \tag{10-19}$$

$$H_e = -\frac{1}{2}\nabla_r^2 + V_{Ae} + V_{Ce} + (V_{AC} - W) \tag{10-20}$$

The unperturbed wave functions belonging to the arrangement C + (A + e) satisfy

$$\left(H^A - i\frac{\partial}{\partial t}\right) x_j(\vec{r},t) = 0 \tag{10-21}$$

where X_j is given by (8-44) and

$$H^A = -\frac{1}{2}\nabla_r^2 + V_{Ae} \tag{10-22}$$

Correspondingly the unperturbed wave functions Φ_m belonging to the arrangement (C + e) + A, satisfy

$$\left(H^C - i\frac{\partial}{\partial t}\right)\Phi_m(\vec{r},t) = 0 \tag{10-23}$$

where

$$H^C = -\frac{1}{2}\nabla_r^2 + V_{Ce} \tag{10-24}$$

Different Born series can be obtained depending on whether H^A, H^C or $H^o \equiv -\frac{1}{2}\nabla_r^2$ are taken to be the unperturbed Hamiltonian. Starting by choosing H^A as the unperturbed Hamiltonian, we can write

$$\left(H^A - i\frac{\partial}{\partial t}\right)\Psi(\vec{r},t) = -V^A\Psi(\vec{r},t) \tag{10-25}$$

where

$$V^A = H_e - H^A = V_{Ce} + (V_{AC} - W) \tag{10-26}$$

In integral form equation (10-25) becomes,

$$\Psi(\vec{r},t) = X_i(\vec{r},t) + \int d^3r' \int_{\infty}^{\infty} dt' G^A(\vec{r},t;\vec{r}',t')\, V^A\Psi(\vec{r}',t') \tag{10.27}$$

where i denotes the incident channel and G^A is the Green's function for the operator $(i\partial/\partial t - H^A)$. By expanding Ψ in terms of the unperturbed functions X_j, G^A is easily found to be

$$G^A(\vec{r},t);\vec{r}',t') = -i\sum_j \theta(t-t')X_j(\vec{r},t)X_j^*(\vec{r}',t') \tag{10-28}$$

where $\theta(x)$ is the step function $\theta(x)=1,\ x\geq 0;\ \theta(x)=0,\ x<0$.

The amplitude for elastic scattering, or excitation, $a_j(b,\infty)$ is given by

$$a_j(b,\infty) = \lim_{t\to+\infty} \int d^3r X_j^*(\vec{r},t)\Psi(\vec{r},t)$$

$$= \delta_{ij} - i\int d^3r' \int_{\infty}^{\infty} dt' X_j^*(\vec{r}',t')V^A\Psi(\vec{r}',t') \quad (10\text{-}29)$$

The Born series is now obtained by substituting the iterative solution of the integral equation (10-27)

$$\Psi = (1 + G^A V^A + G^A V^A G^A V^A \ldots\ldots) X_i \quad (10\text{-}30)$$

in the right hand side of (10-29) and we find

$$a_j(b,\infty) = \delta_{ij} - i(X_j|V^A + V^A G^A V^A + \ldots\ldots|X_i) \quad (10\text{-}31)$$

The amplitude a for charge exchange into the level m can be obtained in various ways. For example, starting from the definition

$$c_m(b,\infty) = \lim_{t\to\infty} \int d^3r \Phi_m^*(\vec{r},t)\Psi(\vec{r},t)$$

$$= \int_{\infty}^{\infty} dt \int d^3r \frac{\partial}{\partial t}\left(\Phi_m^*(\vec{r},t)\Psi(\vec{r},t)\right)$$

and using equations (10-19) and (10-23), it follows that

$$c_m(b,\infty) = -i\int_{\infty}^{\infty} dt \int d^3r \Phi_m^*(\vec{r},t)\left(H_e - H^C\right)\Psi(\vec{r},t)$$

$$= -i(\Phi_m|V^C|\Psi) \quad (10\text{-}32)$$

where

$$V^C = H_e - H^C = V_{Ae} + (V_{AC} - W) \quad (10\text{-}33)$$

Substituting the iterative solution for Ψ, the Born series for c_m becomes

$$c_m(b,\infty) = -i(\Phi_m|V^C + V^C G^A V^A + V^C G^A V^A G^A V^A \ldots|X_i \quad (10\text{-}34)$$

By introducing the Green's function G^C corresponding to the operator $(i\partial/\partial t - H^C)$, the alternative expansion (see Chapter 4, 4- 39) is obtained

$$c_m(b,\infty) = -i(\Phi_m|V^C+V^CG^CV^A + V^CG^CV^CG^CV^A....|X_i) \qquad (10\text{-}35)$$

Finally by expanding the Green's functions G^A or G^C in terms of the Green's function G^O corresponding to the free particle operator$(i\partial/\partial t-H^O)$, a further form of the Born series is easily found

$$c_m(b,\infty) = -i(\Phi_m|V^C + V^CG^OV^A+ .....|X_i) \qquad (10\text{-}36)$$

It has already been shown that $|a_j|^2$ and $|c_m|^2$ are independent of the internuclear potential $(V_{AC}-W)$ which can be removed from (10-19) by a phase transformation[6]. If a finite number of terms is retained in any of the series for charge exchange (10-34), (10-35) or (10-36) the calculated amplitude will depend in some degree on the internuclear potential, and in practise the contribution from the internuclear potential to the first Born approximation is very large. For this reason Oppenheimer (1928) and Brinkman and Kramers (1930) suggested that it would be preferable to remove the internuclear potential by a transformation of the original Schrödinger equation (or by a phase transformation in the impact parameter equation) before writing down the perturbation series. If the internuclear terms are omitted from V^A and V^C, the series (10-36) will be called the Brinkman-Kramers series, and the first order Brinkman-Kramers approximation is

$$c_m^{BK} = - i \; (\Phi_m|V_{Ae}|X_i) \qquad (10\text{-}37)$$

It should be noted that while c_m^{BK} is the correct high velocity limit of the amplitudes (8-90) and (8-91) which were obtained as approximations to the 2-state coupled equations, this limit is only attained at very high velocities for which the overlap integral S is effectively zero. For example, for proton impact on hydrogen and helium over an energy up to 1MeV, the first order approximation (8-91) provides quite reasonable cross sections for capture into the $n\ell$ levels of hydrogen with $n \leq 4$, (Winter and Lin, 1974) and in contrast over the same energy level the Brinkman-Kramers cross sections obtained from (10-37) are quite inadequate, and can be in error by an order of magnitude.

Explicit calculation of the second order Born approximation (Kramer 1972) and of the second order Brinkman-Kramers approximation (Simony and McGuire 1981) for the cross section for capture into the ground state by protons from atomic hydrogen

$$H^+ + H(1s) \rightarrow H(1s) + H^+ \tag{10-38}$$

at energies from 100keV to a few MeV, have shown no improvement over the first order results. This implies that at these energies, even if the Brinkman-Kramers series converges (which has only been proved for short range potentials[7]), the convergence must be very slow.

Some interest attaches to the first Brinkman-Kramers cross section, because there is some evidence, at least for large n, that it provides a reasonable estimate of the ratios of cross sections for capture into the $n\ell$ excited state; also the results of some higher order methods can be expressed by the Brinkman-Kramers cross section multiplied by a slowly varying factor. If A and C are bare nuclei carrying charges Z_A, Z_C so that V_{Ae} and V_{Ce} are unscreened Coulomb potentials, the Brinkman-Kramers cross sections for capture into the level $n\ell$, from any level of the target, can be computed analytically (Sil, 1954). For example for capture from the ground state, the capture cross section into a level n, summed over the degenerate sub-levels is

$$\sigma_n^{BK}(Z_C, Z_A) = n^2 \sigma_1^{BK}(Z_C, Z_A/n) \tag{10-39}$$

where the ground state capture cross section is (in atomic units)

$$\sigma_1^{BK}(Z_C, Z_A) = \frac{2^8 \pi (Z_A Z_C)^5}{5v^2 (Z_A{}^2 + \alpha^2)^5} \tag{10-40}$$

and where

$$\alpha = (v^2 + Z_C{}^2 - Z_A{}^2)/2v \tag{10-41}$$

For large n, the cross section σ_n^{BK} decreases like $1/n^3$, a result which is known as the Oppenheimer rule.

The asymptotic cross section

The nature of the capture of cross sections in the asymptotic limit of high velocities has been studied, on the assumption that the Brinkman-Kramers series converges. Only capture into the 1s ground state from the 1s state of the target will be discussed here[8]. The first order cross section for ground state capture (10-41) becomes for large v

$$\sigma_1^{BK} \sim \frac{2^{18}\pi(Z_A Z_C)^5}{5v^{12}} \qquad (10\text{-}42)$$

The second order Brinkman-Kramers approximation was first obtained in the high velocity limit by Drisko (1955) who showed that

$$\sigma_1^{BK2} \sim \left(0.29458 + \frac{5\pi v}{2^{11}(Z_A+Z_C)}\right)\sigma_1^{\ BK} \qquad (10\text{-}43)$$

This very important result shows that the v^{-12} behavior of the first order term is ultimately overtaken by a v^{-11} behavior which arises from the second order matrix element. In addition, the coefficient of the v^{-12} term is modified by the second order term, and Drisko also showed that in the third order approximation the v^{-11} term was unaltered, but the coefficient of the v^{-12} term was again changed and

$$\sigma_1^{BK3} \sim \left(0.319 + \frac{5\pi v}{2^{11}(Z_A+Z_C)}\right)\sigma_1^{BK} \qquad (10\text{-}44)$$

This result was later confirmed by Shakeshaft (1978). The approach to the limit is very slow and the terms in v^{-11} do not dominate the cross section until energies in excess of 25MeV are attained, and by this energy relativistic corrections are becoming significant and more importantly the dominant capture mechanism for $E \geq$ 9MeV/amu is radiative capture[10].

$$C + (A + e^-) \rightarrow (C + e^-) + A + h\nu$$

It is interesting that the v^{-11} behavior of the cross section had been predicted in a classical model by Thomas (1927) and that the important intermediate states in the second Born matrix element do indeed represent this classical picture. The model depicts the collision as occurring in two steps. In the first step the electron acquires the speed v of the projectile, and is deflected towards the nucleus of the target, while in the second step the electron is deflected without change in speed into a direction parallel to the projectile. These intermediate states are not represented in a truncated discrete atomic orbital expansion, and this is one of the reasons that the continuum part of the expansion must be taken into account, particularly at high velocities.

Before leaving our discussion of the asymptotic cross section, a further contribution to the cross section in the special case of symmetrical resonance should be mentioned. So far. we have discussed the limiting cross section in the straight line impact parameter formalism and this (to order m_e/μ) provides the same results as would be obtained from the full Schrödinger equation for scattering in the forward direction. Charge exchange can also take place, if a collision is made in which the target nucleon is ejected and replaced by the incident nucleon. These 'knock-on' collisions take place at small impact parameters and correspond to scattering through 180° in the center of mass system. This process is only allowed kinematically if the masses of the two nuclei are equal and, if the nuclei are identical, the knock-on collision cannot be distinguished from elastic scattering. In the case of the proton - H(1s) system (10-38), the knock-on cross section is (Shakeshaft and Spruch 1979)

$$\sigma_K = \frac{16}{3}\left(\frac{m_e}{M}\right)^2\left(\frac{1}{v}\right)^6 \tag{10-45}$$

where M is the mass of a proton and m_e is the electron mass. At sufficiently high velocities σ_K becomes important and is about 30% of the forward capture cross section by 10MeV.

The Glauber approximation

In Chapter 6, the many body Glauber approximation was derived. This involved two approximations; the electrons in the target atom were considered to be at fixed positions, and then the scattering of the projectile from these electrons was determined using the eikonal approximation (see particularly (6-104), (6-105)). In heavy particle collisions at high energies, the straight line eikonal approximation is accurate, so that the conditions for the Glauber approximation to be useful depend only on the accuracy of the fixed position assumption. In this method, the total wave function Ψ is expressed as

$$\Psi(\vec{r},t) = X_i(\vec{r},t)\exp -i\int dt' V^A(\vec{r},t') \tag{10-46}$$

where V^A is given by (10-26), and this expression is employed in the matrix element (10-32) to obtain the amplitude $c_m(b,\infty)$. Since the internuclear potential should not alter the charge exchange probability, in applications this is omitted so that $V^C = V_{Ae}$ and $V^A = V_{Ce}$. An analytic expression for the capture amplitude can then be obtained for the case in which V_{Ae} and V_{Ce} are unscreened Coulomb potentials (Mittleman and Quong, 1968; Dewangan 1975, 1977) and for certain cases in which the active electron moves in effective screened potentials (Eichler 1981). The cross sections can be expressed as the product of the Brinkman-Kramers first order cross section a factor that tends to a constant as $v \to \infty$. For example, for capture into the ground state in the $H^+ + H(1s)$ reaction the Glauber cross section σ_G behaves like

$$\sigma_G \sim \frac{23}{48} \sigma_1^{BK} \qquad (10\text{-}47)$$

It is seen that the second order terms which give rise to the amplitude v^{-11} behavior of the capture cross section are not represented in the Glauber approximation, nevertheless at intermediate energies (100keV/amu < E < 1MeV/amu), this method does appear to provide cross sections of reasonable magnitude (Eichler and Chan 1979).

The continuum distorted wave approximation

A method which allows more fully for the second order terms and which treats the initial and final channels symmetrically is the continuum distorted wave (CDW) approximation of Cheshire (1964) (see also Gayet 1972). Let us consider the case of a single active electron moving in the field of two bare nuclei A and C with charges Z_A and Z_C, so that the impact parameter equation is again (10-19) and the potentials V_{Ae}, V_{Ce} and V_{AC} are Coulomb potentials (the effective potential W will be set equal to zero). Distorted waves X_j^D and Φ_m^D are introduced which satisfy the equations

$$\left(H^A + U^A - i\frac{\partial}{\partial t}\right) X_j^D = 0 \qquad \text{(a)}$$
$$\left(H^C + U^C - i\frac{\partial}{\partial t}\right) \Phi_m^D = 0 \qquad \text{(b)} \qquad (10\text{-}48)$$

together with the boundary conditions

$$\underset{t\to-\infty}{\ell t} X_j^D = X_j; \qquad \underset{t\to+\infty}{\ell t} \Phi_m^D = \Phi_m \qquad (10\text{-}49)$$

Provided

$$\underset{t\to-\infty}{\ell t} \int d^3r \Phi_m^{D^*} \Psi = 0 \qquad (10\text{-}50)$$

it is easy to show by an argument similar to that leading to (10-32), that the amplitude for capture into a level m of the atom $(C + e^-)$ is

$$c_m(b,\infty) = -i\int_{\infty}^{\infty} dt \int d^3r\Phi_m^{D^*} (V^C - U^C)\Psi$$

$$= -i(\Phi_m^D|V - U|\Psi) \qquad (10\text{-}51)$$

A distorted wave approximation is obtained if Ψ is approximated by the wave function X_i^D, so that

$$c_m^{DW}(b,\infty) = -i(\Phi_m^D|V^C - U^C|X_i^D) \qquad (10\text{-}52)$$

In the initial channel the interaction between the projectile and the bound electron might be expected to produce in the wave function terms looking like a Coulomb scattering wave function, at least in regions for which r_C is small. Similarly, in the charge exchange channel, the wave function should contain a factor looking like a Coulomb wave function in the coordinate r_A. To see how this can be achieved we write

$$\Psi^+(\vec{r},t) = X_i(\vec{r},t)\ F(\vec{r}_C,t) \qquad (a)$$

$$\Psi^-(\vec{r},t) = \Phi_m(\vec{r},t)\ G(\vec{r}_A,t) \qquad (b) \qquad (10\text{-}53)$$

where Ψ^+ and Ψ^- are two solutions of (10-19) defined so that $F \to 1$ as $t \to -\infty$ and $G \to 1$ as $t \to +\infty$. On substituting into (10-19), equations for F and G are found

$$X_i(\vec{r},t)\left(-\frac{1}{2}\nabla^2 + V_{Ce}(r_C) + V_{AC}(R) - i\frac{\partial}{\partial t}\right) F(\vec{r}_C,t)$$

$$= \vec{\nabla}X_i \cdot \vec{\nabla}F \qquad (a)$$

$$\Phi_m(\vec{r},t)\left(-\frac{1}{2}\nabla^2 + V_{Ae}(r_A) + V_{AC}(R) - i\frac{\partial}{\partial t}\right) G(\vec{r}_A,t)$$

$$= \vec{\nabla}\Phi_m \cdot \vec{\nabla}G \qquad (b) \qquad (10\text{-}54)$$

By setting the right hand sides of (10-54) to zero, exact solutions can be obtained for F and G, similar in character to Coulomb scattering functions for the potentials V_{Ce} and V_{Ae} respectively. These solutions are

$$F = N(\nu_C)\exp\left[i\nu\log(vR-v^2t)\right]{}_1F_1(i\nu_C,1,ivr_C+i\vec{v}\cdot\vec{r}_C) \quad \text{(a)}$$

$$G = N^*(\nu_A)\exp\left[-i\nu\log(vR-v^2t)\right]{}_1F_1(-i\nu_A,1,-ivr_A-i\vec{v}\cdot\vec{r}_A) \quad \text{(b)}$$

$$(10\text{-}55)$$

where

$$N(\nu) = \exp(\pi\nu/2)\Gamma(1-i\nu)$$

$$\nu_A = Z_A/v, \quad \nu_C = Z_C/v, \quad \nu = Z_AZ_C/v$$

The distorted wave functions are now taken as

$$X_i^D = X_iF \text{ and } \Phi_m^D = \Phi_mG \quad (10\text{-}56)$$

Using (10-54b), together with (10-48b) which defines U^C, it is found that

$$(V^C - U^C)\Phi_m^D = \vec{\nabla}\Phi_m\cdot\vec{\nabla}G \quad (10\text{-}57)$$

from which

$$c_m^{DW}(b,\infty) = -\,i\int_{\infty}^{\infty}dt\int d^3r\ X_i^D(\vec{\nabla}\Phi_m^*\cdot\vec{\nabla}G) \quad (10\text{-}58)$$

Numerical cross sections can be obtained, starting from (10-58), without further approximation.

The cross section for capture into the 1s ground state in the CDW approximation has the remarkable property that it coincides with the second Born approximation in the high velocity limit. For capture into excited states the CDW cross section contains the leading v^{-11} terms, but with coefficients that differ (but not by a large factor) from those given by the second Born approximation. No distorted wave method can allow properly for the mutual coupling of the initial and final channels and this sets a lower limit on the applicability of the CDW method. The relevant parameters are the electronic energies of the initial or final states, and Belkić et al (1979) have deduced empirically that the CDW model predicts accurate cross sections when the incident energy is greater than 80keV/amu X (the greater of the ionization potentials of the initial and final levels.) A detailed comparison of the results of CDW calculations with experiment has been given by Belkić et al (1979), who have also discussed some other higher order calculations such as the impulse approximation. As examples, the cross sections for capture into all excited states for (a) He^{++} incident or He and (b) Li^{3+} incident in H(1s) are shown in Fig. 10-5.

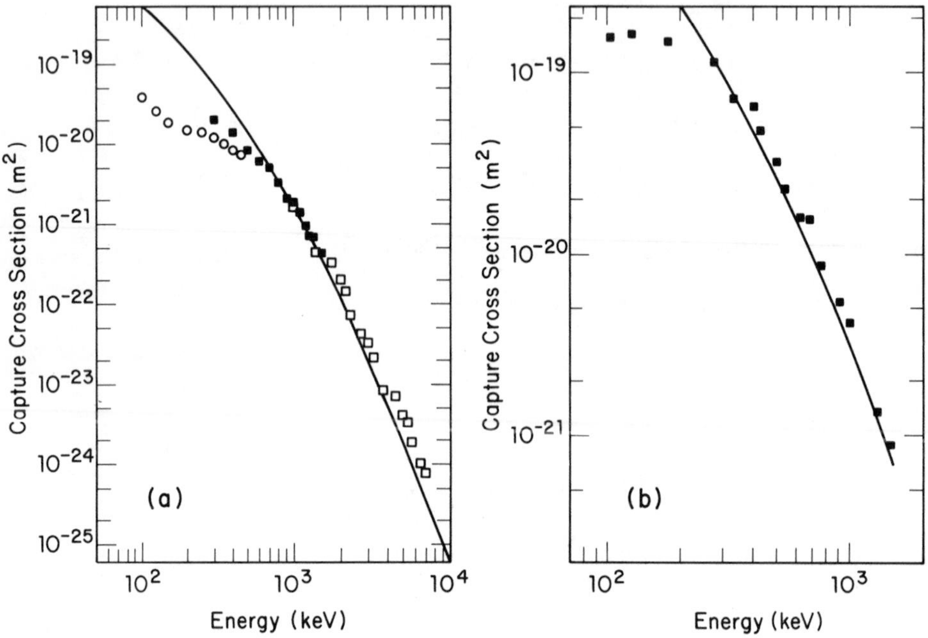

Figure 10-5 Total capture cross sections in the CDW approximation for (a) $He^{++} + He \rightarrow He^{+} + He^{+}$
(b) $Li^{3+} + H \rightarrow Li^{2+} + H^{+}$

Theoretical calculations (a) Belkić et al (1979)
(b) Belkić and Gayet (1979)

Experimental data (a) ○○ Allison (1958)
■ Pivovar et al (1962)
□ Heveplund et al (1976)
(b) ■ Shah et al (1978)

10-3 THE CLASSICAL MODEL

Several models have been developed in which both the electronic and nuclear motions in an ion-atom collision are described by classical mechanics. At first sight, since classical results are obtained in the limit of large quantum numbers, it would seem inappropriate to attempt to describe scattering by the ground state of an atom in this way, however, the most complete classical model is that due to Abrines and Percival (1966) which has been used with considerable success[11] to calculate the cross sections for the scattering of both fully and partially stripped ions by atomic hydrogen in the ground state. This success is related to the fact that the cross section for two-body scattering via a pure Coulomb potential is the same in both classical and quantum mechanics. Consider the system of a fully stripped ion C, charge Z_C, a proton A, charge $Z = 1$, and an electron. Initially ($t \to -\infty$) let the electron be in a classical orbit about the proton and the ion C to be moving parallel to the Z axis, with velocity v along a trajectory defined by an impact parameter b. For any particular set of initial conditions defining the electron orbit, the classical equations of motion can be integrated and the response of the system observed. In the center of mass system, either the six Lagrangian or the corresponding twelve Hamiltonian equations can be employed. After the collision, that is as $t \to \infty$, the electron will be found in orbit about A, in orbit about C or free from both A and C, which can be interpreted as excitation (or elastic scattering), charge exchange and ionization respectively. To obtain cross sections the calculation must be repeated for a sufficiently large range of impact parameters b, and for a given b, an average must be carried out over all possible initial configurations, of the electron-proton system which represent ground state hydrogen. This average is carried out by random sampling of the assumed initial distribution and for this reason this model has become known as the classical trajectory Monte-Carlo model (CTMC). In practice, about a thousand classical trajectory calculations must be made to obtain a statistically significant result. Since the initial electron-proton system is to represent ground state atomic hydrogen, the energy of each electron-proton orbit must be equal to ε_0, ($\varepsilon_0 = -0.5$ a.u.). It can then be shown, for fixed ε_0, the distribution of the square of the angular momentum L^2 is uniform in the interval $0 \leq L^2 \leq L_m^2$ where $L_m^2 = 1/(2|\varepsilon_0|)$ (in atomic units). The orbits are ellipses and the eccentricity of the ellipse is determined by L^2 and $|\varepsilon_0|$.

Six independent coordinates are required to define the initial conditions of the electronic motion. Two of these are ε_0, and $\beta=(L/L_m)^2$, two more can be taken to be (θ,ϕ) the polar angles of the major axis of the elliptical orbit and χ an angle specifying the plane of the orbit. The microcanonical ensemble of initial orbits is uniformly distributed in $\mu = \cos\theta$, over $-1 \leq \mu \leq 1$ and in ϕ and χ over the interval 0 to 2π. The four parameters (β,μ,θ,ϕ) determine the initial orbit (for a given value of ε_0) and a fifth parameter can be used to specify the initial position of the electron on a particular orbit. The calculations are then carried out over a random selection of the five parameters.
In this particular microcanonical ensemble, the distribution of electron momenta is

$$\rho(\vec{p}) = \frac{8p_o^{\,5}}{\pi^2}\,(p^2 + p_o^{\,2})^{-4}$$

where $p_o^{\,2} = 2|\varepsilon_0|$ and this is exactly the momentum distribution in the 1s level of hydrogen. This is a very special property of the Coulomb potential and accounts for the success of the model.

This classical model appears to provide cross sections for both ionization and charge exchange which are usefully, but not highly accurate over an energy range from ~50keV/amu to ~300keV/amu. The lower limit is presumably related to the fact that the system is becoming more 'molecular' in character and the upper limit to the difficulty of obtaining results with sufficient statistical significance. For example the computed cross section for the ionization of H(1s) by proton impact agrees with the experimental data over 80keV < E < 200keV to within 20%. For electron capture by He^{2+} from H(1s) and Li^{3+}H(1s) the classical cross sections lie a little above the results of the coupled channel calculations we have discussed, which are themselves a little larger than the experimental data[12].

NOTES

1. For example Bottcher and Flannery (1971) and Ritchie (1971) have shown that electron exchange is only important in the reaction H(1s) + H(1s) → H(1s) + H (n = 2) for v << 1 a.u. Of course some reactions can only take place through electron exchange, such as H(1s) + He(^{1}S) → H($n\ell$) + He($n\,^3L$), and in these cases the approximate wave function must be fully antisymmetrized in all the electron coordinates.

2. Systems which have been investigated using the coupled channel approximation include p + H, H + H, p + He, H + He, He^+ + H ...., see for example Flannery and McCann (1974); Bell et al (1973, 1974) and Bell and Kingston (1978). Further references are given by Bransden (1979).

3. See Bransden and Issa (1975).

4. These calculations have been reviewed by Bell and Kingston (1974, 1976).

5. See Bransden and Dewangan (1979).

6. Starting from the full Schrödinger equation it can be shown that the internuclear potential can only contribute to the total cross section for an inelastic process in terms of the order m_e/μ where m_e is the mass of the electron and μ the reduced mass of the heavy particles. The impact parameter formalism corresponds to the limit $m_e/\mu \to 0$ (McCarroll and Salin 1968).

7. The proof of convergence for short range potentials has been given by Shakeshaft and Spruch (1973). A lucid and detailed review of the asymptotic behavior of capture cross sections has been given by Shakeshaft and Spruch (1979), and other interesting discussions have been given by Belkić et al (1979) and Greenland (1982).

8. Results have been obtained for capture into excited states by Briggs and Dubé (1980).

9. Some details are given by Bransden (1965).

10. See Briggs and Dettmann (1977); Lee (1978).

11. See in particular Olson and Salop (1977); Salop (1979).

12. Detailed comparisons between the theoretical predictions and the data are given in the reviews of Greenland (1982) and Janev and Presnyakov (1981).

PROBLEMS

10-1 Consider the excitation of ground state atomic hydrogen to the 2s level by proton impact in the first order impact parameter approximation.

(a) Show that

$$V_{2s,1s}(R) = -\frac{2.2^{\frac{1}{2}}}{27}(2 + 3R)\, e^{-3R/2}$$

where $V_{2s,1s}$ is defined by (10-6)

(b) hence obtain the result

$$a_{2s}(b,\infty) = -\frac{i2.2^{\frac{1}{2}}}{27}\int_0^{\infty}(2 + 3R)e^{-3R/2}\cos\,(3t/8v)dt$$

(c) Evaluate $a_{2s}(b,\infty)$ and obtain the result

$$P_{2s}(b,v) = |a_{2s}(b,\infty)|^2$$

$$= \frac{2^{13}b^4v^2}{81(1+16v^2)^2}\left(K_2\left(\frac{3b}{8v}(1 + 16v^2)^{\frac{1}{2}}\right)\right)^2$$

where K_2 is a modified Bessel function of the second kind.

10-2 Consider the infinite set of equations obtained by letting $N\to\infty$ in (10-5). For all j with $j>2$ approximate the equations by only retaining the coupling between the channel j and the channels k = 1 and k = 2, so that

$$i\dot{a}_j \cong \sum_{k=1}^{2} V_{jk}e^{i(\eta_j-\eta_k)t}a_k, \qquad j > 2$$

Substitute the solutions of these equations into the equations for j = 1 and j = 2 to obtain the impact parameter analogue of the second order potential method developed in Chapter 6.

10-3 In problem 2, discuss how the second order kernels might be approximated (a) using closure (b) using a pseudostate basis.

10-4 In problem 2, write down the equivalent potentials in a pair of coupled channels in a third order approximation.

10-5 In the notation of Section (10-2) prove that

$$\int d^3r \int_{\infty}^{\infty} dt\, \Phi_m^{*} V^{C} \chi_i = \int d^3r \int_{\infty}^{\infty} dt\, \Phi_m^{*} V^{A} \chi_i$$

and show that this relation does not hold if the bound state wave functions contained in Φ_m and χ_i are only known approximately. This is known as the'post-prior' discrepancy.

10-6 Starting from (10-37) evaluate the cross section for the charge exchange reaction

$$H^{+} + H(1s) \rightarrow H(1s) + H^{+}$$

The easiest approach is to start by taking the Fourier transforms of $\phi_{1s}(r_C)$ and $r_A^{-1}\phi_{1s}(r_A)$, where ϕ_{1s} is the hydrogenic ground state wave function.

Chapter 11

ELECTRON SCATTERING BY DIATOMIC MOLECULES

The scattering of electrons or atoms by molecules presents a theoretical problem of considerably greater complexity than those we have already considered, because the scattering amplitude depends on the orientation of the molecule and because of the extra rotational and vibrational degrees of freedom involved. At low velocities the interaction between a molecule and other systems is often governed by the long range polarization forces which can be calculated from perturbation theory. We shall not discuss all such processes here, but we shall examine some of the methods that have been used to discuss the scattering of electrons by diatomic molecules, making no attempt at completeness. Many detailed calculations have been carried out for scattering by the hydrogen molecular ion and for the neutral hydrogen molecule which serve as prototypes for electron-molecule collisions in the same way as the scattering of electrons by hydrogen and helium atoms serves as a prototype of electron-atomic collisions.

11-1 MOLECULAR WAVE FUNCTIONS

The fundamental approximation in molecular physics has already been discussed in earlier chapters, where it was explained that, since the ratio of the mass of the electron to that of the nuclei is small, the electrons can be considered to a first approximation as moving in the field of the stationary nuclei. The complete Hamiltonian for a diatomic molecule is expressed as the sum of two terms by writing:

$$H = -\frac{\hbar^2}{2\mu}\nabla_R^2 + H_e \tag{11-1}$$

where μ is the reduced mass of the two nuclei which will be labeled A and B, and $\vec{R}$ is the internuclear line. The electronic wave functions and energies are then defined by the eigenvalue equation:

$$\{H_e(R,\vec{r}\,') - \varepsilon_n(R)\}\psi_{n,\Lambda}(R,\vec{r}\,') = 0 \tag{11-2}$$

where R enters as a parameter and $\vec{r}\,'$ stands for the coordinates of all the electrons collectively, in a frame of reference moving with the molecule with the Z′ axis along the internuclear line. The component of the total orbital angular momentum of the electrons, along the nuclear axis, is $\Lambda\hbar$ and the terms with $\Lambda = 0,1,2$ are denoted by Σ, Π and Δ as before. Each electronic state is characterized by the total spin S and the terms can be designated as $^{(2S+1)}\Sigma$, $^{(2S+1)}\Pi$.... In addition to invariance under rotations about the internuclear line, the system is invariant under reflections in any plane passing through the axis of the molecule. Such reflection changes the sign of the component of the angular momentum along the internuclear axis, so that, as we have already remarked, the states with non-zero values of Λ are doubly degenerate. In the case of Σ states such a reflection can only alter the wave function by a constant c, whose square is unity since a double reflection restores the original situation. Taking c to be real we must have either $c = +1$ or $c = -1$ and there are two distinct states, for one of which the wave function changes sign under reflection and for one of which the wave function is unaltered under reflection. These states are denoted by Σ^- and Σ^+ respectively. When the molecule consists of two nuclei having the same charge, the electronic wave functions divide into even and odd classes under reflection about the mid-point of the internuclear line, as discussed in Chapter 9, giving rise to the additional classification of gerade (even) and ungerade (odd) states.

The exact wave function can be expanded in the form (in what follows we shall suppress the spin variables)

$$\Psi(\vec{R},\vec{r}) = \sum_n \psi_{n,\Lambda}(R,\vec{r}\,')P_{n,\Lambda}(\vec{R}) \tag{11-3}$$

where the wave functions $P_{n,\Lambda}(\vec{R})$ representing the nuclear motion satisfy the coupled equations

$$\int d^3r' \psi^*_{m,\Lambda}(H - E) \sum_n \psi_{n,\Lambda} P_{n,\Lambda} = 0$$

The functions $\psi_{m,\Lambda}$ form an orthogonal set, and if in these functions are normalized to unity for each value of R, we have

$$\left(-\frac{\hbar^2}{2\mu}\nabla_R^2 + \varepsilon_n(\vec{R}) - E\right) P_{n,\Lambda}(\vec{R}) = \sum_m U_{nm}(\vec{R}) P_{m,\Lambda}(\vec{R})$$

where the coupling terms depend on the matrix elements of ∇_R^2 and $\vec{\nabla}_R$ with respect to the electronic wave functions. Since m/μ is small the rate of change of the functions $\psi_{n,\Lambda}$ with R can be neglected in the lowest approximation, so that $U_{nm} \approx 0$ and each molecular level can be represented by a single term in the expansion (11-3). This is known as the Born-Oppenheimer separation.

Although it is convenient to calculate the functions $\psi_{n,\Lambda}$ in the body fixed frame of reference, taking the internuclear line as axis, the wave function $\Psi(\vec{R},\vec{r})$ is required in a frame of reference with a fixed orientation in space. If the body fixed frame of reference has cartesian axes X′, Y′, Z′, with Z′ along the internuclear axis, and the space fixed frame of reference, with the same origin, has axes X, Y, Z, then the rotation that brings the X′, Y′, Z′ axes into the X, Y, Z axes can be defined by Euler angles α,β,γ, where the rotation is carried out in the following order:

(a) a rotation through an angle α about the Z′ axis;
(b) a rotation through an angle β about the new Y axis;
(c) a rotation through an angle γ about the new Z axis.

The polar coordinates Θ, Φ of $\vec{R}$ with respect to the space fixed frame of reference are then identical with the Euler angles β,γ. The relationship between the coordinates X, Y, Z or X′, Y′, Z′ of a point P in the two frames is

$$X = X'(\cos\alpha\cos\gamma - \cos\beta\sin\alpha\sin\gamma) -$$

$$- Y'(\sin\alpha\cos\gamma + \cos\beta\cos\alpha\sin\gamma) +$$

$$+ Z'\sin\beta\sin\gamma$$

$$Y = X'(\cos\alpha\sin\gamma + \cos\beta\sin\alpha\sin\gamma) -$$

$$- Y' (\sin\alpha \sin\gamma - \cos\beta \cos\alpha \cos\gamma) -$$

$$- Z' \sin\beta \cos\gamma,$$

$$Z = X' \sin\beta \sin\alpha + Y' \sin\beta \cos\alpha + Z' \cos\gamma. \quad (11\text{-}4)$$

Using these relations[1] the wave equation satisfied by $P_{n,\Lambda}(\vec{R})$ can be obtained in the space fixed frame. If the electron spin is not coupled to the orbital motion of the electrons, it is found that $P_{n,\Lambda}(\vec{R})$ is the product of a radial function $p_{n,\Lambda,j}(R)$ and an eigenfunction of J^2 and J_z denoted by $Q_{\Lambda,j,m}$, where $\vec{J}$ is the total orbital angular momentum[2] of the system,

$$P_{n,\Lambda}(\vec{R}) = R^{-1} p_{n,\Lambda,j}(R) Q_{\Lambda,j,m}(\beta,\gamma) \quad (11\text{-}5)$$

The functions $Q_{\Lambda,j,m}(\beta,\gamma)$ reduce to the ordinary spherical harmonics $Y_{j,m}(\beta,\gamma)$ if $\Lambda = 0$. For $\Lambda \neq 0$ they are related to the rotation matrices $D^j(\alpha,\beta,\gamma)$; see Edmonds (1957). As usual, $j(j + 1)\hbar^2$ and $m\hbar$ are the eigenvalues of J^2 and J_z respectively. The radial functions satisfy the equation

$$\left\{-\frac{\hbar^2}{2\mu}\left(\frac{d^2}{dR^2} - \frac{j(j+1) - \Lambda^2}{R^2}\right) - E + \varepsilon_{n,\Lambda}(R)\right\} p_{n,\Lambda,j}(R) = 0 \quad (11\text{-}6)$$

If the interaction energy $\varepsilon(R)$ possesses a minimum at a value of R,as in Fig. 11-1 curve (a),a stable molecular state is possible, and the electronic state is said to be attractive. The nuclear motion in this state will be confined to the potential well, the penetration of the wave function into the potential barrier being very small. If the interaction energy $\varepsilon(R)$ does not possess a minimum, as in curve (b) the molecule is unstable and will dissociate. In both cases, for large R, $\varepsilon(R)$ will tend to the sum of the energies of the separated atoms. The equilibrium position of the bound molecule is at the internuclear separation R_0, where R_0 is the root of the equation

$$\frac{\partial\varepsilon(R)}{\partial R} = 0$$

In the case of a bound molecular level, an expansion can be made about the equilibrium distance R_0, in which case (11-6) reduces to the equation

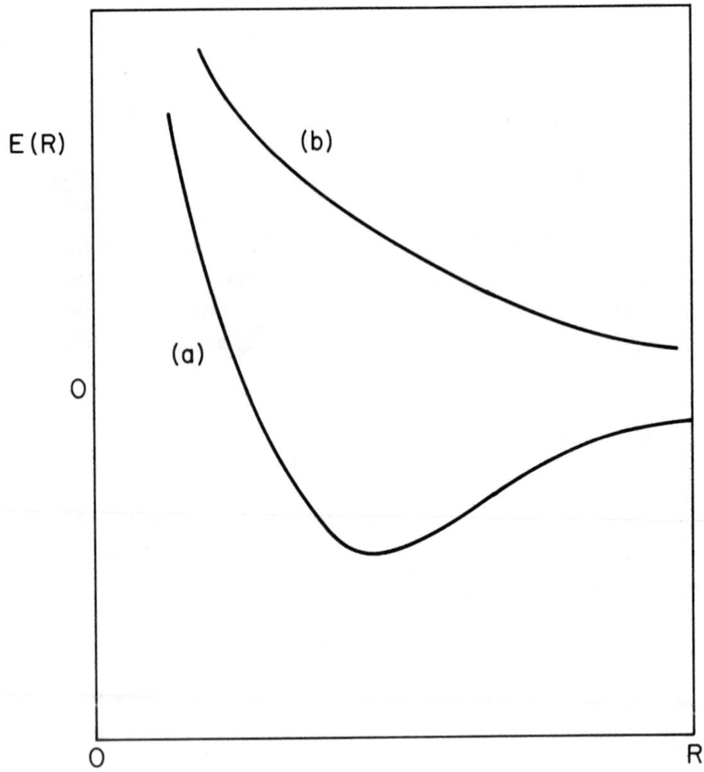

Figure 11-1 The electronic energy $\varepsilon(R)$ of a diatomic molecule as a function of the internuclear distance R. If the molecule is stable $\varepsilon(R)$ possesses a minimum (curve a). If $\varepsilon(R)$ does not possess a minimum the molecule will dissociate (curve b).

$$\left(-\frac{\hbar^2}{2\mu}\frac{d^2}{dR^2} + \frac{1}{2}(R - R_o)^2 \left.\frac{\partial^2 \varepsilon_{n,\Lambda}}{\partial R^2}\right|_{R=R_o}\right) P_{n,\Lambda,j}(R) = E_\nu P_{n,\Lambda,j}(R) \tag{11-7}$$

where

$$E_\nu = E - \varepsilon_{n,\Lambda}(R_o) - \frac{\hbar^2}{2\mu}\,\frac{j(j+1)-\Lambda^2}{R_o{}^2} \tag{11-8}$$

We shall refer to $\varepsilon_{n,\Lambda}(R_o)$ as the electronic energy of the molecule, to

$$E_{rot} = \frac{\hbar^2}{2\mu}\left(\frac{j(j+1)-\Lambda^2}{R_o^{\,2}}\right) \tag{11-9}$$

as the rotational energy, and to E_ν as the vibrational energy. The eigenvalues E_ν can be obtained by recognizing that (11-7) is the equation of a one dimensional oscillator, so that

$$E_\nu = \hbar\omega\left(\nu + \frac{1}{2}\right) \qquad \nu = 0,1,2,\ldots\ldots \tag{11-10}$$

with

$$\mu\omega^2 = \left(\frac{\partial^2\varepsilon(R)}{\partial R^2}\right)_{R=R_o}$$

More accurate values can be obtained from numerical solutions of the radial wave equation (11-6). The vibrational wave functions in this approximation are oscillator wave functions and are labeled by the vibrational quantum number ν for each set of quantum numbers n, Λ and j.

The electronic energy of the diatomic molecule is of the order of a few electron volts, for example in the ground state of molecular hydrogen $\varepsilon(R_o) = 4.7$ ev. This may be compared with the vibrational energy which is proportional to $1/\sqrt{\mu}$, and is an order of magnitude smaller and the rotational energy which is proportional to $1/\mu$ and is smaller still. For hydrogen, the vibrational energy is determined by $\hbar\omega$ which has the value 0.54 ev, and the rotational energy by $(\hbar^2/2\mu R_o^{\,2})$ which has the value 7.6×10^{-3}ev. Thus the vibrational levels split each electronic level into levels which lie much closer together than the spacing of the electronic levels themselves, and the rotational motion causes a further fine splitting of the vibrational levels. As the characteristic times associated with the electronic, vibrational and rotational motions are of the order $\hbar/\varepsilon(R_o)$, $1/\omega$ and $2\mu R_o^{\,2}/\hbar$ respectively, it is seen that the Born-Oppenheimer approximation in which the nuclei are treated as stationary for the purpose of calculating the electronic wave functions is usually sufficiently accurate[3].

The electronic wave functions

To be useful in a practical calculation of a scattering cross section, reasonably simple approximations to the electronic wave functions must be employed. These functions can be classified as single centered or two centered according to whether they are explicit functions of $\vec{r}_i$, the position vector of the ith electron with respect to the center of mass of the nuclei or of $(\vec{r}_{iA}, \vec{r}_{iB})$ the position vectors of the ith electron with the nuclei A and B. In the former representation it is easy to obtain the correct wave function in the united atom limit, while in the latter the separated atom limit arises naturally.

Single center wave functions

As an example of the construction of a single center wave function, we may consider the case of the hydrogen molecular ion H_2^+. In the united atom limit, the ground state of H_2^+ goes over into the 1s state of the helium ion He^+. This suggests that a simple variational approximation to the $(1s\sigma_g)$ state of H^+ would be

$$\psi_g(R,\vec{r}) = \sqrt{\frac{Z^3}{\pi}}\, e^{-Zr}, \tag{11-11}$$

where $\vec{r}$ is measured from the mid-point of the internuclear line and $Z(R)$ is a variational parameter which is a function of R, such that as $R \to 0$, $Z(R) \to 2$, the charge on the helium nucleus. As the lowest ungerade state in the united atom limit is the (2p) level of the helium, the $(2p\sigma_u)$ level of H_2^+ (designated $(\sigma_0 1s)$ in the separated atom limit) might be represented as

$$\psi_u(R,\vec{r}) = \sqrt{\frac{Z^5}{32\pi}}\, r \cos\theta\, e^{-Zr/2}. \tag{11-12}$$

More elaborate trial functions can be formed by taking linear combinations of functions of this hydrogenic type, or of some members of some other complete set. For instance Hagstrom and Shull (1959) have used combinations of the functions $f_{n,\ell,m}(\vec{r})$, where

$$f_{n,\ell,m}(\vec{r}) = R_{n\ell}(2Zr)Y_{\ell,m}(\theta,\phi), \tag{11-13}$$

and

$$R_{n\ell}(2Zr) = (2Z)^{3/2}\{n(n+\ell+1)!\}^{-3/2}\{(n-\ell-1)!\}^{1/2} \times$$
$$\times (2Zr)^{\ell} L^{2\ell+2}_{n-\ell+1}(2Zr)e^{-Zr} \quad n \geq \ell - 1 \tag{11-14}$$
$$|m| \leq \ell$$

This set is discrete and orthonormal. For a many electron

diatomic molecule, the wave function can be built up from correctly symmetrized products of these one electron functions. The molecular orbital wave function possesses cusps at the position of the nuclei A and B, and (except for R = 0) it is difficult to represent these discontinuities using single centered wave functions, and this is one of the reasons why expansions based on such wave functions are in general rather slowly convergent. For excited states the method is very successful, because the mean radius of the charge distribution is greater than the internuclear separation and the further the electron is from the center of the molecule, the more the two nuclei look like a single charge at the center of the molecule.

A different kind of single center wave function, that represents the cusps at A and B in a natural manner is due to Temkin (1963). Taking the midpoint of AB, the internuclear line, as origin, the electronic wave function for H_2 satisfies the Schrödinger equation (atomic units),

$$\left(-\frac{1}{2}\nabla_r^2 - \frac{1}{|\vec{r}+\vec{R}/2|} - \frac{1}{|\vec{r}-\vec{R}/2|} + \frac{1}{R} - \varepsilon(R)\right)\psi(R,\vec{r}) = 0 \tag{11-15}$$

On expanding the potential in terms of the angle θ between $\vec{r}$ and $\vec{R}$, this becomes

$$\left(-\frac{1}{2}\nabla_r^2 - \sum_{\ell}{}' V_\ell(r,R)P_\ell(\cos\theta) + \frac{1}{R} - \varepsilon(R)\right)\psi(R,\vec{r}) = 0 \tag{11-16}$$

where the prime denotes that the sum is over even values of ℓ only. The wave functions of either symmetry can also be expanded in terms of spherical harmonics, taking $\vec{R}$ as the axis we have that

$$\psi_{g,\lambda}(R,\vec{r}) = \sum_n{}' r^{-1}\phi_{n,\lambda}(r,R)Y_{n,\lambda}(\theta,\phi) \tag{11-17}$$

$$\psi_{u,\lambda}(R,\vec{r}) = \sum_n{}'' r^{-1}\phi_{n,\lambda}(r,R)Y_{n,\lambda}(\theta,\phi) \tag{11-18}$$

where the single and double primes denote sums over even and odd values of n respectively. The radial functions then satisfy, using (11-16)

$$\left(\frac{d^2}{dr^2} - \frac{\ell(\ell+1)}{r^2} + \varepsilon(R) - \frac{2}{R}\right)\phi_{\ell,\lambda}(r,R) +$$

$$+ 2\sqrt{\frac{4\pi}{2\ell+1}}\sum_L{}'\sum_n V_L(r,R)C^{\lambda 0\lambda}_{\ell L n}\phi_{n,\lambda}(r,R) = 0 \qquad (11\text{-}19)$$

where (see Appendix B, equation 19)

$$C^{\lambda 0\lambda}_{\ell L n} = \int Y^*_{\ell,\lambda}\, Y_{L,0}\, Y_{n,\lambda}\, d\Omega$$

$$= \left(\frac{(2L+1)(2n+1)}{4\pi(2\ell+1)}\right)^{\frac{1}{2}} (Ln00|\ell 0)(Ln0\lambda|\ell\lambda) \qquad (11\text{-}20)$$

In the lowest order approximation, the ($1s\sigma_g$) ground state of $H_2{}^+$ is represented by $\phi_0{}^0$ which satisfies

$$\left(\frac{d^2}{dr^2} + \frac{6}{R} + \varepsilon\right)\phi_0{}^0 = 0, \qquad 2r < R,$$

$$\left(\frac{d^2}{dr^2} + \frac{4}{r} - \frac{2}{R} + \varepsilon\right)\phi_0{}^0 = 0, \qquad 2r > R. \qquad (11\text{-}21)$$

The change in form of the equation at $r = r/2$ allows the correct representation of the cusps at these points. The function $\phi_1{}^0$ similarly represents the lowest order approximation to ($2p\sigma_u$). This method is capable of producing accurate wave functions even when a few terms in the expansion are taken[4]. In fact a single term is often sufficient.

Two center wave functions

In the separated atom limit, the wave functions for $H_2{}^+$ must become equal to the wave function of a hydrogen atom, centered either on proton A or on proton B. The lowest order wave functions for the ($\sigma_u 1s$), ($\sigma_g 1s$) states could be represented by the simple variational forms

$$\psi_{g,u}(R,\vec{r}) = 2^{-\frac{1}{2}}\left(\phi_{1s}(Z,r_A) \pm \phi_{1s}(Z,r_B)\right) \qquad (11\text{-}22)$$

where $\phi_{1s}(Z,r)$ is a hydrogenic function

$$\phi_{1s}(Z,r) = \sqrt{\frac{Z^3}{\pi}}\, e^{-Zr} \qquad (11\text{-}23)$$

and the variational parameter $Z(R)$ is such that as $R \to \infty$, $Z(R) \to 1$. Clearly better approximations are obtained by taking sums of terms of this general type.

For many electron atoms there are two ways of building up a suitable wave function. We may take products of functions, each of which describe the motion of a single electron in the field of the two nuclei and this is known as the molecular orbital method. For example, the wave function for the neutral hydrogen molecule could be written as

$$\psi(R,\vec{r}_i) = \chi(\vec{r}_1)\chi(\vec{r}_2)\sigma(1,2), \qquad (11\text{-}24)$$

where $\vec{r}_i$ is the position vector of the ith electron from the center of mass, $\sigma(1,2)$ is a spin function and $\chi(\vec{r})$ is a molecular orbital, which can be represented as in equation (11-22)

$$\chi_{g,u}(\vec{r}_i) = 2^{-\frac{1}{2}}\left(\phi_{1s}(Z,r_{iA}) \pm \phi_{1s}(Z,r_{iB})\right) \qquad (11\text{-}25)$$

Alternatively, we may start from the separated atom limit. In the case of molecular hydrogen the wave function at large R becomes equal to the product of two hydrogen wave functions, and approximations to the lowest states are

$$\psi_{g,u}(\vec{r}_1,\vec{r}_2;R) = 2^{-\frac{1}{2}} N_{g,u}(R) \Big(\phi_{1s}(Z,r_{1A})\phi_{1s}(Z,r_{2B}) \pm$$

$$\pm \phi_{1s}(Z,r_{2A})\phi_{1s}(Z,r_{1B})\Big) \sigma^{\mp}(1,2) \qquad (11\text{-}26)$$

where the upper signs correspond to the gerade (g) and the lower to the ungerade (u) states. Because of the Pauli principle the lowest g state is a singlet, $^1\Sigma_g$, and the spin function $\sigma^-(1,2)$ is

$$\sigma^-(1,2) = 2^{-\frac{1}{2}}[\alpha(1)\beta(2) - \beta(1)\alpha(2)] \qquad (11\text{-}27)$$

and the lowest u state is the triplet, $^3\Sigma_u$,

$$\sigma^+(1,2) = \begin{cases} \alpha(1)\alpha(2) \\ 2^{-\frac{1}{2}} \ \alpha(1)\beta(2) + \beta(1)\alpha(2) \\ \beta(1)\beta(2) \end{cases} \qquad (11\text{-}28)$$

The factor $N_{g,u}(R)$ is a normalization factor determined by the equation

$$(N_{g,u}(R))^{-2} = 1 \pm \int \phi_{1s}(r_{1A})\phi_{1s}(r_{2B})d^3r. \qquad (11\text{-}29)$$

In the molecular orbital approximation there are different ways of combining the single electron orbitals $\chi_{g,u}$ with the correct symmetry. For example, the lowest states of H_2 are

$$\begin{aligned}
\psi_g^{\,1} &= \chi_g(r_1)\chi_g(r_2)\sigma^-(1,2), \\
\psi_g^{\,2} &= \chi_u(r_1)\chi_u(r_2)\sigma^-(1,2), \\
\psi_u^{\,1} &= \left\{\chi_g(r_1)\chi_u(r_2) - \chi_g(r_2)\chi_u(r_1)\right\}\sigma^+(1,2), \\
\psi_u^{\,2} &= \left\{\chi_g(r_1)\chi_u(r_2) + \chi_g(r_2)\chi_u(r_1)\right\}\sigma^-(1,2).
\end{aligned} \qquad (11\text{-}30)$$

Each of these configurations corresponds to a different energy, with $\psi_g^{\,1}$ corresponding to the lowest $^1\Sigma_g^+$ state.

As in problems concerning atomic structure, in place of single electron functions depending on variational parameters, wave functions of self consistent field type can be calculated. Finally it should be noted that the orbitals for a single electron moving in the Coulomb fields of two nuclei can be obtained exactly because the Schrödinger equation can be separated in elliptic coordinates (λ,μ,ϕ) where

$$\lambda = \frac{r_A + r_B}{R}, \quad \mu = \frac{r_A - r_B}{R} \qquad (11\text{-}31)$$

and ϕ is the azimuthal angle of the plane containing r_A and r_B, and for H_2^+ the wave functions $\psi = F(\lambda)G(\mu)\Phi(\phi)$ are known exactly (Bates et al., 1953). Potential energy curves for the systems in which we are most interested, H_2 and H_2^+ are shown in Figs. 11-2 and 11-3.

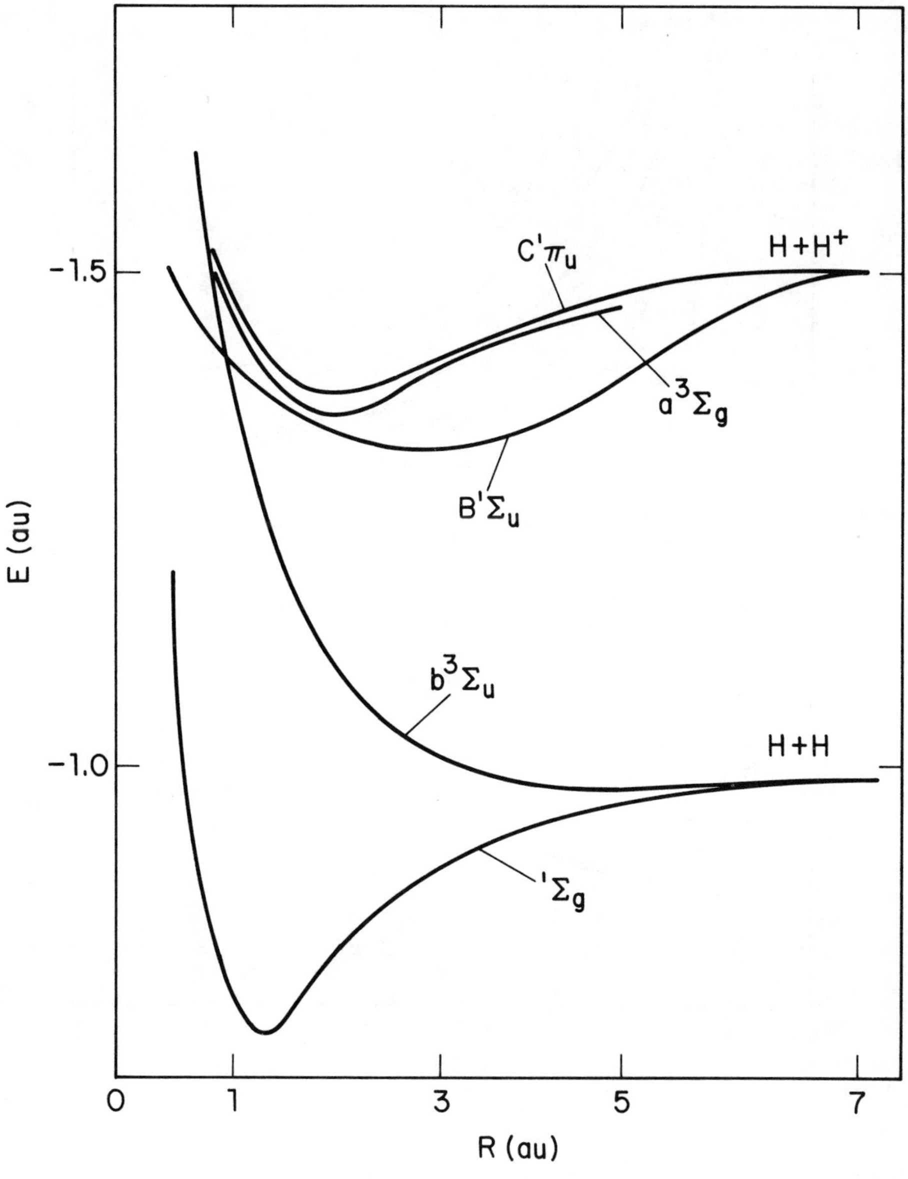

Figure 11-2 Potential energy curves for hydrogen

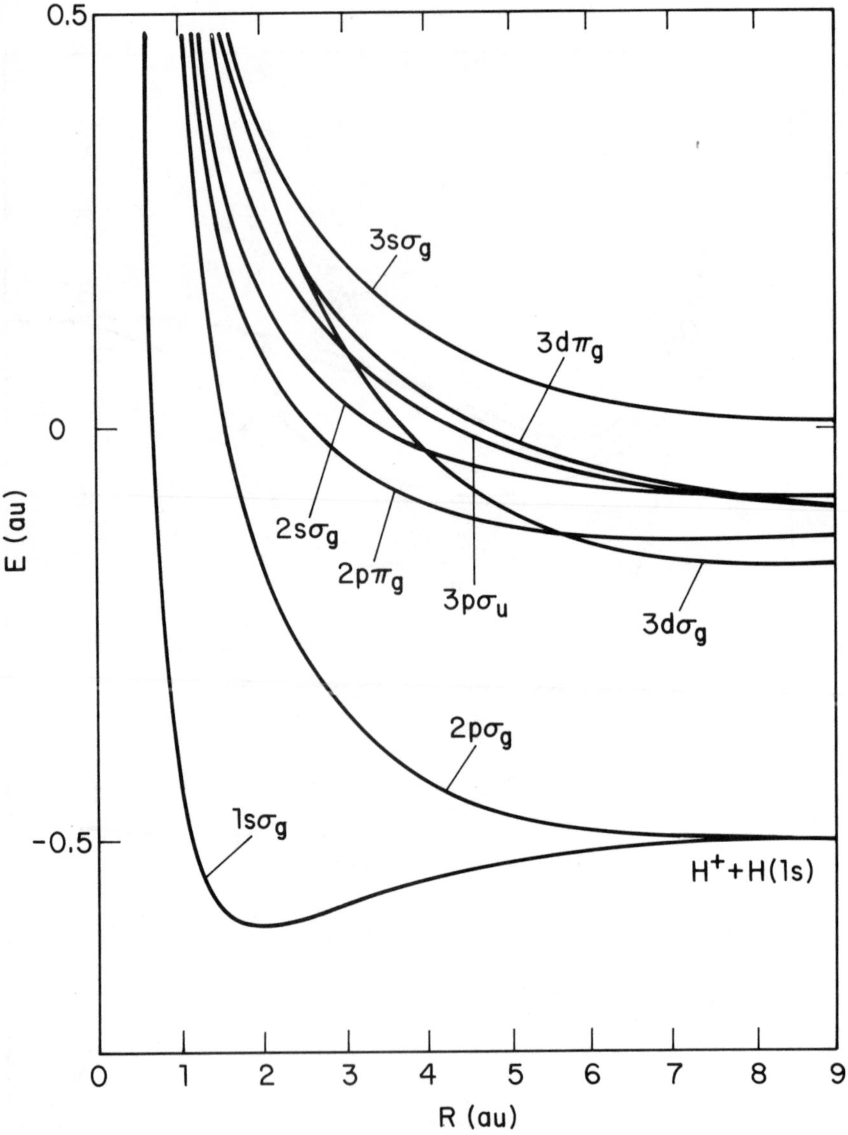

Figure 11-3 Potential energy curves for the hydrogen molecular ion.

11-2 HIGH ENERGY SCATTERING: THE BORN AND OCHKUR APPROXIMATIONS

The internal state of a diatomic molecule is specified by the electronic configuration n, the vibrational quantum number ν and the angular momentum quantum numbers j, Λ as well as the spin s. An electron of sufficient energy may excite the molecule to a state specified by the set of quantum numbers (n', ν', j', Λ', s') or be scattered elastically.

When the velocity of the incident electron is greater than the velocity of the target electron it is reasonable to use Born's approximation to calculate the cross section for a given excitation or elastic scattering process. In the high velocity region exchange effects will be unimportant, with the exception of transitions in which the spin of the target changes, which take place entirely through electron exchange. The rotational motion of the nuclei is so slow compared with the electronic motion that in calculating electronic excitation rates, the internuclear line can be considered to be in a fixed direction in space (Θ,Φ), and the differential cross section for an electronic transition summed over all final rotational states is obtained simply by averaging over all orientations of the internuclear line. This will be shown in the context of the Born approximation, but is correct in general. Some general statements can also be made about the final vibrational states of importance in excitation. The electronic transitions are fast compared with the vibrational motion of the nuclei, and may be considered to take place at a fixed value of R. For example in Fig. 11-4 curves (a) and (b) represent the interaction energy in two electronic states. The vibrational motion of the nuclei is such that the wave function is small beyond the classical turning points. If these are R_1 and R_2, centered about the equilibrium position R_0, then the probability of finding the value of R outside the region $R_1 < R < R_2$ is small. The transitions from the state (a) to the state (b) will take place with an appreciable probability only within this range of values of R, and the final vibrational states of importance will be those which have classical turning points in the same interval. This is known as the Frank-Condon principle. If the interaction curve is attractive, as in Fig.11-4(a), the vibrational levels excited will be bounded, but if the curve is repulsive as in Fig. 11-4(b), the nuclear motion will be unbounded and the molecule will dissociate. Various other possibilities exist; for example, the state represented by

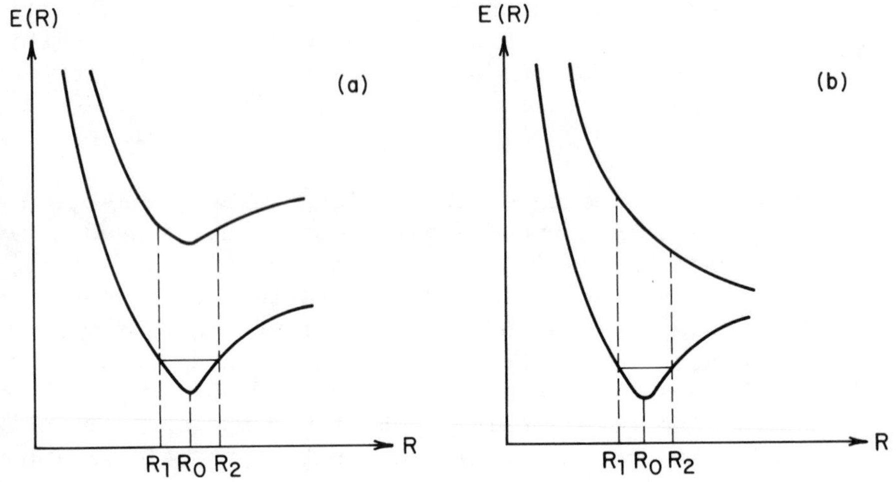

Figure 11-4 The Frank-Condon principle

the upper curve may be subject to auto ionization and the transition proceeds in the two steps:

$$\begin{aligned} e + (AB) &\rightarrow (AB)^* + e \\ &\rightarrow A + B^+ + 2e \end{aligned} \tag{11-32}$$

The scattering amplitude for a transition from the state $i \equiv (n,\nu, j,\Lambda)$ to the state $f \equiv (n', \nu', j', \Lambda')$ can be written down in the Born approximation, just as for electron-atom scattering, and (in atomic units)

$$\begin{aligned} -2\pi f_{fi}(\theta,\phi) = \int d^3x \int d^3r \int d^3R \; e^{-i\vec{k}_f \cdot \vec{x}} \Psi_f(\vec{R},\vec{r}) \; \times \\ \times \; V(\vec{R},\vec{r},\vec{x}) \; e^{i\vec{k}_i \cdot \vec{x}} \Psi_i(\vec{R},\vec{r}) \end{aligned} \tag{11-33}$$

where the perturbation V is

$$V = \sum_i \frac{1}{|\vec{x} - \vec{r}_i|} - \frac{Z_A}{x_A} - \frac{Z_B}{x_B} \tag{11-34}$$

The position vector of the scattered electron with respect to center of mass of the nuclei A and B is $\vec{x}$, and x_A and x_B are the distances of the scattered electron from A and B respectively. The integration $\int d^3r$ denotes an integration over all the bound electron coordinates and Ψ_f, Ψ_i are the final and initial wave functions of the molecule.

For the particular case, $n = n' = 0$, Ψ_f and Ψ_i are

$$\Psi_f(\vec{R},\vec{r}) = \psi_{n'}(\vec{R},\vec{r})\ R^{-1}p_{\nu'}(R)Y_{j,m}(\Theta,\Phi)$$

$$\Psi_i(\vec{R},\vec{r}) = \psi_n(\vec{R},\vec{r})R^{-1}p_\nu(R)Y_{j,m}(\Theta,\Phi) \tag{11-35}$$

It should be noted that the vibrational wave functions $p_\nu(R)$ depend on the electronic state n and also on j (and in general Λ) as well as the vibrational quantum number ν.

The terms in Z_A/x_A and Z_B/x_B in (11-34) only contribute to elastic scattering and for inelastic scattering the amplitude can be written as

$$f_{fi}(\theta,\phi) = \int d^3RM(\vec{R})\left[R^{-2}p^*_{\nu'}(R)p_\nu(R)\right]\left[Y^*_{j',m'}(\Theta,\Phi)\right.$$
$$\left. Y_{j,m}(\Theta,\Phi)\right], \tag{11-36}$$

where

$$M(\vec{R}) = -\frac{2}{K^2}\int d^3r\psi^*_{n'}(\vec{r},\vec{R})\psi_n(\vec{r},\vec{R})\sum_i \exp(i\vec{K}\cdot\vec{r}_i) \tag{11-37}$$

and we have made use of (6-31) to perform the integration over $\vec{x}$. The momentum transfer $\vec{K}$ is as usual defined as $\vec{K} = \vec{k}_f - \vec{k}_i$.

As a rule, the experiments refer to excitation cross sections summed over all final rotational states. This sum can be performed if it is remembered that the energy separation of the rotational states is very small compared with that of the electronic and vibrational states, so that to a good approximation $M(R,\Theta,\Phi)$ and $p_{\nu'}(R)$ are independent of j' and m'. We can then use the closure property of the $Y_{j',m'}$ to obtain

$$\sum_{j',m'} |f_{fi}(\theta,\phi)|^2 = \int d\Omega(\Theta,\Phi) \left| \int_0^\infty p_\nu(R) p^*_{\nu'}(R) M(\vec{R}) \times \right.$$

$$\left. \times \; Y_{j,m}(\Theta,\Phi)\, dR \right|^2 \qquad (11\text{-}38)$$

In exactly the same way, if we neglect the dependence of $\vec{k}_f$ on the energy of the final vibrational level, the sum over all final vibrational states can be performed, using the closure property of $p_\nu(R)$. Then for an initial spherically symmetrical rotational state,

$$Y_{j,m} = \frac{1}{\sqrt{4\pi}} \qquad \text{for } j = m = 0$$

and

$$\sum_{j',m',\nu'} |f_{fi}(\theta,\phi)|^2 = \frac{1}{4\pi} \int d^3R \, |R^{-2} p_\nu(R)|^2 \, |M(\vec{R})|^2 \qquad (11\text{-}39)$$

$M(\vec{R})$ is the scattering amplitude for excitation at a fixed orientation (Θ,Φ) of the internuclear line and is a slowly varying function of R compared with the function $p_\nu(R)$. The total cross section for excitation of the level n′, summed over all final states of nuclear motion is then

$$\sigma_{n'n} = \frac{k_f}{4\pi k_i} \int_{-1}^{+1} d\cos\Theta \int_0^{2\pi} \phi \int_0^\infty dR \, |p_\nu(R)|^2 \, |M(\vec{R})|^2 \qquad (11\text{-}40)$$

This result expresses the approximation that was discussed a little earlier, that is, the cross section can be calculated for a fixed orientation of the internuclear axis and subsequently averaged over all values of cos Θ and Φ.

Excitation of H_2^+

Extensive calculations of the excitation of H_2^+ by electron impact have been carried out by Peek (1964, 1965, 1967) who also considered the cases of excitation by proton and hydrogen atom impact[5]. The important transitions are from the ground state ($1s\sigma_g$) to the excited states ($2p\sigma_u$), ($2p\pi_u$) and ($2s\sigma_g$), where we have used the united atom designations. The strongest transition is to the ($2p\sigma_u$) state and as this state is repulsive, this excitation leads to dissociation:

$$e + H_2^+(1s\sigma_g) \rightarrow e + H_2^+(2p\sigma_u)$$
$$\rightarrow e + H\ (1s) + p. \tag{11-41}$$

In this work, Peek used the exact electronic wave functions of H_2^+ calculated by Bates et al. (1953). The LCAO approximation was employed in the earlier work of Ivash (1958) and where comparison is possible the computed cross sections agree to within 20%, suggesting that the approximate wave functions may be good enough for many purposes. Writing the cross section arising from the initial vibrational state ν as σ_ν, where

$$\sigma_\nu = \int_0^\infty \sigma(R)\,|p_\nu(R)|^2 dR, \tag{11-42}$$

and

$$\sigma(R) = \frac{k_f}{4\pi k_i}\int_{-1}^{+1} d\cos\theta \int_0^{2\pi} d\phi \int d\Omega(\hat{R})\,|M(\vec{R})|^2 \tag{11-43}$$

The behavior of $\sigma(R)$ as a function of R and σ_ν as a function of ν can be studied. In Table 11-1, $\sigma(R)$ is shown for the equilibrium value $R_0 = 2.0$ and for the values of R near the classical turning points.

Table 11-1

Cross section for the $(1s\sigma_g) \rightarrow (2p\sigma_u)$ excitation of H_2^+ (Peek, 1964)

(Atomic units)

	(a)			(b)	
E(ev)	$\sigma(R = 1.4)$	$\sigma(R = 2.0)$	$\sigma(R = 3.2)$	σ_0	σ_3
50	0.426	0.977	3.25	1.09	1.92
100	0.384	0.635	1.92	0.698	1.17
200	0.197	0.396	1.11	0.431	0.691
300	0.148	0.295	0.745	0.320	0.502
400	0.120	0.230	0.612	0.248	0.383

(a) $\sigma(R)$ — For definition see text

(b) σ_ν — Cross section for excitation in which the final vibration state is ν.

It is seen that the variation of $\sigma(R)$ with R is important and it is not sufficient to evaluate (R) at $R = R_0$ and treat it as a constant. The corresponding values of σ_ν are shown for $\nu = 0$ and $\nu = 3$. The cross section increases sharply with increasing ν, and this is shown particularly well in Fig. 11-5, where σ_ν is shown as a function of incident energies for all nineteen bound vibrational states associated with the lowest electronic state of H_2^+.

These results may be compared with measurements by Dunn and Van Zyl[6] (1967). If in the experiment each vibrational level of the $(1s\sigma_g)$ state of H_2^+ is populated by a fraction n_ν of the total number of ions in the $(1s\sigma_g)$ level, the measured cross section is

$$\sigma = \sum_\nu n_\nu \left[\sigma_\nu(2p\sigma_u) + \sigma_\nu(2s\sigma_g)\right] + \bar{\sigma}, \qquad (11\text{-}44)$$

where $\bar{\sigma}$ represents the cross section for excitation and ionization in all other levels. $\bar{\sigma}$ has been estimated using a closure approximation by Peek (1967). Remarkable agreement has been obtained between the calculated cross section and the measurements, illustrated in Fig. 11-6. The measurements which were carried out for energies from 10 to 150 ev, fitted the empirical formulae

$$\sigma = \frac{1}{E}(217 \log_{10} E - 184)\pi, \qquad (11\text{-}45)$$

where σ is atomic units and E is in electron volts, showing the characteristic $(\log(E)/E)$ asymptotic behavior of a dipole transition.

The calculations for proton impact show that, as expected, at high velocities the electron and proton cross section are the same at the same relative velocity. At lower velocities the proton is more efficient than the electron in dissociating the molecule because a greater range of momentum transfers, $(K_{max} - K_{min})$, is allowed.

Electron scattering by H_2

The interaction energy curves of some low lying states of H_2 have been shown in Fig. 11-2. The ground state (designated X) is a singlet state $^1\Sigma_g^+$ in which both electrons are in the united atom configurations $(1s\sigma_g)$ tending in the separated atom limit to two hydrogen atoms in the ground state. The H_2 molecule is stable against dissociation into two hydrogen atoms by 4.4 ev. Two ground state hydrogen atoms can also be brought together in the triplet spin state. In this case, the interaction is repulsive and the correspondinc

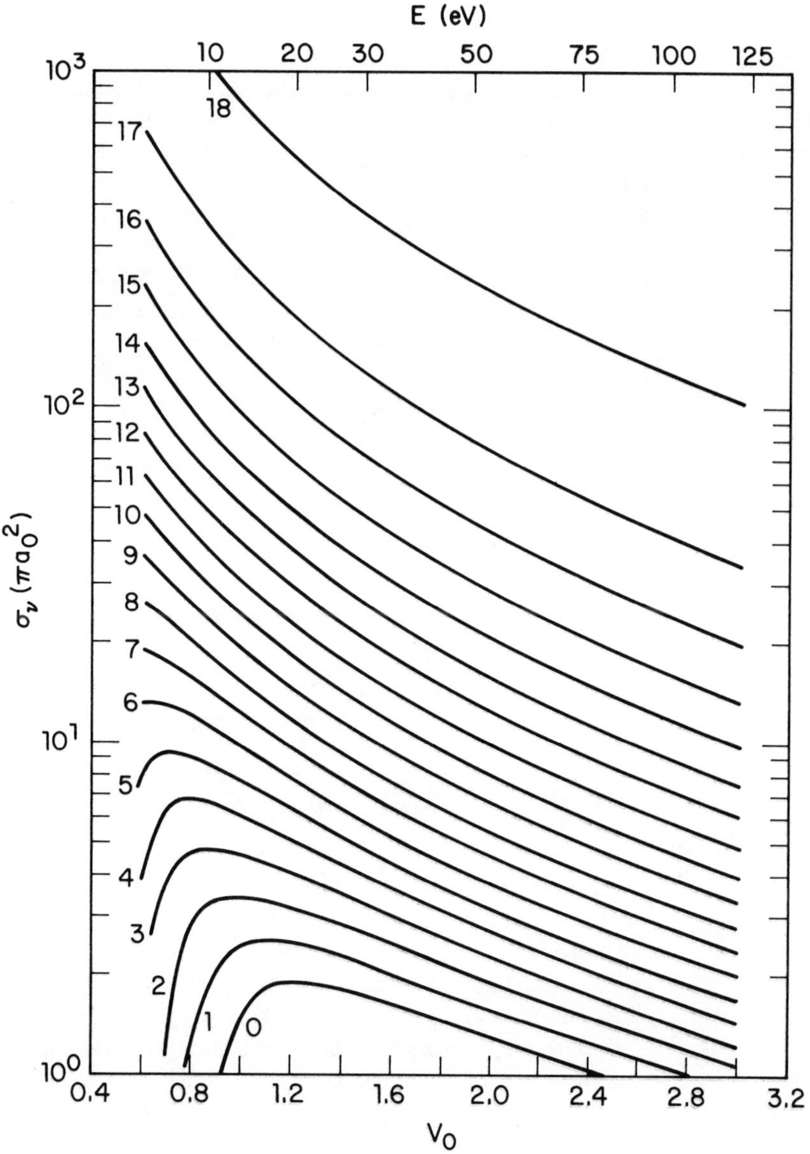

Figure 11-5 The cross sections σ_ν for an electron exciting the transition $1s\sigma_g \rightarrow 2p\sigma_u$ in H_2^+, for all nineteen bound vibrational states of the ground state of H_2^+. The lower scale is the relative velocity and the upper is the electron energy. The level $2p\sigma_u$ lies in the continuum so the process is dissociative. (Peek, 1964, 1965, 1967).

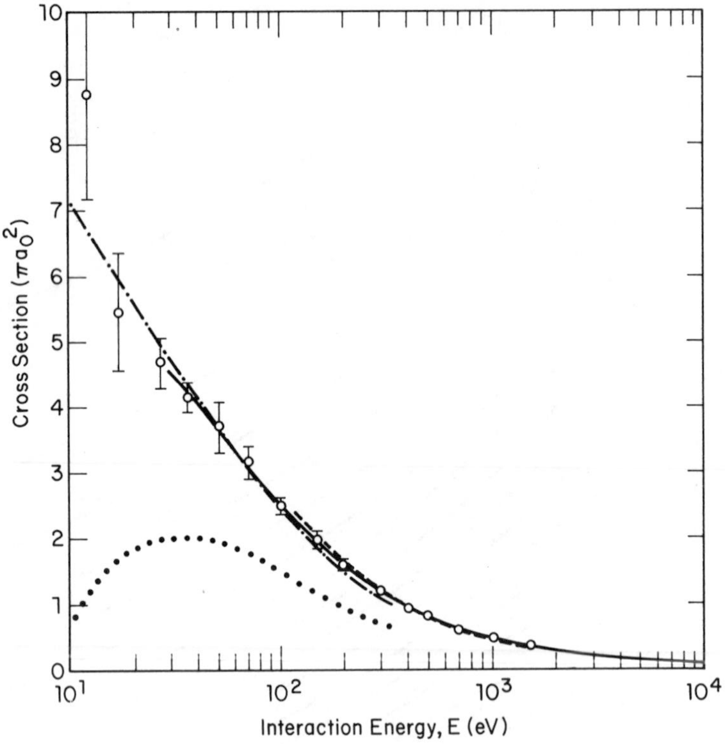

Figure 11-6 The cross section for the dissociation of H_2^+ by electron impact, averaged over vibrational levels.

o o o o Experimental data (Dunn and Van Zyl, 1967)

———— Calculated cross section (Peek, 1966).

.... Calculated cross section for dissociation from the lowest vibrational state of the ground state (Peek, 1966).

$^3\Sigma_u^+$ state of H_2 is unstable. Next come the states that correspond to H(1s) + H(n = 2) in the separated atom limit; these are the $^1\Sigma_n^+$, $^1\Pi_n$ and $^1\Sigma_g^+$ states, designated the B, C and E states respectively. Above the lowest triplet state, $^3\Sigma_u^+$ (designated b) lies the $^3\Sigma_g^+$ (designated a) which is attractive. The correlations for these states are shown in Table 11-2.

Both elastic scattering by the ground state and the excitation of the ground state to the low lying singlet state have been discussed within the Born approximation. In the

Table 11-2

Correlations for H_2

United atom	Term	Separated atom
He(^1S, 1s, 1s)	$X^1\Sigma_g^+$	H(1s) + H(1s)
He(2^3P, 1s, 2p)	$b^3\Sigma_u^+$	H(1s) + H(1s)
He(3^1P, 1s, 3p)	$B^1\Sigma_u^+$	H(1s) + H(2s)
He(2^3S, 1s, 2s)	$a^3\Sigma_g^+$	H(1s) + H(2s)
He(2^1P, 1s, 2p)	$C^1\Pi_u$	H(1s) + H(2p)
He(2^1S, 1s, 2s)	$E^1\Sigma_g^+$	H(1s) + H(2s)

early work of Massey and Mohr (1932), exchange effects were computed using the plane wave or Born-Oppenheimer approximation. As we saw earlier, this approximation is not as a rule reliable and in the more recent work of Khare and Moiseiwitsch (1965, 1966) an improved first order exchange method was used to calculate the exchange scattering amplitude. Khare and Moisewitsch concluded that the Born approximation was reliable at electron impact energies in excess of 100ev.

As an alternative the Ochkur or Ochkur-Rudge approximations to the exchange amplitude may be investigated. As in the case of scattering by atoms, the exchange amplitude in the Ochkur approximation can be expressed in terms of the direct amplitude by the simple formula

$$g_{fi} = \frac{K^2}{2k_i^2} f_{fi} \tag{11-46}$$

Khare (1966a,b) has calculated the cross section for excitation of the B, C and D levels in this approximation using the single center wave functions of Huzenaga (1957). It was assumed that $\sigma(R)$, defined by (11-43) could be treated as a constant and it was computed at the equilibrium distance $R = R_0$. In this the dependence on the initial vibrational state is removed and using (11-46) the differential cross section per unit momentum transfer is

$$\frac{d\sigma}{dK} = \frac{K}{2k_i^2} \int d\Omega(\hat{R}) \left|M(\vec{R})\right|^2 \left(1 - \frac{K^2}{2k_i^2}\right)^2 \tag{11-47}$$

The excitation cross sections for the B and C levels rise steeply from the thresholds (at 11.4 and 12.4eV respectively) to a maximum near 50eV. It is only in the vicinity of this maximum and at lower energies that exchange is important and near 50eV, the exchange interaction reduces the cross section by from 8 to 10%. In Fig. 11-7 the theoretical cross sections of Khare and earlier results of Roscoe (1944), who employed two-center wave functions, are compared with the experimental data of Greider (1964).

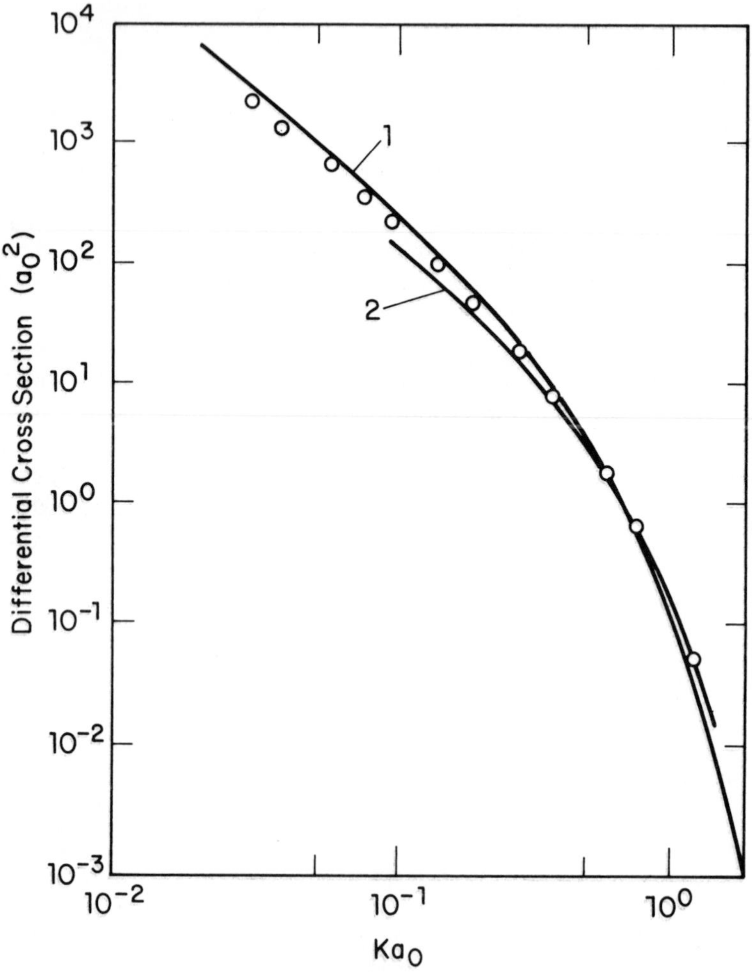

Figure 11-7 Excitation of the sum of the B and C states of hydrogen at 25keV

o o o o o Experimental cross section (Greider, 1964).

1, 2 Calculated cross section in the Born approximation (Roscoe, 1944; Khare, 1966).

The energy of the incident electron was 25keV. At this energy and for small values of the momentum transfer, the first Born approximation should be accurate and the accuracy of the computed cross sections depends on the quality of the molecular wave functions employed. At large angles, for which K is large, the first Born approximation will not be adequate at high energies, and double scattering terms will dominate the cross section in the case of the excitation of atoms (see Chapter 6).

Excitation of the triplet states has also received a good deal of attention (Khare, 1967; Cartwright et al., 1967). As this process can only occur through exchange, the results depend critically on the approximation used to estimate the exchange amplitude. Cartwright et al. show that there are considerable differences between the cross sections calculated in the Ochkur approximation and in Rudge's modification of the Ochkur approximation and also that the results are sensitive to the details of the assumed ground state H_2 wave function. For later developments of the Born approximation the work of Chung and Lin (1978), and the references therein should be consulted.

Interesting applications of the semi-classical impact parameter method to electron-molecule excitation have been reported by Hazi (1981), using a method originally developed by Seaton (1961, 1962). Using a straight line trajectory for the incident electron, and treating the rotational and vibrational levels of the molecule as degenerate, the first order excitation cross section is written down which is similar to (10-9) for atomic excitation. The computational problem is then simplified by replacing the interaction by its asymptotic form for large x. In other words for a dipole transition, the leading term is

$$\sum_i \frac{1}{|\vec{x}-\vec{r}_i|} \sim \sum_i \frac{1}{x^2} r_i \cos\theta_i .$$

With this approximation the integral over the impact parameter b, diverges for small b, but a lower limit to the integration b_0, can be introduced, for example by requiring that the cross section coincides with the Born cross section at high energies. Hazi has applied this method to a number of transitions in H_2, N_2 and F_2 for energies between 20 and 100 eV and has found some improvement over the usual Born approximation at the lower energies. As the incident energy is decreased the Born approximation begins to gail for the lower partial waves, while the higher partial waves may still be represented accurately. The reason for the success of the Seaton model is that the lower partial waves are removed (corresponding to small impact parameters) and replaced by the semi-empirical cut-off parameter b_0.

An impulse approximation

When the wave length of the incident electron is small compared with the internuclear distance, the molecule tends to behave like two independent atomic scattering centers. The scattering amplitude can then be expanded in a multiple scattering series in which each term describes a succession of scatterings at each center. In the lowest approximation, the scattering amplitude can be represented as a sum of the scattering amplitudes from each atom in the molecule, weighted by suitable phase factors that allow for the displacement of each atom from the center of mass of the molecule. If the position vector of each atom in the molecule, with respect to the center of mass, is $\vec{R}_i$, then the outgoing spherical wave arising from elastic scattering at the ith atom from an incident plane wave exp $(i\vec{k} \cdot \vec{x})$ is

$$f_i(\theta) \frac{e^{ik|\vec{x} - \vec{R}_i|}}{|\vec{x} - \vec{R}_i|} e^{i\vec{k}\cdot\vec{R}_i} \tag{11-48}$$

where $f_i(\theta)$ is the scattering amplitude proper to the atom i. The factor $\exp(i\vec{k}\cdot\vec{R}_i)$ allows for difference in phase of the incident wave between the center of mass and the scattering center. For large $|x|$, (11-48) becomes

$$\left(f_i(\theta) e^{i(\vec{k}-\vec{k}')\cdot\vec{R}_i} \right) \frac{e^{ikx}}{x} \tag{11-49}$$

where $\vec{k}'$ is the final momentum of the scattered electron $(|k'| = |k|)$.

The differential cross section for elastic scattering from the molecule becomes

$$\frac{d\sigma}{d\Omega} = \left| \sum_i e^{i\vec{K}\cdot\vec{R}_i} f_i(\theta) \right|^2$$

$$= \sum_{ij} f_i^*(\theta) f_j(\theta) \exp i\vec{K} \cdot (\vec{R}_i - \vec{R}_j), \tag{11-50}$$

In the case of a diatomic molecule i and j take the values 1 and 2 and $\vec{R}_1 - \vec{R}_2 = \vec{R}$ where R is the internuclear distance. Averaging over all orientations of the internuclear axis

$$\left(\frac{d\sigma}{d\Omega}\right)_{av} = \frac{1}{4\pi}\int \sum_{ij} f_i^*(\theta) f_j(\theta) \exp\left(i\vec{K}\cdot(\vec{R}_i - \vec{R}_j)\right) d\Omega(\hat{K})$$

$$= \sum_{i,j=1}^{2} f_i^*(\theta) f_j(\theta) \frac{\sin KR}{KR} \tag{11-51}$$

To a sufficient accuracy R can be set equal to R_0 the equilibrium internuclear distance. When both atoms are identical we have that

$$\left(\frac{d\sigma}{d\Omega}\right)_{av} = 2\left(\frac{d\sigma}{d\Omega}\right)^A \left(1 + \frac{\sin KR_0}{KR_0}\right) \tag{11-52}$$

where $(d\sigma/d\Omega)^A$ is the cross section for scattering from each atom alone. The most important correction to this formula will arise from double scattering in which the electron scatters first from one and then from the other atom. There is some evidence that this is small at higher energies (Hoerni, 1956). Bullard and Massey (1933) discussed the scattering of electrons by nitrogen in this way for energies between 30 and 780 eV, and fair agreement with the observed angular distribution was obtained. Further work along these lines has been reviewed by Craggs and Massey (1959).

11-3 LOW ENERGY SCATTERING

At energies below those for which the Born approximation is accurate coupled channel partial wave approximations can be introduced which parallel the various methods discussed in Chapters 5 and 6 for the scattering of electrons by atoms. A great simplification is achieved in the fixed nuclei or adiabatic approximation in which the calculation is carried out with the nuclei fixed at the equilibrium positions. It is then possible to work in the body-fixed coordinate frame, not only for the bound electrons but also for the scattered electron. At the end of the calculation a unitary transformation can be made to the laboratory (space-fixed) frame to obtain the differential cross section. Such an approach will break down if the incident energy is not large compared with the spacing of the rotational levels and in this case, the problem should be formulated in the laboratory frame (see Section 11-4). It is possible to work entirely in the body-fixed frame, even at low energies, in a region where all the distances r_i and x are small, provided a frame transformation is made to the space-fixed frame in the asymptotic region and this approach (Chang and Fano, 1972) retains much of the simplicity of the body-fixed frame approach. The connection between the inner and outer region can be made in terms of the R-matrix, which was introduced in a one channel context in Chapter 2 (see for example a study of $e^- - CO$ scattering by Chandra, 1977).

The earliest fixed-nuclei models were introduced by Stier (1932) and Fisk (1936, 1937) who analyzed the scattering data from a number of homonuclear molecules in terms of an effective (optical model) potential for which a parametric form was assumed, the parameter being chosen to fit the data. The first calculations based on molecular wave functions and allowing for exchange were by Massey and Ridley (1956), who treated the case of electron scattering by the ground state of hydrogen. They assumed a molecular wave function of the self consistent field type given by Carlson (1938) and expressed the wave function in the form (for s wave scattering)

$$\Psi(\vec{x},\vec{r}_1,\vec{r}_2,\vec{R}) = \mathcal{A}F(\vec{x})\Psi_H(\vec{r}_1,\vec{r}_2,\vec{R})\sigma(1,2,3) \tag{11-53}$$

where Ψ_H is the molecular wave function, σ is the spin wave function and $\mathcal{A}$ is an operator that antisymmetrizes the wave function with respect to the three electrons. A parametric form was assumed for $F(\vec{x})$, the wave function of relative motion of the incident electron and the molecule,

$$F(\vec{x}) = (1 + a^2)^{-1/2}\{C(\xi - 1)\}^{-1}\Big[\sin C(\xi - 1) + \{a + be^{-\gamma(\xi-1)}(1 - e^{-\gamma(\xi-1)})\}\cos C(\xi - 1)\Big]$$

where ξ was defined in terms of the distances x_A and x_B of the incident electron from the two nuclei,

$$\xi = \left(\frac{x_A + x_B}{R}\right) \quad \text{and} \quad C = kR/2$$

The parameters a and b were determined by the Kohn variational principle and the zero order phase shift was given by

$$\eta = \left(\tan^{-1}(a) - \frac{1}{2}kR\right)$$

The results agreed quite well with the measurements of Ramsauer and Kollath (1930) at energies up to 10 eV provided the exchange terms were included. This work was extended to higher order phase shifts by Carter et al. (1958).

The coupled equations

As an example of scattering of an electron by a molecule in a Σ state (Λ=0), let us consider the $e^- - H_2^+$ system containing two electrons - one bound electron and the scattered electron. If $\vec{r}_1$ and $\vec{r}_2$ are the position vectors of the electrons with respect to the center of the internuclear line as origin, a coupled channel wave function can be written as

$$\Psi^{\pm}(\vec{r}_1,\vec{r}_2) = \sum_n [\psi_n(R,\vec{r}_2)F_n^{\pm}(\vec{r}_1) \pm \psi_n(R,\vec{r}_1)F_n^{\pm}(\vec{r}_2)] \quad (11\text{-}53)$$

where the sum is over a number of electronic levels of the H_2^+ molecule. The wave function is spatially symmetric if the + sign is taken and thus corresponds to scattering in a singlet spin state, and spatially antisymmetric if the - sign is taken corresponding to a triplet state.

The scattering functions $F_n^{\pm}(\vec{r})$ can be expanded in a partial wave series

$$F_n^{\pm}(\vec{r}) = \sum_{\ell} r^{-1} f^m_{n,\ell}(r)\; Y_{\ell,m}(\theta,\phi) \quad (11\text{-}54)$$

and it should be noted that the radial functions depend on the magnetic quantum number m, in contrast to the corresponding atomic case. Both $\vec{r}_1$ and $\vec{r}_2$ are defined in the body fixed frame with the internuclear line as the Z axis. To keep the discussion simple, consider the case in which only the ground state is retained in the expansion , so that only elastic scattering is allowed. The extension to inelastic scattering is straightforward and parallels the work of Chapter 6. The ground state wave function is the $(1s\sigma_g)$ function and can be represented either by a single center or a two center expansion. Although we have restricted the discussion to a single electronic state, the radial wave functions satisfy equations coupling the different values of ℓ. The equations are found by requiring

$$\int \psi_g^*(R,\vec{r}_2)Y^*_{\ell,m}(\theta,\phi)[H - E]\Psi^{\pm}(\vec{r}_1,\vec{r}_2) = 0 \quad (11\text{-}55)$$

and are of the form

$$\left(\frac{d^2}{dr^2} - \frac{\ell(\ell+1)}{r^2} + k^2\right) f^m_{\ell}(r) = 2\sum_{\ell'} (V^m_{\ell\ell'} \pm K^m_{\ell\ell'}) f^m_{\ell'}(r) \quad (11\text{-}56)$$

The potential $V^m_{\ell\ell'}$ is the direct (non-exchange) potential and $K^m_{\ell\ell'}$ is an exchange kernel.

The T-matrix in the body-fixed frame is defined as usual by the asymptotic form of the radial functions. For each ℓ', a set of functions is found such that

$$f_\ell^m(r) \sim \sin(kr-\ell\pi/2)\delta_{\ell\ell'} + T_{\ell\ell'}^m \exp(ikr-\ell\pi/2) \qquad (11\text{-}57)$$

The transition matrix in the space fixed frame is obtained by a unitary rotational transformation defined by the Euler cycles (α,β,γ) of the internuclear line. It can be shown that (Temkin et al 1969, see also Burke and Sin Fai Lam, 1970, Chandra, 1975), the scattering amplitude in the laboratory system is

$$f(\alpha,\beta,\gamma;\theta,\phi) = \Sigma T_{\ell\ell'}^m D_{mm'}^\ell(\alpha,\beta,\gamma)\left(D_{om}^{\ell'}(\alpha,\beta,\gamma)\right)^* Y_{\ell'm'}(\theta,\phi) \qquad (11\text{-}58)$$

where the sum is over ℓ, ℓ', m, m$'$ and the D functions are the rotation matrices defined by Edmonds (1957). The differential cross section average over all orientations of the internuclear line is

$$\bar{\sigma}(\theta,\phi) = \frac{1}{8\pi^2}\int |f(\alpha,\beta,\gamma;\theta,\phi)|^2 d\alpha d\gamma d\cos\beta \qquad (11\text{-}59)$$

The differential cross section for excitation of a rotational level j$'$ from an initial level j can also be obtained approximately, from the scattering amplitude

$$f_{j'j}(\theta,\phi) = \int d\alpha \int d\gamma d\cos\beta\ Q_{j'}^* f(\alpha,\beta,\gamma;\theta,\phi) Q_j \qquad (11\text{-}60)$$

where $Q_{j'}$ and Q_j are the rotational eigenfunctions. The angular integration in (11-60) can be performed analytically and it should be emphasized that the matrix elements $T_{\ell\ell'}^m$ are independent of α,β and γ.

The coupled channel model can be improved in different directions. More terms can be added in the expansion over molecular levels, or polarization potentials can be introduced or both. To introduce polarization (that is distortion of the molecule in the field of the incident electron) in a non-empirical way, Temkin and Vasavada (1967) showed how polarized orbitals could be introduced into single center molecular wave functions and applied the method to the calculation of elastic scattering of electrons by H_2^+. Later work on the e-H_2 system was carried out by Lane and Henry (1968).

Because of the numerical difficulties of treating the exchange kernel, attempts have been made to replace the exchange interaction by an equivalent local potential[7], for example Morrison and Collins (1978) have studied elastic scattering of electrons by H_2 and N_2 and their cross sections agree well with those of Buckley and Burke (1977) who solved the full integro-differential equations. Other methods for dealing with exchange include the expansion of the exchange kernel on a finite basis thus representing the kernel by a sum of separable potentials, which as we have seen is a soluble problem (Collins et al 1980).

Other numerical techniques which have been employed to solve the coupled equations include, the reduction of the corresponding integral equations to coupled algebraic equations (Schneider and Collins 1981, 1982) and the use of the Schwinger variational method discussed in Section 4-4 (Watson and McKoy, 1979).

L^2 methods

The region in which the interaction between a scattered particle and a target is strong and is of limited extent, and in such a region the total wave function for the whole system of target + scattered particle can be expanded in a set of normalizable L^2 functions to any desired degree of accuracy. From such a representation of the wave function, which is accurate in a region of finite extent, scattering information can be extracted in different ways - for example, fitting to the solutions in the asymptotic region or by using T-matrix element weighted to emphasize the region in which the approximate wave function is accurate.

These ideas have been applied to the scattering of electrons by molecules in several ways. The R-matrix approach, which introduces a definite boundary between inner and outer regions has been used by Schneider and his colleagues to discuss the e-H_2, e-N_2 and e-F_2 systems (Schneider 1975; Schneider and Hay 1976; Morrison and Schneider 1977) and by Burke et al (1977) and Buckley et al (1979) who also studied e-H_2 and e-N_2. The cross section obtained by Schneider (1975) who included pseudostates to represent polarization effects for e-H_2 elastic scattering is shown in Fig. 11-8. It is seen to agree quite well with the experimental data near the cross section maximum at 2eV.

A different approach to obtaining L^2 wave functions is due to Rescigno et al (1974). This starts by introducing a non-local potential V between the scattered electron and the target molecule. The transition operator is then[8]

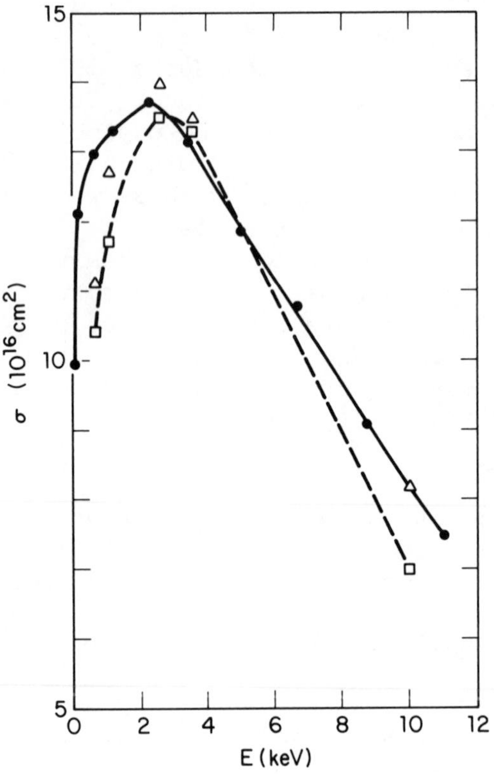

Figure 11-8 The total e-H_2 cross section at low energies
——— Schneider (1975)
- - - - Klonover and Kaldor (1978)
Δ Δ Δ Δ Data of Linder and Schmidt (1971)

$$T = V\ (1 + G + V) \tag{11-61}$$

and since (see 4-159)

$$G^+ = RG_o^{\ +} \tag{11-62}$$

where G_o is free particle Green's function and

$$R = [1 - G_o^{\ +}V]^{-1} \tag{11-63}$$

the transition operator can be written as

$$T = [1 - G_o^{\ +}V]^{-1}V \tag{11-64}$$

The scattering amplitude for scattering from a plane wave state $|\vec{k}_i)$ to a state $|\vec{k}_j)$ is

$$f\ (\theta,\phi) = -\ (2\pi)^{-1}\ (\vec{k}_j|T|\vec{k}_i) \tag{11-65}$$

The complicated non-local optical potential is now expanded on a finite basis of Gaussian functions ϕ_j. These functions are particularly suitable because multi centre integrals can be performed analytically. For example, if r_A and r_B are the positions of an electron with respect to nuclei A and B in a diatomic molecule integrals such as

$$\int d^3r\ \exp(-\lambda r_A^{\ 2})\ \exp(-\mu r_B^{\ 2})V$$

can be evaluated easily, where V is a Coulomb potential function such as $1/r_A$ or $1/r_B$.

In the finite basis the construction of the resolvent R becomes a matter of solving a set of linear equations, so that the matrix elements T_{jk} of T in this basis are found easily. The scattering amplitude is then

$$f(\theta,\phi) = -\ (2\pi)^{-1} \sum_{jk}(\vec{k}_f|\phi_j)T_{jk}(\phi_k|\vec{k}_i) \tag{11-66}$$

Klonover and Kaldor (1978, 1979) have applied this method to e-H_2 scattering, allowing for both the static exchange and polarization interactions in the construction of the optical potential. Their results for the total cross section are shown in Fig. 11-8 and compare well with experiment and are similar to those obtained from R-matrix approach.

11-4 LONG RANGE FORCES AND ROTATIONAL EXCITATION

It is not until very low energies are reached that the energy loss through rotational excitation becomes important compared with elastic scattering. However, at low energies, the most important interaction is the long range part of the effective potential seen by the scattered electron. This is much more effective in producing rotational excitation than the short range part of the interaction, because the short range interaction will only scatter low energy electrons in the $\ell=0$ partial wave. In contrast, the long range interaction can be quite effective in producing significant scattering in the states of non-zero angular momentum, and it is these states that are important in rotational excitation. The theoretical formulation of low energy rotational excitation must be carried out in the space-fixed (laboratory) frame of reference and the rotational levels of the molecule are not treated as being degenerate.

The effective interaction between the scattered electron and the molecule can be expressed as an optical model potential $V(\vec{x},\vec{R})$ where $\vec{x}$ is the position vector of the electron relative to the center of mass of the molecule and $\vec{R}$, is, as usual, the internuclear separation. The static first order approximation to $V(\vec{x},\vec{R})$ is

$$V_s(\vec{x},\vec{R}) = \int d^3r|\psi_0(\vec{r}_i,\vec{R})|^2 \left\{ \sum_i \frac{1}{|\vec{x} - \vec{r}_i|} - \frac{Z_A}{x_A} - \frac{Z_B}{x_B} \right\} \quad (11\text{-}67)$$

where ψ_0 is the ground state electronic wave function of the molecule and the integration is over the coordinates of the bound electrons. The distance of the scattered electron from each nucleus is x_A and x_B, so that for a homonuclear molecule

$$x_A = |\vec{x} + \tfrac{1}{2}\vec{R}|,$$

$$x_B = |\vec{x} - \tfrac{1}{2}\vec{R}|.$$

From (11-33) the scattering amplitude for rotational or vibrational excitation of a molecule in a Σ level, without a change in the electronic state is given in the Born approximation by

$$-2\pi f_{fi}(\theta,\phi) = \int d^3R \int d^3x\, R^{-1} p^*_{\nu'}(R) Y^*_{j',m'}(\Theta,\Phi) \exp(-i\vec{k}_f\cdot\vec{x}) \times$$

$$\times V(\vec{x},\vec{R}) R^{-1} p_\nu(R) Y_{j,m}(\Theta,\Phi) \exp(i\vec{k}_i\cdot\vec{x}) \quad (11\text{-}68)$$

Following earlier work of Massey (1935), Wu (1947), Morse (1953) and Carson (1954) approximated $V(\vec{x},\vec{R})$ by the sum of two potentials depending on x_A and x_B respectively. For a homonuclear molecule V was written as

$$V(\vec{x},\vec{R}) \approx U(x_A) + U(x_B), \quad (11\text{-}69)$$

where U(r) had the parametric form

$$U(r) = -r^{-1}(1 + Zr)e^{-2Zr} \quad (11\text{-}70)$$

The parameter Z(R) was an effective nuclear charge represented in the form

$$Z = \alpha + (R - R_0)\beta. \tag{11-71}$$

The parameters α and β were determined from variational calculations and for molecular hydrogen the numbers $\alpha = 1.166$ a.u., $\beta = -0.23$ a.u. were obtained for an equilibrium distance of $R_0 = 1.4$ a.u.

This interaction is short range in character and does not succeed in reproducing the experimental results, either for rotational or for vibrational excitation, the calculated cross section being an order of magnitude too small. To investigate the forces of longer range, $V(\vec{x},\vec{R})$ can always be expanded in a multipole series for $x > R$. If the molecule is in a Σ state, the system is axially symmetrical about $\vec{R}$ so that, the expansion of V can be written as

$$V(\vec{x},\vec{R}) = -\sum_{n=0}^{\infty} \frac{u_n(R)}{x^{n+1}} P_n(\cos \alpha), \tag{11-72}$$

where α is the angle between $\vec{x}$ and $\vec{R}$. To see the significance of the terms in this series we can approximate $V(\vec{x},\vec{R})$ by $V_s(\vec{x},\vec{R})$, given by (11-67) for a homonuclear molecule. The static potential $V_s(\vec{x},\vec{R})$ can be written as

$$V_s(\vec{x},\vec{R}) = -\frac{Z}{|\vec{x} - \vec{R}/2|} - \frac{Z}{|\vec{x} + \vec{R}/2|} + \int d^3r' \frac{\rho(r',R)}{|\vec{x} - \vec{r}'|} \tag{11-73}$$

where $\rho(\vec{r},\vec{R})$ is the charge density in the molecule. For Σ states, ρ is axially symmetrical about $\vec{R}$. Expanding the denominators in (11-73) and comparing with (11-72), we see that $u_n(R) = 0$ for n odd, because $V_s(\vec{x},\vec{R}) = V_s(-\vec{x},\vec{R})$ for both gerade and ungerade states. For even n,

$$u_n(R) = 2Z\left(\frac{R}{2}\right)^n - \int d^3r' \rho(\vec{r}',\vec{R}) r'^n P_n(\cos \alpha') \tag{11-74}$$

where α' is the angle between $\vec{r}'$ and $\vec{R}$, and if the molecule is neutral $u_0(R)$ is zero. In discussing rotational excitation, the average of $V(\vec{x},\vec{R})$ over the ground state vibrational function $p_0(R)$ is required and the Born approximation reduces to

$$-2\pi f_{fi}(\theta,\phi) = \int d^3x \int_{-1}^{+1} d\cos\Theta \int_0^{2\pi} d\Phi Y^*_{j',m'}(\Theta,\Phi)\exp(-i\vec{k}_f\cdot\vec{x}) \times$$

$$\times \; U(x, \cos\alpha) Y_{j,m}(\Theta,\Phi)\exp(i\vec{k}_i\cdot\vec{x}) \qquad (11\text{-}75)$$

where

$$U(x, \cos\alpha) = \int_0^\infty |p_0(R)|^2 V(\vec{x},\vec{R})dR \qquad (11\text{-}76)$$

For a homonuclear molecule, and in the approximation $V = V_s$ it is seen from (11-74) that for large x, $U(x, \cos\alpha)$ behaves like

$$U(x, \cos\alpha) \sim - \sum_n \frac{C_n}{x^{n+1}} P_n(\cos\alpha) \qquad (11\text{-}77)$$

where the sum runs over even values of n and the quantities C_n are constants. The lowest term contributing to the rotational excitation of a homonuclear molecule in a Σ level is the quadrupole term with $n = 2$. Gerjuoy and Stein (1955a,b) discussed the rotational excitation of H_2 and N_2 retaining the term alone. When this is done the cross section in the Born approximation can be evaluated analytically. The result depends on the quadrupole moment ($Q \equiv C_2$) of the molecule and on the integral

$$\int_{-1}^{+1} d\cos\Theta P_{j'}(\cos\Theta) P_2(\cos\Theta) P_j(\cos\Theta) \qquad (11\text{-}78)$$

which gives rise to the selection rule

$$j' = j \pm 2 \qquad (11\text{-}79)$$

The calculated cross sections are:

$$\sigma_{j,j+2} = \frac{8Q^2}{15}\pi\frac{k_f}{k_i}\frac{(j+2)(j+1)}{(2j+3)(2j+1)}$$

$$\sigma_{j,j-2} = \frac{8Q^2}{15}\pi\frac{k_f}{k_i}\frac{j(j-1)}{(2j-1)(2j+1)} \qquad (11\text{-}80)$$

The quantity that is measured experimentally is the rate at which an electron with velocity v loses energy through rotational excitation. This is

$$\frac{dW}{dt} = v \sum_j N_j \left[\sigma_{j,j+2} (E_{j+2} - E_j) - \sigma_{j,j-2} (E_j - E_{j-2}) \right] \tag{11-81}$$

where N_j is the number of molecules per unit volume and the rotational energy levels are E_j where (in atomic units)

$$E_j = \frac{j(j+1)}{2\mu R_o^2} \tag{11-82}$$

The energy loss per collision is

$$\left(\frac{dW}{dt} \frac{1}{nv\sigma(\text{total})} + \frac{2n}{m} W \right) \tag{11-83}$$

where n is the number density of the molecules and σ(total) is the total cross section. Combining (11-80), (11-81) and (11-83), the mean energy loss per collision divided by the elastic energy loss becomes

$$\lambda = 1 + \frac{32Q^2\pi}{15} \left(\frac{1}{2\mu R_o} \right) \left(\frac{1}{W} \frac{\mu}{2m} \right) \tag{11-84}$$

For nitrogen, λ is ten-times the number expected from elastic loss alone and the computed value of λ, with $Q = - 1.1$, is the same order of magnitude as that measured which is $\lambda \sim 10$ for electron energies W between 0.1 and 0.6 eV. The quadrupole moment of hydrogen is smaller, (Q =).46), than for nitrogen and the computed value of λ is about 2, but this is about half the measured value obtained by Crompton and Sutton (1952).

The above discussion based on the static potential V_s is not completely adequate because it makes no allowance for the distortion of the molecule in the field of the incident electron. The first term of importance is the dipole distortion which is proportional to x^{-4} at large values of x. The general form of the long range interaction, modified to take polarization into account is (averaged over the vibrational ground state), for a homonuclear molecule,

$$U(x, \cos\alpha) = - \frac{\alpha}{2x^4} - \left(\frac{\alpha'}{2x^4} + \frac{Q}{x^3} \right) P_2(\cos\alpha), \tag{11-85}$$

where two new terms arise because the molecule can have different polarizabilities along and perpendicular to the internuclear axis, α_{11} and α_τ respectively. In terms of

$$\alpha = \frac{1}{3}(\alpha_{11} + 2\alpha_{\tau}),$$

$$\alpha' = \frac{2}{3}(\alpha_{11} - \alpha_{\tau}). \qquad (11\text{-}86)$$

The importance of the polarization terms was first pointed out by Dalgarno and Moffatt (1963). For H_2 we have that $\alpha = 5.328$, $\alpha' = 1.25$, while for N_2, $\alpha = 12.0$ and $\alpha' = 4.2$.

For heteronuclear molecules, the odd terms in the series (11-77) no longer vanish by symmetry, and the lowest terms in the expansion of U are

$$U(x, \cos\alpha) \sim -\frac{\alpha}{2x^4} - \frac{\mu}{x^2} P_1(\cos\alpha) - $$

$$- \left(\frac{\alpha'}{2x^4} + \frac{Q}{x^3}\right) P_2(\cos\alpha) + \ldots\ldots, \qquad (11\text{-}87)$$

where μ is the permanent dipole moment of the molecule.

The polarization terms arise naturally in a coupled channel calculation provided a suitable pseudostate is included in the basis and both the R-matrix and polarized orbital calculations which were referred to in the last section are adequate in this respect. To obtain cross sections on a semi-empirical basis the polarization terms can be cut-off at short distances to obtain an effective potential, such as:

$$U(x, \cos\alpha) = -\left(\frac{\alpha}{2x^4} + \frac{\mu}{x^2} P_1(\cos\alpha) + \left(\frac{\alpha'}{2x^4} + \frac{Q}{x^3}\right) P_2(\cos\alpha)\right) \times$$

$$\times \left(1 - \exp(-\lambda x^6)\right)$$

where λ is an adjustable parameter determined so that the computed cross section fits the scattering data.

<u>The general theory of rotational excitation</u>

To obtain an improved theory of rotational excitation, it is necessary to go beyond the Born approximation, as well as using a potential that allows for all the long range effects[9]. We start from the Schrödinger equation (in atomic units) for the system composed of the incident electron and the target molecule:

$$\left(-\frac{1}{2}\nabla_R^2 - \frac{1}{2}\nabla_x^2 + H_e + V - E\right)\Psi = 0 \qquad (11\text{-}88)$$

where H_e is the electronic Hamiltonian and V is the interaction between the incident electron and the molecule. As we are interested for the moment in transitions that leave the molecule in the lowest electronic and vibrational levels, a projection operator $\mathcal{P}$, such that for large x, is introduced

$$\mathcal{P}\Psi(\vec{x},\vec{r}_i,\vec{R}) \to \psi_o(\vec{R},\vec{r}_i)R^{-1}p_o(R)F(\vec{x},\Theta,\Phi) \tag{11-89}$$

A suitable form of $\mathcal{P}$ is the integral operator:

$$\mathcal{P}= \psi_o(\vec{R},\vec{r}_i)R^{-1}p_o(R)\int_0^\infty R'dR'\int d^3r_i'\psi_o^*(\vec{R}',\vec{r}_i')p_o^*(R') \tag{11-90}$$

Introducing $\mathcal{Q} = 1 - \mathcal{P}$, we see that $\mathcal{P}\Psi$ satisfies the equation

$$\mathcal{P}\left(-\frac{1}{2m}\nabla_x^2 + H_R + U - E'\right)\mathcal{P}\Psi = 0 \tag{11-91}$$

where H_R is the Hamiltonian associated with the rotational motion of the molecule and U is the effective potential

$$U = \mathcal{P}\left(H_e + V - \frac{1}{2\mu}\nabla_R^2 - H_R + \varepsilon\right)\mathcal{P} + \mathcal{P}H\mathcal{Q}\frac{1}{\mathcal{Q}(H-E)\mathcal{Q}}\mathcal{Q}H\mathcal{P} \tag{11-92}$$

The energy E′ is equal to (E - ε) where ε is the sum of the electronic and vibrational energies of the molecule in the ground state. The effective potential U is non-local, and contains the effects of exchange, as well as all polarization effects. To the extent that the Born-Oppenheimer separation is valid the first term in U just involves the average of the static interaction $V_S(\vec{x},\vec{R})$ given by equation (11-67) over the vibrational ground state. Equation (11-91) can be written as a wave equation for $F(\vec{x};\Theta,\Phi)$ in the form

$$\left(-\frac{1}{2m}\nabla_x^2 + H_R + U(x, \cos\alpha) - E'\right)F(\vec{x};\Theta,\Phi) = 0 \tag{11-93}$$

where the long range part of U is local and is given by (11-77).

For molecules in a Σ state, the eigenfunctions of H_R are the spherical harmonics $Y_{j,m}(\Theta,\Phi)$ and

$$H_R Y_{j,m}(\Theta,\Phi) = E_j Y_{j,m}(\Theta,\Phi),$$

$$E_j = \frac{1}{2\mu R_o^2}j(j + 1) \tag{11-94}$$

The simultaneous eigenfunctions of the total angular momentum J, the angular momentum of the molecule j and of the electron

ℓ are given by (see Appendix B)

$$\mathcal{Y}^{JM}_{j\ell}(\theta,\phi;\Theta,\Phi) = \sum_{mn} (j\ell mn|JM) Y_{jm}(\Theta\Phi) Y_{\ell n}(\theta,\phi) \qquad (11\text{-}95)$$

where M is the Z component of $\vec{J}$. As F is an eigenfunction of J and M, it can be expanded as

$$F(\vec{x};\Theta,\Phi) = \sum_{j,\ell} x^{-1} f_{j,\ell}(x) \mathcal{Y}^{JM}_{j\ell}(\theta,\phi;\Theta,\Phi). \qquad (11\text{-}96)$$

Inserting this expression into the wave equation (11-93), it is found that the radial functions $f_{j,\ell}$ satisfy

$$\left(\frac{d^2}{dx^2} - \frac{\ell(\ell + 1)}{x^2} - k_j^2\right) f_{j,\ell}(x) =$$

$$= \sum_{j',\ell'} 2(j,\ell|U|j',\ell') f_{j',\ell'}(x) \qquad (11\text{-}97)$$

where

$$k_j^2 = \frac{2m}{h^2} (E' - E_j)$$

and

$$(j,\ell|U|j',\ell') = \int d\Omega(\theta,\phi) \int d\Omega(\Theta,\Phi) \left(\mathcal{Y}^{JM}_{j\ell}\right)^* U \mathcal{Y}^{JM}_{j',\ell'} \qquad (11\text{-}98)$$

Having chosen a form for the effective potential U, the coupled radial equations for $f_{j,\ell}(x)$ can be solved with the usual boundary conditions, discussed in Chapter 4, to find a K matrix with elements $K^J_{j,\ell;j',\ell'}$. Explicit formulae for constructing the cross section from the computed K matrix, or S matrix elements have been given by Arthurs and Dalgarno (1960).

Several calculations have been carried out within this formalism using single center molecular wave functions. For rotational excitation of H_2 by electron impact Henry and Lane (1969) solved the coupled equations for j = 0 and j = 2 (for each value of J) and allowed for exchange and polarization both of which are important. Good agreement was found with the experimental data of Crompton et al (1969) -(see Fig. 11-9).

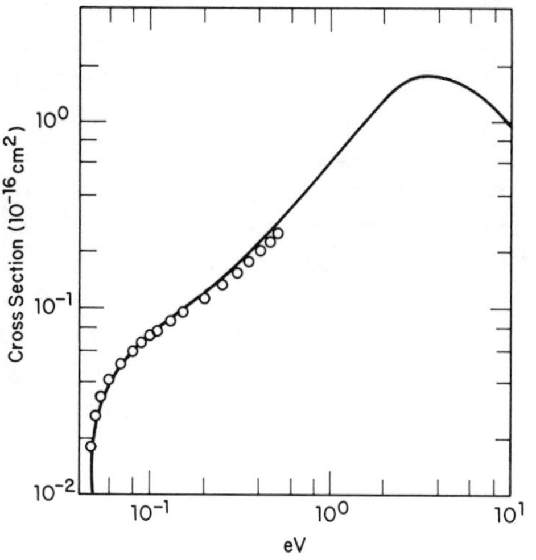

Figure 11-9 The cross section for excitation of j = 2 rotational level of H_2 by electron impact on the ground state.

——— Cross section computed by Henry and Lane (1969)

o o o Experimental data of Crompton et al (1969)

In the case of heteronuclear molecules, scattering by the permanent dipole moment is important. If it is assumed that this is the only potential of importance, the wave equation of the scattered electron becomes

$$\left(-\frac{1}{2}\nabla_x^2 - E - \frac{\mu \cos \alpha}{x^2}\right)F(\vec{x}) = 0 \qquad (11\text{-}99)$$

Mittleman and Holt (1965) have shown that an exact solution of this equation can be obtained, since the equation is separable in spherical polar coordinates, but the omitted short range effects are of importance.

Vibrational excitation

The theory of vibrational excitation can be developed along the same lines as that for rotational excitation. It is found that the short range potential alone provides cross sections (in the Born approximation) that are of an order of magnitude smaller than those observed (Carson, 1954). To allow for the long range interactions, the Born approximation amplitude (11-68) can again be used in conjunction with the multipole expansion (11-72). The calculations of Takayanagi

(1965) show that the quadrupole interaction is not capable of increasing the cross section sufficiently, but that when allowance is made for the polarization potential (α/x^4), cross sections of the correct order of magnitude can be obtained. However in Takayanagi's calculations a cut-off at small x was introduced, so that the results are somewhat uncertain. There is no difficulty in formulating the distorted wave approximation, and Takayanagi has shown that the influence of distortion leads to a further increase in the magnitude of the cross section.

A different approach to the same problem was followed by Bardsley et al. (1966a,b). Using a variational method of Herzenberg they have shown that two levels of the negative hydrogen ion H_2^- exist with the configurations $(1s\sigma_g)^2 (2p\sigma_u)^2\ \Sigma_u^+$ and $(1s\sigma_g)\ (2p\sigma_u)^2\ {}^2\Sigma_g^+$. At energies in the region 0-12 eV, these states can be formed in an electron collision with a hydrogen molecule

$$e + H_2 \to H_2^{-*}$$

The compound state H_2^{-*} can then decay into an electron-hydrogen molecule channel, in which the hydrogen molecule may be excited to the first or second vibrational levels

$$H_2^{-*} \to e + H_2(\nu = 0,1,2).$$

Alternatively, as the potential energy curves of the H_2 levels are repulsive, the negative molecular ion can decay into a hydrogen atom and a negative hydrogen ion

$$H_2^{-*} \to H + H^-. \qquad (11\text{-}100)$$

The calculation of the cross section for vibrational excitation or of dissociative attachment $(e + H_2 \to H + H^-)$ via a compound state follow the general principles outlined in Chapter 7. The existence of the H_2^- states gives rise to a broad peak from 2 to 6 eV in the excitation cross section. This is shown in Fig. 11-10 and is in harmony with the measurements of Schultz (1964), Englehart and Phelps (1963) and Ramien (1935). The cross section for dissociative attachment is shown in Fig. 11-11 and again good agreement is obtained with the experimental work of Rapp et al (1965).

The cross sections obtained in this way are similar to those found by Takayanagi using the distorted wave method. The reason for this is that the H_2 resonance is a shape resonance and is not a virtual bound state, associated with the opening of a new threshold, and the distorted wave potential is of the correct shape and depth to support such a resonance.

Compound negative ion states have also been used by Chen (1965) to investigate vibrational excitation of N_2, and also by Herzenerg (1967), and Chen and Peacher (1968) in calculating the rate of associative detachment, which is the inverse reaction to (11-100).

$$H + H^- \rightarrow H_2^* + e.$$

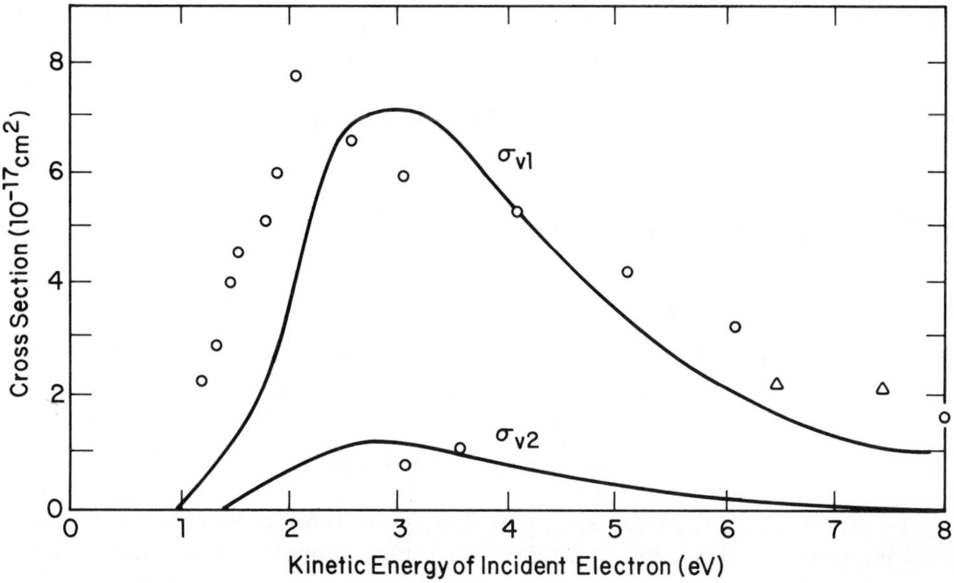

Figure 11-10 Cross sections for excitation of the two lowest vibrational states of hydrogen, showing the influence of the $^2\Sigma_u$ metastable state of H_2^-.

——— Calculated cross section (Bardsley et al., 1966).

o o o Δ Experimental cross section (Schultz, 1944).

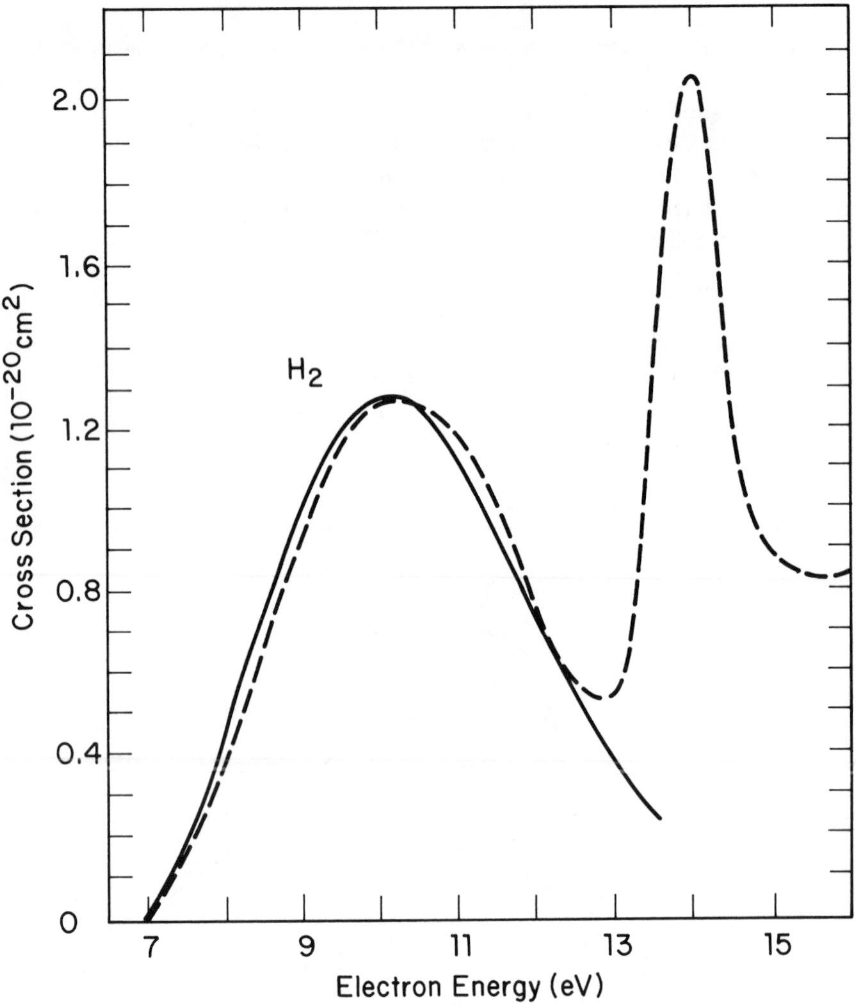

Figure 11-11 Cross section for the dissociation of the hydrogen by electron impact via the formation of the $^2\Sigma^+$ resonance in H_2^-.

———— Calculated cross section (Bardsley et al., 1966).

- - - - - Experimental cross section (Rapp et al., 1965).

Calculations in the body-fixed frame

Provided the collision line is short compared with the characteristic time of vibration, cross sections for vibrational excitation can be calculated using the fixed nuclei approximation. The amplitude for an electron to be scattered into the direction (θ,ϕ), in the laboratory system, from a molecule with fixed internuclear separation R and orientation given by the Euler angles α,β,γ, $f(\alpha,\beta,\gamma;\theta,\phi)$ is calculated for a range of values of R, by any of the fixed nuclei methods. From f, the amplitude for given initial and final rotational levels is calculated (as a function of R) by (11-60). The amplitude for rotational-vibrational excitation from a level ν,j to a level ν',j' is given by

$$f_{fi}(\theta,\phi) = \int_0^\infty dR\, p^*_{\nu'}(R) f_{j'j}(R,\theta,\phi) p_\nu(R)$$

This approximation is successful except near the energy at which a compound intermediate state is formed, because the life time of such states is not always short compared with the time of vibration. For example the fixed nuclei approach is accurate for the e-H_2 system for which the life times of the $^2\Sigma_u^+$ compound level is less than 10^{-15} sec, but not for the e-N_2 system which is dominated by a $^2\Pi_g$ level of life time comparable to the vibrational period. In this case a hybrid model has been introduced (Chandra and Temkin 1967a,b) in which the vibrational levels are coupled using an eigenfunction expansion method, but the orientation of the molecule is fixed, thus simplifying the treatment of the rotational motion. Still other possibilities exist and for further information the reviews of Burke (1979) and Lane (1981) can be consulted.

NOTES

1. A full account of the properties and theory of diatomic molecules has been given by Herzberg (1950), see also Pilar (1968).

2. The total orbital angular momentum $\vec{J}$ is the sum of $\vec{L}_e$ and $\vec{L}_n$ where $\vec{L}_e$ is the orbital angular momentum of the electrons and $\vec{L}_n$ that of the nuclei. Since $\vec{L}_n$ is in a direction at right angles to the inter-nuclear line, the component of $\vec{J}$ along the inter-nuclear line is equal to Λh. It follows that $j \geq \Lambda$.

3. Further information about the elementary properties of molecules can be found in the text by Bransden and Joachain (1982).

4. For an application to $(HeH)^{++}$, see Rabinovitch (1965).

5. For other related work see Kerner (1953) and Bates and Holt (1965).

6. Other measurements of the dissociation cross section by Dance et al (1967) are essentially in agreement with those of Dunn and Van Zyl.

7. An account of the different exchange potentials that have been proposed and of applications to electron-atom scattering has been given by Bransden and McDowell (1977, 1978).

8. This is the same as (4-38) with $V_\beta = V_\alpha = V$.

9. In this section the work of Arthurs and Dalgarno (1960) has been followed.

PROBLEMS

11-1 Obtain the equations (11-21) for the function ϕ_0^0 and find the corresponding equations satisfied by ϕ_1^0

11-2 Show that (11-38) can be obtained from (11-36).

11-3 Using the first order impact parameter approximation, find an expression for the cross section for the $1s \rightarrow 2p$ excitation of atomic hydrogen in the dipole approximation in which the interaction is replaced by its leading term at large distances. Discuss the excitation of the $1s\sigma_g$ level of H_2^+ to the $2p\sigma_u$ level in the same approximation.

11-4 Show that the expansion coefficients $u_n(R)$ given by (11-74) follow from equations (11-73) and (11-72).

11-5 Using the integral (11-78) verify the j dependence of the cross sections (11-80).

APPENDIX A

UNITS AND ATOMIC CONSTANTS

Since the only electromagnetic quantity used in this book is the Coulomb interaction between two charges q_1, q_2, electrostatic units have been used and this potential is written as $V(r) = q_1 q_2/r$. To convert formula to SI units it is only necessary to replace $q_1 q_2$ by $q'_1 q'_2/(4\pi\varepsilon_0)$, where ε_0 is the permitivity of free space and $q'_1 q'_2$ are the charges expressed in Coulombs.

In most of the later part of the book atomic units are used in which $m = e = \hbar = 1$, where m is the mass and e the magnitude of the charge of the electron and $\hbar$ is Planck's constant divided by 2π. The values of the most important atomic units are given in Table A1 and a few frequently required atomic constants are given in Table A2.

Collision cross sections are given either in atomic units, ($a_0{}^2$) or in units of cm^2 depending on the units employed in the original research papers.

Table A1

Atomic Units

Quantity	Unit	Significance	Value
Mass	m	Electron mass	9.10953×10^{-31}kg
Charge	e	Electronic charge	e.s.u. 1.60219×10^{-19}C
Length	a_0	Bohr radius of atomic hydrogen	5.2918×10^{-11}m
Velocity	v_0	Electron velocity in first Bohr orbit	2.18769×10^{6}ms^{-1}
Time	a_0/v_0	Time for electron to traverse first Bohr orbit	2.41889×10^{-17}S
Energy	e^2/a_0	Twice the ionization potential of hydrogen (with infinite nuclear mass)	4.35981×10^{-18}J 27.2116 eV
Angular momentum	$\hbar$	Planck constant divided by (2π)	1.05459×10^{-34}JS
Cross sections	a_0^2	Mainly used for differential cross sections	2.800×10^{-21}m^L
OR	πa_0^2	Mainly used for total cross sections	8.79735×10^{-21}m^L

Table A2

Atomic constants and conversion factors

Planck's constant	h	6.62618×10^{-34}Js 2π a.u.
Velocity of light	c	2.99792×10^{8}ms^{-1} 137 a.u.
Magnitude of the charge on the electron	e	1.60219×10^{-19}c 1 a.u.
mass of the electron	m	9.10953×10^{-31}kg 1 a.u.
mass of the proton	M	1.67265×10^{-27}kg 1836M
Ionization potential of hydrogen (infinite nuclear mass)	I	2.17991×10^{-18}J 13.6058 eV $\frac{1}{2}$ a.u.
permitivity of free space	ε_o	8.85419×10^{-12}Fm^{-1}
1 electron volt	eV	1.60219×10^{-19}J
1 angstrom	Å	10^{-10}m

APPENDIX B

ANGULAR MOMENTUM : USEFUL RESULTS AND THE CLEBSCH-GORDAN COEFFICIENTS

SPHERICAL HARMONICS AND LEGENDRE POLYNOMIALS

In Section 4-3 we introduced the spherical harmonics $Y_{\ell m}(\theta,\phi)$, which are the simultaneous eigenfunctions of the orbital angular momentum operators L^2 and L_z,

$$L^2 Y_{\ell m} = \ell(\ell + 1)\hbar^2 Y_{\ell m}; \quad L_z Y_{\ell m} = m\hbar Y_{\ell m} \tag{B1}$$

where $\ell = 0, 1, 2, \ldots$ and $m = -\ell, -\ell + 1, \ldots \ell - 1, \ell$. They satisfy the orthonormality relation

$$\int Y^*_{\ell' m'}(\theta,\phi) Y_{\ell m}(\theta,\phi) d\Omega = \delta_{\ell\ell'}\delta_{mm'}; \quad (d\Omega = \sin\theta d\theta d\phi) \tag{B2}$$

and the closure relation

$$\sum_{\ell=0}^{\infty} \sum_{m=-\ell}^{\ell} Y^*_{\ell m}(\theta,\phi) Y_{\ell m}(\theta',\phi') = \delta(\Omega-\Omega') \tag{B3}$$

where

$$\delta(\Omega-\Omega') = \frac{1}{\sin\theta}\delta(\theta-\theta')\delta(\phi-\phi')$$

In the special case $m = 0$, the spherical harmonics are given by

$$Y_{\ell 0} = \sqrt{\frac{2\ell + 1}{4\pi}}\, P_\ell(\cos\theta) \tag{B4}$$

where the functions $P_\ell(\cos\theta)$ are the Legendre polynomials.

Let $\vec{r}_1$ and $\vec{r}_2$ be two vectors having polar angles (θ_1,ϕ_1) and (θ_2,ϕ_2) respectively, and let θ be the angle between them. It can be shown that

$$P_\ell(\cos\theta) = \frac{4\pi}{2\ell + 1} \sum_{m=-\ell}^{+\ell} Y^*_{\ell m}(\theta_1,\phi_1)Y_{\ell m}(\theta_2,\phi_2) \qquad \text{(B5)}$$

which is known as the addition (or biaxial) theorem of the spherical harmonics. A useful expansion is

$$\frac{1}{|\vec{r}_1 - \vec{r}_2|} = \sum_{\ell=0}^{\infty} \frac{(r_<)^\ell}{(r_>)^{\ell+1}} P_\ell(\cos\theta) \qquad \text{(B6)}$$

which, using (B5), may also be written as

$$\frac{1}{|\vec{r}_1 - \vec{r}_2|} = \sum_{\ell=0}^{\infty} \sum_{m=-\ell}^{+\ell} \frac{4\pi}{2\ell + 1} \frac{(r_<)^\ell}{(r_>)^{\ell+1}} Y^*_{\ell m}(\theta_1,\phi_1)Y_{\ell m}(\theta_2,\phi_2) \qquad \text{(B7)}$$

It can also be shown that

$$\frac{\exp[ik|r_1 - r_2]}{|\vec{r}_1 - \vec{r}_2|} = ik \sum_{\ell=0}^{\infty} (2\ell+1)j_\ell(kr_<)[j_\ell(kr_>)+in_\ell(kr_>)]P_\ell(\cos\theta) \qquad \text{(B8)}$$

where j_ℓ and n_ℓ are spherical Bessel and Neumann functions respectively. The formula giving the expansion of a plane wave in Legendre polynomials, is

$$e^{i\vec{k}\cdot\vec{r}} = \sum_{\ell=0}^{\infty} (2\ell + 1)i^\ell j_\ell(kr)P_\ell(\cos\theta) \qquad \text{(B9)}$$

where θ is the angle between the vectors $\vec{k}$ and $\vec{r}$.

ADDITION OF ANGULAR MOMENTA. THE CLEBSCH-GORDAN COEFFICIENTS

Consider a aystem described by two angular momenta J_1 and J_2, such that the components of J_1 commute with the components of J_2. For example, J_1 and J_2 could be the angular momenta of different particles, or the orbital and spin angular momenta of a single particle. The normalized simultaneous eigenfunctions of J_1^2 and J_{1z} corresponding to eigenvalues $j_1(j_1 + 1)\hbar^2$ and $m_1\hbar$ will be denoted by $\psi_{j_1m_1}$ and similarly, the normalized eigenfunctions of J_2^2 and F_{2z} corresponding to eigenvalues $j_2(j_2 + 1)\hbar^2$ and $m_2\hbar$ will be denoted by $\psi_{j_2m_2}$. The simultaneous eigenfunctions of J_1^2, F_{1z}, J_2^2 and F_{2z}, are then given by the product functions

$$\psi_{j_1m_1;j_2m_2} = \psi_{j_1m_1} \times \psi_{j_2m_2} \tag{B10}$$

and for a given j_1 and j_2, there are $(2j_1 + 1) \times (2j_2 + 1)$ of these functions.

Now consider the total angular momentum

$$\vec{J} = \vec{J}_1 + \vec{J}_2 \tag{B11}$$

Since J^2, J_z, J_1^2 and J_2^2 all commute, these operators possess a set of simultaneous eigenfunctions, which we shall write as $\Phi_{j_1j_2}^{jm}$ where

$$J^2\Phi_{j_1j_2}^{jm} = j(j + 1)\hbar^2\Phi_{j_1j_2}^{jm}$$

$$J_z\Phi_{j_1j_2}^{jm} = m\hbar\Phi_{j_1j_2}^{jm} \tag{B12}$$

For a given j, there are $(2j + 1)$ values of m with $-j \leq m \leq j$ and j can take any of the values $|j_1 - j_2|, |j_1 - j_2| + 1 \ldots (j_1 + j_2)$. Again there are $(2j_1 + 1) \times (2j_2 + 1)$ of the functions $\Phi_{j_1j_2}^{jm}$, which can be related to the function (B10) by a unitary transformation:

$$\Phi_{j_1j_2}^{jm} = \sum_{m_1m_2} (j_1j_2m_1m_2|jm)\psi_{j_1m_1;j_2m} \tag{B13}$$

The coefficients $(j_1j_2m_1m_2|jm)$ are called Clebsch-Gordan coefficients. These coefficients vanish unless $m = m_1 + m_2$ and $|j_1 - j_2| \leq j \leq j_1 + j_2$, and possess the following important properties:

Orthonormality relations

$$\sum_{m_1m_2} (j_1j_2m_1m_2|jm)(j_1j_2m_1m_2|j'm') = \delta_{jj'}\delta_{mm'}$$

$$\sum_{j,m} (j_1j_2m_1m_2|jm)(j_1j_2m_1'm_2'|jm) = \delta_{m_1m_1'}\delta_{m_2m_2'} \tag{B14}$$

Symmetry properties

$$(j_1j_2m_1m_2|jm) = (-1)^{j_1+j_2-j}(j_2j_1m_2m_1|jm)$$

$$= (-1)^{j_1+j_2-j}(j_1j_2 - m_1 - m_2|j - m)$$

$$= (-1)^{j_1-m_1}\left(\frac{2j+1}{2j_2+1}\right)^{1/2}(j_1jm_1-m|j_2 -m_2) \qquad \text{(B15)}$$

In Table B1 the coefficients $(j_1j_2m_1m_2|jm)$ are tabulated for the cases $j_2 = \frac{1}{2}$ and $j_2 = 1$. By using the symmetry relations, all the coefficients with any one of j_1j_2 or j equal to $\frac{1}{2}$ or to 1, can be found.

Useful notations

When adding two orbital angular momenta L_1 and L_2, we shall write (B13) in the explicit position representation as

$$\mathcal{Y}^{\ell m}_{\ell_1\ell_2}(\theta_1\phi_1;\theta_2\phi_2) =$$

$$= \sum_{m_1m_2}(\ell_1\ell_2m_1m_2|\ell m)Y_{\ell_1m_1}(\theta_1,\phi_1)Y_{\ell_2m_2}(\theta_2,\phi_2) \qquad \text{(B16)}$$

where $\mathcal{Y}^{\ell m}_{\ell_1\ell_2}$ is a simultaneous eigenfunction of L_1^2, L_2^2, L^2 and L_z, and $L = L_1 + L_2$. Similarly, when adding an orbital angular momentum L with a spin angular momentum S, so that $J = L + S$ we shall often write

$$\mathcal{Y}^{jm}_{\ell s}(\theta,\phi) = \sum_{m_\ell m_s}(\ell s m_\ell m_s|jm)Y_{\ell m_\ell}(\theta,\phi)\chi_{sm_s} \qquad \text{(B17)}$$

where χ_{sm_s} is a spin wave function.

Integrals of products of spherical harmonics

It can be shown that the product $Y_{\ell_1m_1}(\theta,\phi)Y_{\ell_2m_2}(\theta,\phi)$ can be expressed as a series by:

$$Y_{\ell_1 m_1}(\theta,\phi) Y_{\ell_2 m_2}(\theta,\phi) = \sum_{\ell=|\ell_1-\ell_2|}^{\ell_1 \ell_2} \sum_{m=-\ell}^{\ell} \left(\frac{(2\ell_1+1)(2\ell_2+1)}{4\pi(2\ell + 1)}\right)^{1/2}$$

$$\times \qquad (\ell_1\ell_2 00|\ell 0)(\ell_1\ell_2 m_1 m_2|\ell m) Y_{\ell m}(\theta,\phi) \qquad \text{(B18)}$$

This enables us to evaluate the integral of a product of three spherical harmonics, which is

$$\int Y_{\ell_1 m_1}(\theta,\phi) Y_{\ell_2 m_2}(\theta,\phi) Y_{\ell_3 m_3}(\theta,\phi) d\Omega$$

$$= (-1)^{m_3} \left(\frac{(2\ell_1 + 1)(2\ell_2 + 1)}{4\pi(2\ell_3 + 1)}\right)^{1/2} (\ell_1\ell_2 00|\ell_3 0)(\ell_1\ell_2 m_1 m_2|\ell_3 -m_3)$$

(B19)

Table B1

Clebsch-Gordan coefficients for $j_2 = \frac{1}{2}$

$$(j_1 \tfrac{1}{2} m_1 m_2 | jm)$$

j	$m_2 = \frac{1}{2}$	$m_2 = -\frac{1}{2}$
$j_1 + \frac{1}{2}$	$\left(\frac{j_1 + m + \frac{1}{2}}{2j_1 + 1}\right)^{1/2}$	$\left(\frac{j_1 - m + \frac{1}{2}}{2j_1 + 1}\right)^{1/2}$
$j_1 - \frac{1}{2}$	$-\left(\frac{j_1 - m + \frac{1}{2}}{2j_1 + 1}\right)^{1/2}$	$\left(\frac{j_1 + m + \frac{1}{2}}{2j_1 + 1}\right)^{1/2}$

Table B2

Clebsch-Gordan coefficients for $j_2 = 1$

$(j_1 1 m_1 m_2 | jm)$

j	$m_2 = 1$	$m_2 = 0$	$m_2 = -1$
$j_1 + 1$	$\left(\frac{(j_1 + m)(j_1 + m + 1)}{(2j_1 + 1)(2j_1 + 2)}\right)^{1/2}$	$\left(\frac{(j_1 - m + 1)(j_1 + m + 1)}{(2j_1 + 1)(j_1 + 1)}\right)^{1/2}$	$\left(\frac{j_1 - m)(j_1 - m + 1)}{(2j_1 + 1)(2j_1 + 2)}\right)^{1/2}$
j_1	$\left(\frac{(j_1 + m)(j_1 - m + 1)}{2j_1(j_1 + 1)}\right)^{1/2}$	$\left(\frac{m^2}{(j_1(j_1 + 1)}\right)^{1/2}$	$\left(\frac{(j_1 - m)(j_1 + m + 1}{2j_1(j_1 + 1)}\right)^{1/2}$
$j_1 - 1$	$\left(\frac{j_1 - m)(j_1 - m + 1)}{2j_1(2j_1 + 1)}\right)^{1/2}$	$-\left(\frac{(j_1 - m)(j_1 + m)}{j_1(2j_1 + 1)}\right)^{1/2}$	$\left(\frac{(j_1 + m + 1)(j_1 + m)}{2j_1(2j_1 + 1)}\right)^{1/2}$

APPENDIX C

FURTHER READING

To go beyond the introductory material presented in this book, the reader should consult the review and periodical literature to which many references have been given. In addition it may prove useful to consult the following more advanced, or more specialized books:

(A) BOOKS ON THE GENERAL THEORY OF NON-RELATIVISTIC COLLISIONS

M.L. Goldberger and K. Watson, "Collision Theory" (Wiley, New York, 1964).

C.J. Joachain, "Quantum Scattering Theory", 2 vols. 2nd.Edit. (North-Holland, Amsterdam, 1979).

R.G. Newton, "Scattering theory of waves and particles" (McGraw Hill, New York, 1966).

J.R. Taylor, "Scattering theory : the quantum theory of non-relativistic collisions" (Wiley, New York, 1972).

(B) BOOKS ON ATOMIC OR MOLECULAR COLLISION THEORY

M.S. Child, "Molecular Collision Theory" (Academic Press, New York, 1974).

S. Geltman "Topics in Atomic Collision Theory" (Academic Press, New York, 1964).

M.R.C.McDowell and J.P. Coleman, "Introduction to the theory of ion-atom collisions" (North Holland, Amsterdam, 1970).

H.S.W. Massey, E.H.S. Burhop and H.B. Gilbody
"Electronic and ionic impact phenomena"
5 vols, 2nd. Edit. (O.U.P. Oxford, 1969-1974).

N.F.Mott and H.S.W. Massey "Theory of Atomic Collisions"
3rd Edit. (O.U.P. Oxford, 1965).

E.E. Nikitin, "Theory of Elementary Atomic and Molecular
Processes in Gases" (Trans. M.J. Kearsley)
(O.U.P., Oxford, 1974).

REFERENCES

(The page number or numbers on which a citation appears are given in brackets following each reference).

Aberth, W., Lorents, D.C., Marchi, R.P. and Smith, F.T. (1965) *Phys. Rev. Let.* 14, 776 (390)

Abrines, R. and Percival, I.C. (1966) *Proc. Phys. Soc.* 88, 861, 873 (423)

Alfaro de V. and Regge, T. (1965) *Potential Scattering* North Holland, Amsterdam (56)

Allison, S.K. (1958) *Rev. Mod. Phys.* 30, 1137 (422)

Altick, P.L. and Moore, E. (1967) *Proc. Phys. Soc.* 92, 853 (317)

Altshuler, S. (1953) *Phys. Rev.* 89, 1278 (67, 108)

Andrick, D. and Bitsch, A. (1975) *J. Phys. B* 10, L673 (242, 247)

Armstead, R.L. (1968) *Phys. Rev.* 171, 91 (218, 219, 220, 221)

Arthurs, A.M. (1961) *Proc. Camb. Phil. Soc.* 57, 904 (354)

Arthurs, A.M. and Dalgarno, A. (1960) *Proc. Roy. Soc.* A256, 540 (466, 472)

Auger, P. (1925) *J. Phys. Rad.* 6, 205 (329)

Baker, M. (1958) *Ann. Phys. (N.Y.)* 4, 271 (80, 165)

Ball, J.S., Chen, J.C.Y. and Wong, D.Y. (1968) *Phys. Rev.* 173, 202 (195)

Baluja, K.L., McDowell, M.R.C., Morgan, L.A. and Myerscough, V.P. (1978) *J. Phys. B* 11, 715 (268)

Bardsley, J.N., Herzenberg, A. and Mandl, F. (1966a,b) *Proc. Phys. Soc.* 89, 305, 321 (468, 469, 470)

Bardsley, J.N. and Nesbet, R.K. (1973) *Phys. Rev.* A8, 203 (262)

Bargman, V. (1949) *Rev. Mod. Phys.* 21, 488 (46)

Basu, D., Mukherjee, S.C. and Sural, D.P. (1978) *Phys. Repts.* 42c, 145 (363, 389)
Bates, D.R. (1958) *Proc. Roy. Soc.* A247, 294 (357)
Bates, D.R. (1960) *Proc. Roy. Soc.* A257, 22 (397)
Bates, D.R., Boyd, A.H. and Prasad, S.S. (1965) *Proc. Roy. Phys. Soc.* 85, 1121 (302)
Bates, D.R. and Carson, J.R. (1956) *Proc. Roy. Soc.* A234, 207 (377)
Bates, D.R. and Griffing, G.W. (1953) *Proc. Phys. Soc.* A66, 961 (408)
Bates, D.R. and Griffing, G.W. (1954) *Proc. Phys. Soc.* A67, 663 (408)
Bates, D.R. and Griffing, G.W. (1955) *Proc. Phys. Soc.* A68, 90 (408)
Bates, D.R. and Holt, A.R. (1965) *Proc. Phys. Soc.* 85, 691 (471)
Bates, D.R. and Holt, A.R. (1966) *Proc. Roy. Soc.*A292, 168 (368, 386)
Bates, D.R., Ledsham, K. and Stewart, A.L. (1953) *Proc. Roy. Soc.* A246, 28 (377, 438, 445)
Bates, D.R. and McCarroll, R. (1962) *Adv. Phys.* 11, 39 (386)
Bates, D.R. and Massey, H.S.W. (1943) *Phil. Trans.* A239, 296 (245)
Bates, D.R. and Massey, H.S.W. (1947) *Proc. Roy. Soc.* A192, 1 (245)
Bates, D.R. and Moisiewitsch, B.L. (1954) *Proc. Phys. Soc.* A67, 805 (398)
Bates, D.R. and Sprevak, D. (1970) *J. Phys. B* 3, 1483 (389)
Bates, D.R. and Williams, D.A. (1964) *Phys. Rev.* 131, 229 (388, 389)
Bayfield, J.E. (1969) *Phys. Rev.* 185, 105 (361)
Baz, A.I. (1959) *Adv. Phys.* 8, 349 (176)
Belkić, D. (1978) *J. Phys. B* 11, 3529 (412)
Belkić, D. and Gayet, R. (1977) *J. Phys. B* 10, 1923 (422)
Belkić, D., Gayet, R. and Salin, A. (1979) *Phys. Repts.* 56., 279 (421, 422, 425)
Bell, K.L. and Kingston, A.E. (1974) *Adv. in Atom. Molec. Phys.* 10, 53 (302)
Bell, K.L. and Kingston, A.E. (1976) In *Atomic Processes and Applications* (Eds. P.G.Burke and B.L.Moisiewitsch), p. 493 North-Holland, Amsterdam (425)
Bell, K.L. and Kingston, A.E. (1978) *J.Phys. B* 11, 1259 (425)
Bell, K.L., Kingston, A.E. and McIlvern, W.A. (1973) *J. Phys. B* 6, 1246 (425)
Bell, K.L., Kingston, A.E. and Winter, T.G. (1974) *J. Phys. B* 7, 1339 (425)

Bell, R.J. (1961) *Proc. Phys. Soc.* 78, 903 (408)
Berrington, K.A., Burke, P.G. and Sin Fai Lam, A.L. (1975) *J. Phys. B* 8, 1459 (262)
Biberman, L.M. and Norman, G.E. (1964) *Soviet Physics (J.E.T.P.)* 18, 1353 (125, 129)
Bhadra, K., Callaway, J. and Henry, R.J.W. (1979) *Phys. Rev. A* 19, 1841 (269)
Blankenbecler, R. (1964) In *Strong Interactions and High Energy Physics*, Ed. R.G.Moorhouse, Oliver and Boyd, Edinburgh, p.411 (71, 81)
Blankenbecler, R. and Sugar, R. (1964) *Phys. Rev.* 136, B472 (81, 195, 246, 252)
Blatt, J.M., Biedenharn, L.C. (1952) *Rev. Mod. Phys.* 24, 258 (156)
Blau, R., Rosenberg, L. and Spruch, L. (1975) *Phys. Rev.* A12, 1859 (246)
Bonham, R.A. and Fink, M. (1976) *High Energy Electron Scattering,* Van Nostrand Reinhold, New York (306)
Bonham, R.A. and Konaka, S. (1978) *J. Chem. Phys.* 69, 525 (278)
Bottcher, C. and Flannery, M.R. (1971) *J.Phys. B* 3,1600 (424)
Bransden, B.H. (1965) *Adv.Atom.Molec.Phys.* 1, 85 (425)
Bransden, B.H. (1969) In *Lectures in Theoretical Physics* Vol. XI, Gordon and Breach (425)
Bransden, B.H. (1969) In *Case Studies in Atomic Collisions* Eds. E.W.McDaniel and M.R.C.McDowell, North-Holland, Amsterdam (247)
Bransden, B.H. (1972) *Rep. Prog. Phys.* 35, 949 (363)
Bransden, B.H. (1979) In *Atomic and Molecular Processes in Controlled Thermonuclear Fusion* Eds. M.R.C.McDowell and A.M. Ferendeci, pp.185-206, Plenum Press, New York (363)
Bransden, B.H. (1979) *Adv.Atom.Molec.Phys.* 15, 263 (425)
Bransden, B.H. and Coleman, J.P. (1972) *J.Phys.B* 5,537 (264)
Bransden, B.H. and Dewangan, D.P. (1979) *J.Phys.B* 12, 1377 (306, 425)
Bransden, B.H., Dewangan, D.P. and Noble, C.J. (1979) *J. Phys. B* 12, 3563 (410)
Bransden, B.H. and Issa, M. (1975) *J. Phys. B* 8, 1088 (425)
Bransden, B.H. and Joachain, C.J. (1982) *Physics of Atoms and Molecules,* Longman, London (10, 55, 56, 195, 214, 246, 247, 271, 322, 400, 471)
Bransden, B.H. and McDowell, M.R.C. (1977) *Phys. Repts.* 30, 207 (262, 269, 288, 293, 305, 306, 472)
Bransden, B.H. and McDowell, M.R.C. (1978) *Phys. Repts.* 46, 249 (262, 269, 288, 293, 305, 306, 472)

Bransden, B.H. and McKee, J. (1956) *Proc. Phys. Soc. A* 69 422 (168)
Bransden, B.H. and McKee, J. (1957) *Proc. Phys. Soc. A* 70 398 (168)
Bransden, B.H. and Noble, C.J. (1981) *J.Phys. B* 14, 1849 (362)
Bransden, B.H. and Noble, C.J. (1982) *J.Phys. B* 15, 451 (362, 363)
Bransden, B.H. and Sin Fai Lam, A.L. (1966) *Proc. Phys. Soc.* 87, 653 (362)
Bransden, B.H., Smith, J.J. and Winters, K.H. (1978) *J. Phys. B* 11, 3095 (304)
Bransden, B.H., Smith, J.J. and Winters, K.H. (1979) *J. Phys. B* 12, 1267 (304)
Bransden, B.H. and Winters, K.H. (1976) *J. Phys. B* 9, 1115 (269)
Brenig, W. and Haag, R. (1959) *Fortschritte der Physik* 7, 183 (3)
Brenig, W. and Haag, R. (1963) English trans. in *Quantum Scattering Theory*, Ed. M.Ross, Indiana Univ. Press, Bloomington (3)
Briggs, J.S. (1976) *Repts. Prog. Phys.* 39, 217 (384, 389, 400)
Briggs, J.S. and Dettmann, K. (1977) *J. Phys B* 10, 1113 (425)
Briggs, J.S. and Dubé, L. (1980) *J. Phys. B* 13, 771 (425)
Briggs, J.S. and Taulbjerg, K. (1978) In *Structure and Collisions of Ions and Atoms* Ed. I.A. Sellin,p.105, Springer-Verlag, Berlin and New York (384, 389, 400, 408)
Brillouin, L. (1926) *Comptes Rendu* 183, 24 (96)
Brinkman, H.C. and Kramers, H.A. (1930) *Proc. Acad. Sci. Amsterdam* 33, 973 (415)
Buckley, B.D. and Burke, P.G. (1977) *J.Phys. B* 10, 725 (457)
Buckley, B.D., Burke, P.G. and Vo Ky Lan (1979) *Comput. Phys. Comm.* 17, 175 (457)
Bullard, E.C. and Massey, H.S.W. (1933) *Proc. Camb. Phil. Soc.* 29, 511 (453)
Burgess, A. (1961) *Mem. Soc. Roy. Sci. Liege* 4, 299 (276)
Burgess, A. (1964) *3rd Int. Conf. on Elec. & Atom. Coll.* London (1963) North-Holland, Amsterdam, p.237 (276)
Burhop, E.H.S. (1952) *The Auger Effect*, Camb. Univ. Press, London (314)
Burke, P.G. (1968) *Adv.Atom.Molec.Phys.*4, 173 (329)
Burke, P.G. (1979) *Adv.Atom.Molec.Phys.*15, 471 (471)
Burke, P.G., Cooper, J.W. and Ormonde, S. (1969) *Phys. Rev.* 183, 245 (305)

Burke, P.G., Gallaher, D.F. and Geltman, S. (1969) *J. Phys. B* 2, 869 (227)

Burke, P.G., Mackey, I. and Shimamura, I. (1979) *J. Phys. B* 10, 2497 (457)

Burke, P.G. and McVicar, D. (1965) *Proc.Phys.Soc.* 86, 989 (317, 321, 322)

Burke, P.G. and Mitchell, J.F.B. (1973) *J.Phys.B* 6, 320 (260)

Burke, P.G. and Robb, W.D. (1975) *Adv.Atom.Molec.Phys.* 11, 143 (107, 225)

Burke, P.G. and Schey, H. (1962) *Phys.Rev.* 126, 163 (226)

Burke, P.G. and Seaton, M.J. (1971) *Meth. in Comp. Phys.* 10, 1 (225)

Burke, P.G. and Sin Fai Lam, A.L. (1970) *J.Phys. B* 3, 64 (456)

Burke, P.G. and Taylor, A.J. (1966) *Proc. Phys. Soc.* 88, 549 (228, 234, 302)

Burke, P.G., Taylor, A.J. and Cooper, J.W. (1966) *Phys. Rev. Let.* 17, 345 (317, 323)

Burke, P.G., Taylor, A.J., Cooper, J.W. and Ormonde, S. (1967a) *Vth Int. Conf. on Elec. & Atom. Coll.* Leningrad, p.376 (255, 257, 305, 317, 319)

Burke, P.G., Taylor, A.J., Cooper, J.W. and Ormonde, S. *Proc. Phys. Soc.* 92, 345 (305)

Burke, P.G. and Webb, T.G. (1970)*J. Phys. B* 3, L131 (260)

Butler, S.E. and Dalgarno, A. (1980) *Astro. J.* 241,838 (398,9)

Butler, S.E., Heil, T.G. and Dalgarno, A. (1980) *Astro. J.* 241, 442 (384)

Byron, F.W. and Joachain, C.J. (1966) *Phys.Rev.* 146, 1 (239)

Byron, F.W. and Joachain, C.J. (1973) *Phys.Rev.A*8, 1267 (278)

Byron, F.W. and Joachain, C.J. (1977) *Phys. Repts.* 34c, 233 (107, 278, 295, 306)

Byron, F.W. and Joachain, C.J. (1981) *J. Phys. B* 14, 2429 (264, 265)

Byron, F.W., Joachain, C.J. and Piraux, B. (1980)*J. Phys. B* 13, L673 (304)

Byron, F.W., Joachain, C.J. and Piraux, B. (1982)*J. Phys. B* 15 (In press) (304)

Byron, F.W. and Latour, C.J. (1976) *Phys. Rev.* A13, 649 (278)

Callaway, J. (1973) *Comp. Phys. Comm.* 6, 265 (246)

Callaway, J. (1978a) *Phys. Repts.* 45, 89 (225,227,258,260,305)

Callaway, J. (1978b) *Phys. Lett.* 65A, 199 (227)

Callaway, J. (1980) *Adv. in Phys.* 29, 7 (225, 227, 269)

Callaway, J. and Bartling, J.R. (1966) *Phys. Rev.* 150, 69 (334)

Callaway, J. and Bauer, E. (1965) *Phys. Rev.* 140, A1072 (334)

Callaway, J. and Dugan, A.F. (1967) *Phys. Rev.*163, 26 (333)

Callaway, J., Henry, R.J.W. and Msezane, A.P. (1979) *Phys. Rev.* A19, 1416 (276, 329)

Callaway, J., LaBahn, R.W. Pu, R.T. and Duxler, W.M. (1968) *Phys. Rev.* 168, 12 (243, 244, 247)

Callaway, J., McDowell, M.R.C. and Morgan, L.A. (1975) *J. Phys. B* 8, 2181 (260, 305)

Callaway, J., McDowell, M.R.C. and Morgan, L.A. (1976) *J. Phys. B* 9, 2043 (260, 305)

Callaway, J. and Wooten, J.W. (1974) *Phys. Rev. A* 9, 1924 (305)

Carlson, C.A. (1938) *Proc. Camb. Phil. Soc.* 34, 204 (454)

Carson, T.R. (1954) *Proc. Phys. Soc. A* 67, 908 (460, 467)

Carter, C., March, N.H. and Vincent, D. (1958) *Proc. Phys. Soc.* 71, 2 (454)

Cartwright, D.C. and Kupperman, A. (1967) *Phys. Rev.* 163, 86 (451)

Case, K.M. (1950) *Phys. Rev.* 80, 797 (55)

Castillejo, L., Percival, I.C. and Seaton, M.J. (1960) *Proc. Roy. Soc. A* 254, 259 (246)

Chadan, K. (1968) *Nuov. Cim.* 53B, 12 (94)

Chamberlain, G.E. (1965) *Phys. Rev. Let.* 14, 581 (329)

Chamberlain, G.E. and Heideman, H.G.M. (1965) *Phys. Rev. Let.* 15, 337 (318, 329)

Chandra, N. (1975) *J. Phys. B* 8, 1338 (456)

Chandra, N. (1977) *Phys. Rev. A* 16, 80 (454)

Chandra, N. and Temkin, A. (1967a) *Phys. Rev.* A13, 188 (471)

Chandra, N. and Temkin, A. (1967b) *Phys. Rev.* A14, 507 (471)

Chang, E.S. and Fano, U. (1972) *Phys. Rev. A* 6, 173 (454)

Chen, J.C. (1965) *J. Chem. Phys.* 60, 3513 (469)

Chen, J.C. and Peacher, J.L. (1968) *Phys. Rev.*168, 56 (469)

Cheshire, I.M. (1964) *Proc. Phys. Soc.* 84, 89 (419)

Cheshire, I.M. and Sullivan, E. (1967) *Phys.Rev.*160, 4 (368)

Cheshire, I.M., Gallaher, D.F. and Taylor, A.J. (1970) *J. Phys. B* 3, 813 (364)

Child, M.S. (1974) *Molecular Collision Theory*, Academic Press, London (107, 368)

Child, M.S. (1978) *Adv. Atom. Molec. Phys.* 14, 1 (107)

Chung, S. and Lin, C.C. (1978) *Phys. Rev. A* 17, 1874 (451)

Collins, L.A., Robb, W.D. and Morrison, M.A. (1980) *Phys. Rev. A* 21, 488 (457)

Compton, K.T. and Boyce, J.C. (1928) *J.Frank.Inst.* 205, 497 (310)

Cooper, J.W., Ormonde, S., Humphrey, C.H. and Burke, P.G. (1967) *Proc. Phys. Soc.* 91, 285 (317)

Coulter, P.W. and Garrett, W.R. (1978) *Phys. Rev. A* 18, 1902 (236)

Craggs, J.D. and Massey, H.S.W. (1979) In *Handbuch der Physik* Ed. S. Flugge, vol.37/1, Springer, Berlin, p. 314 (453)
Crees, M.A., Seaton, M.J. and Wilson, P.M.H. (1978) *Comp. Phys. Comm.* 15, 23 (225)
Crompton, R.W., Elford, M.T. and Robertson, A.G. (1970) *Aust. J. Phys.* 23, 667 (244)
Crompton, R.W., Gibson, D.K. and McIntosh, A.I. (1969) *Aust. J. Phys.* 22, 715 (466, 467)
Crompton, R.W. and Sutton, D.J. (1952) *Proc. Roy. Soc.* A215, 467 (463)
Crooks, J.B. and Rudd, M.E. (1970) *Phys. Rev. Let.* 25, 1599 (411)
Crothers, D.S.F. (1971) *Adv. in Phys.* 20, 405 (400)
Crothers, D.S.F. and Hughes, J.G. (1978a) *Proc. Roy. Soc.* A359, 345 (389)
Crothers, D.S.F. and Hughes, J.G. (1978b) *Phil. Trans. Soc.* A292, 539 (389)
Czanak, Gy., Taylor, H.S. and Yaris, R. (1971) *Adv. Atom. Molec. Phys.* 7, 287 (238)
Dalgarno, A. (1954) *Proc. Phys. Soc.* A67, 1010 (398)
Dalgarno, A. (1966) *Adv. Atom. Molec. Phys.* 2, 1 (333)
Dalgarno, A., Drake, G.W.F., and Victor, G.A. (1968) *Phys. Rev.* 168, 12 (216)
Dalgarno, A. and Henry, R.J.W. (1964) *Proc. Phys. Soc.* 83, 157 (336)
Dalgarno, A. and Lynn, N. (1957) *Proc. Phys. Soc.* A70, 223 (216)
Dalgarno, A. and Moffatt, R.J. (1963) *Proc. Nat. Acad. Sci. India,* A33, 531 (464)
Dalgarno, A. and Poots, G. (1954) *Proc. Phys. Soc.*A69,615 (388)
Dalgarno, A. and Yadav, H.N. (1953) *Proc.Phys. Soc.*A66,173 (387)
Dalitz, R.H. (1961) *Rev. Mod. Phys.* 33, 471 (177)
Damburg, R. and Peterkop, R. (1962) *Proc. Phys. Soc.* 80, 1073 (325)
Damburg, R. and Karule, E. (1967) *Proc. Phys. Soc.* 90, 637 (226)
Dance, D.F., Harrison, M.F.A., Rundel, R.D. and Smith, A.C.H. (1967) *Proc. Phys. Soc.* 92, 577 (472)
de Heer, F.J., McDowell, M.R.C. and Wagenaar, R.W. (1977) *J. Phys. B* 10, 1945 (265)
Delos, J.B. (1981) *Rev. Mod. Phys.* 53, 287 (400)
Delves, L.M. (1958a) *Nuc. Phys.* 8, 258 (176)
Delves, L.M. (1958b) *Nuc. Phys.* 9, 391 (176)
Dettmann, K., Harrison, K.G. and Lucas, M.W. (1974) *J. Phys. B* 7, 269 (412)

Dettmann, K. and Leibfried, G. (1969) *Z. Physik.* 218, 1 (185)

Dewangan, D.P. (1975) *J. Phys. B* 8, 419 (418)

Dewangan, D.P. (1977) *J. Phys. B* 10, 1083 (418)

Donaldson, F.G., Hender, M.A. and McConkey, J.W. (1972) *J. Phys. B* 5, 1192 (269)

Drachman, R. and Temkin, H. (1972) In *Case Studies in Atomic Collision Physics*, Eds. E.W. McDaniel and M.R.C. McDowell, North-Holland, Amsterdam, Vol. II p.394 (246)

Drisko, R.M. (1955) *Thesis: Carnegie Inst. Tech.* (417)

Dunn, G.H. and Van Zyl, B. (1967) *Phys. Rev.* 154, 40 (446,448,47

Duxler, W.M., Poe, R.T. and LaBahn, R.W. (1971) *Phys. Rev. A* 4, 1935 (247)

Edmonds, A.R. (1957) *Angular Momentum in Quantum Mechanics* 2nd. ed. Princeton Press (194, 431, 456)

Eichler, J. (1981) *Phys. Rev. A* 23, 498 (419)

Eichler, J. and Chen, F.T. (1979) *Phys. Rev. A* 20, 104 (419)

Englehart, A.C. and Phelps, A.V. (1963) *Phys.Rev.*131, 2115 (468)

Ermolaev, A.M. and Walters, H.R. (1979) *J. Phys. B* 12 L779 (266, 278, 279)

Ermolaev, A.M. and Walters, H.R. (1980) *J. Phys. B* 13 L473 (266, 278, 279)

Erskine, G.A. and Massey, H.S.W. (1952) *Proc. Roy. Soc.* A212, 521 (168, 170)

Everhart, E. and Helbig, H.F. (1965) *Phys. Rev.* 140, A715 (359)

Faddeev, L.D. (1958) *Soviet Physics J.E.T.P.* 8, 299 (189)

Faddeev, L.D. (1963) *Mathematical Aspects of the three-body problem in Quantum Scattering Theory*, Stekolov Math. Inst. Leningrad, pub. 69 (trans. D.Davey & Co., New York, 1965) (189)

Fano, U. (1961) *Phys. Rev.* 124, 1866 (318)

Feenberg, E. (1932) *Phys. Rev.* 40, 40 (284)

Ferguson, A.F. (1961) *Proc. Roy. Soc.* A264, 540 (388)

Feshbach, H. (1958) *Ann. Phys. (N.Y)* 19, 287 (230)

Feshbach, H. (1962) *Ann. Phys. (N.Y)* 5, 357 (230)

Fisk, J.B. (1936) *Phys. Rev.* 49, 167 (454)

Fisk, J.B. (1937) *Phys. Rev.* 51, 25 (454)

Fitchard, E., Ford, A.L. and Reading, J.F. (1977) *Phys. Rev. A* 16, 1325 (405, 406, 407, 410)

Fite, W.L. and Brackman, R.T. (1958) *Phys. Rev.* 112, 115 (303)

Flannery, M.B. and McCann, K.J. (1974) *J. Phys. B* 7, 840, 1349, 1558 (289, 306, 425)

Fon, W.C., Berrington, K.A., Burke, P.G. and Kingston, A.E. (1978) *J. Phys. B* 11, 325 (262)

Fon, W.C. and Berrington, K.A. (1981) *J. Phys. B* 14, 323 (260)
Fon, W.C., Berrington, K.A., Burke, P.G. and Kingston, A.E. (1981a) *J. Phys. B* 14, 1041 (260)
Fon, W.C., Berrington, K.A., and Hibbert, A. (1981b) *J. Phys. B* 14, 307 (260)
Fonda, L. (1961a) *Nuovo Cim.* 20, 116 (176)
Fonda, L. (1961b) *Ann. Phys. (N.Y.)* 12, 476 (176)
Ford, K.W. and Wheeler, J.A. (1959) *Ann. Phys. (N.Y.)* 7, 259, 287 (103, 107)
Ford, W.M. (1964) *Phys. Rev.* 113, B166 (115, 120)
Ford, W.M. (1966) *J. Math. Phys.* 7, 626 (115, 120)
Fox, L. and Goodwin, E.T. (1949) *Proc. Camb. Phil. Soc.* 45, 373 (57)
Fritsch, W. (1982) *J. Phys. B* 15 (382)
Gailitis, M. (1963) *Sov. Phys. J.E.T.P.* 17, 1328 (329)
Gailitis, M. (1965a) *Sov. Phys. J.E.T.P.* 20, 107 (222, 227, 234, 246, 252)
Gailitis, M. (1965b) In *Cross Sections of Electron Atom Collisions* Ed. V.Veldre, Latv. Acad. Sci. (Riga) p. 155 (222, 227, 234, 246, 252)
Gailitis, M. and Damburg, R. (1963) *Proc. Phys. Soc.* 82, 192 (329)
Gallaher, D.F. and Wilets, L. (1968) *Phys. Rev.* 169, 139 (361, 364, 368)
Garton, W.R.S. (1966) *Adv. Atom. Mol. Phys.* 2, 93 (313)
Gasiorowicz, S. (1966) *Elementary Particle Physics*, Wiley, New York (80)
Gaussorgues, C., Le Sech, C., Masnou-Seewo, F., McCarroll, R and Riera, A. (1975) *J. Phys. B* 8, 239, 253 (389)
Gayet, R. (1972) *J. Phys. B* 5, 483 (419)
Gerjuoy, E. and Stein, S. (1955a) *Phys. Rev.* 97, 1671 (462)
Gerjuoy, E. and Stein, S. (1955b) *Phys. Rev.* 98, 1848 (462)
Gilbody, M.B. and Ireland, J.V. (1963) *Proc. Roy. Soc.* A277, 137 (407)
Glauber, R. (1959) *Lectures in Theoretical Physics*, Eds. W.E. Britten and L.G.Dunham, vol. 1, p.315 (94, 107)
Golden, D.E. (1978) *Adv. Atom. Mol. Phys.* 14, 1 (313, 329)
Greider, J. (1964) *Z. Phys.* 181, 413 (450)
Green, T.A., Stanley, H.E. and Chiang, Y.C. (1965) *Helv. Phys. Acta.* 38, 109 (362)
Green, T.A., Shipsey, E.J. and Browne, J.C. (1982a) *Phys. Rev.* A23, 546, 1346 (382)
Green, T.A., Shipsey, E.J. and Browne, J.C. (1982b) *Phys. Rev.* A25, 1364 (382)
Greenland, P.T. (1982) *Phys. Repts.* 81, 131 (400, 425)

Hagstrom, S. and Shull, H. (1959) *J. Chem. Phys.* 30, 1314 (434)
Hahn, Y. (1965) *Phys. Rev.* 139, 13212 (235, 246)
Hahn, Y., O'Malley, T.F. and Spruch, L. (1962) *Phys. Rev.* 128, 932 (246, 252)
Hahn, Y., O'Malley, T.F. and Spruch, L. (1963) *Phys. Rev.* 130, 381 (246, 252)
Hahn, Y., O'Malley, T.F. and Spruch, L. (1964a) *Phys. Rev.* 134, B397 (246, 252)
Hahn, Y., O'Malley, T.F. and Spruch, L. (1964b) *Phys. Rev.* 134, B1911 (246, 252)
Hatton, G.J., Lane, N.F. and Winter, T.G. (1979) *J. Phys. B* 12, L571 (382)
Harrison, K.G. and Lucas, M.W. (1970) *Phys. Rev.* A33, 142 (411)
Hayes, M.A. and Seaton, M.J. (1978) *J. Phys. B* 11, L79 (329)
Hazi, A.U. (1981) *Phys. Rev.* A23, 2232 (451)
Heil, T.G., Butler, S.E. and Dalgarno, A. (1981) *Phys. Rev.* A23, 1100 (384)
Henry, R.J.W. (1967) *Vth Int.Conf.on Elec. & Atom. Coll.* Leningrad, p. 145 (245)
Henry, R.J.W. (1981) *Phys. Repts.* 68 (263, 269, 276, 329)
Henry, R.J.W., Burke, P.G. and Sin Fai Lam, A.L. (1969) *Phys. Rev.* 178, 218 (305)
Henry, R.J.W. and Lane, N.F. (1969) *Phys. Rev.* 183, 221 (466, 467)
Herzberg, G. (1950) *Spectra of diatomic molecules*, 2nd. ed. Van Nostrand, New York (471)
Herzenberg, A. (1967) *Phys. Rev.* 160, 80 (468, 469)
Herzenberg, A., Kwok, K.L. and Mandl, F. (1964a) *Proc. Phys. Soc.* 84, 345 (323)
Herzenberg, A., Kwok, K.L. and Mandl, F. (1964b) *Proc. Phys. Soc.* 84, 477 (323)
Herzenberg, A. and Mandl, F. (1963) *Proc. Roy. Soc.* A274, 253 (323, 324)
Hoerni, J.A. (1956) *Phys. Rev.* 102, 1530 (453)
Holt, A.R. and Moiseiwitsch, B.L. (1968) *J.Phys.B* 1,36 (279)
Holtsmark, J.A. (1930) *Zeit.f.Physik*, 66, 4a (245)
Hostler, L. (1964) *J. Math. Phys.* 5, 591, 1235 (118)
Hull, M.H. and Breit, G. (1959) *Handbuch der Physik* 41/1, 406 (117)
Hulthén, L. (1944) *K.Fys.Selsk.Lund.Fork.*14,21 (62,63,67,165)
Humberston, J.W. (1979) *Adv.Atom.Mol. Phys.* 15, 101 (247)
Huzenaga, S. (1957) *Prog. Theor. Phys.* 17, 162 (449)
Hvelplund, P., Heinemeier, J., Horsdal-Pederson, E. and Simpson, F.R. (1976) *J.Phys.B* 9, 491 (422)

Inokutu, M. (1971) *Rev. Mod. Phys.* 43, 279 (276)
Ivash, E.V. (1958) *Phys. Rev.* 112, 155 (445)
Janev, R.K. (1976) *Adv. in Atom. Mol.Phys.* 12, 1 (400)
Janev, R.K. and Presynakov, L.P. (1981) *Phys. Repts.* 70, 1 (400, 425)
Jauch, J.M. and Marchland, J.P. (1966) *Helv. Phys. Acta.* 39, 325 (194)
Jeffreys, H. (1923) *Proc. Lond. Math. Soc.* 23(2), 428 (96)
Jost, R. and Pais, A. (1951) *Phys. Rev.* 82, 840 (41)
Kapur, P.I. and Peierls, R. (1937) *Proc. Roy. Soc.* A166, 277 (323)
Karule, E. (1965) *Phys. Let.* 15, 137 (246)
Karule, E. (1972) *J. Phys. B* 5, 2051 (246)
Karule, E. and Peterkop, R. (1964) *Opt.i.Spec.*16, 958 (262)
Karule, E. and Peterkop, R. (1965) *Cross Sections of Electron Atomic Collisions*, Ed. V.Veldre, Latv.Acad.Sci.Riga p3-32 (262)
Kelly, H.P. (1967) *Phys. Rev.* 160, 44 (238)
Kennerly, R.E. and Bonham, R.A. (1978) *Phys. Rev. A* 17, 1844 (247)
Kerner, E.H. (1953) *Phys. Rev.* 91, 1441 (471)
Khare, S.P. (1966a) *Phys. Rev.* 149, 33 (449, 450)
Khare, S.P. (1966b) *Phys. Rev.* 152, 74 (449, 450)
Khare, S.P. (1967) *Phys. Rev.* 157, 107 (451)
Khare, S.P. and Moiseiwitsch, B.L. (1965) *Proc. Phys. Soc.* 85, 821 (449)
Khare, S.P. and Moiseiwitsch, B.L. (1966) *Proc. Phys. Soc.* 88, 65 (449)
Kimura, M. and Thorsen, W.R. (1981a)*Phys. Rev.* A24, 3019 (363)
Kimura, M. and Thorsen, W.R. (1981b)*XIIth Int.Conf.on Elec. & Atom. Coll.* Gatlinburg, p.638-9 (Ed. S.Datz) (382)
Kingston, A.E., Fon, W.C. and Burke, P.G. (1976) *J. Phys. B* 9, 605 (258)
Klein, A. and Zemach, C. (1959) *Ann.Phys.(N.Y.)*7,440 (41)
Kleinman, C.J., Hahn, Y. and Spruch, L. (1968) *Phys. Rev.* 165, 53 (216)
Kleinpoppen, H. and Raible, V. (1965) *Phys. Rev. Let.* 18, 24 (312, 313)
Klonover, A. and Kaldor, V. (1978) *J. Phys. B* 11, 1623 (458, 459)
Klonover, A. and Kaldor, V. (1979) *J. Phys. B* 12, 323 (458, 459)
Knowles, M. and McDowell, M.R.C. (1973) *J. Phys. B* 6, 300 (238, 245)
Kochbach, L. (1976) *Z. Phys. A* 279, 233 (408)

Kohn, W. (1948) *Phys. Rev.* 74, 1763 (62)
Kohn, W. (1952) *Phys. Rev.* 87, 539 (41)
Knudson, S.K. and Thorsen, W.R. (1970) *Canad. J. Phys.* 48, 313 (389)
Kramer, P.J. (1972) *Phys. Rev. A* 6, 2125 (415)
Kramers, H.A. (1926) *Z. Phys.* 39, 828 (96)
Kruger, P.G. (1930) *Phys. Rev.* 36, 855 (310)
Kubach, C. and Sidis, V. (1981) *Phys. Rev.* 23, 110 (384)
Kwok, K.L. and Mandl, F. (1965) *Proc. Phys. Soc.* 86, 501 (324)
Landau, L.D. (1932) *Z. Phys. Sov.* 2, 46 (393)
Landau, L.D. and Lifshitz, E.M. (1958) *Quantum Mechanics* Pergamon Press, Oxford (111, 112, 127)
Lane, N.F. (1980) *Rev.Mod. Phys.* 52, 59 (471)
Lane, N.F. and Henry, R.J.W. (1968) *Phys. Rev.*173, 183 (456)
Langer, R.E. (1937) *Phys. Rev.* 51, 669 (96)
Lassetre, E.N. (1965) *J. Chem. Phys.* 43, 4479 (275)
Lassetre, E.N. (1966) *Phys. Rev. Let.* 17, 345 (306)
Lassetre, E.N. and Jones, E.A. (1964) *J. Chem. Phys.* 40, 1218 (306)
Lassetre, E.N., Krasnow, M.E. and Silvermann, S. (1964) *J. Chem. Phys.* 40, 1242 (306)
Lassetre, E.N. and Silvermann, S. (1964) *J. Chem. Phys.* 40, 2922 (306, 310)
Le Dourneuf, M., Vo Ky Lan and Burke, P.G. (1977) *Comm. At. Mol. Phys.* 7, 1 (262)
Linder, F. and Schmidt, H. (1971) *Z.Naturforsch Teil A*26,1603 (4
Lee, C.M. (1978) *Phys. Rev.* A 17, 566 (425)
Levin, D.A., Rescigno, T.N. and McKoy, V. (1977) *Phys. Rev. A* 16, 157 (107)
Levy, B.R. and Keller, J.B. (1963) *J.Math. Phys.* 4, 54 (128)
Lipsky, L. and Rusek, A. (1966) *Phys. Rev.* 142, 59 (329)
Litchen, W. (1963) *Phys. Rev.* 131, 229 (392)
Litchen, W. (1965) *Phys. Rev.* 139, A27 (400)
Lockwood, G.L. and Everhart, E. (1962) *Phys. Rev.* 125, 567 (389)
Lockwood, G.L., Helbig, H.F. and Everhart, E. (1963) *Phys. Rev.* 132, 2078 (390)
Long, R.L., Cox, D.M. and Smith, S.J. (1968) *J.Res. NBS* 72A, p.521 (258)
Lorents, D.A. and Aberth, W. (1965) *Phys. Rev.* 139, A1017 (390, 391)
Lovelace, C. (1964) In *Strong Interactions and High Energy Physics* Ed. R.G. Moorhouse, Oliver & Boyd, Edinburgh, p.437 (189, 191)

McCarroll, R. and Salin, A. (1968) *J.Phys. B* 1, 163 (425)
McCarthy, I.E., Saha, B.C. and Stelborics, A.T. (1981) *Phys. Rev. A* 23, 145 (264, 265)
McCarthy, I.E., Saha, B.C. and Stelborics, A.T. (1982) *To be published* (264, 265)
McCarthy, I.E. and Wiegold, E. (1976) *Phys. Repts.* 27c, 275 (304, 306)
McCarthy, I.E. and Weigold, E. (1978) *Adv. in Atom.Molec. Phys.* 14, 127 (304, 306)
McGowan, J.W., Williams, J.F. and Curley, E.K. (1969) *Phys. Rev.* 180, 132 (258, 305)
Macek, J. (1970) *Phys. Rev.* A1, 235 (412)
Macek, J. (1970) *Phys. Rev.* A2, 1101 (195)
Macek, J. and Burke, P.G. (1967) *Proc. Phys. Soc.* 92, 351 (256, 305, 323)
Madden, R.P. and Codling, K.C. (1963) *Phys. Rev. Let.* 10, 516 (311, 312)
Madden, R.P. and Codling, K.C. (1965) *Astr. J.* 141, 364 (311, 312, 321)
Madison, D.H. and Shelton, W.N. (1973) *Phys. Rev. A* 7, 499 (268, 269)
Mandl, F. (1967) *Proc. Phys. Soc.* 90, 913 (323)
Manning, I. (1965) *Phys. Rev.* 139, B495 (41)
Manson, S.T., Toburen, L.H., Madison, D.H. and Stolterfoht, N (1975) *Phys. Rev. A* 12, 60 (411)
Marchi, R.P. and Smith, F.T. (1965) *Phys. Rev.* 139, A1025 (391)
Martin, A. (1955) *Nuovo Cimento* 7, 607 (206)
Martin, A. (1965) *Prog.elem.part. and cos. ray phys.* 8, 1 (44)
Martir, M.H., Ford, A.L., Reading, J.F. and Becker, R.L. (1982) *J. Phys. B* (In press) (306)
Martynenko, Y.V., Firsov, O.B. and Chibisov, M.I. (1963) *Soviet Physics (J.E.T.P.)* 17, 154 (128, 129)
Massey, H.S.W. (1935) *Trans. Faraday Soc.* 31, 556 (460)
Massey, H.S.W., Lawson, J. and Thompson, D.G. (1966) In *Quantum Theory of atoms and molecules and the solid state,* Academic Press, New York, p.202 (240)
Massey, H.S.W. and Mohr, C.B. (1932) *Proc. Roy. Soc. A* 135, 258 (449)
Massey, H.S.W. and Moiseiwitsch, B.L. (1951) *Proc. Roy. Soc. A* 135, 483 (63, 221)
Massey, H.S.W. and Moiseiwitsch, B.L. (1953) *Proc. Phys. Soc. A* 66, 406 (172)
Massey, H.S.W. and Moiseiwitsch, B.L. (1954) *Proc. Roy. Soc. A* 227, 38 (285, 286)
Massey, H.S.W. and Ridley, R.O. (1956) *Proc. Phys. Soc. A* 69, 659 (454)

Massey, H.S.W. and Smith, R.A. (1933) *Proc. Roy. Soc. A* 142, 142 (350)
Merzbacher, E. (1970) *Quantum Mechanics*, 2nd. edition Wiley, New York (194, 246)
Milloy, H.B. and Crompton, R.W. (1977) *Phys. Rev. A* 15, 1847 (244)
Mittleman, M.H. (1966) *Phys. Rev.* 147, 69 (238)
Mittleman, M.H. and Quong, J. (1968) *Phys. Rev.* 167, 74 (418)
Moiseiwitsch, B.L. and O'Brien, T.J. (1970) *J. Phys. B* 3 191 (80)
Moores, D.L. and Norcross, D.W. (1972) *J. Phys. B* 5, 1482 (262)
Morgan, L.A., McDowell, M.R.C. and Callaway, J. (1977) *J. Phys. B* 10, 3297 (305)
Morgan, T.J., Geddes, J. and Gilbody, H.B. (1973) *J. Phys. B* 6, 2118 (389)
Morrison, M.A. and Collins, L.A. (1978) *Phys. Rev. A* 17, 918 (457)
Morrison, M.A. and Schneider, B.I. (1977) *Phys. Rev. A* 16, 1003 (457)
Morse, P.M. (1953) *Phys. Rev.* 90, 51 (460)
Morse, P.M. and Allis, W.P. (1933) *Phys.Rev.* 44, 269 (239, 240)
Morse, P.M. and Feshbach, H. (1953) *Methods of Theoretical Physics*, McGraw Hill, New York (30, 37, 55, 93, 96, 99, 112, 203, 204)
Mott, N.F. and Massey, H.S.W. (1965) *Theory of Atomic Collisions*, 3rd. ed. Clarendon Press, Oxford (273)
Murtaugh, T.S. and Reinhardt, W.P. (1972) *J. Chem. Phys.* 57, 2029 (107)
Murtaugh, T.S. and Reinhardt, W.P. (1973) *J. Chem. Phys.* 59, 4900 (107)
Nesbet, R.K. (1975) *Adv. Quant. Chem.* 9, 215 (238)
Nesbet, R.K. (1977) *Adv. in Atom. Molec. Phys.* 13,315 (245,262)
Nesbet, R.K. (1978) *J. Phys. B* 11, L21 (262)
Nesbet, R.K. (1979) *J. Phys. B* 12, L243 (240,242,243, 244)
Nesbet, R.K. (1980) *Variational methods in electron atom scattering theory*, Plenum Press, New York (238, 245)
Neumann, J.V. and Wigner, E. (1929) *Phys.Zeit*, 30, 467 (374)
Newton, R.G. (1959) *Phys. Rev.* 114, 1611 (176)
Newton, R.G. (1961) *J. Math. Phys.* 2, 188 (176)
Nutt, G.L. (1964) *Phys. Rev.* 135, A345 (80, 189)
Nuttall, J. (1970) *The Padé approximant in theoretical physics*, Academic Press, New York (67)
Oberoi, R.S. and Nesbet, R.K. (1973) *Phys. Rev.* A8, 2969 (262)

Ochkur, V.I. (1963) *Soviet Phys. (J.E.T.P.)* 45, 734 (303)
Ochkur, V.I. (1964) *Soviet Phys. (J.E.T.P.)* 47, 1766 (303)
Ochkur, V.I. and Bratsev, V.F. (1965) *Opts. Spect.* 19, 174 (303)
Olson, R.E. and Salop, A. (1977) *Phys.Rev A* 16, 531 (425)
O'Malley, T.F. (1963) *Phys. Rev.* 130, 1020 (128)
O'Malley, T.F. (1964) *Phys. Rev.* 134, A1188 (128)
O'Malley, T.F., Burke, P.G. and Berrington, K.A. (1979) *J. Phys. B* 12, 953 (240)
O'Malley, T.F. and Geltman, S. (1965) *Phys. Rev.* 137, A1344 (314, 316, 317, 318)
O'Malley, T.F., Spruch, L. and Rosenberg, L. (1961) *J. Math. Phys.* 2, 491 (128)
O'Malley, T.F., Spruch, L. and Rosenberg, L. (1962) *Phys. Rev.* 125, 1300 (128)
Oppenheimer, J.R. (1928) *Phys. Rev.* 32, 361 (415)
Park, J.T., Alday, J.E. and George, J.M. (1975) *Phys. Rev. Let.* 34, 1253 (406)
Park, J.T., Alday, J.E.,George, J.M. and Peacher, J.L. (1976) *Phys. Rev. A* 14, 608 (365)
Park, J.T., Alday, J.E., George, J.M., Peacher, J.L. and McQuire, J.H. (1977) *Phys. Rev. A* 15 508 (367,406,407)
Pauli, M. and Trautmann, D. (1978) *J.Phys. B* 11, 667 (408)
Peach, G. (1965) *Proc. Phys. Soc.* 85, 709 (302, 303)
Peach, G. (1966a) *Proc. Phys. Soc.* 87, 375 (302, 303)
Peach, G. (1966b) *Proc. Phys. Soc.* 87, 381 (302, 303)
Peek, J.M. (1964) *Phys. Rev.*134, 877 (444, 445, 446, 447)
Peek, J.M. (1965) *Phys. Rev.*140, A11 (444, 445, 446, 447)
Peek, J.M. (1966) *Phys. Rev.*143, 33 (387)
Peek, J.M. (1967) *Phys. Rev.*154, 52 (444, 445, 446, 447)
Percival, I.C. (1957) *Proc. Phys. Soc.* 70, 494 (71)
Percival, I.C. (1960) *Phys. Rev.* 119, 159 (71)
Percival, I.C. and Seaton, M.J.(1957) *Proc. Camb. Phil. Soc.* 53, 654 (156, 225)
Peterkop, P.K. (1977) *Theory of Ionization of atoms by Electron Impact*, Trans.E.Aronson, Ed. D.G.Hummer (Colorado Assoc. Univ. Press) (306)
Pilar, F.L. (1968) *Elementary Quantum Chemistry* McGraw Hill, New York (471)
Pivovar, L.I., Tubaer, V.M. and Novikov, M.T. (1962) *Soviet Phys. (J.E.T.P.)* 15, 1035 (422)
Poet, R. (1978) *J. Phys. B* 11, 3081 (260)
Ponce, V.H. (1979) *J. Phys. B* 12, 3731 (369)
Potapov, V.S. (1973) *Soviet Phys. (J.E.T.P.)* 36, 1105 (280)
Power, J.D. (1973) *Phil.Trans. Roy.Soc. A* 274, 663 (400)
Predazzi, E. (1966) *Ann.Phys. (N.Y.)* 36, 228, 250 (94)
Pu, R.T. and Chang, E.S.(1966) *Phys.Rev.* 151, 31 (238)

Rabinovitch, H. (1965) *J. Chem. Phys.* 43, 3144 (471)
Rai Dastidar, T.K. and Bhattacharya, S.S. (1976) *Ind. J. Phys.* 50, 731 (392)
Ramien, H. (1931) *Z. Phys.* 70, 353 (468)
Rapp, D. and Dinwiddie, P. (1972) *J. Chem. Phys.* 57, 4919 (361, 362)
Rapp, D., Sharp, T.E. and Brighton, D.D. (1965) *Phys. Rev. Let.* 14, 573 (468, 470)
Ramsauer, C. and Kollath, R. (1929) *Ann. Phys. (Leipzig)* 3, 536 (128)
Ramsauer, C. and Kollath, R. (1930) *Ann. Phys. (Leipzig)* 5,4,91 (454)
Ramsauer, C. and Kollath, R. (1932) *Ann. Phys. (Leipzig)* 12, 529 (247)
Reading, J.F., Ford, A.L. and Becker, R.L. (1981) *J. Phys. B* 14, 1995 (367, 405, 406, 407)
Reeh, H. (1960) *Z.f. Naturforsch* 15A, 377 (216)
Register, D. and Poe, R.T. (1975) *Phys. Let.* 51A, 431 (219, 220, 221)
Reinhardt, W.P. (1979) *Comp. Phys. Comm.* 17, 1 (81)
Reinhardt, W.P., Oxtoby, D.W. and Rescigno, T.N. (1972) *Phys. Rev. Let.* 28, 401 (80)
Rescigno, T.N., McCurdy, C.W. and McKoy, V. (1974) *Phys. Rev. A* 10, 2240 (457)
Riley, M.E. and Green, T.A. (1971) *Phys. Rev. A* 4, 619 (369)
Risberg, V. (1956) *Arch. Math. Nat.* 53, 1 (71)
Ritchie, B. (1971) *Phys. Rev. A* 3, 656 (424)
Roscoe, R. (1941) *Phil. Mag.* 31, 349 (450)
Rosenberg, L. (1965) *Phys. Rev.* 135, B1348 (246)
Rosenberg, L. and Spruch, L. (1959) *Phys. Rev.* 116, 1034 (67)
Rosenberg, L., Spruch, L. and O'Malley, T.F. (1960) *Phys. Rev.* 118, 184 (69, 230)
Ross, M.H. and Shaw, G.L. (1961) *Ann. Phys. (N.Y.)* 13, 147 (178)
Rowntree, S.P., Burnett, T., Henry, R.J.W. and Weatherford, C.A. (1976) *Comp. Phys. Comm.* 11, 27 (225)
Rudd, M.E. (1964) *Phys. Rev. Let.* 13, 503 (310, 312)
Rudd, M.E. (1965) *Phys. Rev. Let.* 15, 580 (310, 312)
Rudd, M.E. and Lang, D.V. (1965) *IVth Int.Conf. on Elec. & Atom. Coll.* Quebec, (312)
Ryufuku, H. and Watanabe, T. (1978) *Phys. Rev.A* 18, 2005 (357)
Ryufuku, H. and Watanabe, T. (1979a) *Phys. Rev.A* 19, 1538 (357)
Ryufuku, H. and Watanabe, T. (1979b) *Phys.Rev.A* 20, 1828 (357)
Salin, A. (1969) *J. Phys. B* 5, 979 (412)
Salop, A. (1979) *J. Phys. B* 12, 919 (425)

Schinke, R. and Kruger, H. (1976) *J. Phys. B* 9, 2469 (389)
Schneider, B.I. (1975) *Phys. Rev. A* 11, 1957 (457)
Schneider, B.I. and Collins, L.A. (1981) *Phys. Rev. A* 24, 1264 (457)
Schneider, B.I. and Collins, L.A. (1982) *J. Phys. B* 15, L335 (457)
Schneider, B.I. and Hay, P.J. (1976) *Phys. Rev. A* 13, 2049 (457)
Schneiderman, S.B. and Russek, A. (1969) *Phys. Rev.* 181, 311 (369)
Schram, B.L., de Heer, F.J., Van der Wiel, M.J. and Kistermaker, J. (1965) *Physica* 31, 94 (303)
Schultz, G.J. (1963) *Phys. Rev. Let.* 10, 104 (313)
Schultz, G.J. (1964) *Phys. Rev. Let.* 13, 383 (312)
Schultz, G.J. (1964) *Phys. Rev.* 135, A988 (468, 469)
Schultz, G.J. and Fox, R.E. (1957) *Phys.Rev.*106, 1179 (286)
Schultz, G.J. and Philbruck, J.W. (1964) *Phys. Rev. Let.* 13, 476 (329)
Schwartz, C. (1961) *Phys. Rev.* 124, 1468 (79)
Schwinger, J. (1964) *J.Math. Phys.* 5, 1606 (120)
Scott, T. and Bransden, B.H. (1981) *J. Phys. B* 14, 2277 (236, 264)
Seaton, M.J. (1955) *C.R. Acad. Sci. (Paris)* 240, 1317 (126)
Seaton, M.J. (1957) *Proc. Phys. Soc.* A70, 620 (126)
Seaton, M.J. (1961) *Proc. Phys. Soc.* 77, 174 (327, 451)
Seaton, M.J. (1962) *Proc. Phys. Soc.* 79, 1105 (451)
Seaton, M.J. (1966) *Proc. Phys. Soc.* 88, 801,815 (329)
Seim, W., Muller, A. and Salzborn, E. (1980) *Phys. Let.* 80A, 20 (363)
Seim, W., Muller, A., Wirkner-Bott, I. and Salzborn, E. (1981) *J. Phys. B* 14, 3475 (363)
Shah, M.B., Goffe, T.V. and Gilbody, H.B. (1978) *J. Phys. B* 11, L233 (363, 422)
Shakeshaft, R. (1976) *Phys. Rev. A* 14, 1626 (365)
Shakeshaft, R. (1978) *Phys. Rev. A* 18, 1930 (361,362,365,366)
Shakeshaft, R. (1978) *Phys. Rev. A* 18, 2047 (284)
Shakeshaft, R. (1978) *Phys. Rev. A* 17, 1011 (417)
Shakeshaft, R. and Spruch, L. (1973) *Phys.Rev.A*8, 206 (425)
Shakeshaft, R. and Spruch, L. (1979) *Rev. Mod. Phys.* 51, 369 (185, 195, 418, 425)
Shipsey, E.J., Brown, J.C. and Olson, R.E. (1981) *J. Phys. B* 14, 869 (384)
Siegert, A.J.F. (1939) *Phys. Rev.* 56, 750 (324)
Sil, N.C. (1954) *Ind. J. Phys.* 28, 232 (416)
Simony, P.R. and McQuire, J.H. (1981) *J. Phys. B* 14, L737 (415)

Simpson, J.A. (1964) In *Atomic Collision Processes* Ed. M.R.C.McDowell, North-Holland, Amsterdam, p. 128 (310)

Simpson, J.A., Mielczierek, S.R. and Cooper, J.W. (1964) *J. Opt. Soc. Am.* 54, 269 (312)

Sin Fai Lam, A.L. (1976) *J. Phys. B* 9, 101 (262)

Sin Fai Lam, A.L. and Nesbet, R.K. (1973) *Phys. Rev. A* 7, 1987 (246, 262)

Sloan, I.H. (1964) *Proc. Roy. Soc.* A281, 151 (218)

Smith, F.J. (1964) *Proc. Phys. Soc.* 84, 889 (386)

Smith, F.J. (1966) *Planet. Space Sci.* 14, 929 (337)

Smith, F.J. (1967) *Proc. Phys. Soc.* 92, 866 (387)

Smith, F.T., Lorents, D.C., Aberth, W. and Marchi, R.P. (1965) *Phys. Rev. Let.* 15, 742 (392)

Smith, J.J., Winters, K.H. and Bransden, B.H. (1979) *J. Phys. B* 12, 1723 (304)

Smith, K., Henry, R.J.W. and Burke, P.G. (1967) *Phys. Rev.* 157, 51 (262)

Smith, K., McEachran, R.P. and Fraser, P.A. (1962) *Phys. Rev.* 126, 147 (226)

Spruch, L. and Rosenberg, L. (1960)*Phys. Rev.*117, 1143 (230)

Spruch, L. (1962) *Lectures in Theoretical Physics*, Eds. W.E. Brittin, B.W. Downs and J. Downs, *Interscience New York* 4, p.161 (107)

Spruch, L. (1976) *IXth Int. Conf. on Elec. & Atom. Coll.* Seattle, p. 685 (107)

Stebbings, R.F., Young, R.A., Orley, C.L. and Ehrhart, H. (1965) *Phys. Rev.* 138, A1317 (362)

Stein, T.S., Kauppila, W.E., Pol, V., Smart, J.H. and Jesion, G. (1978) *Phys. Rev.* A17, 1600 (243, 247)

Stier, H.C. (1932) *Z. Phys.* 76, 439 (454)

Sternheimer, R.M. (1954) *Phys. Rev.* 96, 951 (218)

Stückelberg, E.C.G. (1932) *Helv. Phys. Acta* 5, 320 (393)

Swan, P. (1954) *Proc. Roy. Soc.* A228, 10 (206)

Takayanagi, K. (1965) *J. Phys. Soc. Jap.* 20, 562 (468)

Tambe, B.R. and Henry, R.J.W. (1976a) *Phys. Rev. A* 13, 224 (245, 262)

Tambe, B.R. and Henry, R.J.W. (1976b) *Phys. Rev. A* 14, 512 (245, 262)

Taylor, A.J. and Burke, P.G. (1967) *Proc. Phys. Soc.* 92, 336 (305)

Teller, E. (1936) *J. Chem. Phys.* 41, 109 (374)

Temkin, A. (1957) *Phys. Rev.* 107, 1004 (245, 246)

Temkin, A. (1960) *Phys. Rev. Let.* 4, 566 (246)

Temkin, A. (1962) *Phys. Rev. Let.* 6, 354 (228, 229)

Temkin, A. (1963) *J. Chem. Phys.* 39, 161 (485)

Temkin, A. (1964) *IIIrd Int. Conf. on Elec. & Atom. Coll.* London, 1963 (229)
Temkin, A. and Bhatia, A.H. (1964) *Rev. Mod. Phys.* 36, 1050 (229)
Temkin, A. and Lamkin, J.C. (1961) *Phys. Rev.* 121, 788 (217)
Temkin, A. and Sullivan, E. (1963) *Phys. Rev.* 129, 1250 (229)
Temkin, A. and Vasavada, K.V. (1967) *Phys. Rev.* 160, 109 (456)
Temkin, A., Vasavada, K.V., Chang, E.S. and Silver, A. (1969) *Phys. Rev.* 186, 57 (456)
Thomas, E.W. and Bent, G.D. (1967) *Phys. Rev.* 164, 143 (408)
Thomas, L.D. and Nesbet, R.K. (1975a) *Phys. Rev. A* 11, 170 (245, 262)
Thomas, L.D. and Nesbet, R.K. (1975b) *Phys. Rev. A* 12, 1729 (245, 262)
Thomas, L.D., Yarlagadda, B.S., Czanak, Gy. and Taylor, H.S. (1973) *Comput. Phys. Comm.* 6, 316 (238)
Thomas, L.D., Yarlagadda, B.S., Czanak, Gy. and Taylor, H.S. (1974) *J. Phys. B* 7, 1719 (268, 269, 305)
Thomas, L.H. (1927) *Proc. Roy. Soc.* A114, 561 (417)
Thompson, D.G. (1966)*Proc. Roy. Soc.* A294, 160 (245)
Tully, J. (1960) *M.Sc. dissertation, University of London* (276)
Vaaber, J. and Taulbjerg, K. (1981) *J.Phys. B* 14, 1815 (400)
Vo Ky Lan (1971) *J. Phys. B* 4, 658 (246)
Vogt, E. and Wannier, G.H. (1954) *Phys. Rev.*95, 1190 (129)
Walker, D.W. (1971) *Adv. in Phys.* 20, 257 (195, 276)
Watson, D.K. and McKoy, V. (1979)*Phys. Rev. A*20, 1474 (457)
Wentzel, G. (1926) *Z. Phys.* 38, 518 (96)
Whiddington, R. and Priestly, M. (1934) *Proc. Roy. Soc. A* 145, 462 (310)
Wigner, E.P. (1955) *Phys. Rev.* 98, 145 (32, 49)
Wigner, E.P. and Eisenbud. L. (1947) *Phys.Rev.* 72, 29 (83)
Williams, J.F. (1975) *J. Phys. B* 8, 1683 (222, 257, 265)
Williams, J.F. (1976) *J. Phys. B* 9, 1519 (257)
Williams, J.F. (1979) *J. Phys. B* 12, 265 (247)
Williams, J.F. (1981) *J. Phys. B* 14,1197 (259)
Williams, J.F. and Willis, B.A. (1974) *J. Phys. B* 7, L61 (259, 305)
Winters, K.H., Clark, C.D., Bransden, B.H. and Coleman, J.P. (1974) *J. Phys. B* 7, 788 (266)
Winters, K.H. (1978) *J. Phys. B* 11, 149 (269)
Winter, T.G. (1982) *Phys. Rev. A* 25, 697 (362, 367)

Winter, T.G. and Hatton, G.J. (1980) *Phys. Rev. A* 21, 793 (382)

Winter, T.G. and Lin, C.C. (1974) *Phys. Rev. A* 10, 2141 (362, 415)

Wu, T.Y. (1947) *Phys. Rev.* 71, 111 (460)

Yau, A.W., McEachran, R.P. and Stauffer, A.D. (1978) *J. Phys. B* 11, 2907 (247)

Yost, F.L., Wheeler, J.A. and Breit, G. (1936) *Phys. Rev.* 49, 174 (117)

Zener, C. (1932) *Proc. Roy. Soc. A* 137, 696 (393)

SUBJECT INDEX